H. Eberle
E. Gonser
H. Hermeling †
M. Hornberger
R. Kilgus
R. Kupke
D. Menzer
A. Moll
W. Ring

Clothing Technology

... from fibre to fashion

Sixth Edition

VERLAG EUROPA-LEHRMITTEL · Nourney, Vollmer GmbH & Co. KG
Düsselberger Straße 23 · 42781 Haan-Gruiten · www.europa-lehrmittel.de

Europa-Nr.: 62218

Authors

Hannelore Eberle	Director of Studies	Ravensburg
Elke Gonser	Lecturer	Metzingen
Hermann Hermeling †	Dipl.-Ing (FH), Principal	Frankfurt
Marianne Hornberger	Diplom-Modellistin, Lecturer	Munich
Renate Kupke	Senior Lecturer	Stuttgart
Dieter Menzer	Dipl.-Ing (FH)	Nussloch
Andrea Moll	Instructor	Darmstadt
Werner Ring	Dipl.-Ing (FH), Director of Studies	Eningen

Editor and Team Leader:
Werner Ring, Dipl.-Ing (FH), Director of Studies, Eningen
Roland Kilgus, Principal, Neckartenzlingen (German Editions 1 to 9)

Fashion Drawings: Studio Salo-Döllel, Aufkirchen bei Erding

Picture Processing: Design Department, Verlag Europa-Lehrmittel, Ostfildern

This book was produced according to the latest German Industrial Standards (DIN-Blätter). Conformance is strictly limited to the DIN-Blätter. The DIN-Blätter are published by: Beuth-Verlag GmbH, Burggrafenstrasse 6, 10787 Berlin.

Tenth German Edition 2013

Print 5 4 3 2

All prints of the same edition are interchangeable, excepting correction of printing errors.

Sixth English Edition 2014

Translation: Cotton Technology International, 27 Winnington Road, Marple, Stockport SK6 6PD, England
http://www.cottontech.co.uk

ISBN 978-3-8085-6226-0

http://www.europa-lehrmittel.de
Cover design: braunwerbeagentur, 42477 Radevormwald
Setting & layout: Satz+Layout Werkstatt Kluth GmbH, 50374 Erftstadt
Printing: Stürtz GmbH, 97080 Würzburg

Preface 10th German Edition

This is a vocational book, directed primarily at students of the clothing industry: cutting, sewing, and assembly for fashion and mass markets. However, it will also be found useful in either college- or industry-based training for managers and technologists, and as a general reference work.

A key feature of the book is its concise and compact design. The chapters generally follow the flow of textile and clothing manufacture. Each page is complete in itself. Particular emphasis has been laid on providing a simple layout and straightforward language, which students will find easy to grasp. Numerous colour diagrams are an effective aid to the comprehension of some of the more difficult topics. These coloured illustrations are a particularly useful feature of the chapters on Commercial Terminology and the History of Clothing.

The book is organised largely according to the different technological sectors, but teaching requirements have also been kept in mind. There are fifteen chapters:

- Fibres
- Labelling of Textiles
- Functions of Textiles
- Ecology
- Yarns
- Textile Fabrics
- Dyeing and Finishing
- Commercial Terminology
- Leather and Fur
- Clothing Manufacture
- Company Management
- Garment Sizing
- Product Development
- Product Groups
- History of Clothing

Improvements for the 10th Edition: The sections on Labelling of Textiles, Functions of Textiles, Ecology, Yarns, Fabrics, Dyeing and Finishing, Commercial Terminology, Company Management, Product Development, and Product Groups have been rewritten or extended according to the latest technical developments. Many illustrations have been enhanced by the use of colour or changed to reflect current fashion trends.

We would like to give special thanks to the persons, companies and associations listed on *page 307 ff* for their assistance in the clarification of questions and for the provision of pictorial material.

Many clothing companies today employ offshore manufacturing. Therefore, it is useful to note that "*Fachwissen Bekleidung*" has been translated into English ("*Clothing Technology*") and from there into several other European languages. Maybe this can provide some stimulus to intra- and extra-European communication via the language of technology. The new generation will need competence in both language and technology to succeed in an era of global market competition.

We would welcome any suggestions for improving or supplementing the material in this book.

Eningen, Summer 2013 — Editor and authors

Preface 6th English Edition

Fachwissen Bekleidung is now in its tenth edition and has been a firm favourite in the German-speaking area of Europe since it first appeared in 1989. So far as we are aware, the book is unique in its scope and presentation, so it was perhaps natural that a demand should arise for an English-language version.

Although this English edition follows quite faithfully the general content and layout of the German, it is not always a literal translation. There are several instances in the original where the treatment of the subject matter naturally has a distinctively central-European bias. In the English, an attempt has been made to present a more international perspective. Wherever possible, ISO or ASTM or EN standards have been referenced rather than DIN.

For an international readership, there is always the problem of whether to use British or North American terminology. For this edition, wherever there is a conflict between the British and American traditions, the British has generally been selected, although the American is often acknowledged and occasionally preferred – *Fairchild's Dictionary of Textiles (7th Ed.)* has been frequently consulted.

The German approach to Work Measurement has been retained, as a valid and comprehensive example of the technique. Most of Chapter 12 on Garment Sizing has been completely rewritten for the English edition.

Stockport, Winter 2013–14

Allan Heap & Jill Stevens
Cotton Technology International

Contents

1 Fibres

1.1 Overview
1.1.1 Sources and Demand for Textile Fibres 6
1.1.2 Classification of Textile Fibres 7
1.2 Natural Fibres: Vegetable
1.2.1 Cotton 8
1.2.2 Flax 12
1.2.3 Seed, Bast, and Hard Fibres 15
1.3 Natural Fibres: Animal
1.3.1 Wool 16
1.3.2 Hairs 20
1.3.3 Silk 21
1.4 Man-made Fibres: Fundamentals
1.4.1 Composition of Textile Fibres 25
1.4.2 Fibre-forming Materials 26
1.4.3 Spinning Man-made Fibres 27
1.5 Man-made Fibres: Natural Polymers
1.5.1 Overview 28
1.5.2 Viscose, Modal 29
1.5.3 Lyocell 31
1.5.4 Cupro 32
1.5.5 Acetate, Triacetate 32
1.6 Man-made Fibres: Synthetic Polymers
1.6.1 Overview 33
1.6.2 Polyamide, Nylon 34
1.6.3 Polyester 36
1.6.4 Acrylic, Modacrylic 38
1.6.5 Elastomerics, Fluorofibres, Chlorofibres, Olefins, Vinylals 39
1.7 Man-made Fibres: Inorganic
1.7.1 Glass, Carbon, Metal 40
1.8 Fibre Properties
1.8.1 Fibre Identification 41
1.8.2 Physical Properties 42
1.9 Fibre Blending
1.9.1 Blend Ratios, Aftercare, Labelling 44

2 Labelling of Textiles

2.1 Textile Labelling
2.1.1 Textile Labelling Regulations 45
2.2 Aftercare Labelling
2.2.1 Aftercare Characteristics, Recommendations, Symbols 46

3 Functions of Textiles

3.1 Functions of Clothing
3.1.1 Basic Functions and Requirements 48
3.1.2 Clothing Physiology 49
3.2 Textiles with Particular Functions
3.2.1 Weatherproof Clothing 50
3.2.2 Protective Work Clothing 51
3.2.3 Moisture Transport and Thermoregulation 52
3.2.4 High-tech Textiles 53
3.2.5 Technical Textiles 55

4 Ecology

4.1 Ecology and the Textile Chain
4.1.1 Sustainability 56
4.1.2 Ecology and Textile Production 56
4.1.3 Social Considerations 57
4.1.4 Human Ecology, Utilisation and Disposal 58
4.1.5 Eco-Labelling 59

5 Yarns

5.1 Fundamentals
5.1.1 Overview and Definitions 60
5.2 Spun Yarns
5.2.1 Basic Principles of Spun Yarn Production 61
5.2.2 Manufacture of Spun Yarns 62
5.2.3 Properties and Applications of Spun Yarns 66
5.3 Filament Yarns
5.3.1 Manufacture of Filament Yarns 67
5.3.2 Texturing 67
5.3.3 Textured and Bicomponent Yarns 67
5.3.4 Properties and Applications of Filament Yarns 68
5.4 Folded Yarns, Plied Yarns
5.4.1 Folded Yarns and Cabled Yarns 69
5.4.2 Core Yarns 69
5.5 Fancy Yarns
5.5.1 Properties and Applications of Fancy Yarns 70
5.5.2 Colour, Lustre and Structural Effects 70
5.6 Sewing Threads
5.6.1 Overview and Packaging 71
5.6.2 Quality Requirements 71
5.7 Yarn Fineness
5.7.1 Yarn Numbering Systems 72
5.7.2 Numbering of Single Yarns 72
5.7.3 Numbering of Folded Yarns and Sewing Thread 73

6 Textile Fabrics

6.1 Nonwoven Fabrics
6.1.1 Fabrics Overview 74
6.1.2 Wool Felts and Bonded Webs 74
6.2 Woven Fabrics
6.2.1 Woven Fabric Manufacture 76
6.2.2 Weaving Preparation 77
6.2.3 Weft Insertion Devices 78
6.2.4 Principles of Cloth Construction 79
6.2.5 Plain Weave and its Elaborations 80
6.2.6 Twill Weave and its Elaborations 81
6.2.7 Satin Weave and its Elaborations 83
6.2.8 Colour Woven Fabrics 84
6.2.9 Crêpe Fabrics 85
6.2.10 Fabrics with Three or more Yarn Systems 86
6.2.11 Piqué Fabrics 89
6.3 Knitted Fabrics
6.3.1 Classification of Knitted Fabrics 90
6.3.2 Weft Knitted Fabrics 91
6.3.3 Developments of the Single Jersey Structure 93
6.3.4 Developments of the Rib Structure 94
6.3.5 Developments of Purl and Interlock 95
6.3.6 Spreading, Cutting and Sewing 95
6.3.7 Circular Knits, Flat Knits 96
6.3.8 Warp Knitted Fabrics 97
6.3.9 Stitch-bonded Fabrics 98
6.4 Special Fabrics
6.4.1 Transparent and Open-work Fabrics 99
6.4.2 Laces and Nets 100
6.5 Comparison of Textile Fabrics
6.5.1 Properties and Applications of Textile Fabrics 101

7 Dyeing and Finishing

7.1 Fundamentals
7.1.1 Definition and Objectives 102
7.1.2 Finishing Processes: Overview 102
7.2 Preparation, Intermediate and After-treatment
7.2.1 Singeing, Desizing, Scouring, Mercerizing 103
7.2.2 Bleaching, Optical brightening, Carbonising, Heat setting, Drying, Fixation 104
7.3 Coloration
7.3.1 Dyeing: Fundamentals 105
7.3.2 Dyeing Processes 106
7.3.3 Printing 107
7.4 Finishing
7.4.1 Mechanical Finishing 110
7.4.2 Thermo-Mechanical Finishing 111
7.4.3 Chemical Finishing 112
7.4.4 Garment Processing: Jeans 114
7.5 Coating and Lamination
7.5.1 Coating, Bonding, Laminating 115

8 Commercial Terminology

8.1 Trade Descriptions
8.1.1 Technical Terms for Particular Effects 116
8.1.2 Top Cloths 118
8.2 Accessories, Trimmings
8.2.1 Interlinings 137
8.2.2 Linings 138
8.2.3 Ribbons and Decorations 139
8.2.4 Fastenings 140

9 Leather and Fur

9.1 Leather
9.1.1 Leather Manufacture 141

9.1.2 Leather Types ... 143
9.1.3 Leather Garment Manufacture ... 144
9.2 Fur
9.2.1 Fur Types ... 145
9.2.2 Pelt Preparation ... 146
9.2.3 Pelt Finishing ... 147
9.2.4 From Pelt to Fur Clothing ... 147

10 Clothing Manufacture

10.1 Pattern Construction
10.1.1 Design, Pattern Construction ... 150
10.1.2 Pattern Grading ... 151
10.2 Equipment and Methods for Cutting
10.2.1 Making a Lay Plan ... 153
10.2.2 Types of Lay Plan ... 155
10.2.3 Spreading ... 156
10.2.4 Cutting ... 158
10.2.5 Marking, Preparation for Sewing ... 159
10.2.6 Drawing and Measuring Tools ... 160
10.2.7 Hand Sewing Tools ... 161
10.2.8 Cutting Tools ... 162
10.3 Equipment and Methods for Sewing
10.3.1 Types of Sewing Machine ... 164
10.3.2 Sewing Machines, Overview ... 165
10.3.3 Construction of a Sewing Machine ... 166
10.3.4 Moving Parts of a Sewing Machine ... 167
10.3.5 Sewing Machine Needles ... 168
10.3.6 Feeding Systems ... 170
10.3.7 Presser Feet and Fabric Guides ... 172
10.3.8 Shuttles, Hooks and Loopers ... 174
10.3.9 Stitch Types ... 175
10.3.10 Seam Types ... 184
10.3.11 Sewing Machine Drives ... 189
10.3.12 Ancillary Mechanisms for High-speed Sewing Machines ... 190
10.3.13 Automatic Sewing Machines ... 191
10.3.14 Automated Sewing Equipment ... 192
10.3.15 Welded Seams, Seam Sealing ... 193
10.4 Problems in Sewing
10.4.1 Seam Puckering ... 194
10.4.2 Fabric Damage, Sewing Faults ... 195
10.5 Equipment and Methods for Pressing and Fusing
10.5.1 Pressing ... 196
10.5.2 Pressing Workstations ... 198
10.5.3 Mechanical Pressing and Finishing ... 200
10.5.4 Fusing ... 201
10.6 Health and Safety
10.6.1 Safety at Work: Signs and Symbols ... 203
10.6.2 First Aid ... 204
10.6.3 The Working Environment ... 204
10.6.4 Working with Hazardous Materials ... 205
10.6.5 Safety in Clothing Manufacture ... 206

11 Company Management

11.1 Garment Making
11.1.1 Industry Sectors and Product Groups ... 208
11.1.2 Garment Production Systems ... 209
11.2 Company Organisation
11.2.1 Company Structure ... 210
11.2.2 Functional Organisation and Communication ... 211
11.2.3 Organisation of a Garment Making Factory ... 212
11.2.4 Production Management ... 213
11.2.5 Material Flow ... 216
11.3 Work Measurement
11.3.1 Time Analysis by the REFA System ... 217
11.3.2 Time Analysis by the MTM System ... 219
11.4 Method Study
11.4.1 Systems and Processes ... 220
11.4.2 Method Study and Ergonomics ... 221
11.5 Quality Management
11.5.1 Fundamentals ... 224
11.5.2 Quality Assurance in a Clothing Company ... 225
11.6 Data Exchange
11.6.1 Information Flow in a Clothing Company ... 228

12 Garment Sizing

12.1 Proportion
12.1.1 Basic Concepts ... 230
12.2 Body Size
12.2.1 Making Body Measurements ... 231
12.3 Garment Size
12.3.1 Basic Considerations, Body Types, Control Dimensions ... 232
12.3.2 Size Intervals, Size Charts, Size Codes ... 233

13 Product Development

13.1 The Collection
13.1.1 Developing a Collection ... 234
13.1.2 Planning a Collection, Quality Levels ... 235
13.1.3 Target Groups ... 236
13.2 Product Design
13.2.1 Elements of Clothing Design ... 238
13.2.2 Design Influences ... 239

14 Product Groups

14.1 Special Groups
14.1.1 Underwear, Nightwear ... 240
14.1.2 Foundation Garments, Swimwear ... 242
14.1.3 Babywear, Childrenswear ... 243
14.1.4 Men's Shirts ... 244
14.1.5 Workwear, Career Apparel ... 245
14.2 Women's, Men's & Boy's Wear
14.2.1 Skirts ... 246
14.2.2 Blouses ... 248
14.2.3 Dresses ... 249
14.2.4 Knitted Outerwear ... 250
14.2.5 Trousers ... 251
14.2.6 Jackets ... 252
14.2.7 Coats ... 253
14.2.8 Women's Outfits ... 254
14.2.9 Men's Outfits ... 255
14.2.10 Formal Dress ... 256
14.3 Sport and Leisure Wear
14.3.1 Requirements for Sport and Leisure Wear ... 257
14.3.2 Construction and Materials ... 258
14.4 Accessories
14.4.1 Headwear ... 260
14.4.2 Other Fashion Accessories ... 261

15 History of Clothing

15.1 Chronological Survey
15.1.1 Style Periods ... 262
15.1.2 Fashion ... 263
15.2 Ancient Times
15.2.1 Ancient Egypt ... 264
15.2.2 Ancient Greece ... 266
15.2.3 Ancient Rome ... 268
15.2.4 Germanic Prehistory and Early Times ... 270
15.3 Middle Ages
15.3.1 Byzantine Middle Ages ... 272
15.3.2 Romanesque ... 274
15.3.3 Gothic ... 276
15.4 Modern Age
15.4.1 Renaissance ... 279
15.4.2 Baroque ... 282
15.4.3 Rococo ... 284
15.5 Neo-Classicism
15.5.1 English Fashion, Directoire and Empire ... 286
15.5.2 Biedermeier ... 288
15.6 Romanticism
15.6.1 Neo-Rococo, and the Victorian Era ... 290
15.7 Recent Times
15.7.1 Belle Époque, Reform, Art Nouveau ... 292
15.7.2 The Twenties ... 294
15.7.3 The Thirties ... 296
15.7.4 The Forties ... 297
15.7.5 The Fifties ... 298
15.7.6 The Sixties ... 299
15.7.7 The Seventies ... 300
15.7.8 The Eighties ... 301
15.8 Modern Times
15.8.1 The Nineties ... 302
15.8.2 The New Millennium ... 303
15.9 Special Terms
15.9.1 Special Terms in Clothing History ... 304

Bibliography ... 306
Acknowledgements ... 307
Index of Technical Terms ... 310

1.1.1 Sources and Demand for Textile Fibres

Sources of Textile Fibres

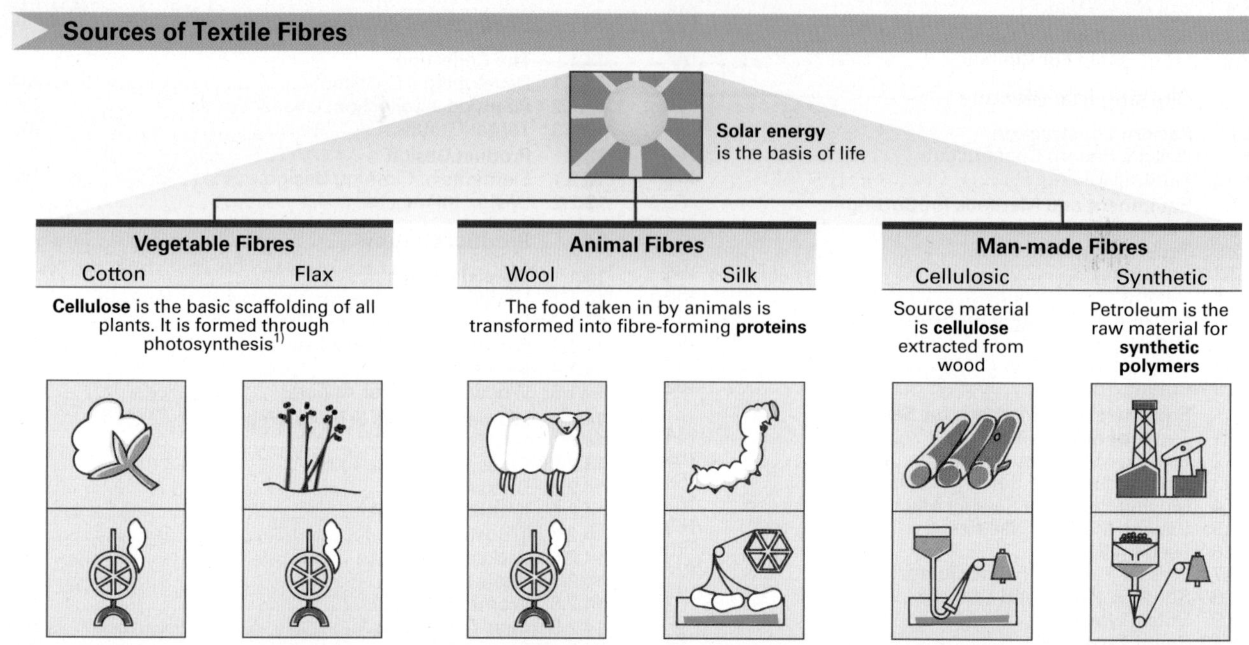

Fibres from plants and animals are constructed from natural **polymers.** Polymers are very large molecules. Cellulosic man-made fibres are formed from the natural polymers of plants (cellulose). The cellulose is dissolved and then forced through spinning jets. Synthetic man-made fibres are derived from petroleum products. Their polymers are formed synthetically (artificially). The common feature of all fibres is that they are constructed from large polymer molecules which lie alongside each other and are bonded together.

1) Synthesis of carbohydrates by green plants from carbon dioxide using solar energy.

Production of Textile Fibres

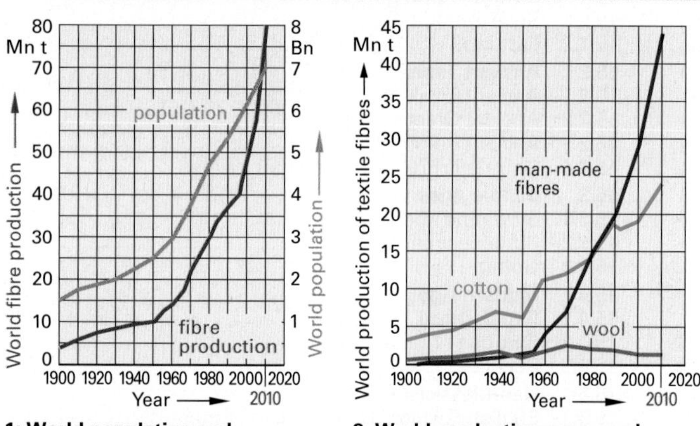

1: World population and fibre production

2: World production: man-made fibres, wool, cotton

The demand for **textiles,** and therefore for textile fibres has increased rapidly due to growing prosperity and the large increase in world population (*Figures 1 and 2*).

Apparel fabrics satisfy the basic requirement of the population for clothing.

Household textiles, e.g. bed and table linen, decorative fabrics, furnishings and blinds, curtains and floor-coverings are utilised in dwellings.

Technical textiles are used in increasing volumes for functional and protective clothing in medicine, packaging, engineering, house and road building, as well as in all forms of transport (including space travel).

The Textile Chain, from Fibre to Consumer

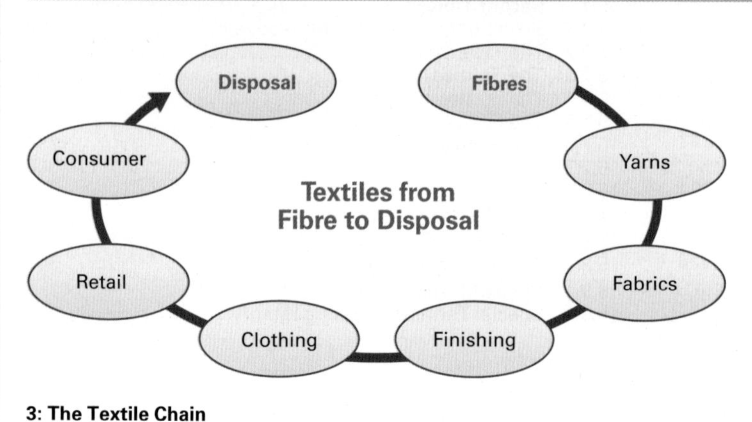

3: The Textile Chain

Figure 3 shows the **textile chain.** Textile **fibres** are spun into **yarns** (spun yarns, filaments) and the yarns are formed into **fabrics** (wovens, knits, nonwovens). The fabrics are **finished** (e.g. bleaching, dyeing, functional finishing). The fabrics are made into **clothing** which is brought to the **consumer** via small **shops** and large **stores.**

The consumer utilises and cares for the clothing.

At the end of the textile chain comes **disposal** e.g. by recycling, landfill or incineration.

1.1.2 Classification of Textile Fibres[1)]

TEXTILE FIBRES[1)]

NATURAL FIBRES

Group Sub-group	Name or Generic Name
Vegetable Fibres	
Seed	Cotton Kapok Coir
Bast	Flax Hemp Jute Ramie
Leaf	Sisal Manila
Animal Fibres	
Wool	Wool Virgin wool
Fine hair	Alpaca Llama Vicuna Guanaco Camel Rabbit Angora Mohair Cashmere Cashgora Yak
Coarse hair	Cattle Horse Goat
Silk	Cultivated Wild (Tussah)
Mineral Fibres	
Rock fibres	Asbestos[2)]

MAN-MADE FIBRES

Group Sub-group	Name or Generic Name
Natural Polymers	
Cellulosic	Viscose Modal Lyocell Cupro Acetate Triacetate
Alginate	Alginate
Rubber	Rubber
Protein	Azlon
Synthetic Polymers	
Elastomeric	Elastane Elastodiene
Fluorofibres	Fluoro
Polyacrylics	Acrylic Modacrylic
Polyamides	Nylon Aramid
Chlorofibres	Vinyl chloride Vinylidene chloride
Polyesters	Polyester
Polyolefins	Polyethylene Polypropylene
Vinylal	Polyvinyl alcohol
Inorganics	
Glass Carbon Metallic	Glass Carbon Metallic

1) Standards for generic names are in ISO 2076 and ISO 6938

2) Asbestos is classified as a hazardous substance; the appropriate health and safety regulations must be observed.

1.2.1 Cotton (1)

Cotton German: Baumwolle French: Coton Spanish: Algodon

History

Archaeological findings in Mohenjo-Daro, in modern Pakistan, and in the Tehuacán valley in Mexico, both dating from about 3000 BC, suggest that the cotton plant was already domesticated and being used for making textiles over 5000 years ago. Cotton fabrics from India, of outstanding fineness and quality, were traded in the Mediterranean area from the time of Alexander, who had established the trade routes to the East. Alexandria became the major dispersal point for these goods. Later the rise to power of the city-state of Venice is said to have been built largely on trade in Indian cotton cloth.

In the 8th century, cotton growing and fabric manufacture were introduced into Spain by the Moors, where it thrived until the expulsion of Islam in the 15th century. Thereafter, the opening of the sea route to India promoted Portugal to the prime source of cotton fabrics.

During the 17th century textile manufacturing expertise and sea power began to concentrate in England which then became the dominant centre of textile manufacture. Meanwhile cotton growing was expanded in North America and the Caribbean. These trends were reinforced in the late 18th century by the invention of the cotton gin in America, and by the development of spinning and weaving machinery, plus the harnessing of water and steam power, in Britain.

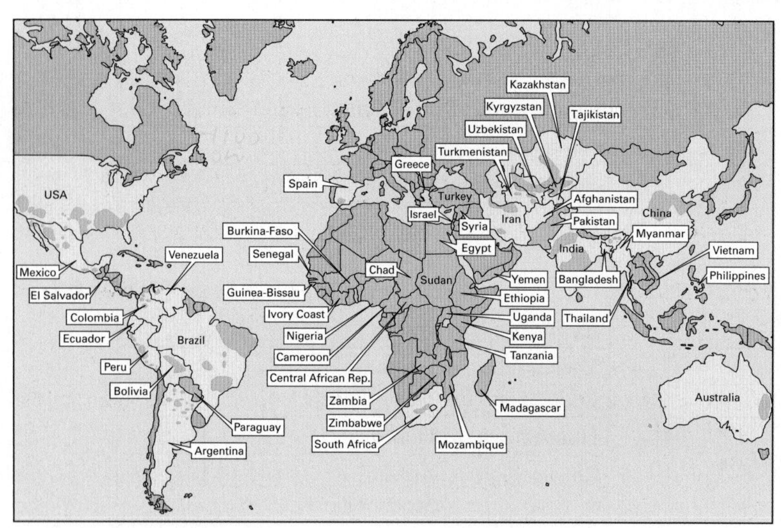

1: Cotton growing regions

Production and Sources

By 1930 cotton accounted for 85% of the world consumption of textile fibres but, during the last half of the twentieth century, its market share fell to about 40% due to the introduction of synthetic fibres. Current annual production (2010-12) is about 26 million tonnes.

Although cotton production has tripled in recent decades, the amount of land utilised has not increased. This is a result of constant improvements in cotton varieties and farming techniques. Cotton is grown in about 80 different countries world-wide (*Figure 1*).

Leading Producers	Others
China India USA Brazil Pakistan Uzbekistan Australia	**Africa:** Egypt, Sudan, East Africa, West Africa **Asia:** Israel, Turkey, Central Asia, East Asia **Latin America:** Mexico, Peru **Europe:** Spain, Greece

2: Cotton field

3: Cotton flower

4: Fruit capsule

5: Open bolls

The Cotton Plant

Cotton is a member of the Mallow family. Its height ranges from 25 cm to over 2 m, depending on variety, climate, and agronomy. It is normally grown as an annual shrub but, in parts of South America and the Caribbean, it is cultivated as a perennial shrub (tree cotton).

From planting to maturity takes between 175 and 225 days. At planting and during its growth, cotton needs plenty of water (*Figure 2*). For ripening, it needs heat. Therefore, the world's cotton belt is located mainly in the tropics and sub-tropics.

After flowering (*Figure 3*), the fruit nodes, located in the calyx (bracts), grow into capsules (bolls) which eventually crack open to reveal the seed hairs (*Figures 4 and 5*). In each boll there are about 30 seeds. The number of hairs on each seed ranges from less than 1000 to more than 10000, depending on the variety.

1.2.1 Cotton (2)

1: Hand picking

2: Machine picking

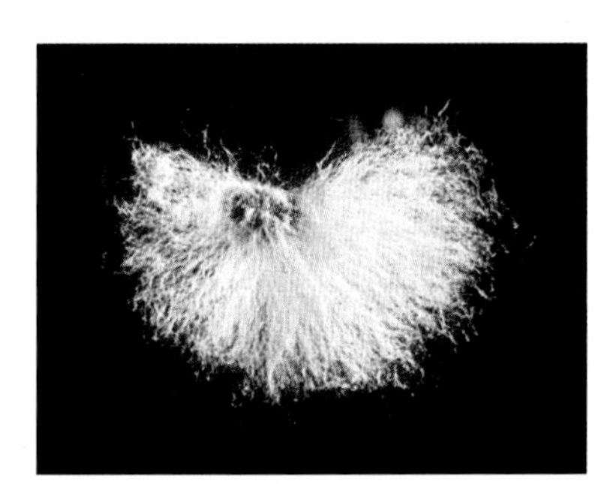

3: Seed with fibres

4: Cotton staple length standards

5: Seeds with linters (left)
Seeds without linters (right)

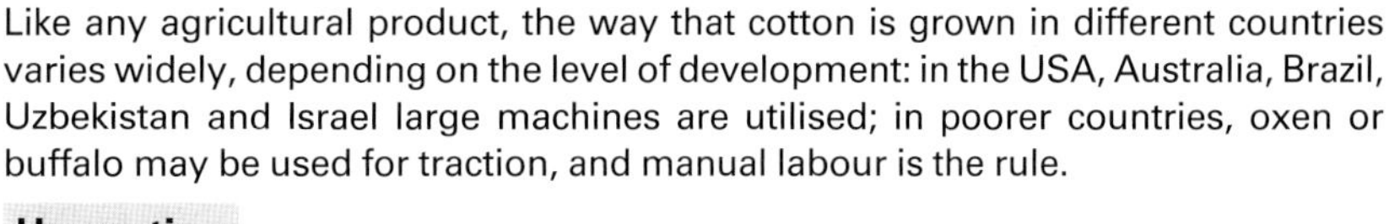

Like any agricultural product, the way that cotton is grown in different countries varies widely, depending on the level of development: in the USA, Australia, Brazil, Uzbekistan and Israel large machines are utilised; in poorer countries, oxen or buffalo may be used for traction, and manual labour is the rule.

Harvesting

Harvesting is either by hand or by picking machines.

Hand picking (*Figure 1*) extends over several weeks. In principle, it has the advantage that only the fully ripened bolls are collected and no leaves are included.

A picking machine (*Figure 2*) will usually harvest the whole crop in one passage. It has a tendency to include some unripe bolls, together with various quantities of dead leaves and other plant parts.

Drying

If the newly-harvested seed-cotton is wet, then it may have to be dried using warm air before it can be stored in large piles to await ginning. In many countries drying is an integral part of the ginning process.

Ginning

Ginning is the separation of the fibres from the seeds (*Figure 3*) using special machines. The separated fibres, called lint, have a staple length of between 15 and 50 mm, depending on the cotton variety (*Figure 4*).

On many types of seed, there are some very short fibres, called **linters.** They are made of cellulose and they find many uses, including the production of man-made fibres. The **seeds** can also be utilised for the production of edible oil, and as cattle feed (*Figure 5*).

100 kg of clean seed-cotton yields about 35 kg of fibre, 62 kg of seed and 3 kg of waste.

Processing into Yarn

Cotton fibres are made into staple fibre yarns predominantly by ring spinning or OE rotor spinning.

Commercial Quality

Commercially, cotton is usually designated according to its variety and origin. Different varieties are grown in different countries – about 40 in the USA alone. Thus the country of origin is only a partial guide to quality. The high-quality, long-staple cottons, such as the Gizas of Egypt and the Pimas of the USA, Peru, and Israel, account for less than 10% of total production. Sea Island cotton, from the West Indies, is a very high quality type produced in vanishingly small quantities. The most common type world-wide is the American Upland cotton, with about 85%.

Naturally-coloured cottons, mostly in brown shades, have been adapted for commercial production on a very limited scale.

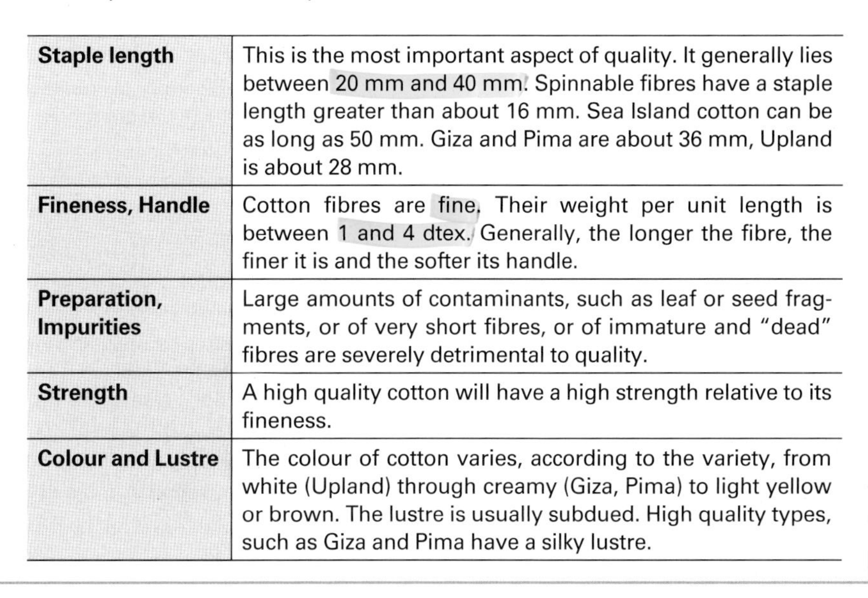

Staple length	This is the most important aspect of quality. It generally lies between 20 mm and 40 mm. Spinnable fibres have a staple length greater than about 16 mm. Sea Island cotton can be as long as 50 mm. Giza and Pima are about 36 mm, Upland is about 28 mm.
Fineness, Handle	Cotton fibres are fine. Their weight per unit length is between 1 and 4 dtex. Generally, the longer the fibre, the finer it is and the softer its handle.
Preparation, Impurities	Large amounts of contaminants, such as leaf or seed fragments, or of very short fibres, or of immature and "dead" fibres are severely detrimental to quality.
Strength	A high quality cotton will have a high strength relative to its fineness.
Colour and Lustre	The colour of cotton varies, according to the variety, from white (Upland) through creamy (Giza, Pima) to light yellow or brown. The lustre is usually subdued. High quality types, such as Giza and Pima have a silky lustre.

1.2.1 Cotton (3)

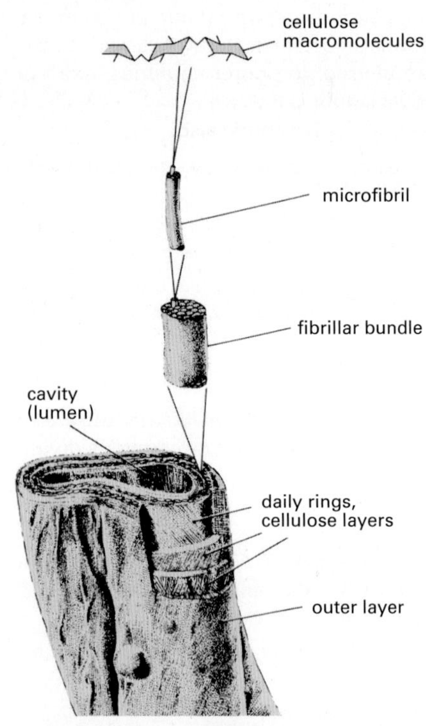

1: Model of the cotton fibre

Construction of the Cotton Fibre (*Figure 1*)

Cotton is composed of cellulose, the foundation of all plants.

Whilst it is growing inside the boll, the fibre is circular (annular) in section. When the boll opens, the fibre begins to dry and it collapses to a kidney-shaped cross-section. At very strong magnification in the electron microscope a suitably prepared cross-section shows daily growth rings, comparable with the annual rings in wood. These are the result of daily deposits of layer upon layer of fresh cellulose, proceeding from the outside inwards. The first-formed outer layer is composed of an especially tough kind of cellulose. At the end of the growth period, a cavity remains at the centre. This is called the Lumen. During drying the fibre twists along its length axis and looks like a flattened, twisted tube. A layer of natural wax coats the surface.

Each cellulose layer is formed from fibrillar bundles composed of individual fibrils (fibril = tiny fibre). The fibrils are made of cellulose macromolecules. The fibrillar bundles of succeeding cellulose layers are inclined at an angle to the length axis of the fibre. Spaces between the ordered lattice of the fibrillar structure, as well as the hollow fibre centre, are easily penetrated by water. Moisture can be stored in the cavities. Sweat can be absorbed and will be removed during subsequent washing. Cotton is stronger when it is swollen by water. This is because the presence of water promotes a more uniform distribution of stresses across and along the cellulose layers.

The high strength of the cotton fibre is a consequence of its construction from highly organised cellulose chain molecules in the fibre interior (crystalline regions). Its low elasticity is due to slippage between the crystalline regions.

Clothing Comfort (*see pages 48, 49*)	
Thermal insulation	Cotton fibres are relatively fine and flexible. Therefore they are often made into textiles which have a relatively low proportion of entrapped air (low specific volume). Warmer, more voluminous materials can be made, however, by appropriate choice of yarn and fabric constructions and through roughening (raising) the surface.
Moisture absorption	Cotton can absorb up to 20% of water vapour without feeling wet. Cotton fabrics absorb liquid very rapidly and can contain up to 65% (wovens) or 90% (knits) of their own weight without dripping. Cotton dries slowly.
Next-to-skin comfort	Cotton is very comfortable next to the skin because of its fineness and softness.

Other Important Properties (*see pages 41, 42, 43*)	
Strength	The strength of cotton is good: 20 to 50 cN/tex in a fibre-bundle tensile test. It is stronger when wet than when dry. Abrasion resistance and durability are good.
Extensibility	The extensibility is relatively low, at about 6 to 10%.
Elasticity/creasing	Cotton has very poor elasticity and therefore it creases easily.
Electrostatic charge	Under normal conditions it develops scarcely any electrostatic charge because it always contains moisture, which conducts the charge away.
Fineness and Handle	Cotton fibres are fine and soft; they have a pleasant handle.

Improvement of Properties by Finishing (*see Chapter 7*)	
Mercerizing	Treatment of cotton under tension with caustic soda solution causes the fibre cross-section to become more circular. This results in higher strength and lustre.
Easy-care finish	The elasticity of cotton, and hence its resistance to creasing, can be improved by cross-linking the cellulose chains, using synthetic resins. There is a consequent reduction in strength and absorptivity, and an increase in the rate of drying.
Anti-shrink finish	Shrinkage is induced in the fabric to avoid such shrinkage appearing after subsequent wet treatments. This process is important for improving the laundering characteristics of cotton textiles – especially when a household tumble dryer is used.
Water repellency	Cotton textiles can be made water repellent by treatment with special chemicals (e.g. silicones).

1.2.1 Cotton (4)

Fibre Identification

Microscopy	Burning Test	Tearing Test	Solubility Test
1: Longitudinal View of a mature fibre mature, im-mature, dead, mercer-ized **2: Cross sections**	**Combustion:** Quick, bright, with afterglow. **Smell:** Like burnt paper. **Residue:** Pale grey, powdery ash.	**Dry tearing:** Short fibres appear at the torn edges (cf. linen). **Wet tearing:** If a spot of water is applied, the yarns will not tear across the wet area (cf. viscose).	**Sulphuric acid:** Dissolves; cotton is destroyed (cf. wool). **Alkalis:** Safe in washing liquors. Caustic soda is utilised in finishing (cf. wool).

Typical Cotton Fabrics

Batiste
Buckram
Bedford Cord
Calico
Cambric
Chintz
Corduroy
Cretonne
Damask
Denim
Drill
Flannelette
Gabardine
Interlock
Oxford
Piqué
Plain rib
Poplin
Terry
Velvet

Fibre Blends (*see page 44*)

Fibre blending allows for the disadvantages of one fibre to be offset by the advantages of another, or for special effects to be achieved, or for the cost to be reduced. Cotton is most often blended with polyester but also with nylon, acrylic, viscose and modal fibres. Blending with synthetic man-made fibres improves the easy-care and durability of clothing. Blending with viscose and modal fibres may be for their lustre and uniformity, whilst preserving good moisture absorption. Modal fibres are a good match for cotton in their strength and extensibility. Blends with other fibres are also possible. The most common blends are 35:65, 50:50, and 70:30 cotton:polyester. Note that different varieties of cotton are frequently blended together in 100% cotton yarns.

Applications

Apparel Fabrics	Accessories	Household Textiles	Technical Textiles
Shirts, blouses, underwear, nightwear, outerwear, rain-wear (water-repellent finish-es), trousers (jeans, chinos), leisure wear, workwear.	Handkerchiefs, laces, ribbons, trimmings, umbrellas.	Bed clothes, table and kitchen cloths, decorative fabrics, furniture coverings, hand and bath towels.	Workwear and protective clothing, awnings, tarpaulins, sewing threads.

Aftercare

The most severe laundering conditions that a fibre could tolerate are seldom those to be recommended for a given item of clothing. Limitations may be imposed, for example, by yarn and fabric construction, type of finish, garment construction and decoration. **Care symbols,** used to indicate the appropriate aftercare regime, are illustrated and explained on *pages 46 and 47.*

Washing	Bleaching	Drying	Ironing	Professional Cleaning
95 60 40 30			steam iron	P W

Textile Labelling

The laws governing product descript-ions allow the name "Cotton" to be applied only to fibres obtained from the seeds of the cotton plant.

International Cotton Emblem

The Cotton Emblem is registered internationally. It serves clearly to identify textiles made from pure cotton and implies good quality. It may not be applied to fibre blends.

3: International Cotton Emblem

1.2.2 Flax[1] (1)

Flax German: Leinen French: Lin Spanish: Lino

1: Egyptian woman in fine linen fabric

History

Linen[2] has been known in civilised societies for thousands of years. Flax was already being cultivated systematically by ancient Egyptians, Babylonians, Phoenicians, and other civilisations between 5000 and 4000 BC.

Mummies from the pyramids of Egypt are wrapped in linen; cotton was unknown in Ancient Egypt until about 400 BC.

The Romans laid down precise procedures for processing flax fibres which were hardly different, in principle, from those used today.

Linen was especially popular in the Middle Ages. It remains to this day a highly valued natural product.

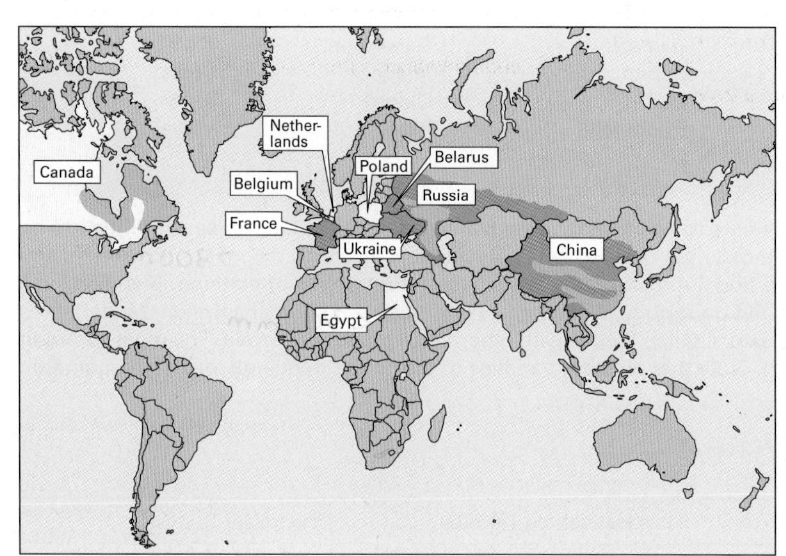

2: Flax growing countries

Production and Sources

World production of flax has been almost constant for the last 25 years at between 600 000 and 700 000 tonnes. This represents less than 1.5% of world fibre production.

The main producing countries, by area (*Figure 2*), are:

Leading Producers	Others
China	Egypt
Russia	Belgium
Belarus	Netherlands
Ukraine	Poland
France	

In recent years, attempts have been made to expand flax production in Europe and the USA.

3: Flax plant

4: Flowering flax

5: Ripe flax

The Flax Plant

Flax fibres are extracted from the stalks of the flax plant (*Figure 3*), which may be grown either for its fibres or for its seed. For fibre extraction, tall varieties with white to light blue flowers and a height of 80 to 120 cm are grown. The shorter types are grown for linseed oil (*Figure 4*).

Flax is an annual plant; it must be re-seeded every year. It thrives in temperate climates. Regions with a maritime climate grow the best flax qualities.

Planting is in March and April, and growth takes 90 to 120 days. The plant has side branches only at the top of the stem, from which the flowers grow. After flowering, the mature plant develops seed capsules the size of peas. The seeds are about 2 mm long and are very rich in oil (*Figure 5*).

Harvesting is in July and August.

[1] Flax: fibres extracted from the flax plant
[2] Linen: yarns made from flax fibres and fabrics made from linen yarns

1.2.2 Flax (2)

1: Flax Harvesting

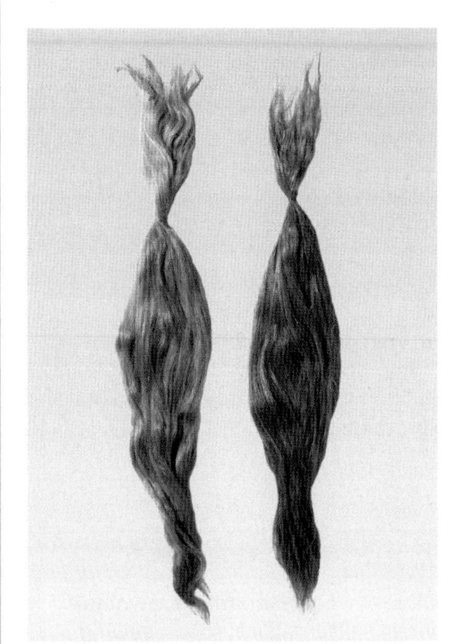

2: Hackled Flax

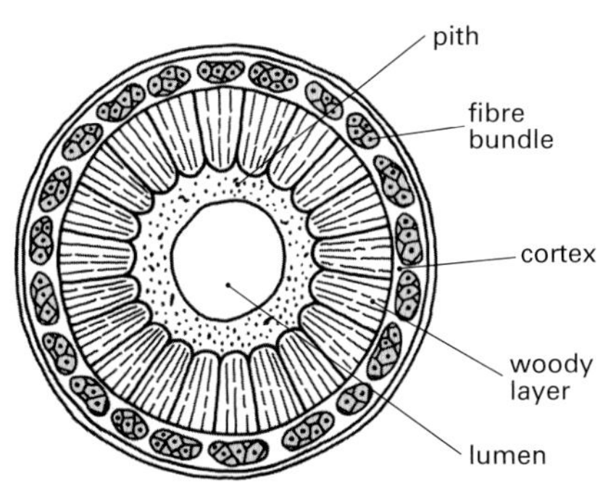

3: Flax stem cross-section, schematic

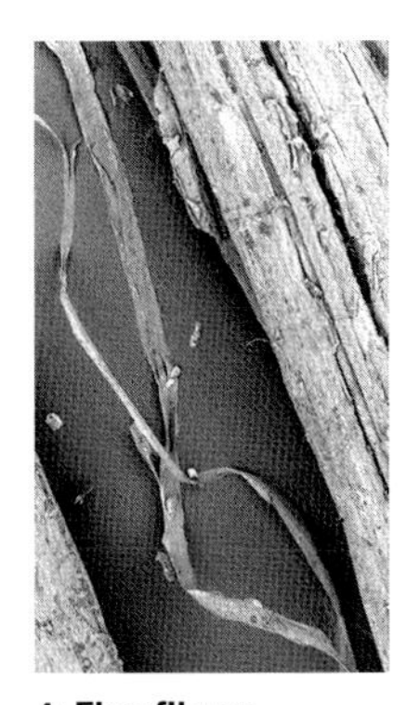

4: Flax fibres, longitudinal view

5: Flax fibres, cross-section

Harvesting and Fibre Extraction

60-70% cellulose

Pulling: Traditionally, the plant was harvested whole, including the roots, in order to preserve the full length of the fibres. Nowadays harvesting machinery is available either for pulling or, more often, for cutting (*Figure 1*).

Drying: Usually, the stalks will be stacked in bundles in the field (stooking) and left to dry out, but drying ovens can also be used.

Retting: Degrading the woody part of the stems so that the fibres are loosened. Retting can be natural, in the field or pond (dew retting), or can be accelerated by using tanks of warm water, with or without extra chemicals.

Extraction of the Fibre Bundles

Roughing out: Removing the seeds and other extraneous material from the stems.

Breaking and Scutching: After loosening the fibres from the wood by retting, the flax straw is broken and the woody parts are removed by scutching. The products are line fibre, with a length of 45 to 90 cm, and scutcher tow, with a length of 10 to 25 cm.

Hackling, Heckling: This is a process of combing out the bast fibres into spinnable fibre bundles (*Figure 2*). The remaining woody particles and short fibres are removed at the same time. The main product is line flax; the by-product is **hackle**, or **heckle tow**.

Roughing out, Breaking, Scutching and Hackling are all part of a single, continuous process.

Processing into Yarn

Line flax: The longer fibres of the line tow are spun into relatively smooth, strong, uniform linen yarns using the linen (wet spinning) process. > 300 mm

Tow flax: The shorter fibres of the hackle tow are spun into coarser, irregular yarns or may be used for blending with other fibres. < 300 mm

Afine, Cottonised flax: The shortest tow fibres may also be chemically and mechanically reduced further – even to their ultimates – so that they are short and fine enough to be blended with cotton.

Construction of a Flax Fibre *(Figures 3 to 5)*

The cross-section of a flax stalk is composed of several layers which have to be removed in order to release the fibre bundles. The fibre bundles extend all the way to the plant roots. They are made up from individual fibres (ultimates) of about 25 to 40 mm in length which are cemented together by a mixture of lignins, pectins and hemicelluloses. This cement comprises about 30% of the dry weight of flax, with the remainder being mainly cellulose. Flax fibres are relatively stiff, and have a smooth surface, without crimp or convolutions.

Clothing Comfort (*see pages 48, 49*)

Thermal insulation: Yarns and fabrics made from the smooth flax fibres do not enclose much air and have relatively poor insulation properties. Linen fabrics feel fresh and cool, a distinct advantage for Summer clothing.

Moisture absorption: Linen is highly absorbent. It takes up water rapidly and releases it quickly again to the surroundings. In hot weather this helps in regulating the microclimate between body and clothing.

Next-to-skin comfort: Fabrics made from flax fibres are comfortable due to the smooth surface and good moisture absorption.

Other Important Properties (*see pages 41, 42, 43*)

Strength: Flax has very good tenacity and durability. It is stronger wet than dry.

Extensibility: The extensibility of flax, about 2%, is the lowest of all apparel fibres.

Elasticity/creasing: Flax has a low elasticity; it creases very easily.

Electrostatic charge: Practically nil, under normal conditions, since the fibre always contains moisture.

Surface, Lustre: Because of its smooth surface, linen fabric has a subdued lustre, does not soil easily, and does not shed lint.

Fineness, Handle: The coarse fibre bundles give linen a firm handle.

Improvement of Properties by Finishing (*see Chapter 7*)

Like cotton, linen fabrics can be given mercerizing and easy-care treatments (*see page 10*).

100kg of stems yields 4kg of flax fibre

1.2.2 Flax (3)

Fibre Identification

Microscopy	Burning Test	Tearing Test	Light Test, Oil Test
fibre ultimate fibre bundle (cross-section)	**Combustion:** Quick, bright, with afterglow. **Smell:** Like burnt paper. **Residue:** Pale grey, powdery ash.	**Dry tearing:** The torn edges are much longer than with cotton. Linen Cotton	When held up to the light, pure linen fabrics show thick places in both warp and weft. An oil spot on a linen fabric is more transparent than on cotton.

Typical Linen Fabrics (with typically irregular yarns)

Crash	Filter cloth	Holland	Interlining
Duck	Half linen (Union)	Huckaback	Mattress ticking

Fibre Blends (*see page 44*)

The most important mixtures are with cotton. "Half linen" or Union is a fabric with cotton warp yarns and linen weft (*see Textile Labelling and Linen Seal, below*). Flax is also mixed with other bast fibres, such as hemp and ramie, and with cellulosic or synthetic man-made fibres, such as modal, polyamide, polyester, or polyacrylics. The linen look (yarn structure, colour and lustre) can be imitated to some extent by synthetic fibres, but without the typical linen properties.

Applications

Apparel Fabrics	Accessories	Household Textiles	Technical Textiles
Leisure wear and Summer wear: blouses, shirts, skirts, trousers, jackets, suits, inter-linings for stiffening.	Pockets, bags, shoes, hats.	Bed clothing, tablecloths, drapes, furniture and wall coverings, mattress lining.	Lace, trimmings, awnings, tarpaulins, ropes, sewing thread.

Aftercare

The most severe laundering conditions that a fibre could tolerate are seldom those to be recommended for a given item of clothing. Limitations may be imposed, for example, by yarn and fabric construction, type of finish, garment construction and decoration. **Care symbols**, used to indicate the appropriate aftercare regime, are illustrated and explained on *pages 46 and 47*.

Washing	Bleaching	Drying	Ironing	Professional Cleaning
95 60 40 30			steam iron	P W

Textile Labelling

The laws governing product descriptions allow the name linen to be used only for fibres originating from the **stems of the flax plant.**

Textiles made from **100% linen** may be described as pure linen. Both warp and weft must be made from pure flax yarns.

The term **"half linen"** may be used for fabrics in which the warp is made only from cotton, the weft is only linen, and the overall **linen content is at least 40%.** The label should state "Cotton warp, linen weft".

Registered Trade Marks

The linen industry of Western Europe (spinners, weavers, knitters) has formed an association to promote linen use and offer certain quality guarantees. It has created a trademarked label for its products and has registered the mark world-wide. The **Masters of Linen Seal** has the form of a stylised **"L"** and is administered by the European Confederation of Linen and Hemp **(CELC)**. It guarantees European traceability of origin of linen products (grown and manufactured in Europe) through the member companies.

Another trademark is that of the German Linen Association, the **Schwurhand Siegel** which, roughly, means the **Sign of the Pledge**. It is a guarantee of quality and is administered by the **Schwurhand-Zeichenverband e.V.** in Bielfeld.

1.2.3 Seed, Bast, and Hard Fibres

Seed Fibre			Properties and Applications
Kapok	**Seed fibre** from the Kapok tree. **Producers:** Brazil, India, Indonesia, Mexico, East and West Africa.	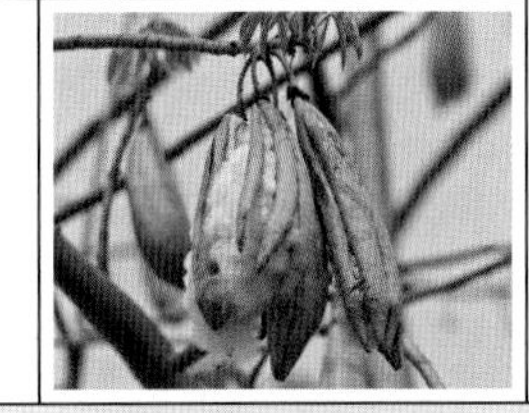	Kapok fibres cannot be spun into yarns because they are very weak. Their density is only 0.35 g/cm³, due to the large air-filled lumen. The fibres are water repellent, fine, soft, and lustrous. **Applications:** Kapok fibres are used as stuffings and waddings for e.g. cushions, bolsters, and mattresses. In addition, Kapok is suitable as filling for life jackets.
Bast Fibres			
Hemp	**Bast fibre** from the stems of the hemp plant. **Producers:** Poland, Hungary, Romania, China, Germany, Netherlands, France.	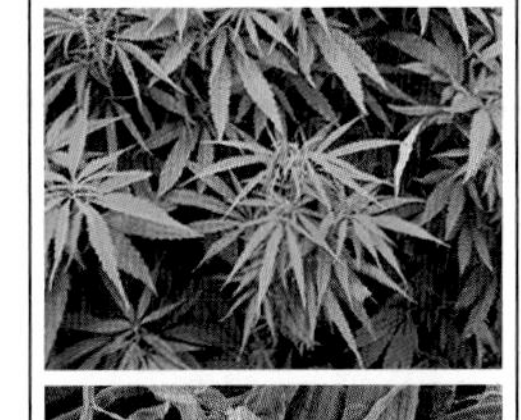	Cultivation of hemp was banned for a while but nowadays specific varieties are allowed for fibre production. Production in Central Europe is increasing due to its environmental friendliness i.e. minimum requirement for fertiliser and pesticides. After cutting down the (up to 3m tall) plants, the fibre extraction processes, and the resulting fibre properties, are similar to Flax. Processing of hemp fibre into apparel takes place mainly in China. **Applications:** Hemp fibre is used mainly in industrial outlets such as insulation in automobiles (ca. 40 kg per family car). Apparel uses are e.g. lightweight shirts and blouses. The seed oil is used for cosmetics and for cattle fodder.
Ramie	**Bast fibre** from the stems of the ramie plant. Also known as Oriental linen or New Zealand Flax. **Producers:** China, Brazil, Central America. Far East	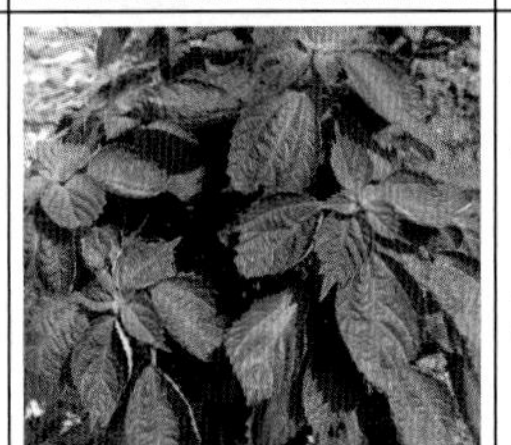	Ramie fibres are strong and high grade bast fibres, similar to flax. They are smooth and uniform, easy to dye and resistant to light. The fibres are white, with a durable lustre and good absorbency, but the handle is somewhat harder than cotton. **Applications:** Ramie is used mainly in technical outlets to make fine, light and durable fabrics for kitchen and table cloths, belts and ribbons. Short, waste fibres may be included in banknotes. Ramie is seldom used for clothing.
Jute	**Bast fibre** from the stems of jute plants. **Producers:** India, Bangladesh, Pakistan.		Jute fibres are very woody and irregular. They tend to have a strong aroma, due to the oils used in processing. Strength, extensibility and elasticity are similar to flax. **Applications:** Jute is manufactured into packaging fabrics, wall coverings (hessian), and base cloths for belts and carpets. Jute can also form the backing cloth for floor coverings.
Hard Fibres for Technical Uses			
Sisal	**Leaf fibre** from the leaves of the sisal plant, a type of agave. **Producers:** Brazil, Indonesia, Mexico, East Africa.	 	Sisal fibres have a high strength and abrasion resistance. They are white in colour, easy to dye, and have good resistance to sea water. **Applications:** Sisal is used for ropes, carpets, nets, and matting.
Manila	**Leaf fibre** from the leaves of a type of banana (Abaca) **Origin:** Philippines (capital: Manila), Ecuador.		Manila fibres are stronger than sisal. They are very resistant to sea water. **Applications:** Manila is used for teabags, banknotes and reinforced plastics, for marine cables and other ropes, also for nets and matting.
Coir	**Seed fibre** from the coconut palm. **Producers:** India, Indonesia, Sri Lanka.	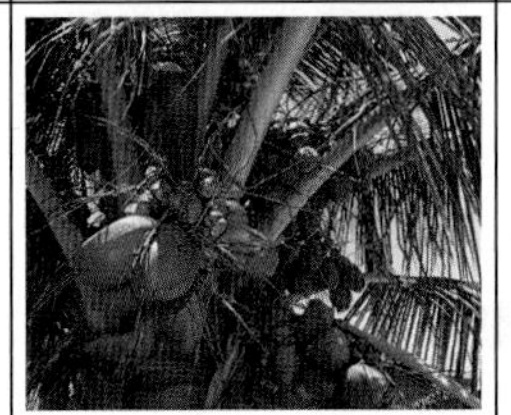	Coir fibres have a very high abrasion resistance, are very durable and have good elasticity. They do not soil easily, are good insulators and are resistant to rotting. They are often used in the raw form. **Applications:** Coir is used primarily for padding materials in the automobile industry, but also for stair-carpets, doormats, floor coverings, stuffed furniture backings, and brushes.
Other Vegetable Fibres			
Fibres extracted from nettle, bamboo, seaweed, hops, kenaf, banana, yucca and other shrubs, trees, or sedges.			

1.3.1 Wool (1)

Wool German: Wolle French: Laine Spanish: Lana

History

Wool felts were known 7000 years ago in China, in Babylon, and in Egypt. Shearing of the wool, rather than pulling, was made possible by the invention of cutting tools in the Iron Age. The Merino sheep, which has the finest wool, was bred in Spain in the 14th century. Sheep breeding began in Australia at the end of the 18th century. Today, Australia rears about 100 million sheep – about 10% of the world's sheep population.

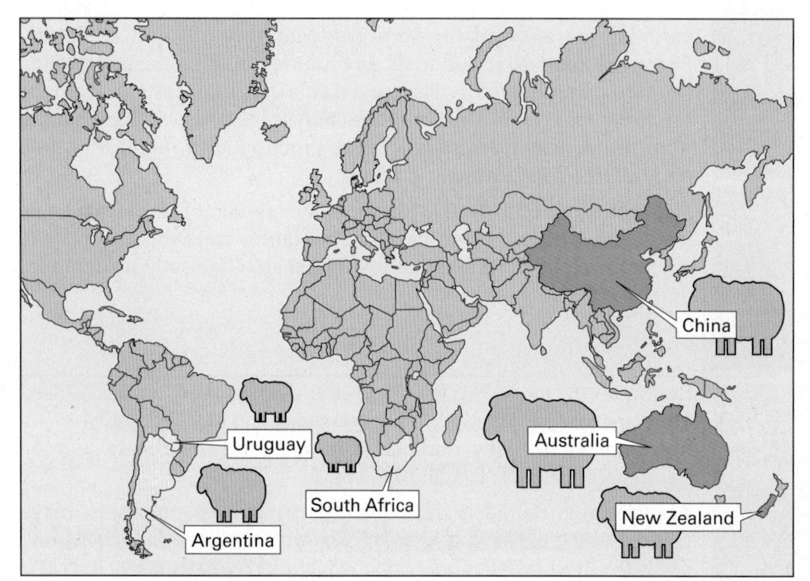

1: Wool producing countries

Production and Sources

During the 20th century, the production of wool roughly doubled. Production of scoured wool is now about 1.3 million tonnes; unscoured wool is about 2.2 million tonnes. This represents about 2% of total world fibre production. Sheep are to be found in almost every country in the world.

The most important wool producers are shown in *Figure 1*.

Leading Producers	Others
Australia	Argentina
China	South Africa
New Zealand	Uruguay

Wool Production

Shearing: The sheep are shorn using electric shears. Care must be taken to avoid injuries and to ensure that the coat is separated intact. This coat is called the **fleece.** Wool from the legs is short and coarse. Because of its lower quality, it is separated from the fleece during shearing.

2: Merino ram

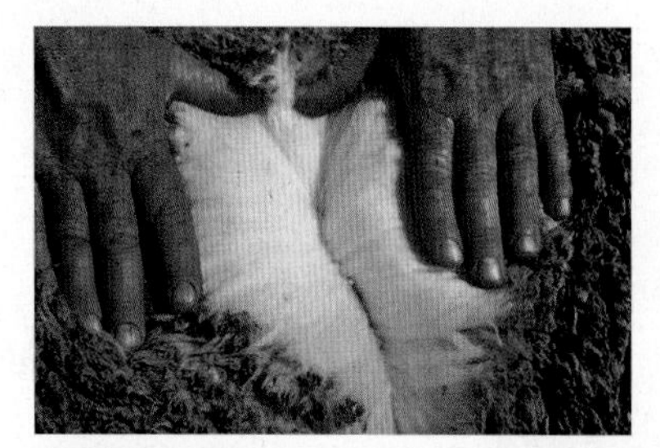

3: Examination

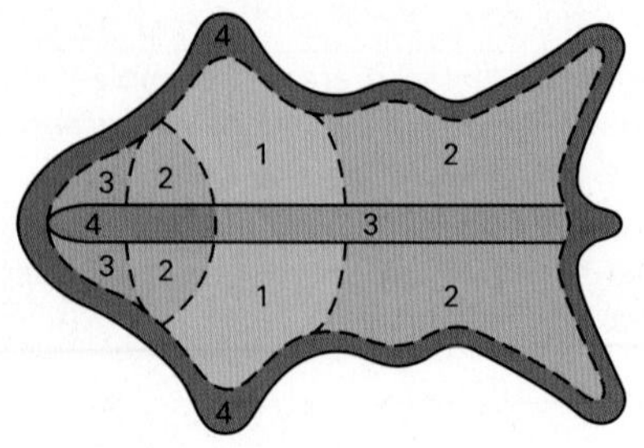

4: Fleece

5: Worsted fabric

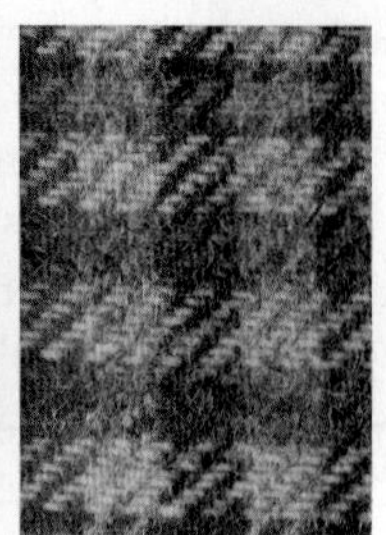

6: Woollen fabric

Classing: After shearing, the fleece is graded into essentially four qualities (1 = best, 4 = worst) (*Figure 4*). The grader classifies the wool according to fineness, crimp, length, impurities, and colour. Heavy contamination is found in the belly area.

Scouring: An unscoured fleece weighs between 1 and 6 kg. The average Australian fleece weighs 4.5 kg. About 40% of this weight is grease (lanolin), dirt, and burs. The dirt and most of the grease are removed by a gentle scouring.

Carbonising: Vegetable impurities are removed, when necessary, by treatment with sulphuric acid.

Processing into yarn: Wool fibres are spun into fine, smooth yarns by the Worsted process and into coarser, more bulky yarns by the Woollen process (*Figures 5 and 6*).

1.3.1 Wool (2)

Classification of Wool

There are hundreds of different types and breeds of sheep. They are classified according to their wool into five basic types: Fine, Medium, Crossbred, Long, and Coarse.

Wool Type	Fine	Medium, Crossbred	Long, Coarse
Breed (examples)	Merino, Rambouillet	Southdown, Corriedale	Lincoln, Romney, Karakul
Fineness, Diameter	finest wools, 15...23 µm[1]	medium fine, 24...30 µm	coarse, over 30 µm
Length	50...120 mm	120...150 mm	over 150 mm
Crimp, Waviness	highly crimped	normal crimp	low crimp, straight
Sources (examples)	Australia, South Africa	Argentina, Uruguay	New Zealand, Great Britain
Applications	fine outerwear, knitted and woven, shawls, socks	heavier, more robust, sporting clothing	carpets, traditional furniture coverings

[1] 1 µm = 1 millionth of a metre = 10^{-6} m

Apart from its fineness, length, crimp, and breed, wool can also be classified according to:

- **Shearing: Lambswool** is from the first shearing, after six months, whilst **Yearling wool** is from the first or second shear after 10-12 months. They are fine, soft, not very strong, with fine tips. **Six-month, Eight-month, Twelve-month wools** are from sheep shorn at intervals of 6, 8 or 12 months.
- **Source: Australian, New Zealand,** etc. **Cape** wool is from South Africa; **Shetland** is typical coarse wool from Scotland.
- **Extraction: Virgin wool** is from living, healthy sheep or lambs. **Dead wool, Fallen wool** is from sheep that have died from natural causes. **Skin wool** has been taken from the skins of slaughtered sheep.
- **Spinning: Worsted wool** is usually fine Merino, spun into fine, smooth, uniform, combed yarns. The very finest and most expensive wools are made into extra-fine combed yarns designated as **super 100s to super 200s. Woollens** are heavier, more voluminous yarns prepared on the woollen spinning system. **Carpet wool** is long, coarse wools for carpet yarns.
- **Recycling: Recovered Wool** is wool that has been recovered mechanically by teasing apart production waste and second-hand clothing. Recovered wool is damaged and is of low quality.

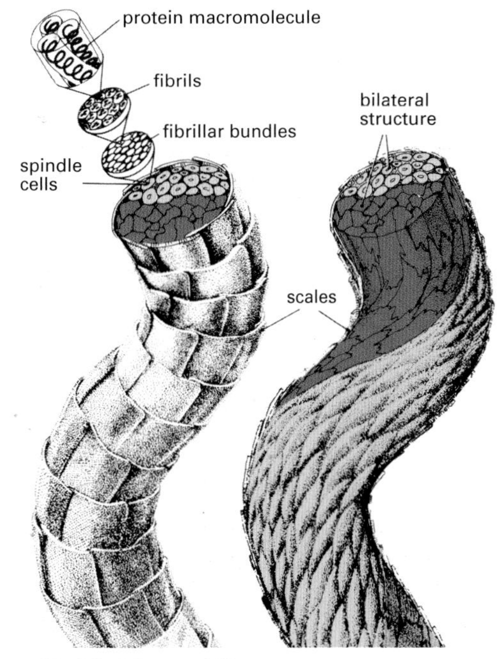

1: Model of the wool fibre

Construction of the Wool Fibre

The wool fibre (*Figure 1*) is made of **protein molecules (keratin).** It is rather similar to human hair. The long-chain protein molecules are formed into **fibrils.** These combine into **fibrillar bundles** which form the mass of the **spindle cells.** This construction gives the wool fibre an extraordinary elasticity. The bulk of the fibre is made from two separate components. These have different chemical constitutions, and they wind in a spiral around each other **(bilateral structure)**. Moisture and temperature have different effects upon the two components, which swell to different extents, causing changes in the overall fibre shape. It is the bilateral structure which causes the fibres to be crimped; finer fibres develop more crimp. Heat and moisture can relax bonds between the protein chains. The bonds are re-formed during cooling and drying, and this is the source of the good smoothing and shaping properties of wool.

Wool absorbs moisture (is hygroscopic). It can absorb about 1/3 of its mass of water vapour without feeling wet. The moisture is released only slowly. In spite of the strong affinity for water of the fibre interior, its surface is water repellent (hydrophobic) because it is covered by an extremely thin skin, the **epicuticle.** This skin causes liquid water to roll up into droplets whilst allowing the passage of water vapour.

The **scales** on the fibre surfaces are capable of hooking onto one another to cause felting, under the influence of water, heat, and mechanical action.

1.3.1 Wool (3)

Clothing Comfort (*see pages 48, 49*)	
Thermal insulation	In smooth, combed yarns, the fine wool fibres are tightly constrained so they can scarcely crimp. Fine combed yarns enclose less air and therefore provide less insulation. Bulky woollen yarns have a looser structure. The fibres can develop their crimp inside the yarn and, due to the large amount of entrapped air, offer excellent protection against cold.
Moisture absorption	Wool is **hygroscopic.** It can absorb up to a third of its weight in moisture vapour without feeling wet, and can chemically bind liquid perspiration. Water vapour is absorbed very rapidly, but water droplets are repelled. Liquid water is absorbed only very slowly. Such behaviour is called **"hydrophobic"**. Wet wool dries very slowly.
Next-to-skin comfort	The softness of wool depends on its fineness. Lambswool and fine Merino wool are especially soft. Fibres that are coarser than about 30 µm can irritate the skin.
Other Important Properties (*see pages 41, 42, 43*)	
Strength	Wool has adequate strength which, nevertheless, is lower than that of most apparel fibres. Textiles made from wool are not particularly durable.
Extensibility	The fibres have very good extensibility, which is greater when wet than dry. Dripping wet wool garments should be laid flat to dry, to avoid stretching.
Elasticity/creasing	Elasticity and "springiness" are excellent. Creases soon drop out of wool clothing (especially under the influence of steam).
Formability	The molecular chains in the wool fibre can be re-oriented under the influence of heat and moisture. In this way, wool fabrics can be more or less durably shaped.
Felting	Felting is the matting together of fibres, under the influence of mechanical action, heat and water. It is facilitated by the scales on the fibre surface, which can hook onto each other. The effect is utilised for the production of felts but it is a disadvantage in the aftercare of wool clothing.
Fineness, Handle	Wool fibres may be fine or coarse, depending on the type. The very finest Merino wools (less than 16 µm) are designated Super 100's. They are sold at special auctions and are made into extremely fine, soft fabrics.
Electrostatic charge	Wool fibres develop only small electrostatic charges because, under normal conditions, they always contain some moisture which conducts the charge away.
Flammability	Wool does not burn easily. It is suitable for protective clothing.
Improvement of Properties by Finishing (*see Chapter 7*)	
Permanent creasing	Ironed creases can be **durably fixed** through heat, pressure and chemicals (Siroset process).
Decatizing	Application of heat, moisture, and pressure **stabilises** and **smoothens** wool textiles. Fabrics have improved handle and lustre, and are then ready for making into clothing.
Anti-felting treatment	Wool can be made **machine-washable** by chemical treatments which greatly reduce the tendency of the fibres to felt.
Soil release	A surface coating is applied, usually a silicone polymer, which **resists soiling** and **facilitates cleaning.**
Flame retardance	**Protection against heat and flames** is good and can be improved by treatment with chemicals that combine with the wool protein molecules.
Carbonising	Removal of **vegetable impurities** using sulphuric acid.
Mothproofing	Treatment of the fabric with e.g. Eulan or Mitin, which make the fibres inedible and to which the moths are averse (household textiles).
Raising	**Fibre ends** are teased out of the textile material to **build a nap.** The weave structure is obscured. Often follows fulling.
Fulling	**Controlled felting** of wool materials. The material shrinks and becomes denser.

1.3.1 Wool (4)

Fibre Identification

Microscopy	Burning Test	Rubbing Test	Solubility Test
Cross-section: round. **Appearance:** overlapping scales, like roof tiles	**Combustion:** small, sputtering flame, self-extinguishing. **Smell:** like burning hair. **Residue:** black, friable cinder.	If a wool fibre is held between thumb and fore-finger (parallel to them), and thumb and finger are rubbed together, then the fibre will travel in one direction. If the fibre is turned around, then it travels in the opposite direction.	**Sulphuric acid:** Cold, concentrated sulphuric acid has scarcely any effect (cf. cotton). **Alkalis:** Boiling 5% caustic soda, and lithium hypochlorite solutions will dissolve wool (cf. cotton).

Typical Wool Fabrics

Afghalaine, Baize, Charmelaine, Cheviot, Donegal, Felt, Flannel, Fleece, Fresco, Loden, Saxony, Serge, Shetland, Tartan, Tricotine, Tweed

Fibre Blends (*see page 44*)

Wool is excellent for blending with synthetic fibres, such as polyester, acrylic, and nylon. Both fibres are complemented in the mixture; the tendency to felting is reduced and the aftercare characteristics are enhanced. In addition, the durability is improved. So long as the proportion of wool is greater than 50%, then its good clothing comfort properties are retained. Common blend ratios are 50:50, 55:45, 60:40, 70:30, and 80:20. Wool is also blended with silk, with cotton, and especially with fine hair fibres.

Applications

Apparel Fabrics	Accessories	Household Textiles	Technical Textiles
Suits, costumes, pullovers, waistcoats, overcoats, dresses, winter blouses.	Gloves, scarves, hats, socks, stockings.	Blankets, carpets, drapes, furnishings.	Fire protection clothing, industrial felts.

Aftercare

The most severe laundering conditions that a fibre could tolerate are seldom those to be recommended for a given item of clothing. Limitations may be imposed, for example, by yarn and fabric construction, type of finish, garment construction and decoration. **Care symbols,** used to indicate the appropriate aftercare regime, are illustrated and explained on *pages 46 and 47.*

Washing	Bleaching	Drying	Ironing	Professional Cleaning
40, 30, hand wash, do not wash Washable wool can be **machine-washed** using the wool programme. Sensitive fabrics are **hand-washed** or **dry-cleaned.**	Do not bleach	Wovens can be hung out; knits should be laid flat. **"Total Easy Care"** can be **tumble dried.** TOTAL EASY CARE WOOL WOOLMARK	•• / •	F P W

Textile Labelling

The regulations governing product labelling allow the terms **New Wool** or **Virgin Wool** to be used only for fibres shorn from a living sheep or lamb. Virgin Wool products must be made from wool fibres which have not previously been spun into yarn or felted, nor previously been incorporated into a finished product. Textiles made from 100% Virgin Wool may be labelled as Pure New Wool, or **Pure Virgin Wool.** An allowance may be made for 0.3% of adventitious foreign fibres, 2% for antistatic dressings, and 7% for visible ornamental effects. New Wool and Virgin Wool descriptors may also be used in **blends** where there is only one other fibre present, and where the proportion of Virgin Wool is at least 25%.

The term **Pure Wool** may also be used for products made from recovered wool.

Trademarks for New Wool and Blends

The trademarks Woolmark® Woolmark Blend® and Wool Blend® serve to identify high quality textiles. As well as the fibre content, the mark guarantees a certain product quality level: colour fastness, strength, and dimensional stability. Licensed use of the mark is governed by strict regulations, supervised and controlled by the Woolmark Company.

Woolmark® is applied to high quality textiles of Pure New Wool. **Woolmark Blend®** is applied to fibre blends where there is only one other fibre, and a Virgin Wool content of at least 50%. It guarantees the same quality levels as for the Woolmark. Wool Blend® is applied to blends having from 30 to 49% of Virgin Wool – especially in functional textiles.

1.3.2 Hairs

Fine Animal Hairs

Fibre Name	Appearance	Description
Alpaca **Llama** **Vicuna** **Guanaco**		Alpaca, llama, vicuna, and guanaco are all types of **llama,** both wild and domesticated, which live in the Andes mountains of South America. They are shorn every two years and the hairs are sorted by colour and fineness. They are fine, soft, lightly crimped, and very warm. They are used in expensive knitted fabrics, jackets, overcoats, and blankets.
Camel		Camel hair is the downy undercoat of the Bactrian (two-humped) **camel.** It is moulted every year, is very fine, soft, lightly crimped and beige in colour. Camels under one year old are blonde, almost white. Their "baby hair" is especially soft and valuable. Camel hair is used for outerwear. The coarser guard hairs, and those of the one-hump camel, are used for interlinings.
Cashmere **Cashgora**		The **cashmere goat** lives in Mongolia and the Himalayan mountains at altitudes up to 5000 m. To withstand the cold, it has an unusually fine undercoat. At the yearly coat change, the under-hairs are separated from the coarser guard hairs and are sorted by colour. Textiles made from cashmere are very soft, light, and lustrous; it is the most expensive hair fibre. The **cashgora goat** is a cross between the cashmere and the angora goats.
Mohair **Yak**		Mohair is the hair of the **angora goat,** which may be shorn twice each year. The best quality comes from Texas, South Africa, and Turkey. The hairs are long, lightly curled, and have a silky lustre. They are white, do not felt easily, and are well suited for dyeing. Mohair is used for outerwear. Yak is the hair of the domesticated **Tibetan ox.**
Angora **Rabbit**		Angora fibre is the hair of the **angora rabbit,** which is farmed in Europe and East Asia. The name derives from Ankara, in Turkey. The rabbits are shorn up to four times each year. The fine, very light hairs are very good at absorbing moisture vapour. Usually, they are blended with wool and used for thermal underwear and ski underwear. In outerwear, inclusion of the coarse guard hairs gives angora fabrics their typical spiky appearance.

Within the Woolmark, and the textile labelling regulations, fine animal hairs have equivalent status to wool, because they have similar properties. So long as they conform to the quality requirements, fine hairs can be labelled with the Woolmark.

Coarse Animal Hairs

Coarse hairs are used mostly for the manufacture of resilient and stable interlining materials. The most important are **Horse hair, Camel hair** (guard hairs), **Cattle hair,** and **Goat hair.**

1.3.3 Silk (1)

Silk German: Seide French: Soie Spanish: Seda

History

According to legend, almost 5000 years ago the Chinese Empress Si Ling Shi (or Lei Zu) observed a silk caterpillar spinning itself into a cocoon. She unravelled the filaments and made a fabric from them.

The Romans paid one pound of gold for a pound of silk fabric. Caterpillar eggs were smuggled into Europe in about 555 AD and, from then on, it was possible to produce silk in the Mediterranean region.

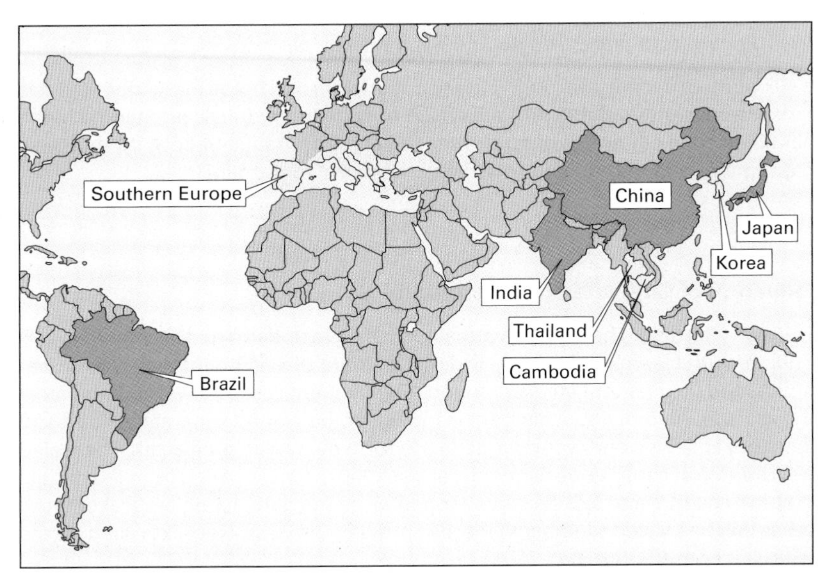

1: Silk producing countries

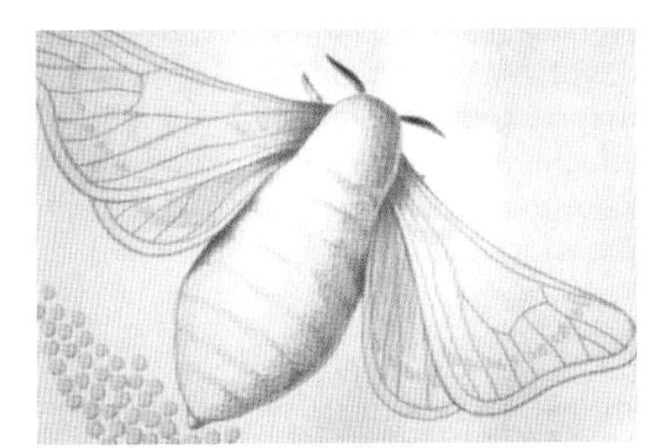

2: Egg-laying female

3: Caterpillar development

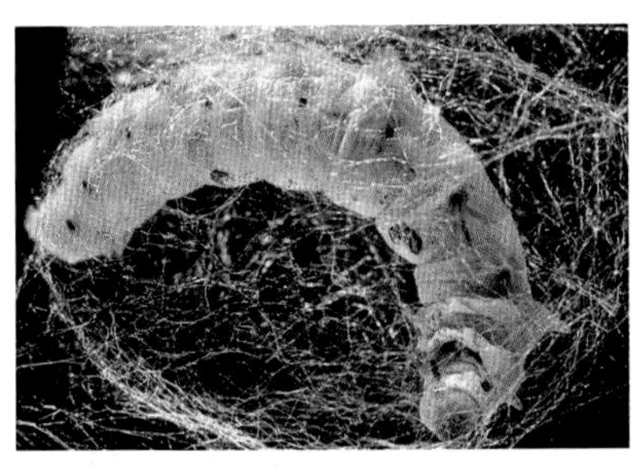

4: Spinning silkworm

5: Cocoons, anchored by floss

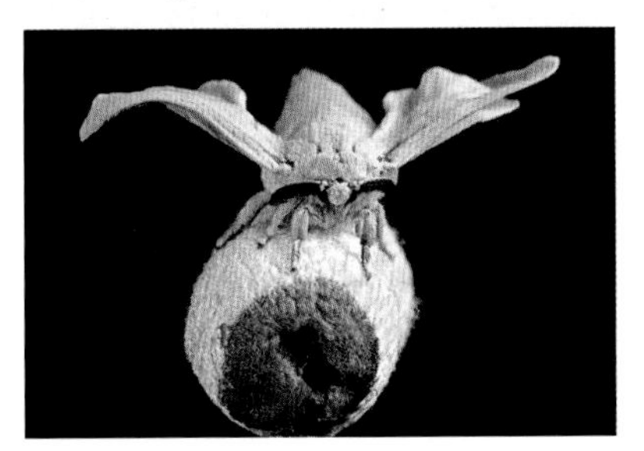

6: Newly emerged moth

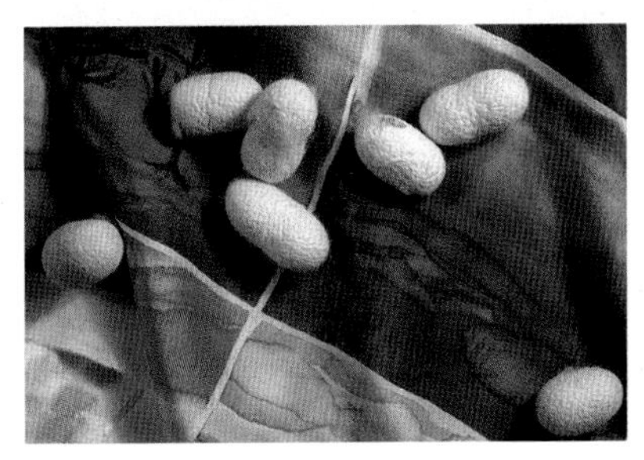

7: Cocoons on silk cloth

Production and Sources

The world production of raw silk is about 140 000 tonnes. This is less than 0.2% of world textile fibre production.

Silk can be produced only where the mulberry tree grows.

The most important producing areas are shown in *Figure 1*.

Leading Producers	Others
China Brazil India Japan	Thailand Cambodia Korea Southern Europe

The Mulberry Silkworm

On emerging from its egg, the mulberry silkworm is only about 2 mm long. It feeds on a large quantity of mulberry leaves (*Figures 2 and 3*).

After about 30 days, and after moulting four times, it will be as large as a middle finger and begins to pupate (*Figure 4*). Straw or twigs are supplied at this stage for the caterpillars to use. The silk fluid **(fibroin,** an animal protein) is extruded from a spinneret located under the lower lip. The spinneret is fed by two glands and the emerging filaments are coated with silk gum **(sericin)**. Spinning takes about 3 days, during which a twin filament of about 3000 m is produced. The silkworm moves its head in a figure-of-eight pattern to create a cocoon about the size of a pigeon's egg. The tangle of loose silk with which the silkworm originally secured its position in the straw, is called **floss,** or **blaze** (*Figure 5*).

The transition from pupa to moth takes about 14 days. The moth dissolves a portion of the cocoon wall and crawls out (*Figure 6*). The moths mate, the female lays, and both die immediately.

The harvest from 50 000 silkworms is about 1000 kg of cocoons (*Figure 7*), which yield about 120 kg of raw silk.

Wild Silk

Beside the mulberry silkworm, there are many wild species. The most important of these is the Tussah.

1.3.3 Silk (2)

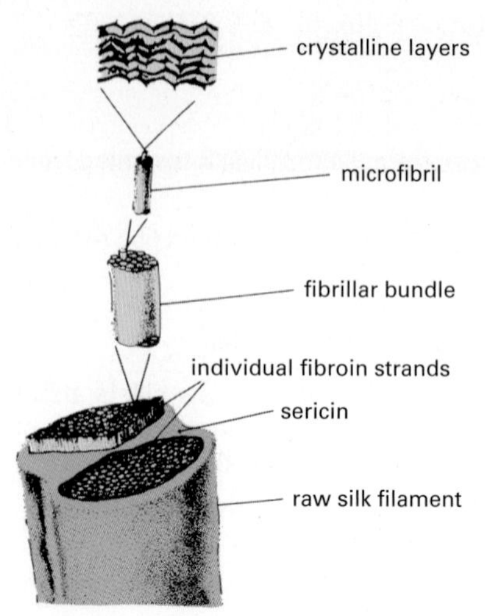

1: Model of a raw silk filament

Construction of the Silk Filament (*Figure 1*)

The basic fibre substance is **fibroin.** Like wool, it is made from long-chain protein molecules. Each of the two individual fibroin filaments is constructed from fibrillar bundles (fibril = tiny fibre) which themselves are made from microfibrils. The microfibrils are built from the protein chains.

The physical, chemical, and clothing-comfort properties of silk are determined by the molecular structure, and the organisation of the polymer chains in the fibre interior. These are disposed in crystalline layers, somewhat like the leaves of a book. This results in high strength and good resilience.

The silk gum, or **sericin,** surrounds the two filaments and holds them together. It is a transparent, water-soluble protein, which may be more or less pigmented in the usual silk-cocoon colours of natural white to yellow or orange-yellow, for mulberry silk, or light brown to reddish-brown or dark brown, for tussah.

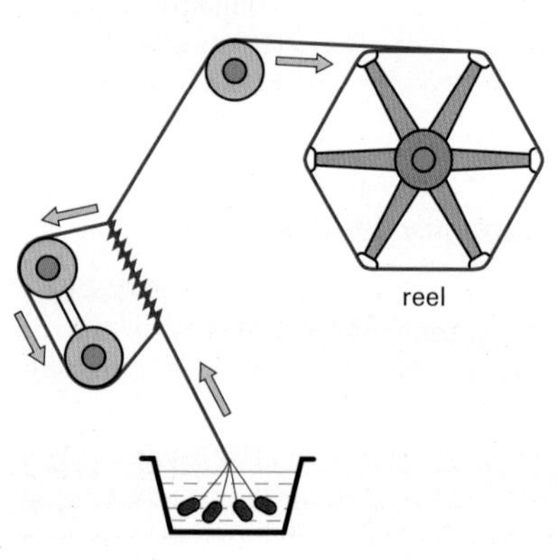

2: Silk reeling

Production of Cultivated (Mulberry) Silk

Reeled silk (Net silk): The silk cultivator needs to have undamaged cocoons. He kills the pupae with steam or dry heat. The cocoons are placed in hot water, to soften the gum, and the filament ends are found. The filaments are then wound up onto a reel (*Figure 2*). An individual filament is too fine to be wound separately, so 7 to 10 of them are collected and wound together to form the **raw** or **greige** silk. The reeled silk is a bundle of continuous filaments, about 1000 m long, coming from the middle part of the cocoon, and still cemented together by the gum. Later, several of these bundles will be twisted together in the silk throwing process. Net silk is used for the finest silk fabrics (*Figure 3*).

Spun silk: Unwindable remnants from the cocoons, together with other waste silk, are first degummed, broken or cut to length, if necessary, and then converted into spun yarns – either by a process similar to the worsted system or one like the woollen system, according to the fibre length. **Schappe** spun silk yarns are made from the longer fibres, separated at a combing machine. They are fine, smooth and regular (*Figure 4*). Schappe is also the name given to silk waste that has been through a fermentation process, instead of the more common alkaline boiling, to remove the sericin gum.

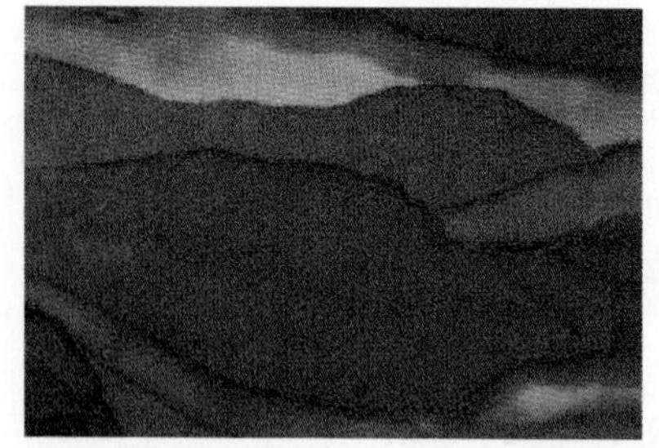

3: Net silk fabric

4: Knitted fabric from spun silk

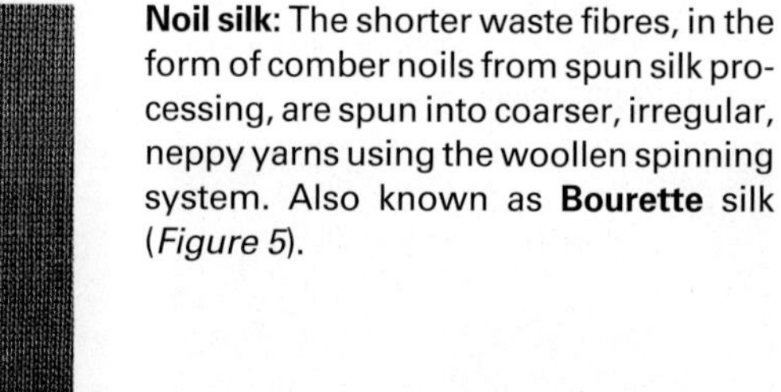

Noil silk: The shorter waste fibres, in the form of comber noils from spun silk processing, are spun into coarser, irregular, neppy yarns using the woollen spinning system. Also known as **Bourette** silk (*Figure 5*).

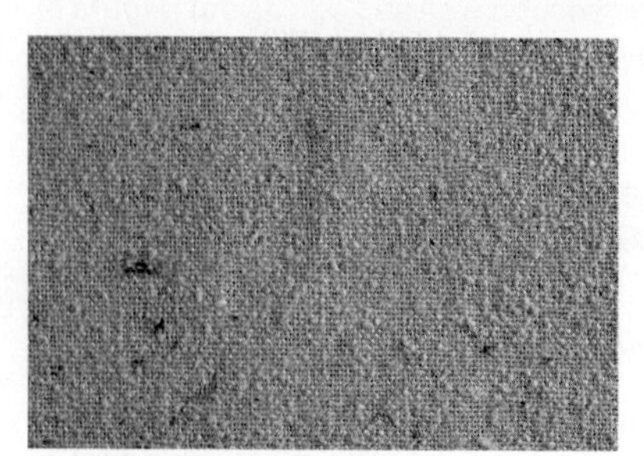

5: Noil (Bourette) silk fabric

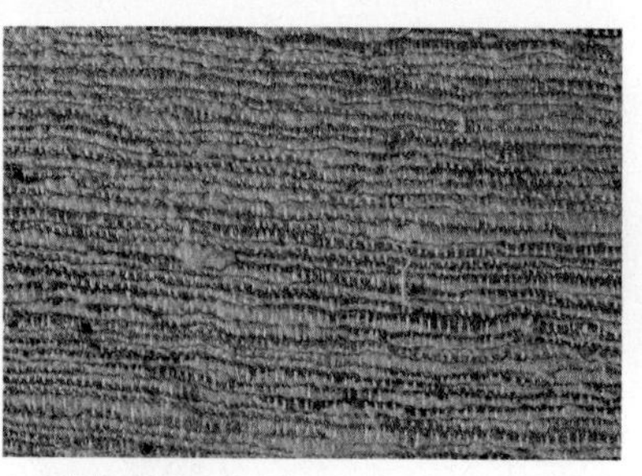

6: Wild silk fabric

Recovery of Wild Silk (Tussah Silk)

The wild Tussah cocoons are gathered from trees and bushes. Wild silk is not easy to degum and usually cannot be reeled. Therefore, it tends to retain its natural reddish or brownish colouring. The filaments exhibit variations in their fineness, which yields the typical wild silk appearance (*Figure 6*).

1.3.3 Silk (3)

Clothing Comfort (*see pages 48, 49*)	
Thermal insulation	Silk is seen as both **cool** and **warming.** Filament silk is made into fine fabrics, with a small volume of enclosed air, which lie smoothly on the skin. This gives a cooling effect. Nevertheless, these fine, compact silk fabrics are good insulators because the layer of warm air, which lies between fabric and skin, is not able to escape very easily.
Moisture absorption	Like wool, it is hygroscopic, and can absorb and hold about 1/3 of its weight of water vapour without feeling wet. Liquids are absorbed rapidly into the non-crystalline regions of the fibre interior.
Next-to-skin comfort	Silk is very **pleasant to wear,** because of its fineness and softness.

Other Important Properties (*see pages 41, 42, 43*)	
Lustre, Fineness, Handle	The most important properties of degummed silk are its **typical lustre,** its **fineness,** and its **pleasant handle.**
Strength	Silk has a very good tenacity.
Extensibility	Extensibility is very good; it lies between 10% and 30%.
Elasticity/creasing	Silk has **outstanding resilience.** With the exception of very fine, smooth, weighted woven fabrics, it does not crease badly and the wrinkles tend to fall out.
Electrostatic charge	Degummed silk will build an electrostatic charge in dry conditions.
Sensitivity	Strong, direct sunlight will weaken silk and cause its colours to fade. Perspiration, deodorant sprays, and perfumes can cause colour changes, and can embrittle the fibre. Therefore underarm linings should be used.
Scroop	When a silk fabric is compressed by hand, it makes a rustling sound somewhat like the crunching of fresh snow.

Improvement of Properties by Finishing (*see Chapter 7*)	
Degumming	The natural silk gum makes knitted and woven raw silk fabrics harsh and rough. The sericin gum is removed by a **gentle boiling in mild alkaline soap** solution.
Weighting	The **weight loss** caused by degumming is **recovered** by the addition of metallic salts or polymeric materials.

Properties of Different Types of Silk (summary)

The properties given above apply mainly to degummed net silk. These properties may vary according to the source (cultivated or wild) the fibre type and processing (net, spun, bourette) and the finishing (raw, degummed, or weighted). The table gives an overview of the most important differences.

Degummed Cultivated Silk	Weighted Cultivated Silk	Wild Silk
• wrinkles little • supple • fine lustre **Net:** • smooth, finest **Spun, Schappe:** • fine, smooth, regular **Noil, Bourette:** • coarser, neppy, irregular	• full • heavy • stiff • wrinkles • less durable • stronger lustre	• coarse (thicker fibre, different cross-section) • usually cannot be degummed • harsh handle • heavier than cultivated silk • darker, duller colours • dull lustre • not so uniform • more sensitive to perspiration

In addition, as with all textile materials, fabric properties are influenced by the weave type and density, and by further processing.

1.3.3 Silk (4)

Fibre Identification

Microscopy	Burning Test	Appearance, Handle	Solubility Test
Cultivated silk degummed	**Combustion:** Small flame, slowly self-extinguishing. **Smell:** Like burning horn or hair. **Residue:** Black, friable cinder.	Degummed cultivated silk is supple, smooth, and lustrous. Net silk: very fine Spun silk: fine Bourette: coarse, neppy Weighted silk: smooth, stiff Wild silk: firm, irregular.	**Sulphuric acid:** Dissolves, destroys (cf. wool). **Lithium hypochlorite:** Dissolves.

Typical Silk Fabrics

Bourette	Crêpe de chine	Organza	Satin crêpe	Wild silk: Tussah
Chiffon	Doupion	Pongé	Taffeta	Honan
Crêpe	Duchesse	Satin	Twill	Shantung

Fibre Blends (*see page 44*)

Silk is usually processed as the pure fibre. It can be blended with practically all apparel fibres – primarily as staple fibre blends. Blends with wool and fine (high quality) animal hairs are valued highly.

Applications

Apparel Fabrics	Accessoires	Household Textiles	Technical Textiles
Dresses, blouses, sophisticated lingerie, ski underwear, formal dress.	Scarves, squares, gloves, ties, hats, handbags.	Drapes, wall coverings, carpets, lampshades, bedclothes.	Sewing threads, embroidery threads, typewriter ribbons, racing bicycle tyres.

Aftercare

The most severe laundering conditions that a fibre could tolerate are seldom those to be recommended for a given item of clothing. Limitations may be imposed, for example, by yarn and fabric construction, type of finish, garment construction and decoration. **Care symbols,** used to indicate the appropriate aftercare regime, are illustrated and explained on *pages 46 and 47.*

Washing	Bleaching	Drying	Ironing	Professional Cleaning
Gentle detergents, minimum agitation, cool rinse, a dash of clear vinegar in the last rinse.			Iron on the back at 120 to 150 °C. Do not press seams. Steam and water can leave stains.	

Textile Labelling

The regulations governing the labelling of textiles stipulate that the word "silk" may be used only for fibres obtained from the cocoon of the silk moth. Phrases such as "artificial silk" and "man-made silk" for man-made fibres, or the use of "silk jersey" and "silk damask" for cotton fabrics are not permitted.

The Silk Seal

The internationally recognised Silk Seal stems from the European Silk Secretariat. It stands for pure silk and good quality.

1: Silk Seal

Outer fabric: 100% silk
Lining: 100% silk

2: Label for a lined silk jacket

1.4.1 Composition of Textile Fibres

1: Atoms

Chemical Elements – Building Blocks of all Materials

All substances (not just textile materials) are constructed out of about 100 basic chemical elements. The smallest individual component in chemistry is the **atom.** Atoms cannot be subdivided by chemical means; they are the basic building blocks of chemical compounds. The most important atoms in fibre-forming materials are Carbon (C), Oxygen (O), Hydrogen (H), Nitrogen (N), and Sulphur (S) (*Figure 1*).

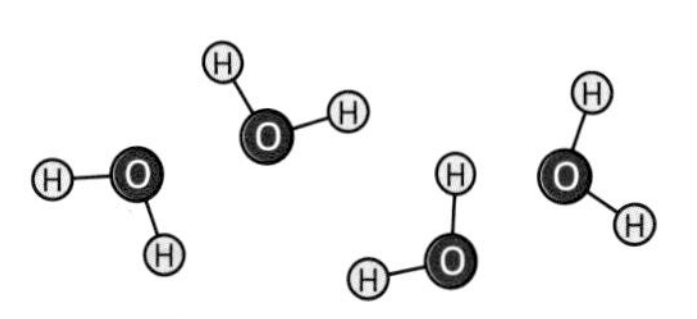

2: Water molecules

Chemical Compounds

Atoms combine to form molecules, the smallest units of a compound. The best-known chemical compound is water (H_2O). Its molecule is a combination of two atoms of hydrogen and one of oxygen (*Figure 2*).

Manufacture of a chemical compound is called **synthesis.**

Separation of a compound into its constituents is called **analysis.**

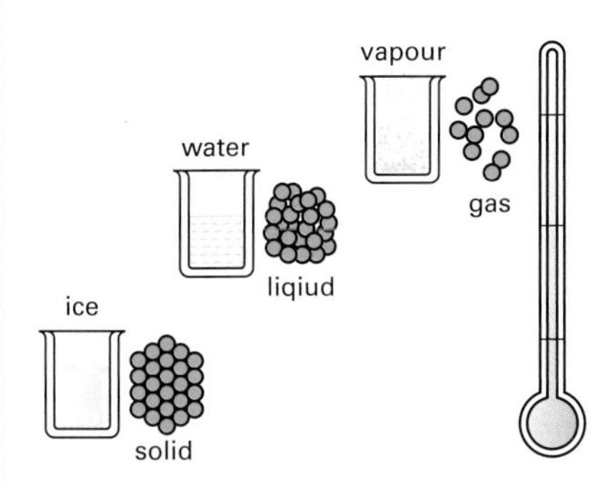

3: Different states of water

Molecular Aggregation

The different physical forms of a compound are called its states (*Figure 3*).

Solid: The molecules are arranged in fixed positions, as for example in crystals of ice. They have very little independent motion.

Liquid: The molecules are held together much more loosely, and can move relatively freely, as in water. The compound is amorphous[1].

Gas: The molecules are free to move independently, as in water vapour.

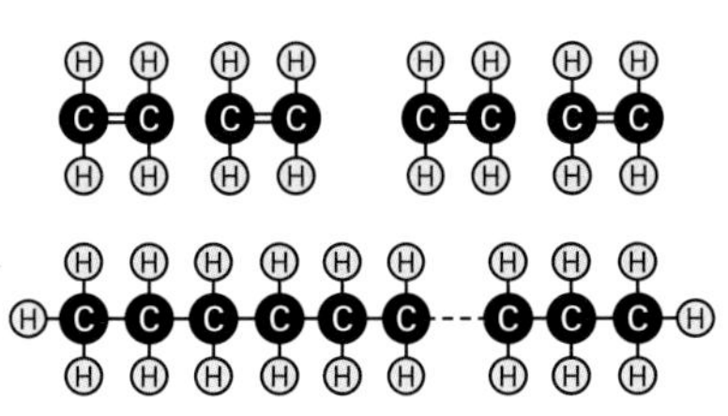

4: Building a molecular chain from small molecules

Macromolecules

Very large molecules are called macromolecules[2]. When macromolecules are constructed in the form of long chains of small units (*Figure 4*), then they are called long-chain macromolecules, or linear **polymers**[3]. All fibres, whether vegetable, animal, or man-made, are constructed from linear polymers which lie alongside each other and are bonded together.

Textile fibre-forming materials are made either from natural or from synthetic linear polymers.

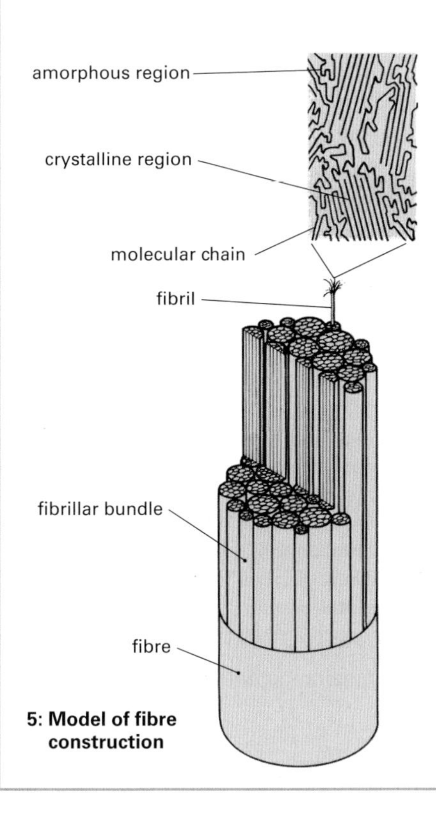

5: Model of fibre construction

Construction and Internal Structure of Fibres

The bulk of the fibre is constructed from fibrillar bundles[4]. The individual fibrils are made from long-chain macromolecules. In vegetable fibres, the molecular chains are primarily those of cellulose; in animal fibres they are proteins. Vegetable cellulose is the raw material for the manufacture of cellulosic man-made fibres. Synthetic man-made fibres are made from synthetic polymers, whose basic raw materials are derived from petroleum. Thus fibre-forming substances can be classified according to the source of their basic raw materials – which also are responsible for many of the basic fibre properties.

Amorphous[1] and Crystalline Regions

The fibre bulk contains amorphous and crystalline[5] regions, depending on the arrangement of the chain molecules (*Figure 5*). The crystalline regions give the fibre its strength, while the amorphous areas allow flexibility. Small molecules, such as water or dyestuffs, can penetrate the amorphous areas but not the crystals. The properties of fibres are governed by the constitution and the organisation of the macromolecules, and by the amorphous and crystalline regions.

[1] amorphous: without form (in fibres the so-called amorphous regions are not truly amorphous; they are much less well ordered than the crystals)
[2] makros (Grk.) = large
[3] poly (Grk.) = many, meros (Grk.) = part
[4] fibril: tiny fibre
[5] crystalline: having regular arrangement of atoms

1.4.2 Fibre-forming Materials

Man-made fibre production comprises three basic steps: conversion of the fibre-forming substance into a fluid by solution or melting; extrusion of the fluid through spinnerets; solidification of the extruded filaments.

Cellulosic Man-made Fibres

Cellulosic man-made fibres are made from natural cellulose polymers, extracted from plants. The macromolecule which has been synthesised by nature may be used as such, or may be chemically modified. To enable cellulose to be spun, it has to be dissolved. There are many different ways to do this, but only four are used in practice.

- **viscose process**
- **cuprammonium process**
- **acetate process**
- **lyocell process**

Synthetic Man-made Fibres

Synthetic fibre-forming materials are made in two steps:

1. Synthesis of reactive precursors. These are small molecules, called **monomers**[1]. Petroleum is the main raw material for their production.
2. Coupling of thousands of monomers to form **polymers.** Two different types of polymerisation reaction are utilised, namely **addition** and **condensation. Homopolymers** are made from a single species of monomer. **Copolymers** are made from two or more different monomers, in any proportions. The monomers may be mixed uniformly or randomly, or may be present in alternating blocks **(block copolymers)**.

Addition Polymerisation

Addition polymers are made by direct coupling of (usually) identical reactive monomers to form long chains, without by-product. Typical addition polymers are polyacrylics, polyvinyl chloride, and polypropylene.

A + A + A + A + A + A ⟶ A A A A A A

monomer monomer monomer monomer polymer

Condensation Polymerisation

Condensation polymers are made by coupling (often) different reactive monomers, with the elimination of a small by-product molecule (often water). Typical textile condensation polymers are polyesters and polyamides.

A + B + A + B + A + B ⟶ A B A B A B

monomer monomer monomer monomer polymer by-product

Block Copolymers

One or more of the starting reactive monomers are pre-formed into blocks which are then co-polymerised. Elastomeric fibres are made from block copolymers, in which one block (soft segment) is much larger than the other (urethane link).

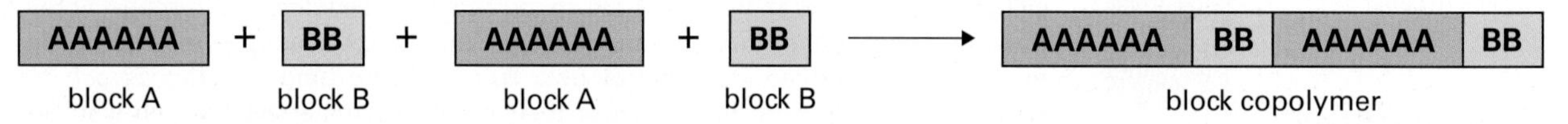

Drawing

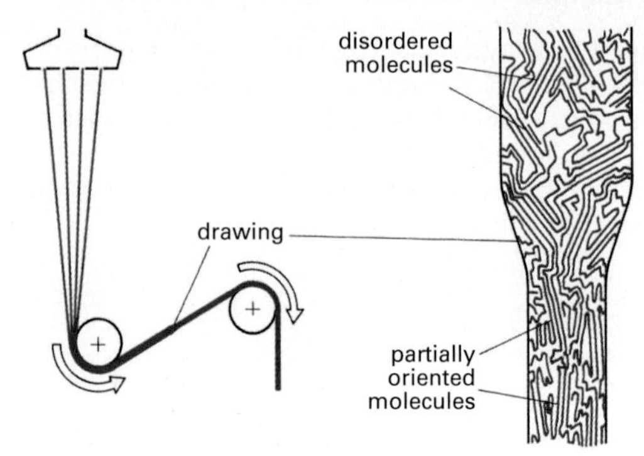

1: Orientation of microfibrils by drawing

The spinning fluid solidifies as it emerges from the spinneret. Inside the filament, the microfibrils are not very well ordered. Drawing the filament down to a thinner section causes the disordered microfibrils to become oriented more in the direction of the filament axis. Crystalline regions are formed within the microfibrils through individual molecular chains bonding together along their length. "Amorphous" regions are between and at the surfaces of the microfibrils. The formation of crystalline microfibrils, and their orientation along the filament axis is what gives the filament its strength and elasticity (*Figure 1*).

Drawing may be done during spinning and also in a separate, subsequent process.

[1] monos (Grk.) = alone

1.4.3 Spinning Man-made Fibres

Man-made Fibre Spinning Processes

There are three major types of process for spinning man-made fibres. They have several basic elements in common: a reservoir and a metering pump for the fibre-forming material; a spinning jet (spinneret); a fluid in which the filaments are formed; a take-up mechanism which draws the filaments and winds them onto a package.

Wet Spinning	Dry Spinning	Melt Spinning
Spinning from a polymer solution		Spinning from a polymer melt
polymer solution, metering pump, take up, spinneret, drawing, winding, coagulation bath	polymer solution, metering pump, warm air, spinneret, solvent, winding, drawing	molten polymer, metering pump, spinneret, cool air, winding, drawing
The polymer solution is extruded into a bath containing chemicals which neutralise the solvent and coagulate (solidify) the filaments.	The polymer solution is extruded into a stream of warm air, which evaporates the volatile solvent and solidifies the filaments.	The molten polymer is extruded into an air stream, which cools the melt and solidifies the filaments.
Examples: viscose, acrylics	Examples: acrylics, acetate	Examples: nylon, polyester

After the filaments have been extruded and solidified, they are drawn out between rollers having different speeds. Drawing can also be a separate process. Spinneret size, plus spinning and drawing conditions determine the final filament diameter.

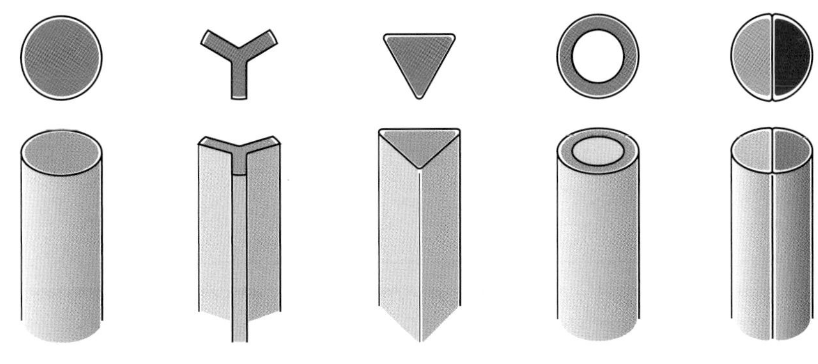

1: Spinneret shapes and fibre cross-sections

The holes in the spinneret may be circular or some other shape, according to requirements. This enables the production of filaments having different cross-sectional shapes (*Figure 1*).

The filament cross-section, and the optional inclusion of delustrants, influences the **lustre** and **handle.**

It is also possible to extrude two different polymers, side-by-side, from a single spinneret to form **bicomponent fibres.**

Terminology of Extruded Filaments

Filaments: The continuous strands of man-made fibres.

Monofilament: When the spinneret has only a single hole.

Multifilament: The bundle of filaments from a multi-hole spinneret.

Textured: Thermoplastic multifilament yarns that have been subjected to a permanent crimping treatment.

The filaments from several spinnerets can be combined into a **tow** and then chopped or broken into **staple fibres.** These are classified as **wool type** or **cotton type,** according to their staple length, diameter and crimp. Man-made staple fibres may be spun into yarns, either alone or as blends with other man-made or natural fibres.

1.5.1 Overview

There are three main types of **natural polymer** man-made textile fibres: **cellulosics, alginates,** and **rubber.** Of these, the only ones of real commercial significance are the cellulosics, made from natural cellulose. **Alginate** fibres are made from seaweed. They are not very stable; they dissolve in soapy water. At one time they found use as soluble fibres (for making temporary joins) but have been replaced by polyvinyl alcohol. **Rubber** fibres are made from latex; they are being extensively replaced by the synthetic elastomers. The so-called **biopolymer fibres** are polyesters derived from plant starch. **Azlon** fibres are made from proteins such as casein (milk), soya protein, and corn protein (zein).

History of Cellulosic Man-made Fibres

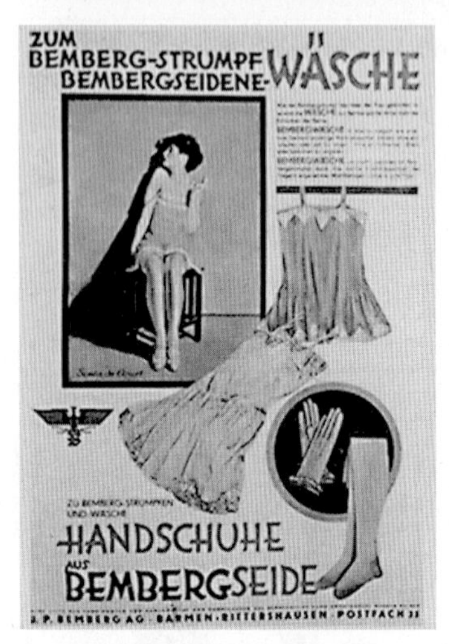

1: Advertising for "Artificial Silk" textiles (1928)

There has always been a desire to find a cheap substitute for silk. Robert Hooke speculated on the idea in 1664 but it was not until the end of the 19th Century that scientists found a way to produce an artificial fibre which looked like silk.

The first soluble cellulose derivative with fibre-forming properties, cellulose nitrate, was prepared in 1832, by Braconnet. Later, it was found to be soluble in a mixture of alcohol and ether, and several more or less successful attempts were made to produce fibres but the processes were never fully developed. It was left to Count Hilaire de Chardonnet to solve the technical problems of "artificial silk"[1)] production. His process was patented in 1885 and the product was named "Chardonnet silk". Yarns and fabrics of Chardonnet silk were shown at the Paris Exhibition in 1889. Commercial production of the first man-made textile fibres began in Chardonnet's factory in Besançon in 1891.

The solubility of cellulose in aqueous ammonia containing copper oxide was discovered in 1857. By 1897, the process had been developed to the extent that fibre production was possible. Commercial production of cuprammonium rayon[1)] or "Bemberg silk" began in Wuppertal in 1904.

The viscose process was developed in England between 1892 and 1898. In this process, cotton was treated with sodium hydroxide and carbon disulphide to yield a thick (viscous) yellow fluid which could be extruded into a coagulation bath.

A further method of cellulosic man-made fibre production followed the laboratory discovery of cellulose acetate, in 1864. A patent application for the dry spinning of cellulose acetate was submitted in 1904.

Thus, the years leading up to 1900 can be seen as the birth of the man-made fibre industry. "Artificial silk" stockings, which arrived after the First World War, precipitated the short skirts of the "Roaring Twenties". A similar revolution took place in "artificial silk" lingerie. A new style in lingerie took over, based on soft, silky, drapable, colourful, and highly resilient locknit fabrics. At first, the cellulosics were produced only as "artificial silk" (continuous filament) yarns but, during the twenties, staple viscose rayon fibres were developed in Germany, where they were called "Zellwolle"[2)]. Further developments of the viscose process led to cellulosic man-made staple fibres with many properties similar to cotton. In recent times a more environmentally friendly organic **solvent spinning process (Lyocell)** has been developed for cellulose. In the past few years, a new type of polyester fibre has been synthesised starting from glucose derived from corn starch **(biopolymers)**.

Classification of Cellulosic Man-made Fibres

Cellulosic man-made fibres can be classified according to the solvent system which is used to convert the cellulose raw material into a spinnable solution.

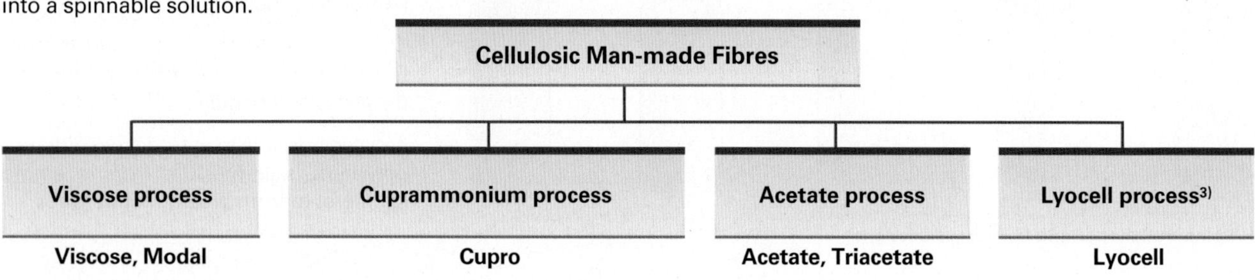

Production of Cellulosic Man-made Fibres

The man-made cellulosics have never captured a very large share of the world market for textile fibres. In 2011, world consumption was about 4.7 million tonnes; about 5.8% of all textile fibres.

The most important of the cellulosics is viscose.

[1)] Artificial silk, rayon: former names for cellulosic filament yarns
[2)] Zellwolle (Ger.) = cellulose-wool
[3)] The so-called bamboo fibres are actually viscose or lyocell made from bamboo cellulose.

1.5.2 Viscose, Modal (1)

Viscose, Modal

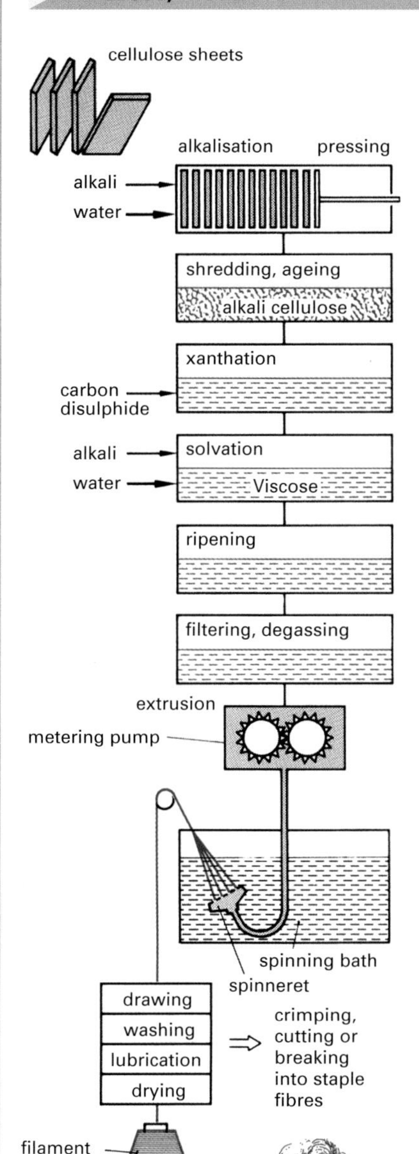

1: The classic viscose process

Manufacture

The raw material for viscose is extracted from eucalyptus, pine, bamboo or beech wood which, after removing the bark, is chipped into fragments the length of matches. Resins and other impurities are extracted in a rather exhaustive procedure. The cellulose is purified and bleached, then pressed into solid sheets.

For fibre production, the cellulose must be dissolved. Using the 100 year old viscose process (*Figure 1*), the cellulose sheets are first steeped in sodium hydroxide solution. This penetrates into the molecular bundles and loosens their structure, to form soda cellulose. After pressing off excess liquor, the soda cellulose is shredded, and then allowed to age. Ageing causes a reduction in the length of the cellulose molecules, which makes them easier to dissolve. Addition of carbon disulphide (Xanthation) converts the cellulose to a form which is soluble in dilute sodium hydroxide to yield the spinning fluid – the viscose – which looks like honey. Delustrants or pigments may be added. The viscose is degassed and filtered and, after ripening, is extruded through fine spinnerets which are immersed in the coagulation bath. The cellulose is regenerated in the spinning bath and solidifies into filaments which are drawn, gathered into a filament yarn, and wound onto a spool. This is followed by a thorough washing, to remove all process chemicals, lubrication (addition of oils) for suppleness, and drying. Staple fibres are made by cutting the filaments to a given length.

Fibre Composition

Viscose: Chemically, the cellulose is scarcely altered by the viscose process. After fibre formation it is again cellulose (*Figure 2*), and is called **regenerated cellulose.** Thus the chemical structure of viscose is comparable to cotton. Nevertheless, the cellulose molecules are much shorter than those of cotton, and their organisation in the fibre is different. This is the main reason for the lower strength of viscose fibres.

Modal fibres are made by a modified viscose process. The spinning conditions are different and the coagulation bath contains additional chemicals. These modifications result in longer cellulose molecules and an improvement of the structure and orientation of the crystalline areas. This yields a higher strength, both wet and dry, and better textile performance properties.

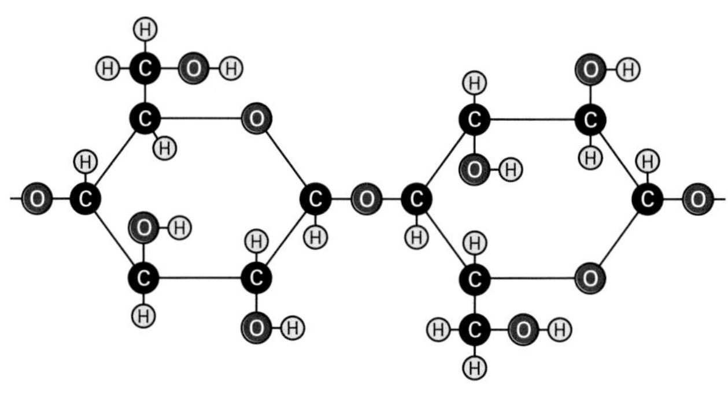

2: Repeat unit of cellulose
(comprising two glucose molecules)

Clothing Comfort (*see pages 48, 49*)	
Thermal insulation	Viscose filament yarns are made into smooth textiles with a low volume of entrapped air (low specific volume). Staple fibre yarns made from viscose or modal can yield textiles with varying specific volumes, so that the insulation properties can be controlled to some extent. The fibre itself has only a small influence on insulation.
Moisture absorption	Viscose and modal are very absorbent. In normal conditions, they absorb 11 to 14% of water vapour. In liquid water, they swell and can absorb 80 to 120% of water. They are more absorbent than cotton.
Next-to-skin comfort	Viscose and modal fibres are fine and soft. They are very comfortable to wear.

1.5.2 Viscose, Modal (2)

Other Important Properties (*see pages 41, 42, 43*)	
Strength	Viscose has a significantly lower dry strength than cotton. The wet strength is low; it is only 40 to 70% of the dry strength. **Modal** has a higher dry strength and much higher wet strength than viscose.
Extensibility	The breaking extension is 15 to 30% – more than double that of cotton.
Elasticity/ creasing	Poor resilience is a feature of all cellulose fibres. Viscose and modal wrinkle easily.
Electrostatic charge	Very low, because the fibres always contain moisture under normal conditions.
Fineness, Handle	As with all man-made fibres, the fineness of viscose and modal can be varied over a wide range.
Coloration	Viscose and modal are excellent substrates for dyeing and printing. Colours are very bright.
Lustre	Can range from high lustre to matt, depending on the fibre cross-section and the addition of delustrants.
Improvement of Properties by Finishing (*see Chapter 7*)	
Easy-care treatments	Viscose fibres swell in water. This causes the fabrics to shrink. Swelling and shrinkage can be reduced by treatment with synthetic resins. The treatment also improves wrinkle recovery but moisture absorbency and abrasion resistance are reduced. Modal fibres swell less than viscose so that, in the absence of chemical finishing, the fabrics are more stable.
Applications	
Filament viscose	Filament viscose is used to produce lustrous fabrics, for effect yarns in woven and knitted fabrics, and for crêpe fabrics. More than half of all lining fabrics are viscose. Other applications are blouses, shirts, dresses, drapes, lingerie, ribbons and trimmings.
Staple viscose	Staple fibres are mostly used in blends with other fibres, where their uniformity, lustre, and absorbency are useful. Cotton, wool, and linen type fabrics can be made.
Modal staple	Modal is produced almost exclusively as staple fibre and is used primarily in blends with cotton or polyester because of its strength, uniformity, and absorbency. The blended fabrics are used in underwear and outerwear.

1: Quality Guarantee for Enka® Viscose

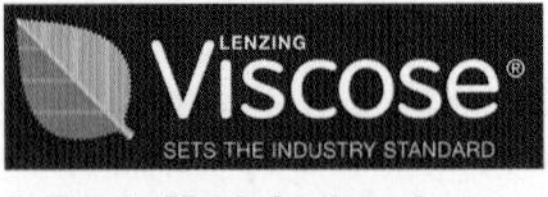

2: Trade Mark for Lenzing Viscose®

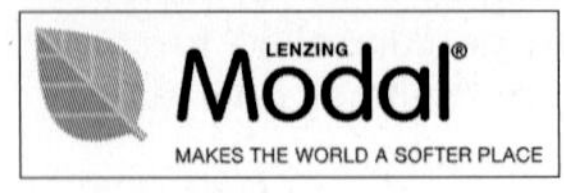

3: Trade Mark for Lenzing Modal®

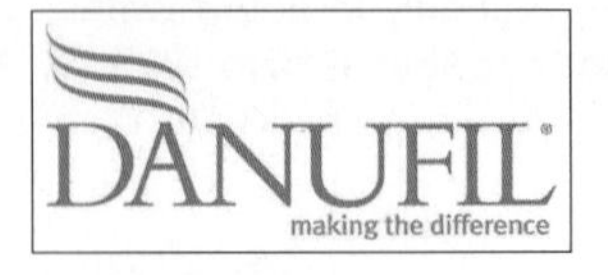

4: Trade Mark for Danufil®, Kelheim Fibres

Fibre Identification

Microscopy	Burning Test	Wet Tearing Test	Solubility Test
Cross-section is usually serrated – depends on spinning conditions	**Combustion:** rapid, bright, with afterglow. **Smell:** like burning paper. **Residue:** pale grey, powdery ash.	Tears straight through a wet spot (cf. cotton).	Sulphuric acid dissolves viscose and modal.

Aftercare

The most severe laundering conditions that a fibre could tolerate are seldom those to be recommended for a given item of clothing. Limitations may be imposed, for example, by yarn and fabric construction, type of finish, garment construction and decoration. **Care symbols,** used to indicate the appropriate aftercare regime, are illustrated and explained on *pages 46 and 47.*

Washing		Bleaching	Drying		Ironing	Professional Cleaning
viscose 40	modal 60		viscose	modal		P

Textile Labelling

The term **Viscose** is reserved for **regenerated cellulose** fibres produced by the viscose process. **Modal** is used for regenerated cellulose fibres with a defined high breaking strength and wet modulus (ISO 2076).

Producer Labels: Examples for Viscose are Enka® Viscose, Lenzing Modal®, Danufil®. Beside these trademarks, the producers provide swing tickets or hang tags for special brands of Viscose, as a guarantee of high quality (*Figures 1 to 4*).

1.5.3 Lyocell

Lyocell[1)]

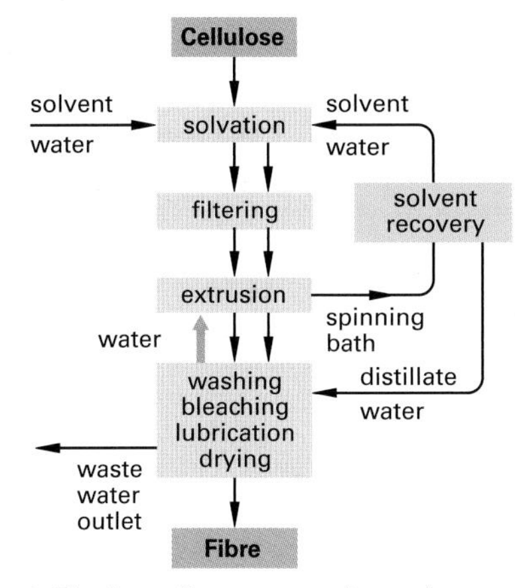

1: The Lyocell process – schematic

Manufacture and Fibre Structure

The raw material for Lyocell manufacture is cellulose derived from wood. For the **Lyocell process,** fluffy cellulose pulp is dissolved directly in an aqueous amine oxide solvent and filtered to form the spinning fluid. This viscous fluid is extruded into hot air and then passes into a water bath where the cellulose is regenerated. Finally, the amine oxide is washed from the bundle of filaments and both solvent and water are recovered for recycling. If required, the filaments are cut into staple fibres, then bleached, softened with a spin finish, dried and baled (*Figure 1*). The process is short and fast, and is **environmentally friendly.** The solvent is almost all recovered and the wastewater is harmless.

Lyocell fibres are essentially pure cellulose, so they are susceptible to degradation by fungi such as mildew. They have a relatively high crystallinity, compared to other regenerated cellulosic fibres. This gives higher strength and is the source of **fibrillation** – partial separation of microfibrillar bundles from the fibre surface under the influence of water and abrasive mechanical action (*Figure 2*).

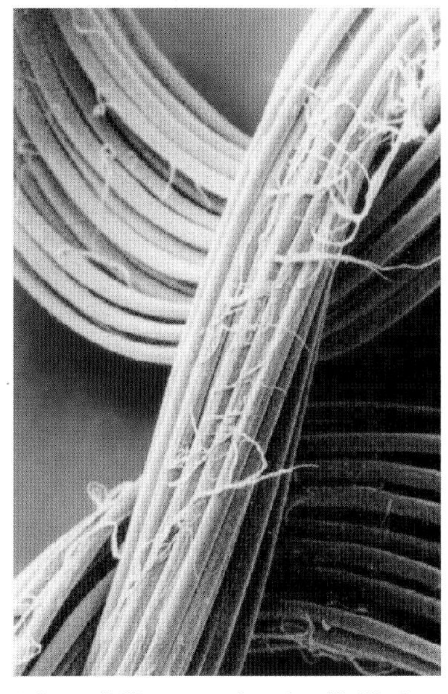

2: Lyocell filaments showing fibrillation

Important Properties (*see pages 41, 42, 43, also 48, 49*)

Lyocell has good dry and wet strength – usually better than other man-made cellulosic fibres. The dry strength is better than a middle grade cotton. Wet strength is lower than the dry strength. The extensibility of staple fibres, at 10 to 14%, is somewhat higher than that of cotton. Elasticity is low, as with all cellulosic fibres.

Fibre fineness can be similar to cotton or wool, ranging from 1.1 to 3.3 dtex.

Clothing comfort properties are comparable to other cellulosic fibres. Moisture absorption is less than viscose but greater than cotton.

Improvement of Properties by Finishing (*see Chapter 7*)

A range of finished fabric effects can be obtained by controlling and manipulating the fibrillation. Possibilities range from complete inhibition (or removal) of fibrillation to deliberate controlled enhancement of the effect.

Mechanical finishing: A peach-skin finish can be obtained by emerizing. Other typical processes are raising and shrinking.

Chemical finishing: Easy-care finishes can be applied – as with all cellulosic fibres. The fibre structure allows especially deep dyeing.

Applications

Potential applications are numerous, ranging from durable denim fabrics through classical suitings to lightweight crêpes and knitted fabrics. Lyocell staple fibres can be blended with cotton or flax as well as wool or fine hair fibres. Lyocell is particularly suited to fleecy fabrics, because of the fibrillation effect.

Aftercare

The most severe laundering conditions that a fibre could tolerate are seldom those to be recommended for a given item of clothing. Limitations may be imposed, for example, by yarn and fabric construction, type of finish, garment construction and decoration. **Care symbols,** used to indicate the appropriate aftercare regime, are illustrated and explained on *pages 46 and 47.*

Washing	Bleaching	Drying	Ironing	Professional Cleaning
60 40				P

3: Trademark and typical end-uses for Lenzing Tencel®

Textile Labelling

Lyocell is the designated generic name for solvent-spun regenerated cellulose fibres (staple and filament)

Trademarks include Tencel®. (*Figure 3*)

1) lyein (Grk) = to dissolve

1.5.4 Cupro
1.5.5 Acetate, Triacetate

Cupro, Cupra

Manufacture and Fibre Composition

Copper oxide and other copper compounds dissolve in aqueous ammonium hydroxide to give blue solutions which are capable of dissolving cellulose. Upon dilution, the cellulose precipitates (solidifies). Use of this mechanism to produce a spinnable fluid is called the cuprammonium process. It is a wet spinning process which has been discontinued in some countries for cost and environmental reasons. Cupro is a regenerated cellulose fibre.

Aftercare

The most severe laundering conditions that a fibre could tolerate are seldom those to be recommended for a given item of clothing. Limitations may be imposed, for example, by yarn and fabric construction, type of finish, garment construction and decoration. **Care symbols,** used to indicate the appropriate aftercare regime, are illustrated and explained on *pages 46 and 47.*

Washing	Bleaching	Drying	Ironing	Professional Cleaning
40				P

Properties, Applications, Identification

As a regenerated cellulose, the important fibre properties are similar to those of viscose. Cupro's pleasant handle and good absorbency are especially prized, but it is not a very important textile fibre. The chief outlets are in filament fabrics, mainly for linings.

Textile Labelling

The **Cupro** (Cupra) designation is reserved for regenerated cellulose fibres produced by the cuprammonium process.

Acetate, Triacetate

Manufacture and Fibre Composition

Acetate and triacetate are **cellulose derivatives.** The three hydroxyl (-OH) groups per glucose unit of cellulose (*see page 29*) are more or less substituted with acetyl (-OCH_3) groups.

Acetate: Cellulose acetate is a dry, granular substance which can be dry-spun from solution in acetone.

Triacetate: Cellulose triacetate is not as soluble in acetone; the spinning solvent is dichloromethane.

Fibre properties depend on the degree of substitution and are quite distinct from those of viscose, modal, and cupro. For example, acetate reacts differently in burning and solubility tests. Triacetate is fully substituted; acetate is about two thirds.

Properties, Applications

Acetate has a sophisticated, subdued lustre, full handle, and elegant drape. It is the closest approach to natural silk. Elasticity and stability are better than viscose. Acetate is thermoplastic and sensitive to dry heat. It has low moisture absorption so that it dries rapidly, but is susceptible to electrostatic charging.

Triacetate has better resistance to heat than acetate, and lower moisture absorbency. It is also thermoplastic; it can be textured, and permanently creased or pleated. The other fibre properties are similar to acetate.

Acetate and triacetate are produced as both filament and staple fibres, for dresses, blouses, and lining fabrics, but the largest end-use is Rhodia® Filter Tow, for cigarette filters.

Fibre Identification

Solubility Test:

Cellulose acetate is soluble in acetone, dichloromethane, glacial acetic acid, and formic acid. It is sensitive to both acids and alkalis.

Burning Test:

Acetates melt in a flame; they burn rapidly, with an acidic smell. The residue is hard and black.

Aftercare

The most severe laundering conditions that a fibre could tolerate are seldom those to be recommended for a given item of clothing. Limitations may be imposed, for example, by yarn and fabric construction, type of finish, garment construction and decoration. **Care symbols,** used to indicate the appropriate aftercare regime, are illustrated and explained on *pages 46 and 47.*

Washing		Bleaching	Drying	Ironing		Professional Cleaning
acetate	triacetate			acetate	triacetate	
30	40					P

Textile Labelling

The textile labelling regulations reserve the terms **Acetate** and **Triacetate** for fibres which have been produced from cellulose acetate.

1.6.1 Overview

History of Synthetic Fibres

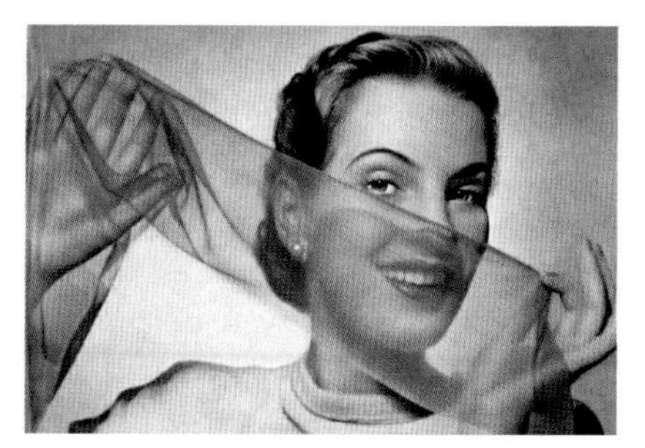

1: Sheer nylon stockings (1952)

In 1925 it was proposed, by the German chemist Staudinger, that textile fibres were formed from linear polymers – very long chain molecules built up from large numbers of simple, small molecules. In natural fibres, the linear polymers are made by plants and animals. Staudinger's insight provided the stimulus for humans to attempt to synthesise linear polymers in the laboratory.

The years between 1931 and 1941 saw the synthesis of polyvinyl chlorides, polyacrylonitriles, polyamides, and polyurethanes. 1941 saw the patent application for polyester; the most important synthetic fibre. The commercial breakthrough for synthetic fibres came in the early 1950's, with the successful introduction, worldwide, of nylon stockings (*Figure 1*). Up to that time, sheer stockings for formal wear had been made from silk or "artificial silk" (regenerated cellulose). A few years later, the knitted, easy-care nylon shirt was launched. The first elastomeric fibre, Lycra, was developed in the USA and was brought to the market in 1959. Today, synthetic fibres account for more than 60% of world textile fibre consumption.

Cellulosic fibres can be regarded as the first generation of man-made fibres; synthetics are the second generation. The third generation, represented by aramids, carbon fibres, and ceramic fibres, were commercialised in the last third of the 20th century. (*see page 7*).

Classification of Synthetic Fibres

One way of classifying synthetic fibres is according to the general chemical mechanisms used for building the linear polymers from small molecules. The basic types are condensation polymers, addition polymers, and block copolymers.

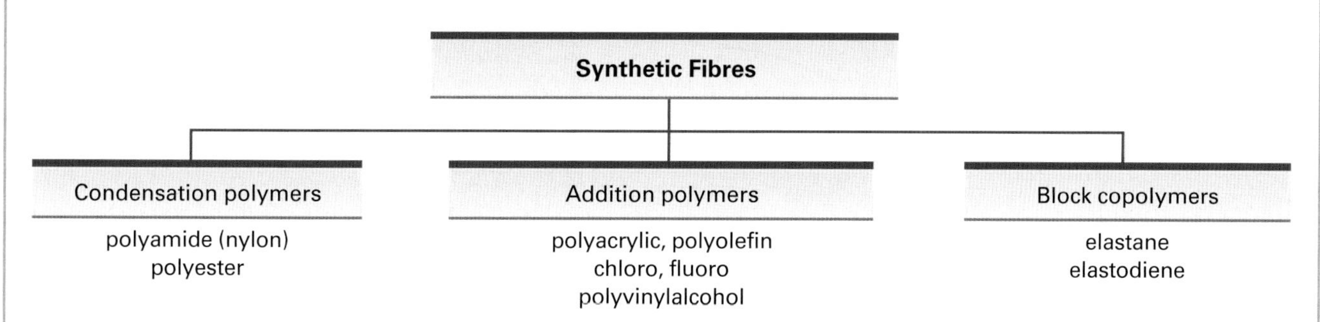

Polycaprolactam (nylon 6) is classified as a condensation polymer, even though it is polymerised by an addition mechanism, because the monomer (caprolactam) is formed by a condensation reaction.

Production of Synthetic Fibres

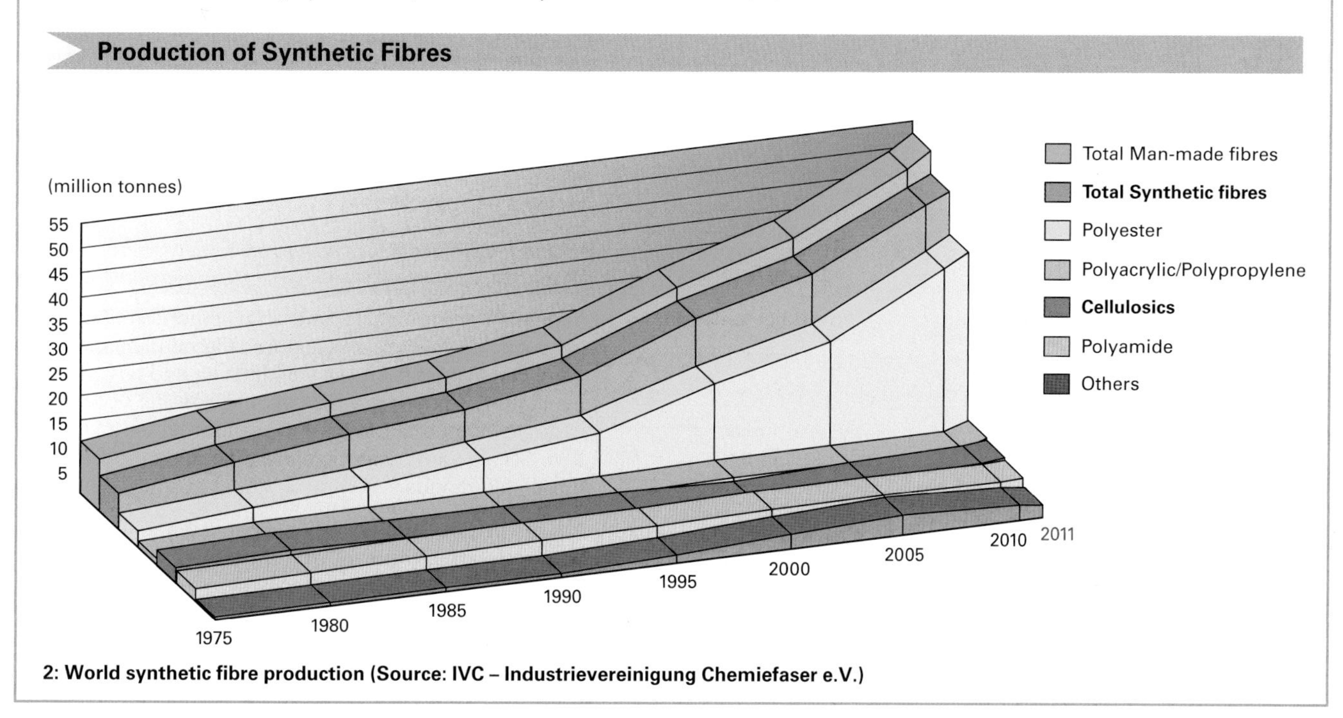

2: World synthetic fibre production (Source: IVC – Industrievereinigung Chemiefaser e.V.)

1.6.2 Polyamide, Nylon (1)

Polyamide, Nylon

Manufacture

The most important polyamides are nylon 6 and nylon 6.6. Nylon 6 is made by polymerising caprolactam (a cyclic amide derived from a particular amino acid) to polycaprolactam. Nylon 6.6 is made by condensation polymerisation of hexamethylene diamine and adipic acid, through the intermediate "nylon salt", to poly (hexamethylene adipamide).

The nylon 6 or 6.6 is melted and either extruded directly or converted into nylon chips for later use. After emerging from the spinneret, the filaments are cooled in a cold air stream and drawn by three to fourfold in length (*Figure 1*).

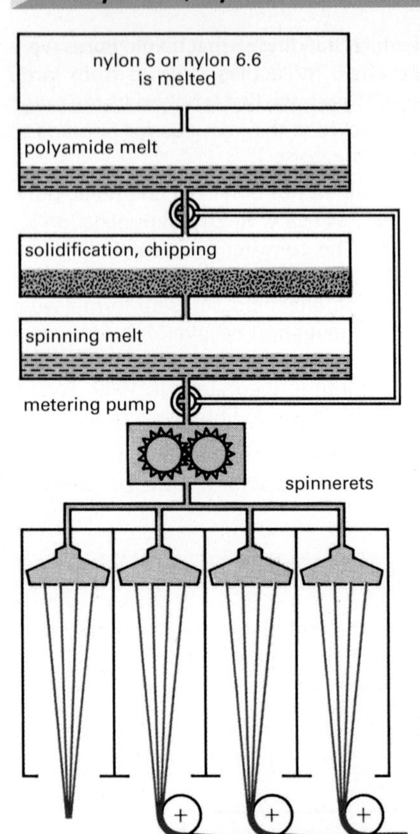

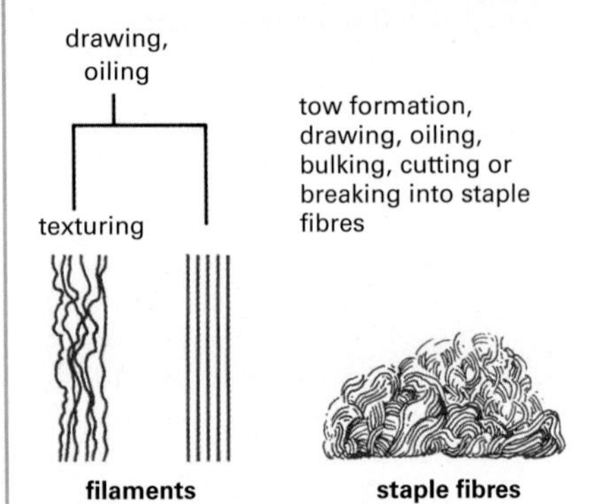

1: Melt spinning of nylon

Fibre Composition

Polyamides are linear macromolecules containing amide groups (-CO-NH-) at regular intervals. Different types of polyamide are made by using starting materials (monomers) of different sizes (different numbers of carbon atoms). Nylon 6 has six carbons in the repeating unit (*Figure 2*); Nylon 6.6 has two sets of six carbons (*Figure 3*).

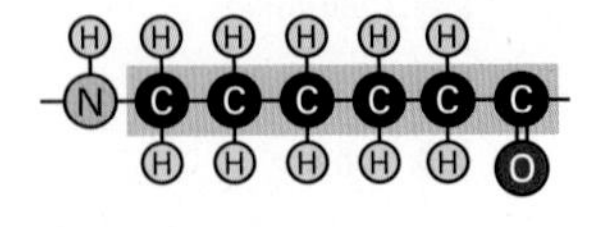

2: Repeat unit of nylon 6

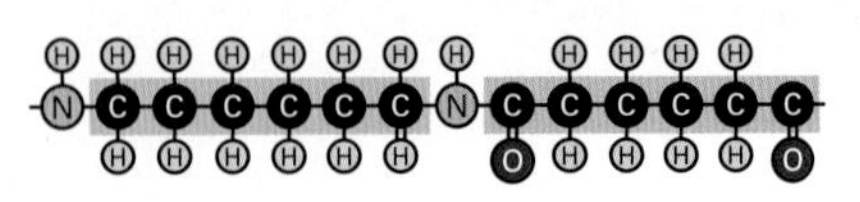

3: Repeat unit of nylon 6.6

Types

Nylon 6 and **nylon 6.6** are used in apparel, household, and technical fabrics. There are special types for particular end uses. Examples are high-bulk, antistatic, and high-lustre types. The newest polyamide types are the so-called **aramids.** These are polyamides which contain a large proportion of aromatic (phenyl) groups. Such fibres tend to have more highly oriented molecules and higher crystallinity; they are therefore stronger and more resistant to high temperatures.

Clothing Comfort (*see pages 48, 49*)	
Thermal insulation	Insulation properties depend on whether the fibre is produced as flat filament, textured filament, or staple yarn. Flat filaments entrap very little air and have low insulation. Texturing increases the specific volume and allows more air to be enclosed for better insulation. Staple yarns may be either fine and smooth or more voluminous.
Moisture absorption	Nylons absorb little water; between 3.5 and 4.5%. In textured yarns, the capillary spaces are capable of transporting liquid water effectively.
Next-to-skin comfort	Fine and soft nylon fibres are utilised for apparel fabrics.

1.6.2 Polyamide, Nylon (2)

1: Nylon sportswear

2: Kevlar® aramid fencing suits

Other Important Properties (*see pages 41, 42, 43*)	
Strength	Nylon is very strong and has excellent abrasion resistance. The wet strength is 80 to 90% of the dry. Aramid fibres have about five times the tensile strength of apparel fibres.
Extensibility	Breaking extension is very high, either wet or dry. Depending on the fibre type it may be from 20 to 80%.
Elasticity/creasing	Nylon is very resilient and wrinkle-resistant.
Electrostatic charge	Very susceptible, but can be reduced by special antistatic treatments.
Fineness, Handle	Fineness ranges from microfibres to coarse fibres (*see page 42*). Fabrics may be fine and soft or firm, according to fibre fineness, fabric construction, and finishing.
Lustre	From matt to high lustre, depending on fibre cross-section and addition of delustrants.
Formability	Is thermoplastic; can be permanently shaped under the influence of heat. This property is utilised for texturing and heat setting.
Chemical resistance	Nylon is resistant to alkalis and many solvents. It is attacked by concentrated acids.
Light resistance	Nylons will yellow and lose strength on long exposure to sunlight. Resistance can be improved by including special chemicals in the spinning melt.
Biological resistance	Nylon is resistant to moulds and fungi. It does not decompose.
Heat resistance	Nylon is sensitive to dry heat.

Applications

Filament yarns, usually textured, are about 80% of nylon production. They are utilised in sheer stockings, lingerie, foundation garments, swimming, sports and leisure wear (*Figure 1*), linings, dresses, and blouses, weatherproof clothing and umbrellas, reinforcing yarns for knitted fabrics, and carpets. Monofilaments are used for sewing yarns.

Staple fibres are blended with wool, cotton, or other man-made fibres for apparel fabrics. They are used in knits, plush, carpet pile, and drapes. They are also used for fleece fabrics.

Aramids are used mostly for fibre-reinforced plastics. They are also utilised in protective clothing such as bullet-proof vests, fencing suits (*Figure 2*), and clothing for forestry workers, racing drivers, and fire fighters.

Fibre Identification

Microscopy: Cross section usually circular but depends on the spinneret.

Burning Test: Shrinks and melts away from the flame with fibre-forming drips. Residue is hard and uncrushable.

Solubility Test: Destroyed by 80% formic acid and concentrated mineral acids. Slightly degraded by dilute organic acids.

Aftercare

The most severe laundering conditions that a fibre could tolerate are seldom those to be recommended for a given item of clothing. Limitations may be imposed, for example, by yarn and fabric construction, type of finish, garment construction and decoration. **Care symbols,** used to indicate the appropriate aftercare regime, are illustrated and explained on *pages 46 and 47.*

Washing	Bleaching	Drying	Ironing	Professional Cleaning
40				P

Textile Labelling

The labelling regulations stipulate the use of the generic name **polyamide,** or **nylon,** without type designation. Trade names can be added. Examples of nylon: Antron®, Bayer-Perlon®, Enka-Perlon®, Tactel®, Rho-Sport®. Examples of **aramids:** Kevlar®, Nomex®.

1.6.3 Polyester (1)

Polyester

1: Polyester chips

2: Flat filaments

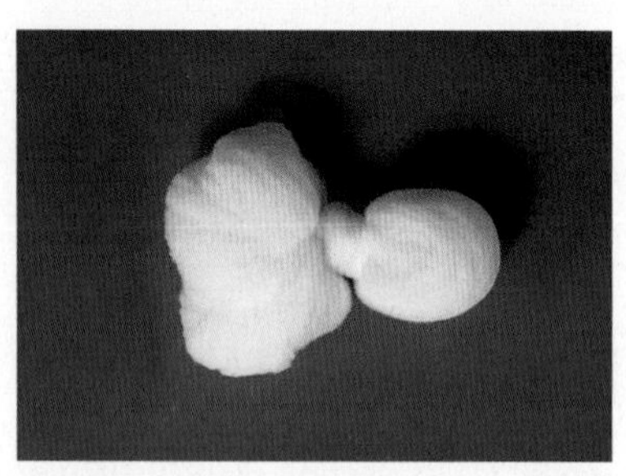

3: Textured filaments

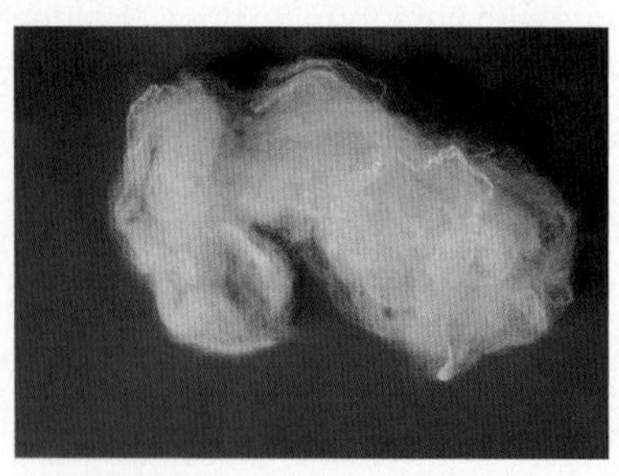

4: Staple fibre

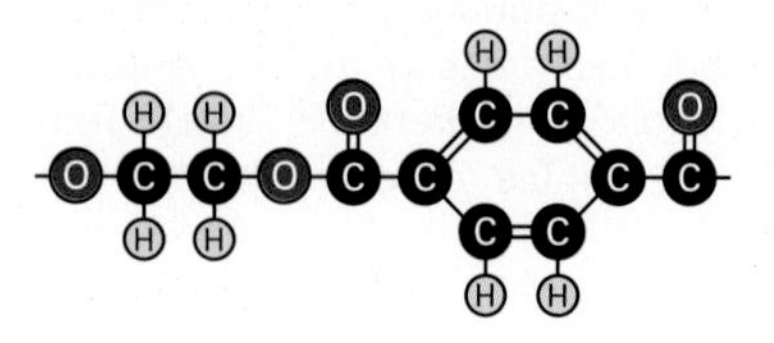

5: Repeat unit of the polyester macromolecule

Manufacture

Terephthalic acid combines with ethylene glycol to form dihydroxyethyl terephthalate. At high temperature and vacuum, condensation polymerisation proceeds to form poly (ethylene terephthalate), which is cast and cut into chips. The polyester chips (*Figure 1*) are melted at about 280 °C and extruded (melt spinning process). After drawing, the flat filaments (*Figure 2*) are usually textured (*Figure 3*) or cut into staple fibres (*Figure 4*).

Fibre Composition

The polyester macromolecule contains the ester group (-CO-O-) at regular intervals (*Figure 5*). Esters are produced by the reaction of an organic acid with an alcohol, with the elimination of water.

Types

In addition to standard polyester fibre, there are special types for particular end-uses. Examples are high strength, flame resistant, heat resistant, high shrink, high crimp, antistatic, low pill, low melting adhesive fibres, hollow, and profiled fibres.

Clothing Comfort (*see pages 48, 49*)	
Thermal insulation	Flat filament yarns enclose little air; textured yarns are better insulators. Staple yarns may be fine and smooth or very bulky, with corresponding poor or good insulation.
Moisture absorption	Polyester scarcely absorbs water. Transport of liquid water in the yarn capillaries can be good, with an appropriate finish.
Next-to-skin comfort	Fine and soft fibres are used for apparel fabrics.

Other Important Properties (*see pages 41, 42, 43*)	
Strength	Polyester and nylon have the highest tensile strength and abrasion resistance of all apparel fibres. The wet strength of polyester is the same as the dry.
Extensibility	The breaking extension is between 15 and 50%; somewhat lower than nylon.
Elasticity/creasing	Polyester is highly resilient; it is very wrinkle-resistant.
Electrostatic charge	Is very high, but can be reduced by antistatic treatments.
Fineness, Handle	Fibre fineness ranges from microfibres to coarse fibres (*see page 42*). Fabrics are fine and soft or stiff depending on the fibre fineness, fabric construction, and finishing.
Lustre	From bright to matt, depending on fibre cross-section and addition of delustrants.
Formability	Polyester is thermoplastic; it can be textured.
Chemical resistance	Unaffected by most acids, alkalis, and solvents. Can be degraded by strong, concentrated acids and alkalis and a few solvents.
Light resistance	Very good.
Biological resistance	Resistant to moulds and fungi; does not decompose.
Heat resistance	Polyester has the best heat resistance of all synthetic fibres used for apparel fabrics.

1.6.3 Polyester (2)

1: Rainwear in polyester microfibres

2: Principle of modern rainwear

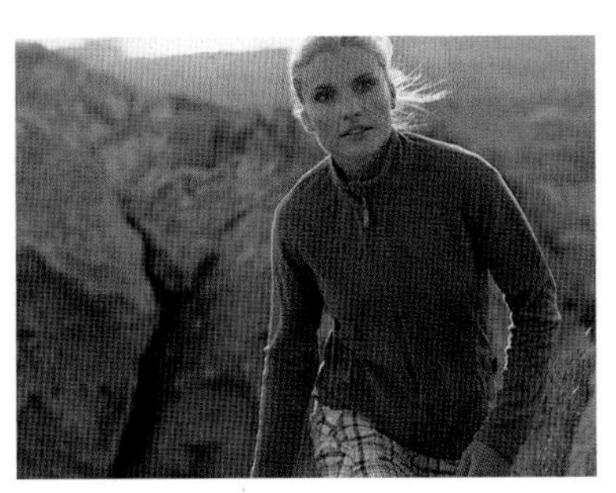

3: Fleece fabric in polyester microfibres

4: Textured polyester sewing thread

5: Home furnishings in fire-resistant polyester

Applications

Polyester is the most versatile of the man-made fibres and, therefore, finds the widest range of uses. About 60% of polyester production is in the form of staple fibres (cotton or wool type).

Staple fibres are used primarily in blends with other fibres, especially wool, cotton, viscose, and modal. The blending level depends on the end use and the other fibre. Common blending ratios are 70:30, 65:35, 55:45, and 50:50, though other blend ratios and other fibres are also used. The most important applications are in suits, costumes, dresses, shirts and blouses, leisure wear, rainwear, workwear, and bed clothing. 100% polyester staple yarns are used for high strength sewing threads and for weaving into furnishing fabrics. The staple fibres are also used as waddings for interlinings or used as filling material for pillows, duvets and quilted articles.

Filament yarns for apparel fabrics are usually textured. These are used in dresses and blouses, ties and scarves. Bulked yarns are used for edge overlocking, because they have good covering power. Flat filament yarns are used in rainwear and linings. Almost all net curtains are made from filament yarns.

Special types of polyester are used in technical end-uses such as personal hygiene and medical products e.g. medicated plasters, Band-Aids and bandages. High tenacity variants are used for tenting, tarpaulins, and tyre cords. Fire-resistant variants are used for furnishing fabrics and drapes in public buildings and transport. *See page 55* for other technical end-uses.

Fibre Identification

Microscopy:

Cross-section is usually circular, but depends on the spinneret. Profiled fibres may be triangular or five-point star (for modified lustre, handle, and soil-hiding properties).

Burning Test:

Melts and shrinks from the flame to form a brownish mass which may drip filaments. Residue is hard and uncrushable.

Solubility Test:

Polyester is soluble only in concentrated sulphuric acid, concentrated potassium hydroxide, tetrachloroethane, and phenols.

Aftercare

The most severe laundering conditions that a fibre could tolerate are seldom those to be recommended for a given item of clothing. Limitations may be imposed, for example, by yarn and fabric construction, type of finish, garment construction and decoration. **Care symbols,** used to indicate the appropriate aftercare regime, are illustrated and explained on *pages 46 and 47.*

Washing	Bleaching	Drying	Ironing	Professional Cleaning
60				P

Textile Labelling

The designated generic name polyester should be used. Trade names may be added.

Examples of the many trademarks are: Coolmax®, Dacron®, Diolen®, Thermolite®, Trevira Perform®, Trevira Polair®, Trevira Bioactive®.

1.6.4 Acrylic, Modacrylic

Acrylic, Modacrylic

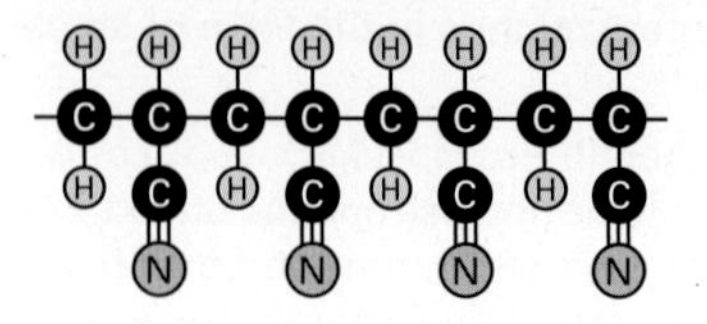

1: Section of a polyacrylonitrile molecule

Manufacture

Acrylonitrile, made from propylene and ammonia, is polymerised to form polyacrylonitrile powder. It is dissolved in dimethylformamide or dimethylacetamide, and either wet or dry spun to acrylic filaments. Polymerisation of the acrylonitrile can also be effected in the solvent, to form the spinning solution directly.

Fibre Composition

The polyacrylic linear chain molecule is built from repeating units of CH_2CHCN (*Figure 1*). There are two broad types of acrylic fibres: normal acrylics and modacrylics (modified acrylics), which are highly resistant to burning.

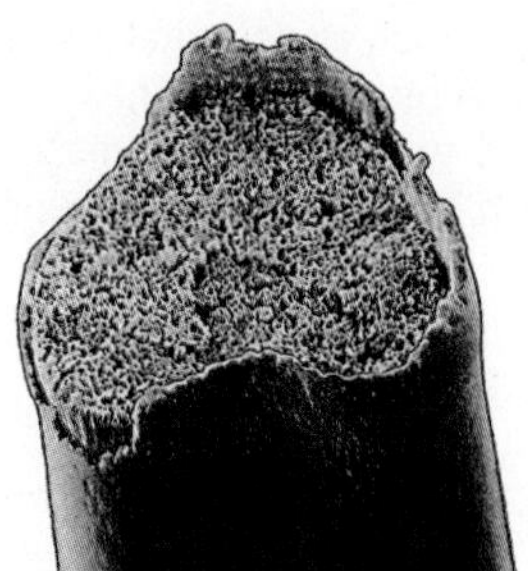
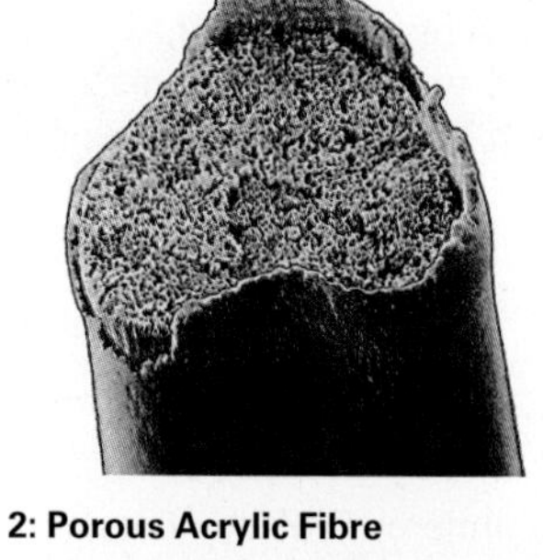

2: Porous Acrylic Fibre

Properties (*see pages 41, 42, 43*)

Acrylics are produced almost exclusively as staple fibres. They have a wool-like handle, low density, and good resistance to light and chemicals. Like all synthetic fibres they are thermoplastic and wrinkle-resistant (though they are susceptible to deformation in steam or hot water).

Acrylic yarns are usually voluminous, and are very soft and warm; somewhat similar to wool in character (*Figure 3*). Heat will cause the fibres to shrink strongly. By mixing such fibres with stabilised fibres in a spun yarn, a subsequent heat treatment will induce bulking in the yarn, due to the shrinkage of the unstabilised fibres. Acrylic yarns usually have a high specific volume.

Applications

Acrylics are spun into staple yarns, either alone or blended, especially with wool. The yarns are made into knitted fabrics, outerwear, blankets, imitation fur, drapes and furnishings, carpets and awnings.

Modacrylics are modified acrylic fibres. Their properties include flame resistance. They are made into protective clothing and drapes.

Porous acrylic fibres (*Figure 2*) contain internal voids which can absorb water. They are made by including up to about 20% of a second, incompatible polymer, such as poly(vinyl acetate), into the spinning solution. After wet spinning, the second polymer is dissolved away leaving a matrix of voids.

3: Warm acrylic clothing

Fibre Identification

Burning Test:

Acrylics shrink and burn with a sooty flame, with melting and dripping. The smell is pungent; the residue is hard and unbreakable.

Solubility Test:

Solvents are dimethylformamide, dimethylacetamide, and nitric acid.

Aftercare

The most severe laundering conditions that a fibre could tolerate are seldom those to be recommended for a given item of clothing. Limitations may be imposed, for example, by yarn and fabric construction, type of finish, garment construction and decoration. **Care symbols,** used to indicate the appropriate aftercare regime, are illustrated and explained on *pages 46 and 47*.

Washing	Bleaching	Drying	Ironing	Professional Cleaning
40 (wash tub)	(crossed-out triangle)	(crossed-out tumble dryer)	(iron, one dot)	P

Textile Labelling

The textile labelling regulations reserve the name **acrylic** for fibres which have been made from at least 85% acrylonitrile. The label must show the generic name acrylic. Trade names may also be given.

Examples: Dolan®, Dralon®, Dolanit®.

For **modacrylics,** the proportion of acrylonitrile must lie between 50% and 85%.

1.6.5 Elastomerics, Fluorofibres, Chlorofibres, Olefins, Vinylals

1: Extensibility of elastane

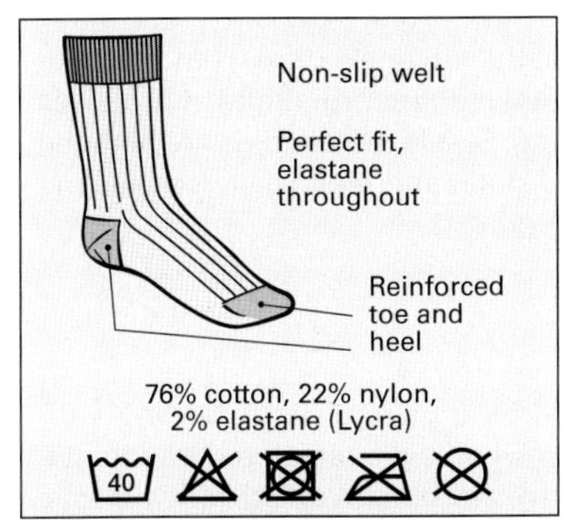

2: Elastane in stretch clothing

Non-slip welt

Perfect fit, elastane throughout

Reinforced toe and heel

76% cotton, 22% nylon, 2% elastane (Lycra)

3: Elastane in socks

4: Protective clothing in Tyvek® staple fibre nonwoven

Fibre	Properties and Application
Elastane **Spandex**	Elastane is manufactured from at least 85% of a segmented **polyurethane**. Its outstanding property is very high elastic recovery. An elastomeric yarn can stretch by up to 500% and recover its original length after unloading. The molecular structure is that of a block copolymer, with alternating hard and soft segments. The short, hard segments are usually aromatic urea derivatives. They can develop inter-molecular bonds to give overall strength and coherence. The much longer, soft segments are polyesters or polyethers. They are amorphous or semi-crystalline, highly extensible and elastic (*Figure 1*). Elastane is made only as filament yarns. The filaments can be very fine, are resistant to light and oxidation, and will withstand domestic laundering. They are used wherever high elasticity is required. The filaments can be used as such (bare) or they can be folded into a textured nylon filament (covered). Bare elastane filaments are used in sheer hosiery (the largest end-use), foundation garments and swimwear. Fabrics with small amounts of elastane (2 to 5%) are used for gentle shape-holding elasticity. Larger amounts (up to 45%) are used in foundation garments. Covered yarns are used in e.g. cotton or wool outerwear, usually at a level of 2 to 5%. They are unseen within the fabric, never coming into contact with the body, providing invisible elasticity and wrinkle resistance (*Figures 2, 3*). Trademarks include Dorlastan®, Lycra®, Roica®.
Fluorofibres PTFE poly(tetra-fluoro-ethylene)	The milky-white polymer is predominantly cast as films, but can also be spun into filament yarns and staple fibres. Fluorofibres are chemically resistant, water repellent, do not absorb any moisture, are practically undyeable, and have a very low frictional coefficient. Gore-Tex® is a microporous PTFE membrane used in all-weather clothing (*see page 50*). Fluoro yarns in sports socks can help to avoid blistering. Trademarks include Teflon®, Hostaflon®.
Chlorofibres PVC poly(vinyl-chloride)	**Polyvinylchloride** is manufactured as filament yarns and staple fibres but it finds only limited use in apparel textiles. Knitted thermal underwear is sometimes made from chlorofibres. They can also be used in protective clothing because of their resistance to certain chemicals. Trademarks include Rhovyl®.
Polyolefins **Polyethylene**	**Polyethylene** has a low density and a low softening temperature. It will not absorb water and is resistant to most chemicals. Therefore, polyethylene nonwovens are used in protective clothing (*Figure 4*). Trademarks include Tyvek®. Technical textiles, such as ropes, cords, nets, and filters are made from narrow strips cut from polyethylene film. Trademarks include Vestolan®.
Polypropylene	**Polypropylene** is manufactured as filament yarns and staple fibres. It also absorbs no water but it does display good capillary wicking. This makes it suitable for use in high-performance sportswear, for transporting perspiration away from the body surface (*see page 49*). Trademarks include Meraklon®, Hahl PP, Monosuisse PP.
Vinylals PVA poly(vinyl-alcohol)	**Polyvinyl alcohol** is manufactured as filament yarns and staple fibres. There are water-soluble and insoluble types. The soluble types are used as ground fabrics for embroidery lace, or as temporary joining or wrapping threads which will later be washed out. Insoluble types are used in technical textiles. Trademarks include Kuralon®.

1.7.1 Glass, Carbon, Metal

1: Protective clothing made from worsted fabric with a small percentage of metal fibres

2: Lurex® multicolor

3: Lustre effect from Lurex® in lamé fabric

Fibre	Properties and Application
Glass	Glass can be manufactured into filament yarns and staple fibres. They **will not burn, do not absorb moisture,** and have **low extensibility.** They are used for drapes, wall hangings, fireproof safety curtains, and reinforced plastics. They are not normally used in clothing. Trademarks include **Fibreglass®**.
Carbon fibres	Carbon fibres have a carbon content of more than 80%. They are made by carbonisation of suitable carbon-based fibrous materials, such as polyacrylonitrile or viscose. Carbonisation is a slow heating process, during which as much as possible of the non-carbon material is driven off, leaving essentially the carbon-rich backbone of the polymer molecule. Carbon fibres are **resistant to temperatures up to about 4000 °C.** Their **high tensile strength and stiffness** can be varied to some extent by the manufacturing conditions. Carbon fibres are used mainly in technical fields such as reinforced plastics for aircraft, machinery and sports equipment. Trademarks include **Sigrafil®, Tenax®.**
Metal fibres	Metal fibres are made as wiredrawn or flat-drawn filaments, staple fibres, and thin strips cut from **metallised plastic films.** Wiredrawn and flat-drawn filaments are finely drawn out metal. In silver and gold colours, they are used predominantly in brocades and decorative cords and braiding. Staple metal fibres are blended with other fibres to provide antistatic and electrically conducting fabrics for protective clothing (*Figure 1*). **Lurex®** The name Lurex® is often used as a general term for any yarn containing metallised plastic films but it is a registered trademark. It is made from a metallised polyester film, overlaid with a plastic coating. The polyester film is first laminated with aluminium and then protected by a layer of plastic lacquer. There are several different types, made with different lacquers, depending on the performance requirements and the end use. The different qualities can tolerate e.g. different washing and ironing temperatures. Their thickness ranges from 0.01 to 0.03 mm and their width from 0.2 to 0.4 mm. The underlying colour is silver but this can be modified by using coloured lacquers. Additional effects can be obtained by combining the Lurex® with a black or white yarn. Colours available include various **silver, gold and bronze effects** but also **blue, red, and green tones.** Multicolour yarns can be obtained by printing the film before it is cut into strips (*Figure 2*). There are also **iridescent, transparent, phosphorescent,** and **reflective** variants. **Lurex®** is most often used in silver or gold as an effect yarn for woven and knitted fabrics. Other colours may be used for fashion fabrics (*Figure 3*).

1.8.1 Fibre Identification

In the absence of proper labels, the fibre type can be established by simple tests.

Microscopy: A good microscope is needed. Cotton and wool have distinctive appearances.

Burning test: A specimen of fibres, yarn, or fabric is held horizontally with forceps. Its behaviour as it approaches the flame, how it burns, the smell and the residue are all observed.

Dry Tearing test: A piece of fabric is snipped and then torn by hand. The length of the broken fibre ends is observed.

Wet Tearing test: A drop of water is applied and the behaviour of the wet place is observed during tearing.

Solubility test: Used mainly to identify fibre blends. The material is immersed in various chemicals for several hours. Acids are used in concentrated form.

Fibre Type			Fibre Composition Polymer type	Microscopy Longitudinal and cross-sectional appearance	Burning Test (untreated fibre) B = burning S = smell R = residue	Other Tests So = solubility test Td = dry tearing Tw = wet tearing
NATURAL FIBRES	vegetable	**cotton**	cellulose	kidney or bean-shape	B: rapid, bright, afterglow S: like burning paper R: pale grey powder	So: dissolved by sulphuric acid Td: short fibre ends, cf. linen Tw: high wet strength, cf. viscose
		flax	cellulose	irregular polygon	B: rapid, bright, afterglow S: like burning paper R: pale grey powder	So: dissolved by sulphuric acid Td: long fibre ends, cf. cotton
	animal	**wool**	keratin (protein)	round to oval	B: slow, sputtering S: burning hair R: friable cinder	So: lithium hypochlorite dissolves animal proteins So: strong alkalis dissolve wool
		silk (degummed)	fibroin (protein)	rounded triangle	B: slow, sputtering S: burning hair R: friable cinder	So: lithium hypochlorite dissolves animal proteins So: sulphuric acid dissolves silk
MAN-MADE FIBRES	cellulosic	**viscose, modal** cupro, lyocell	regenerated cellulose	depends on spinning conditions	B: rapid, bright, afterglow S: like burning paper R: pale grey powder	So: dissolved by sulphuric acid So: viscose is attacked by hydrochloric acid Tw: low wet strength, cf. cotton
		acetate	cellulose acetate	depends on spinning conditions	B: melts, burns, flaming drips S: pungent, vinegar R: sets hard	So: acetate is soluble in acetone and acetic acid So: triacetate is soluble in dichloromethane
	synthetic	**polyester**	poly(ethylene-terephthalate)	depends on spinneret	B: shrinks, melts, burns (smoky), drips in filaments R: sets hard	So: soluble in dichlorobenzene and sulphuric acid
		nylon	polyamide	depends on spinneret	B: shrinks, melts, burns, drips in filaments R: sets hard	So: soluble in formic acid and hydrochloric acid
		acrylic	polyacrylo-nitrile	depends on spinning conditions	B: shrinks, melts, burns (sooty), drips R: sets hard	So: soluble in dimethyl-formamide and nitric acid
		polypropylene	polypropylene	depends on spinneret	B: shrinks, melts, burns, drips R: sets hard	So: soluble in xylol
		elastane	polyurethane	fibrillar	B: shrinks, melts, burns, drips R: sets hard	So: soluble in cyclohexanone and dichlorobenzene

1.8.2 Physical Properties (1)

Fibre Fineness (linear density)[1)]

Linear density is the fibre weight per unit length. The units are tex or dtex (decitex).

tex = mass in grams per kilometre of fibre (or yarn)
dtex = mass in grams of ten kilometres of fibre (or yarn)

The smaller the number, the finer is the fibre. A fineness of 2 dtex indicates that 10 km of fibre has a mass of 2 grams.

Fibre	Fineness range dtex	Micro-fibres	Fine fibres 1 2 3 4 5 6 7	Coarse fibres 8 9 10 11 12 13 14 15 16 17 18 19 Fibre fineness in dtex
Cotton	1...4			
Flax	10...40			
Wool, Hairs	2...50			
Silk	1...4			
Viscose, Modal	1...22			
Acetate	2...10			
Polyester	0.2...44			
Nylon	0.2...22			
Acrylic	0.6...25			
Polypropylene	1.5...40			
Elastane	20...5000			

magnification 250 times

[1)] Different fineness ranges are appropriate for different end-uses

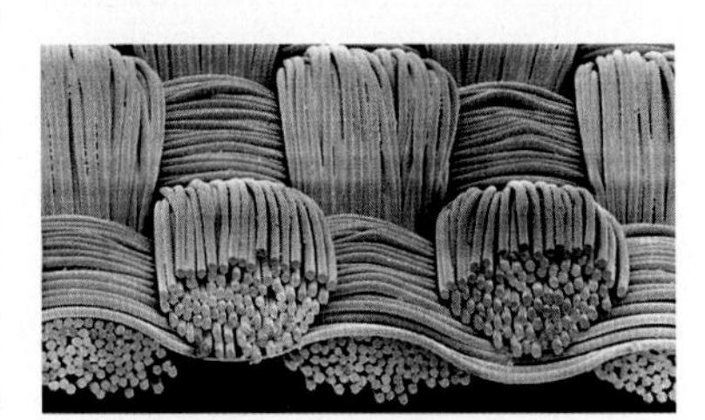

1: Fabric from nylon 78 dtex yarn; 98 filaments of 0.8 dtex

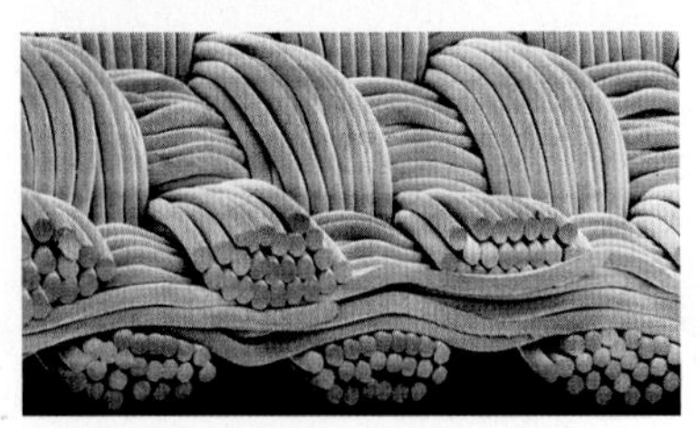

2: Fabric from nylon 78 dtex yarn; 23 filaments of 3.4 dtex

Textile fibres can be classified into **Coarse, Fine,** and **Microfibres.** Apparel fabrics are usually made from fine fibres and microfibres. Finer fibres make softer, denser, and more comfortable fabrics, with better drape (*Figures 1 and 2*).

Microfibres are generally man-made fibres with a linear density of less than 1 dtex. They are predominantly nylon or polyester filament or staple fibres. Microfibre yarns allow the production of **fine and dense fabrics.** Densely woven microfibre fabrics have relatively small capillary spaces. This allows water vapour to pass freely outwards but tends to stop the penetration of raindrops (*see page 50*). Very fine fibres impart a fluid drape and a soft, silky handle. **Polar fleece** is a very warm microfibre **knitted** fabric in a special construction, raised on one or both sides.

Applications for microfibre fabrics are in all-weather clothing and for soft, flowing outerwear materials. Their surface characteristics can be modified in several ways: peach-skin, velvety, crêpe, brushed. Fleecy knits are especially suitable for warm outdoor clothing.

Trademarks for microfibre fabrics include Dralon-Microfibre®, Micromodal®, Tencel Micro®, Trevira Finesse®, Trevira Micro ®.

1.8.2 Physical Properties (2)

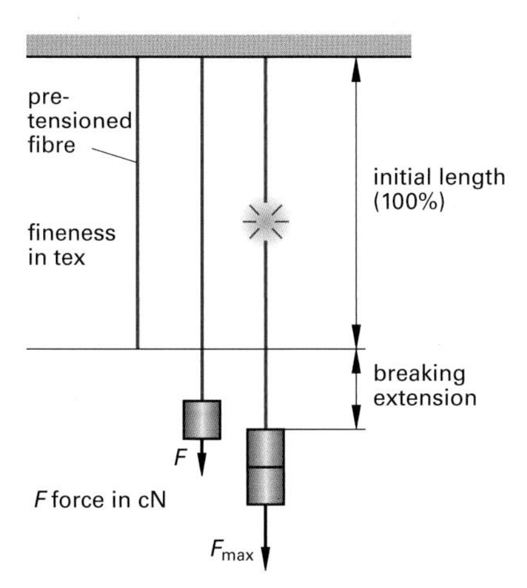

1: Measurement of tenacity and breaking extension

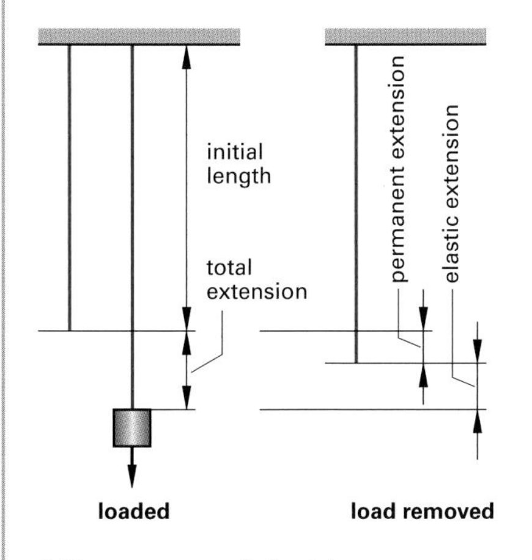

2: Measurement of elasticity

Fibre properties can only be assessed comparatively. Therefore they have been summarised in tabular form. From the wide range of available data, only those properties which are of importance for apparel fabrics are presented.

Fibre Length (staple)

Long fibres allow the production of yarns with low hairiness. The shorter the fibres, the greater the frequency of protruding fibre ends.

Fibre Density

The density of a fibre affects the weight of its fabrics. In general, fibres with a low density allow the production of light, voluminous fabrics.

Moisture Absorption

Most fibres will absorb a certain amount of water from the atmosphere. The amount absorbed depends on the relative humidity of the air. Moisture absorbed by clothing can conduct away electrostatic charges (*see page 49*).

Biological Resistance

Cellulose and protein fibres are decomposed; synthetic fibres are not.

Tenacity

Tenacity is the peak force per unit of fibre fineness obtained during a strength test (*Figure 1*), expressed in cN/tex (cN = 1/100 Newton). The higher the value, the better is the strength, and (usually) the durability of the corresponding fabrics.

Breaking Extension and Elasticity

Together with the fabric construction, fibre extensibility and elasticity influence the general comfort, the formability, the dimensional stability and the wrinkle-resistance of clothing.

Breaking extension (or extension at peak force) is given in percent, based on the initial length (*Figure 1*). Elasticity is the property which allows a fibre to recover its length after it has been extended. Fibres never return completely to the original length; they always retain a greater or lesser part of the extension (*Figure 2*).

Fibre Type	Fineness	Length	Density	Moisture Absorption %		Biological Resistance	Tenacity cN/tex		Breaking Extension		Elasticity
	dtex	mm	g/cm³	standard[1]	high humidity[2]		standard	wet % of dry	standard	wet % of dry	
Cotton	1...4	20...40	1.54[3]	7...11	14...18	poor	25...50	100...110	6...10	100...110	poor
Flax	10...40	450...900	1.43...1.52	8...10	~20	poor	30...55	105...120	1.5...4	110...125	poor
Wool	2...50	50...350	1.32	15...17	25...30	poor[4]	10...16	70...90	25...50	110...140	good
Silk	1...4	~	1.25[5]	9...11	20...40	poor	25...50	75...95	10...30	120...200	very good
Viscose	1...22	38...200	1.52	11...14	26...28	poor	18...35	40...70	15...30	100...130	poor
Modal	1...22	38...200	1.52	11...14	26...28	poor	35...45	70...80	15...30	120...150	poor
Lyocell	1...3.3	34...105	1.5	11...13	~	poor	40...45	80...85	15...17	115...120	poor
Acetate	2...10	40...120	1.29...1.33	6...7	13...15	poor	10...15	50...80	20...40	120...150	good
Polyester	0.6...44	38...200	1.36...1.38	0.2...0.5	0.8...1	very good	25...65	95...100	15...50	100...105	very good
Nylon	0.8...22	38...200	1.14	3.5...4.5	6...9	very good	40...60	80...90	20...80	105...125	very good
Acrylic	0.6...25	38...200	1.14...1.18	1...2	2...5	very good	20...35	80...95	15...70	100...120	very good
Polypropylene	1.5...40	38...200	0.90...0.92	0	0	very good	15...60	100	15...200	100	good
Elastane	20...4000	~	1.15...1.35	0.5...1.5	0.5...1.5	good	4...12	75...100	400...800	100	highest

Values extracted from the Denkendorf Fibre Chart

[1] 20 °C and 65% RH
[2] 24 °C and 96% RH
[3] purified fibre wall only: whole fibre is less dense – about 1.33
[4] attacked by moths
[5] degummed

1.9.1 Blend Ratios, Aftercare, Labelling

Fibre blending is used either to improve performance, by compensating a weakness in the properties of a given fibre type, or to achieve special optical effects. Blending may also influence processing efficiency, yarn fineness, and cost.

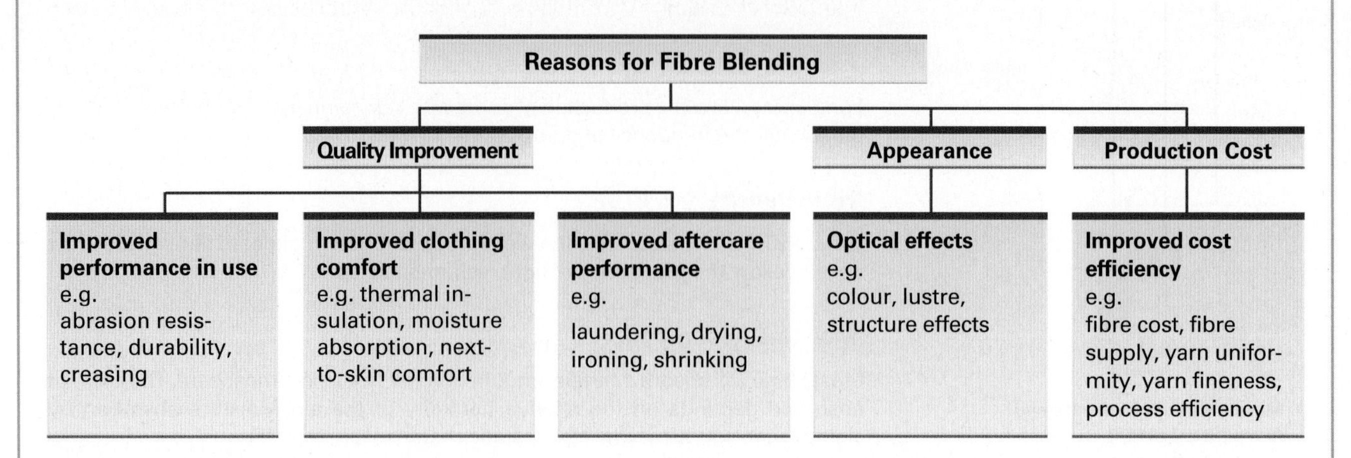

Typical Blends and Blending Ratios

Blending can be effected at either of two stages in textile manufacture:

During **staple yarn production,** by blending different types of fibres.

During **fabric production,** by mixing yarns made from different fibres or filaments. Any combination of natural fibre and man-made fibre yarns is possible, in principle.

1: Combination of two natural fibres

2: Blend of natural and man-made fibres

It is especially advantageous to blend natural fibres with man-made fibres. In this way, the most desirable properties of both fibre types can be exploited, whilst their disadvantages can be partially offset.

The most popular blends are those of wool with polyester, nylon, or acrylics, and of cotton with polyester, nylon, viscose, or modal. The superb clothing comfort properties of the natural fibres are supplemented by the high strength, abrasion resistance, and resilience, and the good aftercare characteristics of the synthetic man-made fibres to make textiles with excellent all-round performance. The cellulosic man-made fibres are valuable blending materials because of their softness and high moisture absorption, and because they can be produced with the ideal length and fineness for making fine yarns.

Special effects can be obtained with man-made fibres through controlling their lustre and shrinking potential. The best staple fibre blends are obtained when the different fibres are closely matched in their extensibility, length, and fineness.

The most common blending ratios are 70:30, 60:40 and 50:50.

Aftercare

In principle, aftercare has to be based on the properties of the most sensitive component. Nevertheless, wool which has not been given an anti-felting treatment can be made machine washable by blending with a high proportion of a synthetic fibre.

Labelling of Blended-fibre Fabrics

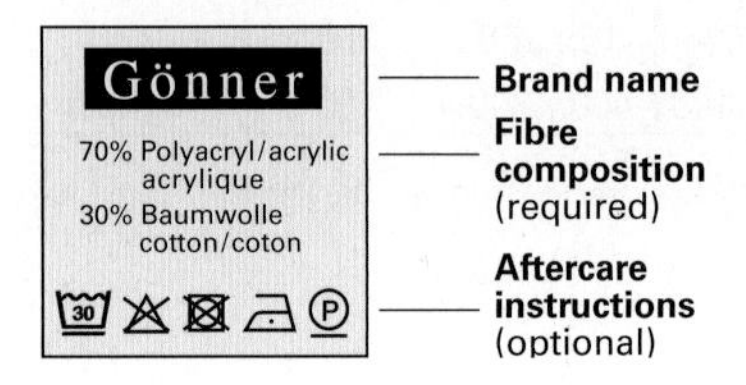

3: Label with aftercare instructions

The labelling regulations require that the components of the blend, and their proportions, be stated in rank order. Natural fibres are indicated by their common names. Man-made fibres must be designated by the generic terms, such as polyester, nylon, etc. Trademarks of individual manufacturers and quality marks may also appear (*see page 45*).

Inclusion of aftercare symbols is optional.

2.1.1 Textile Labelling Regulations

European Textile Labelling Regulations 2012

Label

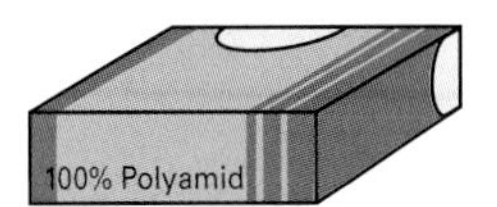

Selvedge

Packaging

1: Location of labelling information

2: Example of a label

100% Silk

Pure Silk

All Silk

80% Nylon
20% Elastane

95% Cotton
5% other fibres

85% Cotton
15% other fibres

Outer fabric: 100% New Wool
Lining: 100% Silk

Outer fabric: 100% Nylon
Lining: Viscose

The Textile Labelling Regulations in various countries constrain trade and industry to display appropriate information so that the consumer can see **which fibre types have been used** to make the product. In the European Union, for example, the regulations stipulate the descriptors that must be used for the different **fibre types** and what **additional information** is important or is permitted.

In addition, textiles, designs, samples and illustrations in catalogues and internet sites must also be labelled, though not newspaper advertisements.

In clothing, fibre content information must be provided on sewn-in labels; in piece goods the information may be woven into the selvedge. If the product is sold in a package (stockings and tights), then the information may be placed on the packaging (*Figure 1*). **Made-to-measure garments are excluded** from the regulations

The Textile Labelling Regulations stipulate the fibre descriptors which may be used. These are given in the **raw materials overview** on *page 7*. For man-made fibres, the **generic names** are used e.g. polyester, viscose. The specific names for linen, wool, and silk are given under the descriptions of the individual fibres. Short forms and abbreviations are not allowed.

Trade marks, brand names, or company names may be placed beside the fibre content, but must be clearly separate. It is recommended, though not prescribed that the aftercare symbols should also be provided (*Figure 2*) (*see pages 46, 47*).

Textiles which are made from only one raw material may be described as "pure" or "all". An allowance of 7% for visible decoration material and 2% for antistatic dressings is given. Coarse, carded yarns are allowed up to 5% of foreign fibres.

With blended products, the percentages by weight of the constituent fibres must be given. The fibres must be listed in decreasing order.

For textiles which are made from several fibres, the designation "other fibres" may be used if a single fibre type is not more than 5% or if two or more fibre types together comprise not more than 15%.

With lined clothing, the fibre content of the main lining material must be given.

Components whose share of the total product weight is less than 30% need not be specified in detail.

Brand Names, Quality Marks, Registered Trademarks

Brand names are used by manufacturers to advise the consumer of the source of the product. In addition, there are **Quality Marks** which indicate that the products, which may be supplied by different manufacturers, conform to certain written quality standards. Brand names and logos can be officially registered at national or regional patent or registration offices. These are **"Registered Trademarks"** which are usually indicated by a superscript R in a circle. National and international regulations govern the use of these marks, and protect them against misuse.

Examples of Quality Marks are the Cotton Emblem, the Linen Seal, The Woolmark, and the Man-made Fibre Seal. Examples of Trademarks include Dolan®, and Trevira® (*Figure 3*).

3: Examples of Registered Quality Marks and Trademarks

2.2.1 Aftercare Characteristics, Recommendations, Symbols (1)

Aftercare Characteristics of Apparel Fabrics

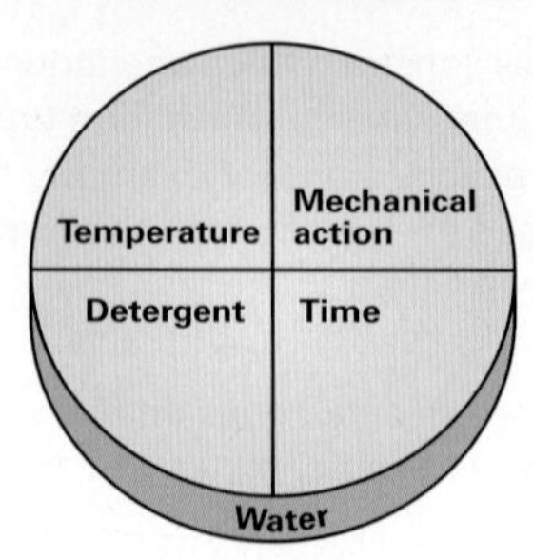

1: Key factors in washing and cleaning

Aftercare requirements form part of the utility value of textiles. If clothing demands laborious and expensive laundering, then its value is so much the less. Aftercare may include airing, washing, bleaching, dry cleaning, drying (laid flat, hanging on a line, or in a tumble dryer) and ironing. Beside the liquid medium (usually water) four factors are important in washing or dry cleaning: temperature, time, detergent, and mechanical action (*Figure 1*). These four have to be optimised. Particular laundering procedures have to be chosen according to the **type of fibre** and its properties, such as strength and sensitivity to chemicals and temperature. Additional limitations may be imposed by **yarn and fabric construction,** or **special finishes.** Clothing with linings and interlinings, such as suits, costumes, jackets and overcoats, must usually be professionally cleaned. Aftercare characteristics can be established by means of laundering tests.

General Recommendations

- Sort the items into groups according to wash temperature, and light/dark colours.
- Follow the dosage instructions for detergents.
- Coloured articles being washed for the first time should be washed separately.
- Avoid detergents that contain bleach with coloured items.
- Pay attention to the degree of soiling of the goods and the hardness of the water.
- Do not overload the machine.
- Wool materials can be machine-washed only if the label confirms it is safe to do so.
- Sensitive items should be turned inside-out or placed in a wash-bag.

Aftercare Symbols: Textile Labelling (ISO 3758; ASTM D5489)

The provision of aftercare symbols is optional. They indicate a recommended procedure which, if followed, should avoid the risk of damage to the textile product. They always indicate the most severe procedure that is acceptable. For fibre blends, the recommendation should be based on the most sensitive component. The precedence of the symbols on the label[1)] is: **Washtub, Triangle, Square, Iron, Circle.**

Care Symbols		Recommendations
	**Washing** (symbol: wash tub) The symbol indicates that water washing, either by hand or by machine, is acceptable. The number in the wash tub indicates the maximum temperature. A line underneath indicates a less severe process (**gentle wash,** lower water level) e.g. for sensitive fibres or easy-care finished fabrics. A double line indicates an especially gentle treatment for **delicates** e.g. wool. **Standard** (built) detergents include water-softening, bleaching and optical brightening agents, anti-redeposition agents and fillers. **Gentle** detergents are used for wool, silk and other sensitive fabrics. They are active at low temperature, have low alkalinity, and do not contain bleaching or optical brightening agents. **Compact** detergents contain no fillers and are active at low temperatures. This saves energy and reduces environmental impact.	**Do not wash** Very delicate wool and silk fabrics should be cleaned professionally. **Hand wash** Normal wool and silk should be washed with gentle detergents. 30 **30 °C Delicates program** Delicate items e.g. wool. 30 **30 °C Gentle program** Sensitive articles of modal, viscose, acrylic, nylon, polyester. 30 **30 °C Normal program for Coloureds** Dark colours in cotton, polyester and blends. 40 **40 °C Delicates program** Delicate articles such as lace underwear, underwired bras, and easy-care wool (*see page 19*). 40 **40 °C Gentle program** Sensitive articles of modal, viscose, acrylic, nylon, polyester. 40 **40 °C Normal program for Coloureds** Dark colours in cotton, polyester and blends. 60 **60 °C Gentle program** Easy-care (permanent press) articles: reduced water, short spin 60 **60 °C Normal program for Coloureds** Coloured items in cotton, modal, polyester and blends. 95 **95 °C Normal program** Boil wash: white cotton or linen without special finishes, colours fast to boiling.

1) The precedence of the symbols was specified by the International Care Labelling Association (Ginetex) in 2006, following consultations with consumers.

2.2.1 Aftercare Characteristics, Recommendations, Symbols (2)

Care Symbols	Recommendations	
Bleaching (symbol: triangle) The symbol indicates whether a bleaching agent may be utilised for brightening and stain removal. An empty triangle means that any bleaching agent can be used, i.e. chlorine or oxygen bleach.	**Do Not Bleach** For sensitive coloured articles: use a bleach-free detergent. **Oxygen Bleach** Use only oxygen bleach (standard detergent). **Chlorine or Oxygen** Either type of bleach may be used.	
Machine Drying (symbol: tumble dryer) The dots indicate drying intensity. The divisions are similar to those for washing and ironing. The symbol gives no information about shrinkage in the tumble dryer.	**Do Not Tumble Dry** Articles that are likely to deform or shrink in a tumble dryer. **Low Heat** Robust articles of polyester, viscose, modal, lyocell. **Medium/Normal Heat** Cotton and linen that are not likely to shrink excessively.	
Natural Drying (symbol: square) Recommendations for natural drying may be given in written or symbol form. These symbols are displayed below the five main symbols (*Figure 2*).	**Line Dry** Fabrics that are susceptible to shrinkage in the tumble dryer. **Drip Dry** Easy-care shirts and blouses with a special drip-dry finish. **Dry Flat** Fabrics that are sensitive to distortion in the wet state e.g. wool.	
Ironing (symbol: iron) The dots indicate the maximum temperature of the iron sole. ••• 200 °C •• 150 °C • 110 °C Shiny or pressure-sensitive materials should be ironed on the reverse and/or under a cloth.	**Do Not Iron** Fabrics that are too sensitive or do not need ironing. **Low Heat** Shiny or pressure-sensitive fabrics: iron with care. **Medium Heat** Steam iron with care, do not stretch. **High Heat** Steam iron. Fabric may be damp if required.	
Professional Dry-cleaning and Wet-cleaning (symbol: circle) The circle indicates recommendations for professional cleaning. The letters indicate acceptable cleaning and stain removal solvents. A line under the circle means a gentle process (reductions in mechanical action). A double line means especially gentle treatment.	**Dry-cleaning** **Do Not Dry-clean** **F = Hydrocarbon solvent** Used for sensitive articles. Perchloroethylene may not be used. **P = Perchloroethylene** Either hydrocarbon or perchloroethylene solvent may be used.	**Wet-cleaning** **Do Not Wet-clean** Cleaning with **water** and very mild mechanical action. Cleaning with **water** and mild mechanical action. Cleaning with **water**. The symbol for wet-cleaning is inserted beneath that for professional cleaning.

Examples of Product Labels

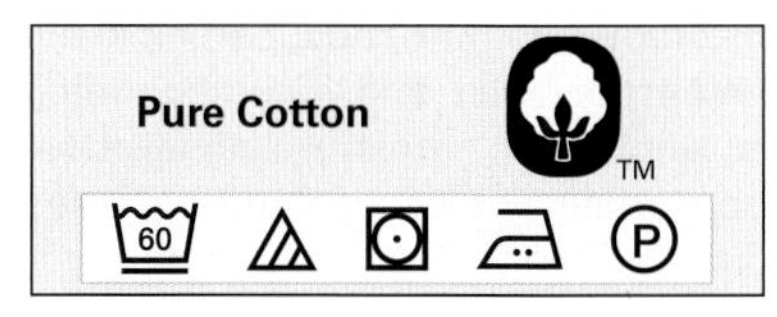

1: Men's Shirt in Easy-care Cotton

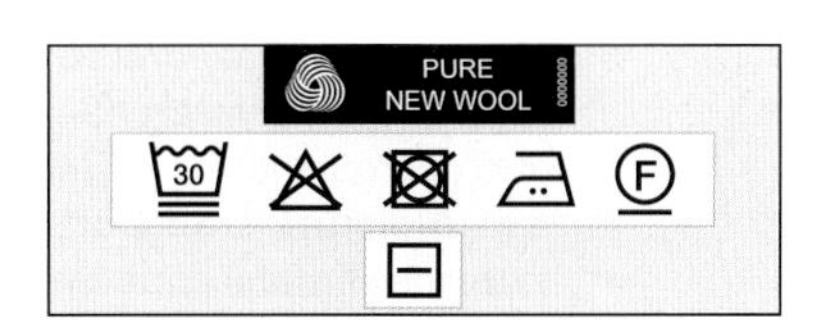

2: Pullover in Machine Washable Pure New Wool

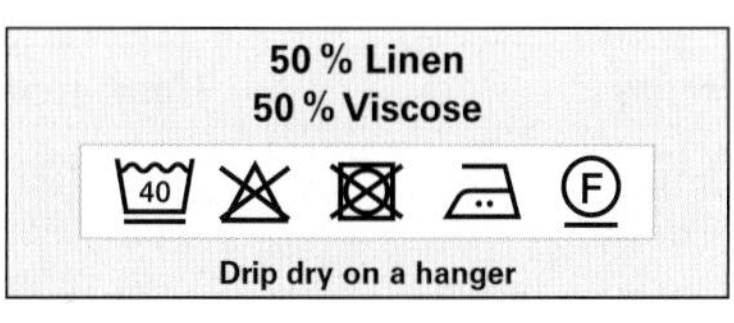

3: Blouse in Easy-care Linen/Viscose Blend.

3.1.1 Basic Functions and Requirements

Basic Functions

Together with food and shelter, clothing is one of the three basic needs of humans. It fulfils many requirements:

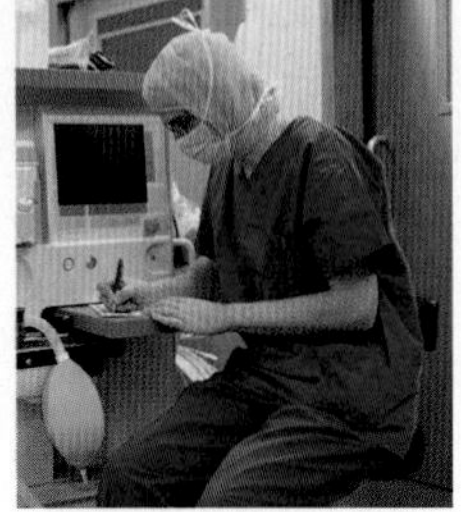

1: Protection

2: Decoration

3: Identification

Protection

Clothing serves as protection against the elements; heat, cold, wind, rain or snow, and against injury at work, in transport, or in sport (*Figure 1*). In addition clothing should supplement the thermal regulation system of the human body. Even in climates where clothing is not required for protection, it may still be used simply to avoid nakedness.

Decoration

Every age has its own fashions for the decorative function of clothing. Through fashion, wearers can proclaim their own personality and individuality. As the old saying goes, "clothing makes the man" (*Figure 2*).

Identification

Clothing can also signal the belonging of an individual to a more or less specific group within a given society or geographical region (*Figure 3*). Examples are traditional costumes, uniforms of police, military or fire services, and the dress codes of social movements such as punk, or football fans.

These basic functions condition the various requirements that are placed upon clothing.

Requirements

General Requirements

Suitability

The basic requirements of protection, decoration, and identification must be satisfied.

Appearance

It should fit properly and present an appearance appropriate to the wishes of the wearer.

Stability

It should maintain its intended form and be sufficiently durable.

Comfort

It should remain comfortable within the range of environments for which it is intended.

Aftercare

It should retain its shape and function through laundering and cleaning.

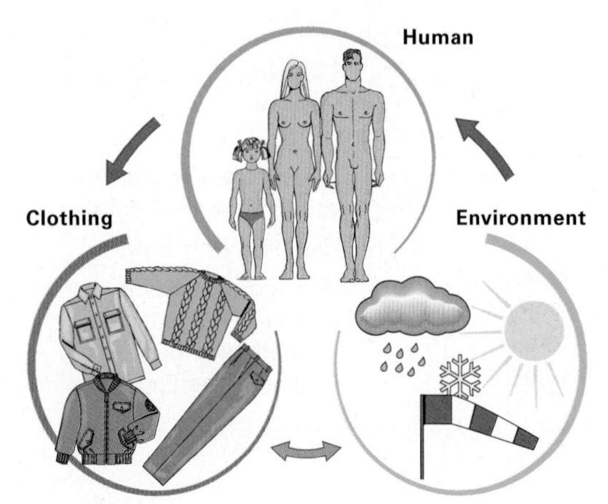

4: Interaction between body and clothing in different environments

Activity	Heat generation
sitting still	ca. 100 Watt
walking	ca. 350 Watt
vigorous sport	ca. 1000 Watt

5: Heat generation by humans

Physiological Requirements

Clothing physiology is the study of the interaction between the human body and its clothing in different environments (*Figure 4*). The comfort of a person in a given situation depends on these interactions.

A person can be subjected to many different environments and his bodily requirements can vary widely. An involuntary, internal regulation system always attempts to maintain the body temperature at about 37°C. Under normal circumstances, heat is continuously being dispersed from the body through the skin (about 90%) and through respiration (about 10%). During vigorous activity, the body produces a great deal of excess heat (*Figure 5*).

If the generation of excess heat is greater than can normally be dispersed, then the body reacts by producing an increased flow of liquid perspiration at the surface of the skin. Evaporation of the perspiration has a strong cooling effect. If the dispersal of heat from the body is greater than that which is being generated internally, then the body begins to chill (hypothermia).

In order for the wearer to be comfortable, clothing must participate in regulating the interchange between the body and its surrounding microclimate through **insulation, ventilation, moisture absorption,** and **moisture transport.** By appropriate choice of clothing, even extreme climatic conditions can be accommodated.

3.1.2 Clothing Physiology

Heat Insulation and Air Exchange

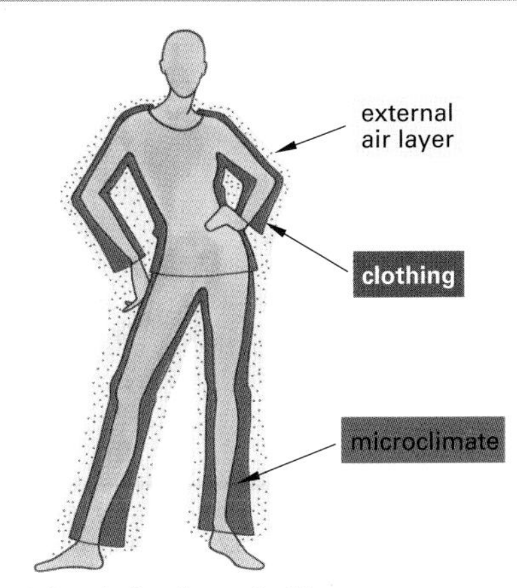

1: Insulation from clothing

To prevent excessive heat losses in cooler climates, the body's natural thermal regulation mechanisms have to be supplemented by **insulation.** For a stationary person, about 50% of the insulation is provided by air trapped inside the clothing, about 30% by the external air layer, and about 20% by the fibres. Thus, the enclosed air is the most important insulator (*Figure 1*). Bulky constructions, having a large volume of enclosed air have good insulation properties and are especially suitable for winter clothing. Thin, smooth fabrics are better for warm environments.

To maintain an equable balance of heat and moisture in the **microclimate,** between skin and clothing, some **ventilation** is required. Air exchange is regulated mainly by three factors.

Firstly it depends on the **surface texture,** mediated by fibre type, yarn and fabric construction, and finishing.

Secondly it depends on the **garment construction.** Tight-fitting garments will restrict ventilation and may lead to discomfort due to a build-up of heat and moisture. Loose garments can promote ventilation like a chimney.

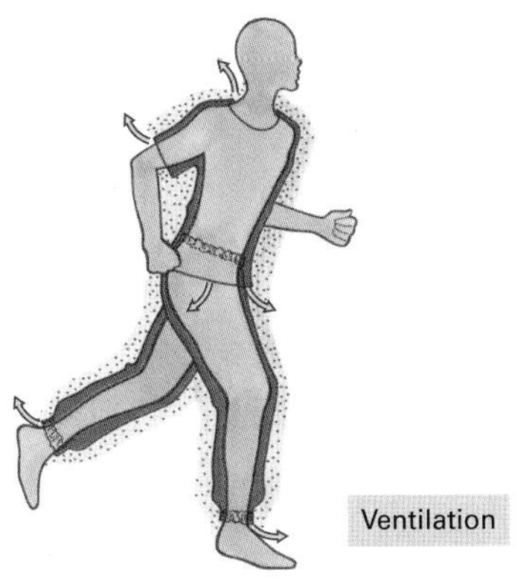

2: Air exchange affects the microclimate

The third influence is **motion** which can be provided externally by wind or by transportation (such as a bicycle), or internally by the pumping action of body movements such as working or running (*Figure 2*). Motion disturbs one or more of the various air layers and thus reduces heat insulation considerably.

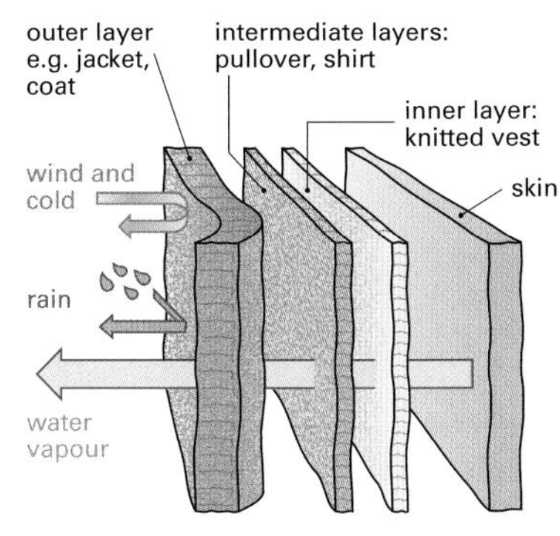

3: Principle of layering

A very effective supplement to the human thermoregulation system is obtained by providing more or fewer **layers** of clothing (*Figure 3*). The **soft-shell** or **shell-suit** is a thin, lightweight, closely-woven material which provides good insulation by limiting the escape of air. It is used e.g. for winter sports.

Wind-chill is the apparent reduction in temperature, felt at the skin surface, caused by air movement. The size of the effect, from a pleasant cooling breeze to a bitter freezing blast, depends on the temperature and moisture content of the air, as well as the wind speed (*Figure 4*).

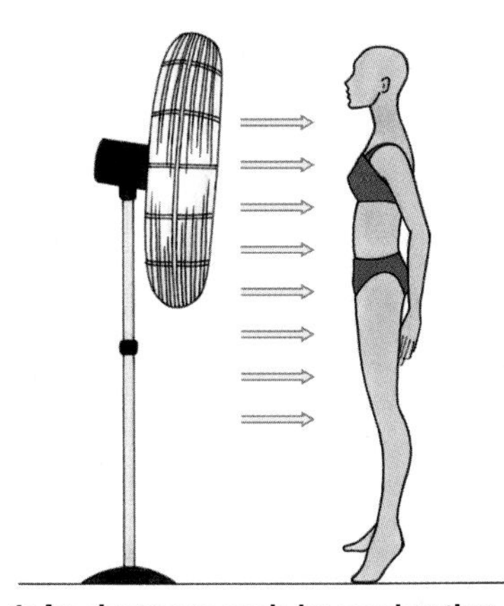
4: An air stream cools by accelerating evaporation

Moisture Absorption and Moisture Transport

The human thermoregulation system dispenses dry heat and more or less moisture, according to the heat load. This moisture has to be taken up and dispersed by the clothing. This is accomplished by absorption into the fibres and by capillary transport in the spaces between the fibres.

At normal levels of heat stress and low to medium levels of perspiration, **hygroscopic** (absorbent) fibres are preferable (*see data on page 43*). Their absorptivity is quite sufficient to take up the released moisture and to transport it, by diffusion within the fibres, to the surface where it is evaporated into the external air layer. When perspiration rates are very high, then more liquid moisture may be formed than can be transported by diffusion. This excess of liquid has to be transported by capillary action (wicking) in the spaces between the fibres. **Capillary wicking** is much faster than diffusion so greater quantities of moisture can be transported to the outside. However, if the rate of evaporation at the surface is much less than the rate of generation of liquid perspiration at the skin, then the fabric may become saturated which leads to the uncomfortable **"wet cling"** effect. Moreover, as absorbent fibres become saturated they swell, which has the effect of reducing the average size of the capillaries and slowing the rate of wicking.

Because fabrics made from non-absorbent (synthetic) fibres dry more rapidly, the wet cling effect may persist for a shorter time. Special double-layer fabrics have been developed for sportswear in which the inner layer of the fabric comprises a non-absorbent, synthetic yarn with excellent wicking properties whilst the outer layer is made of an absorbent fibre such as cotton (*see page 52*). Liquid perspiration is transported rapidly through the inner layer to the outer where it is stored and evaporated. The inner layer remains (or quickly becomes) dry so the wet cling effect is avoided or minimised.

Next-to-Skin Comfort

The sensation of contact of clothing with the skin can be very comfortable (softness, suppleness) or it can be unpleasant (scratching, prickling, clinging). These sensations depend mainly on the fineness of the fibres and their moisture content. Coarse fibres tend to yield scratchy and prickly sensations.

Perspiration can build a film on a smooth fabric surface, which can cling to the skin and feel uncomfortable. A similar effect can arise on dry skin through static charging of the fabric. An irregular or hairy fabric surface makes fewer contacts with the skin. This allows the air to move more freely between skin and clothing.

3.2.1 Weatherproof Clothing

Modern apparel fabrics may be called upon to satisfy special demands, such as weather protection, moisture transport, thermal regulation, better wearing comfort, protection against radiation, chemicals, micro-organisms, and smog. Thus the term **Functional Clothing** has arisen.

An important sector of functional clothing is **Weatherproof** or **All-weather Clothing.** European standard EN 343 lists the requirements for clothing intended for protection against bad weather (rain, wind, and low temperatures).

1: Weatherproof clothing

The main purpose of weatherproof clothing (*Figure 1*) is to keep out wind and rain, but also cold, whilst allowing perspiration moisture to escape from the body. If these requirements are not met then, even under normal conditions of exertion, either the body becomes soaked with perspiration or the clothing becomes wet, which can lead to hypothermia.

There are various textile constructions which are more or less capable of fulfilling these requirements. Liquid water is prevented from entering by having fabrics with a dense, smooth and hydrophobic (non-wetting) surface and by membrane systems such as Gore-Tex® and Sympatex®. Insulation against cold can be provided by quilted and padded structures that enclose pockets of still air. Water vapour can diffuse outwards between the yarns and fibres, driven by the higher temperature and vapour pressure on the inside of the garment (*Figure 2*).

Garments constructed from such fabrics are of special value to hikers, construction workers, farmers, police and emergency services.

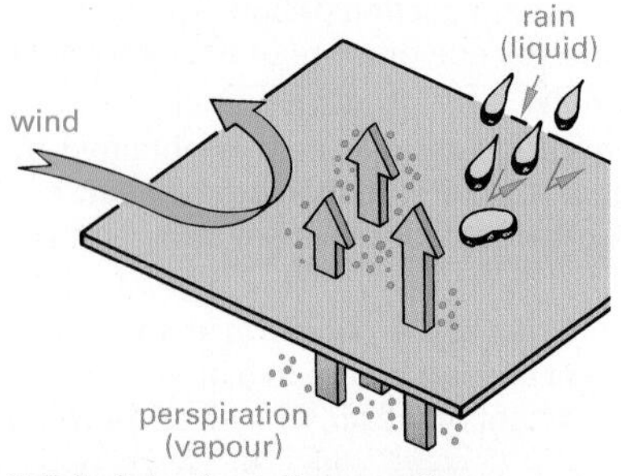

2: Principle of weather proofing

Traditional Weather Protection

Heavily-milled and raised wool fabrics and densely-woven fabrics of cotton, nylon, or polyester, with a hydrophobic finish will resist the penetration of water for a certain time (*Figure 3*). However, with continuous exposure to severe conditions, clothing made from such materials will eventually become wet and its protective value will diminish. Hydrophobic finishes are applied to fabrics for raincoats, sport and leisure-wear. Often a soil-release finish is applied at the same time. After laundering or dry-cleaning the finish may need to be renewed.

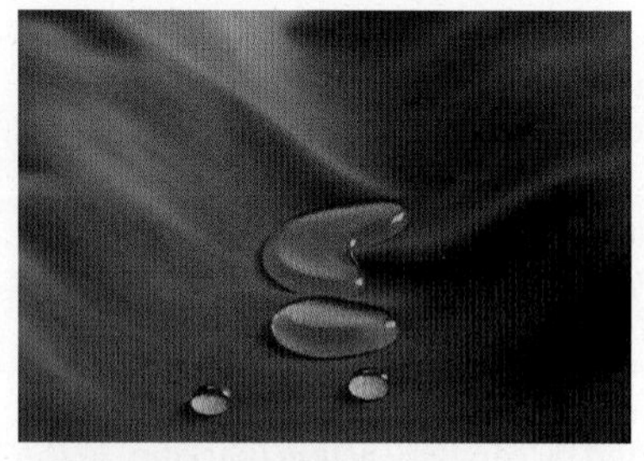

3: Water resistant fabric

Modern Weather Protection

Modern textile constructions are impermeable to water, or resist wetting for a longer time, whilst allowing water vapour to diffuse through. When made from synthetic fibres they are also easy-care. Three basic systems can be distinguished.

Microporous membranes

These are very fine films, about 0.02 mm (the thickness of domestic cling-film), containing very fine pores. They are used either by laminating onto a textile structure or by interleaving between two fabrics (*Figure 4*). In Gore-Tex® the membrane is made from polytetrafluoroethylene (PTFE).

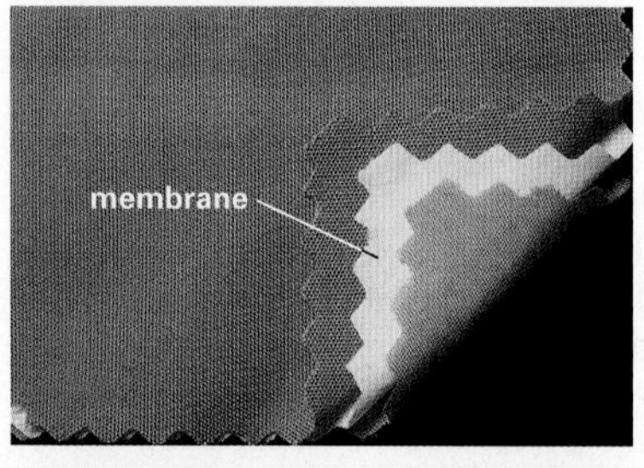

4: Fabric with membrane lining

Hygroscopic membranes

Hygroscopic means water-absorbing. They take up the perspiration and transport the vapour through the continuous film to the outside. Sympatex® is a hygroscopic membrane made from polyester (*Figure 5*).

Microfibre fabrics with a hydrophobic finish

This is a development of the traditional technology, in which very fine synthetic fibres are used to make tightly woven fabrics having very small pores. These are better able to **resist wetting and penetration** by liquid water whilst still **allowing water vapour to diffuse.** As with the traditional fabrics, a hydrophobic finish enhances the water resistance. Examples are Tactel® in nylon and Trevira Finesse® in polyester.

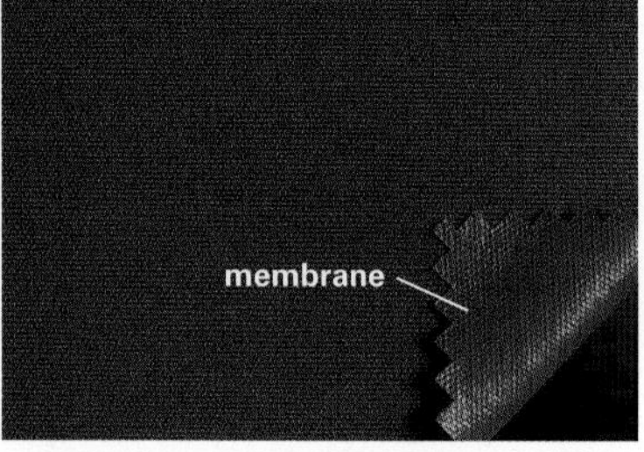

5: Fabric with laminated membrane

3.2.2 Protective Work Clothing

An important segment of the Functional Textiles area is **Protective Clothing,** both for occupational and leisure pursuits. Occupational clothing is often not solely concerned with protection. Comfort, "breathability", lightness, durability, weather resistance and launderability have become the basic requirements for modern, image conscious career apparel ("Corporate Fashion") in such areas as restaurants, hotels, airlines, filling stations, banks and postal services, etc.

Some of the basic requirements and test methods are given in the cited European standards.

1: Low temperature protection

Low Temperature Protection (*e.g. EN 14058*)

Protection against extreme cold, snow and ice is afforded by multiple-layer constructions including e.g. quilted and wadded fabrics, bulky fleeces, etc. (*Figure 1*). Enclosed still air is a most effective insulator.

Applications include winter sports, cool-room workers, polar researchers and astronauts.

2: High temperature protection

High Temperature Protection (*e.g. EN ISO 11612*)

Protection against extreme heat, flames and sparks is provided by flame retardant finished wool fabrics, special synthetic fibres, and by lamination e.g. with aluminium (*Figure 2*).

Applications include furnace, forge and foundry, glass and ceramics workers, welders, fire fighters and racing drivers.

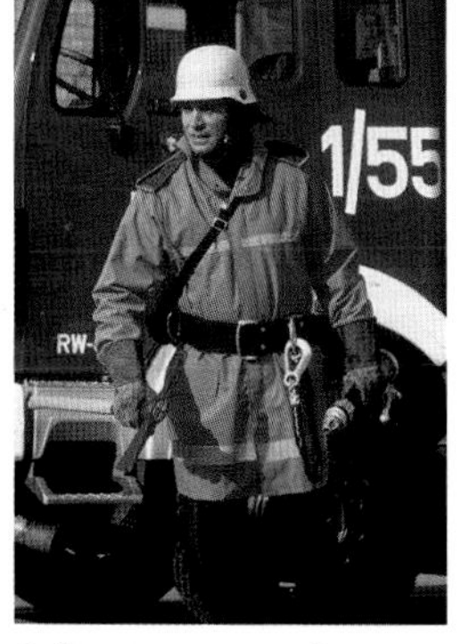

3: Emergency services

Injury Protection (*e.g. EN 381*)

Protection against severe mechanical forces is required in many occupations. Police and military may require bullet-proof clothing.

High resistance to such forces is obtained from leather or from aramid fibres, such as Kevlar®, Nomex® and Twaron®, which can be stronger than steel, often in multi-layer constructions.

Applications include mountaineers, welders, foundry workers, motor cyclists, fencers, police, fire and emergency services and military (*Figure 3*).

Chemical Protection (*e.g. EN 13034*)

Protection from smoke, poisonous chemicals, strong acids and alkalis, and harmful vapours etc. requires fabrics that are impervious to liquids and gases.

Such protection is given by special coated fabrics or nonwovens and by rubber.

Applications include chemical workers, fire and emergency services.

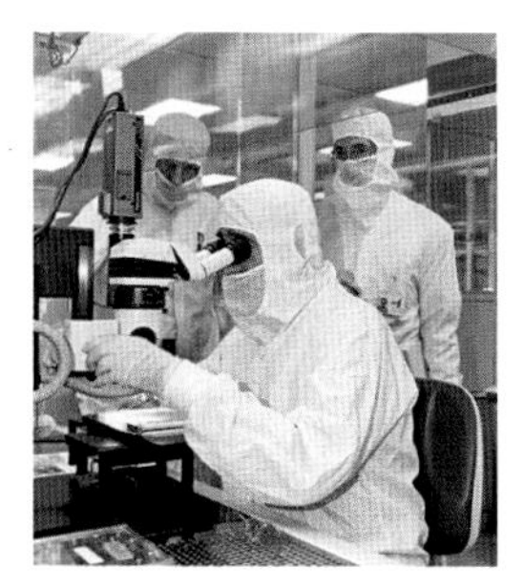

4: Clean room protection

Clean Room Suits (*e.g. EN ISO 13982-1*)

The manufacture of microelectronic devices, optical instruments, medical and pharmaceutical products and satellite technology requires a completely dust- and particle-free environment.

Humans are a major source of contamination so they have to be provided with appropriate clothing, often including head covering, made from nonwoven materials such as Tyvek® or closely-woven polyester blends (*Figure 4*).

Protection against Bacteria, Radiation, and Electrostatic Charge

(*e.g. EN 14026, 1073-2, 1149*)

Doctors, surgeons, hospital workers and medical researchers require protection from bacteria. This is provided by dense fabrics with smooth surfaces for low particle retention and easy cleaning.

Protection against radiation, for workers in X-ray departments, nuclear energy, or welding is provided by special fibres or leather.

In areas where flammable vapours, or excess oxygen may be present, such as operating theatres, it is very important to avoid the build-up (and discharge) of static electricity. This is achieved by the use of special finishes and by the inclusion of a small percentage of metal fibres in the fabrics (*see page 40*).

3.2.3 Moisture Transport and Thermoregulation

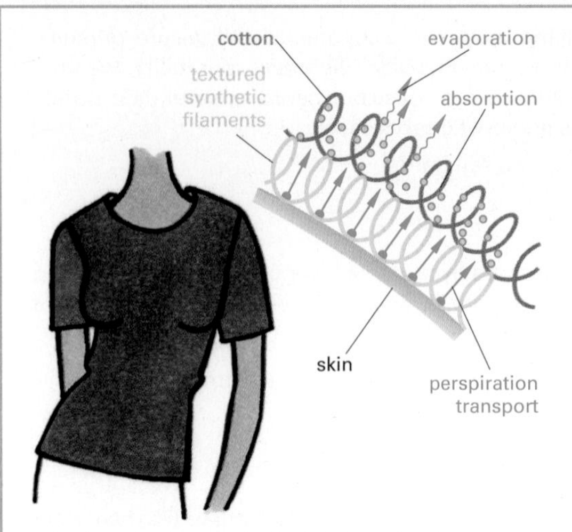

1: Moisture transport in double-layer fabrics

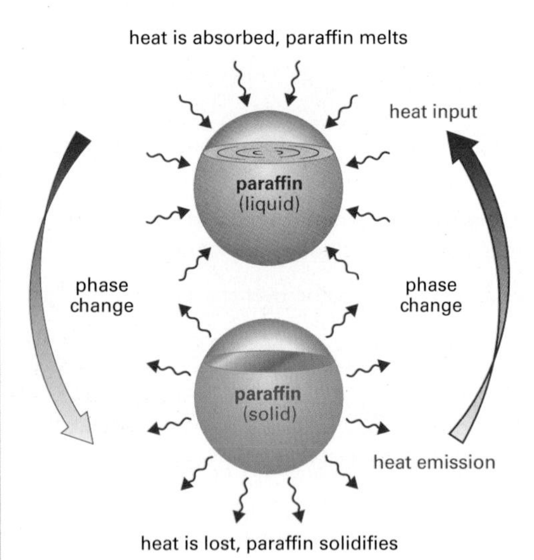

2: Encapsulated paraffin as a heat buffer

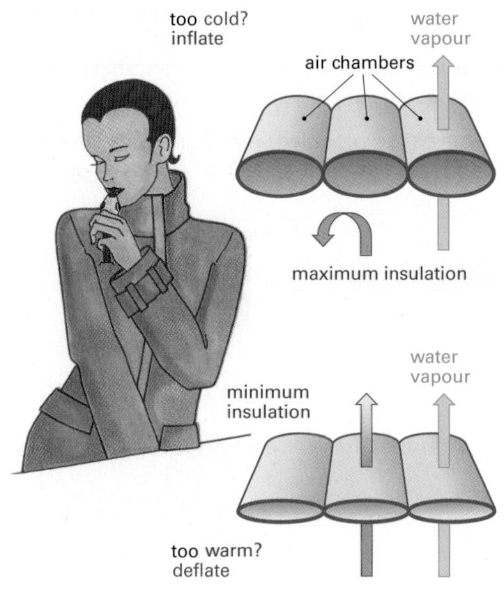

3: Insulation via air chambers

Modern textiles can be provided with specific functional attributes such as **moisture transport** and **thermal regulation.** At the same time, they can be lightweight and easy-care. The closer to the skin an item of clothing is worn, the more that attributes such as fabric extensibility, wearing comfort, and clever tailoring are appreciated.

Moisture Transport

In everyday circumstances, underwear made of cellulosic fibres such as cotton and its blends with viscose, modal or lyocell can deal perfectly well with the normal levels of perspiration that the human body generates. However, at high levels of physical exertion, such as in sport – when sweating may be heavier and more prolonged – cellulose fibres can become saturated and develop an uncomfortable "wet cling".

Special **double-layer** fabrics have been developed for sportswear in which the inner layer of the fabric comprises a non-absorbent, synthetic yarn with excellent **capillary[1] wicking** properties whilst the outer layer is made of an absorbent fibre such as cotton. Liquid perspiration is transported rapidly through the inner layer to the outer where it is stored and gradually evaporated (*Figure 1*).

Special polyester fibres such as Coolmax® are made with a wettable surface and **longitudinal grooves** that promote wicking of liquid perspiration away from the body for evaporation at the surface. They are especially useful for active sports such as cycling.

Thermal Regulation

It is possible to exploit a change of phase (solid to liquid or vice versa) to provide a heat buffer. For a given material, the change from solid to liquid requires a given quantity of heat: the latent heat. Conversely, when a liquid solidifies, the same quantity of heat is given up. The so-called microencapsulated **phase-change materials** (microPCM)[2] consist of an encapsulated paraffin wax substance which melts at around normal body temperature. The capsules, made from e.g. polyurethane, are extremely small and can be incorporated in fibres, fabrics, or films. When a garment containing microPCM is first put on, it absorbs some of the wearer's body heat and the wax melts. If the person then goes out into a cold environment, the wax is caused to freeze and the latent heat is released, providing a buffer against the cold. If the person then does some heavy activity (e.g. skiing) the body produces more heat and the wax melts again, providing a buffer against the heating. As the skier sits in the ski lift, the wax will again freeze, releasing its latent heat once more. (*Figure* 2). Outlast® and schoeller®-PCMTM are examples of trademarks in this field.

Still air will insulate a body from external cold and will trap warmth inside. Garments can be constructed with **inflatable chambers** to take advantage of this effect. The garment is provided with a tube containing a valve which can be used to either inflate or deflate the chambers. The more the chambers are inflated, the greater the insulation effect. The wearer adjusts the degree of inflation to suit the current conditions (*Figure 3*). In the AIRVANTAGE® system of W.L. Gore, the chambers are constructed from a membrane which is impervious to liquid water but allows the passage of water vapour.

A similar system is available as a down-filled quilt with air chambers. Inflation or deflation of the chambers allows the optimum warmth to be achieved – for example to allow for seasonal temperature changes.

Direct electric heating can also be built into a fabric or garment by weaving or sewing in fine conducting fibres which can be connected to a battery pack placed in the breast pocket of, say, a hiking jacket.

[1] Capillary: a fine tube; in this case the spaces between fibres or filaments.
[2] see, for example, www.microteklabs.com/micropcm.html.

3.2.4 High-Tech Textiles (1)

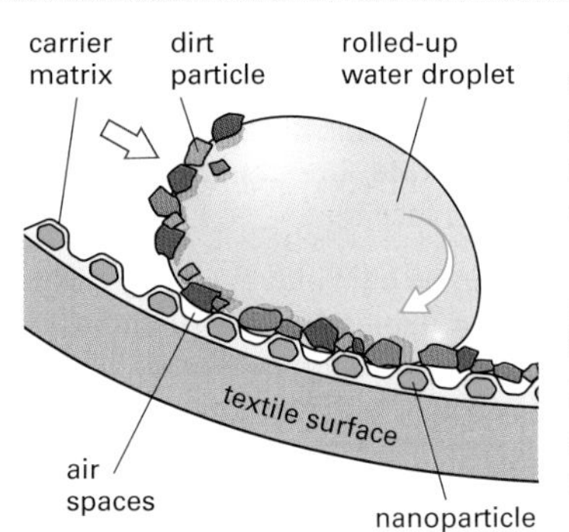

1: Nanoparticle coating

2: Label for textiles with nano-finishing

3: Label for clothing with UV protection

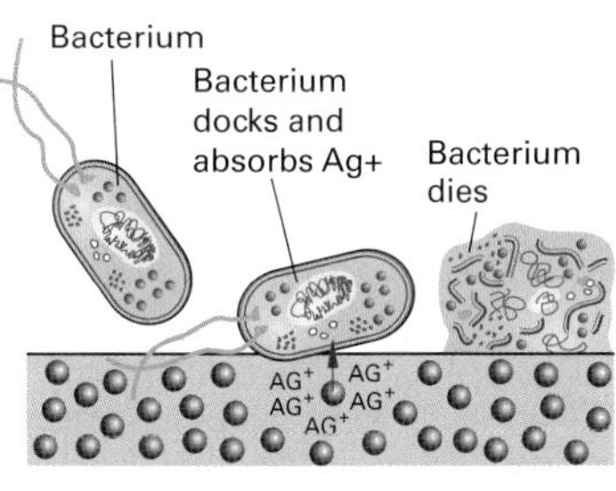

4: Antibacterial action with Silver ions (Ag^+)

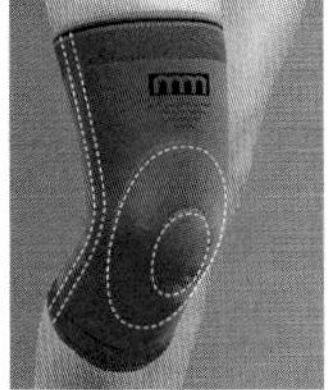
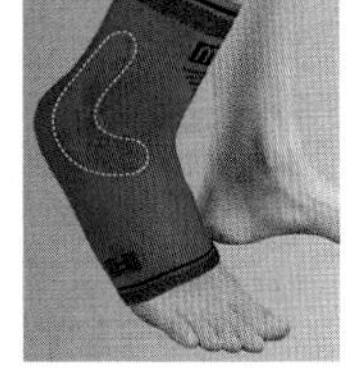

5: Specialised knee and ankle supports

The term **High-Tech Textiles** is used to describe clothing that is designed to enhance human wellbeing, or to provide extra protection against health hazards such as bacteria and solar radiation, using the latest technology. This is achieved through selection of particular fibre types, special textile constructions, application of certain chemicals, and processes based on advanced biotechnology.

Nanotechnology

Nanotechnology[1)] is a collective term for technologies that are concerned with particles of a size less than 100 nanometres. A nanometre is one thousand millionth of a meter (10^{-9} m). Nanotechnology has various applications in textiles.

- Production of very fine fibres, having a cross-sectional diameter of less than 100 µm (1 µm = 10^{-6} m).
- Inclusion of nanoparticles in the fibre spinning solution or melt ("nanocomposite fibres")
- Coating the fibre surface with nanoparticles ("nano surface coating"). Nanoparticles form a surface with extremely fine nodules (ca. 109 nodules per cm^2) (*Figure 1*).

Various substances can be produced in nanoparticle form, e.g. silver, zinc, silicon, and plastics, resulting in various surface properties. Recent developments include **anti-stick/ self-cleaning, bacteriostatic** and **UV protective** properties.

The influence, if any, on the environment and human health of man-made nanoparticles has not yet been adequately researched. It has been suggested that all textiles containing nanoparticles should be labelled as such.

Figure 2 shows a label issued by the Textile Research Institute at Denkendorf, Germany.

Protection against Ultraviolet (UV) Radiation

Ultraviolet is a part of natural sunlight and is essential for human wellbeing, but over-exposure to UV can lead to skin damage or even cancer. Textile fibres are more or less transparent so, if effective UV blocking is required, then the fabrics have to be thick, densely woven, and dyed or printed with dark colours. Additional protection can be provided by the deposition in the fibres or fabric of selected pigments which either absorb or disperse the UV rays.

Figure 3 shows a label issued by the Hohenstein Test Institute.

Textiles Containing Silver

Silver has been known for centuries as an effective means to prevent the build-up and spread of bacteria and fungi: thus, the use of silver in textiles, for example in sportswear, to prevent the generation of excessive body odours. Silver can be included in textiles in various ways to achieve a **bacteriostatic effect.**

- Silver filaments can be twisted together with a carrier yarn.
- Individual filaments (ca. 20%) can be coated with silver and then twisted together with untreated filaments.
- Silver salts can be included in the polymer melt when spinning (*Figure 4*).
- Textile fabrics can be impregnated with a solution containing silver nanoparticles.

Textile Supports, Bandages, and Prostheses

Supports, bandages and prostheses are used to stabilise, support, immobilise, or correct the operation of limbs and joints (*Figure 5*). They are usually used directly on the body, so they need to have good physiological properties plus high extensibility and elasticity. They are usually made from knitted fabrics, possibly double-layer structures, constructed from fine, synthetic microfibre, multifilament yarns with a large proportion of elastomeric.

1) nano (grk) = dwarf: in science nano is a prefix meaning 10^{-9}

3.2.4 High-Tech Textiles (2)

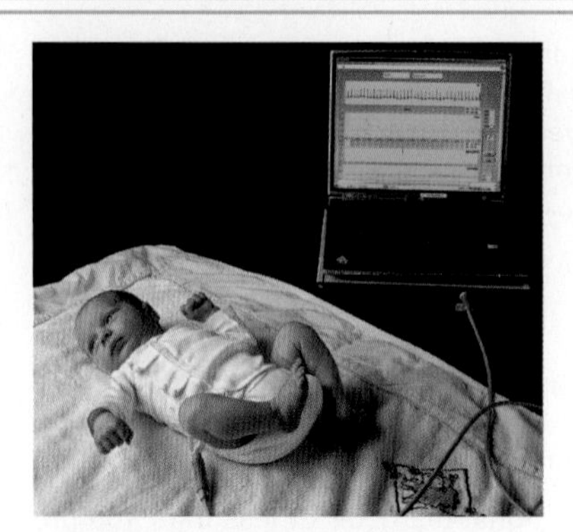

1: Healthcare: Integrated baby monitoring system

Smart clothing is the name given to clothing with built-in electronic devices. Other terms include **wearable electronics, e-textiles, intelligent textiles,** and **personal health monitoring.** Electronic components, sensors and telecommunications systems are integrated into the clothing so that data such as heart rate, breathing rate, body temperature, etc. can be transmitted to a data-processing facility.

Personal Health Monitoring and diagnostic functions can be built into everyday clothing. Examples are the rapid detection of health risks for babies (*Figure 1*), and data relay (including alarm communication, if necessary) in the diagnosis and care of chronic health conditions. Such arrangements allow those at risk to continue with their normal lives, at home, whilst under medical surveillance. This preservation of their quality of life is especially important for the elderly – an ever-increasing proportion of the population.

Sport and Leisurewear with Integrated Monitoring of Vital Functions

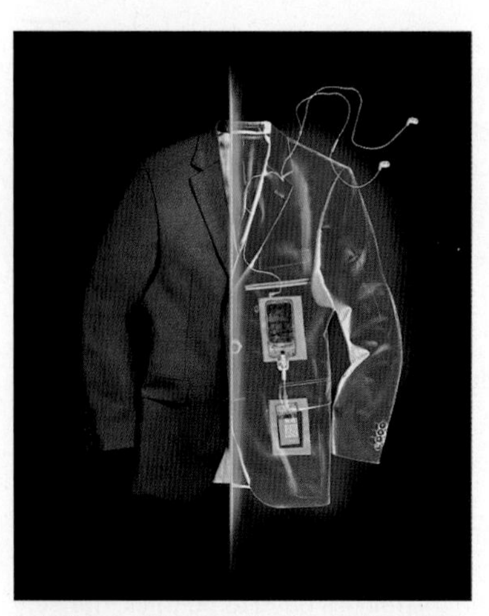

2: Leisure: Integrated communications technology

For professional sportsmen and women, as well as fitness enthusiasts, data monitoring and relay, built into **sportswear** can be a valuable aid to training or intensive exercise. During training, data from ECG, pulse, and blood pressure readings etc. can be relayed to a (remote or proximate) recording station to guide the build-up, duration and intensity of effort. Quite apart from their obvious application in extreme sports, even normal leisure pursuit gear can be supplemented by safety features such as automatic position tracking and emergency communication devices.

Normal **leisurewear** can be provided with consumer electronics and communications devices (*Figure 2*).

Textiles with Integrated Drug Delivery Systems

Textile fibres and fabrics can also be provided with reservoirs for active medical agents, e.g. for the treatment of chronic skin conditions or lesions. The reservoirs are in the form of complex molecules, such as cyclodextrins, and hollow fibres. The substances stored in these reservoirs are released to the skin surface over an extended time period.

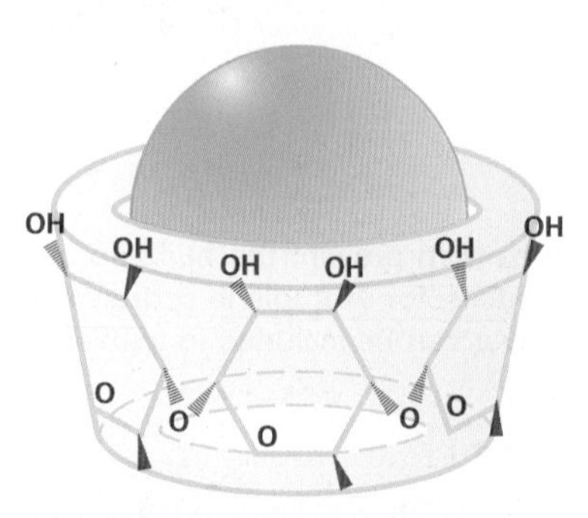

3: Cyclodextrin molecule with included active agent

Cyclodextrins are sugars in which six, seven or eight molecules of glucose are combined to form a ring in the shape of a hollow, truncated cone (*Figure 3*). The orientation of the molecules is such that the external surface of the cyclodextrin is hydrophilic and the inside is relatively hydrophobic. This construction is capable of forming **inclusion compounds** with hydrophobic molecules. Thus the target molecule is encapsulated by the cyclodextrin from which it can later be released by the action of heat or moisture. Typical uses are the absorption of odour-causing molecules from perspiration (later removed by normal washing) or the gradual release of skin emollients or fragrances.

Hollow fibres (*Figure 4*) can also deliver a controlled dose of active agent, for example as part of a soluble dressing for wounds. The active agent, e.g. Seraticin[1)], is deposited inside the hollow fibres, together with an enzyme which promotes the gradual disintegration of the fibres so that, when the healing process is complete, the dressing falls away.

Different types of active agents can be distinguished for the different end-uses.

Plant-based agents for skin care	**Animal-based agents** for wound dressing	**Metallic agents** to treat allergies	**Synthetic agents** for skin care and odour control	**Micro-organisms** for wound dressing
Aloe Vera Vitamin C Vitamin E Alginate Ginko	Seraticin[1)] Hirudin[2)] Krill enzyme[3)]	Silver	Skin emollients Fragrances	Viruses that attack and disrupt bacteria

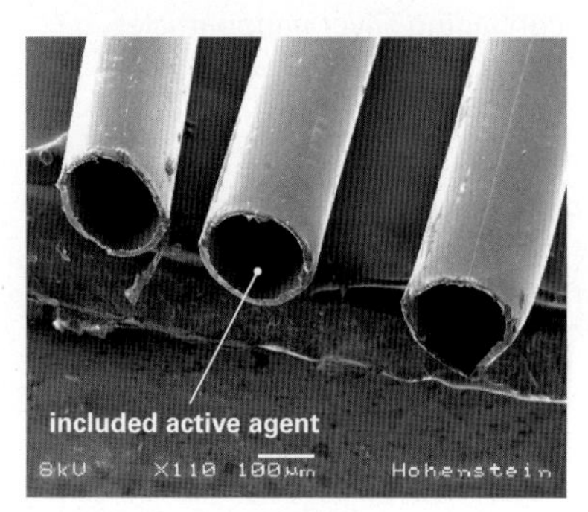

4: Hollow cellulosic fibres

1) Seraticin is a novel antibiotic able to kill 12 different strains of MRSA, as well as E. coli and C. difficile.
2) Hirudin is an anticoagulant occurring naturally in the saliva of medicinal leeches.
3) Krill enzymes are used for the treatment (dissolving) of dead tissue.

3.2.5 Technical Textiles

The term Technical Textiles was coined, by the promoters of the TechTextil® trade exhibitions, as a catch-all phrase to encompass all of the textile materials that were considered suitable for showing at these trade fairs, i.e. primarily industrial fabrics but also any apparel fabrics that incorporate relatively advanced technology for specialised applications. The range of materials included is very wide, from ultra-light concrete reinforcement, to composite materials for cars and aeroplanes, to medical implants and prostheses. Also included are new developments in fibre technology, especially in the nano-region, and these are giving rise to a large increase in Technical Textiles.

In the apparel sector, Technical Textiles are used for **protective clothing,** workwear, **personal health protection,** and **sportswear.** Clearly, there is a significant overlap between Technical Textiles and **Functional Textiles.**

The main sectors of Technical Textiles are shown below.

Protech

Protective Clothing Safety at Work

Membrane systems; special fibres; fabrics and coatings for protection against extreme weather, cold, heat and flames, corrosive materials, dangerous chemicals, etc.

Sporttech

Sport and Leisure

Membrane systems; special fibres; yarns and knitted or woven fabrics, for particular activities: sky-diving, biking, skiing, hiking, mountaineering, water sports, etc.

Oekotech

Environmental Protection, Waste Disposal, Recycling

Fibres, nonwovens, filters and sieves, made from recycled materials, for household textiles, packaging and industrial textiles.

Medtech

Medical Textiles

Superfine fibres, circular knits, warp knits and woven fabrics for textile implants; wound dressings containing active agents; surgical ligatures, etc.

Clothtech

Clothing

Technical innovations in man-made fibre production, yarn and fabric development, and processing for the clothing and footwear industries.

Buildtech

Building

Nonwovens, composites, special fabrics and membranes for construction and civil engineering: e.g. in roads, dams, reinforcements, roofing, awnings and coverings, facades, etc.

Mobiltech

Transport

Fibre-reinforced plastics and composites for bodywork in lorries and aeroplanes; cordage for ropes, hoses, strapping, belting; sound proofing materials in hemp; three-dimensional fabrics for car seats.

Indutech

Industrial

Superfine fibres for filter pads and filtration plants; special textiles for cleaning uses; fibres and circular knits for caulking and padding; transport belts for the engineering, chemical and electrical industries.

Agrotech

Agriculture

Fabrics for shading systems; webs and warp knits for irrigation and drainage systems; windshields; silo components, plant containers for farming and forestry; garden and industrial landscaping materials.

Geotech

Geo Textiles

Fibre-reinforced plastics, textile webs and warp knits for irrigation and drainage systems; road building, civil engineering, dams and landfill sites.

Hometech

Home Textiles

Technical developments in textile materials for furniture, upholstery, carpets and floorcoverings.

Packtech

Packaging

Technical textiles such as webs, woven fabrics and circular knits for packaging, garment-making and transport of goods.

The pictograms are promulgated by TechTextil® an exhibition of the Frankfurt Trade Fair Company (Messe Frankfurt).

4.1.1 Sustainability
4.1.2 Ecology and Textile Production (1)

Ecology is the study of the relationships between life and its physical environment. Conservation of and responsibility for the environment is a duty of all human enterprises, since every generation must bequeath a safe and healthy environment to the next. The key concept is **sustainability:** the ability to meet current requirements without compromising the needs of future generations. It is convenient to subdivide the subject into three areas, namely **social, environmental** and **economic** influences. Textiles are worn in intimate contact with the body; they form a personal environment which should be benign.

The environmental influence of a textile product, over its whole life cycle, can be divided into five broad areas: **Production, Utilisation, Disposal, Society, Humanity.**

Life-cycle Analysis[1)2)] attempts to quantify the impact upon the environment of a product throughout its whole lifetime. It considers the consumption of raw materials, energy, chemicals, water, etc. in production, transportation, utilisation, and disposal.

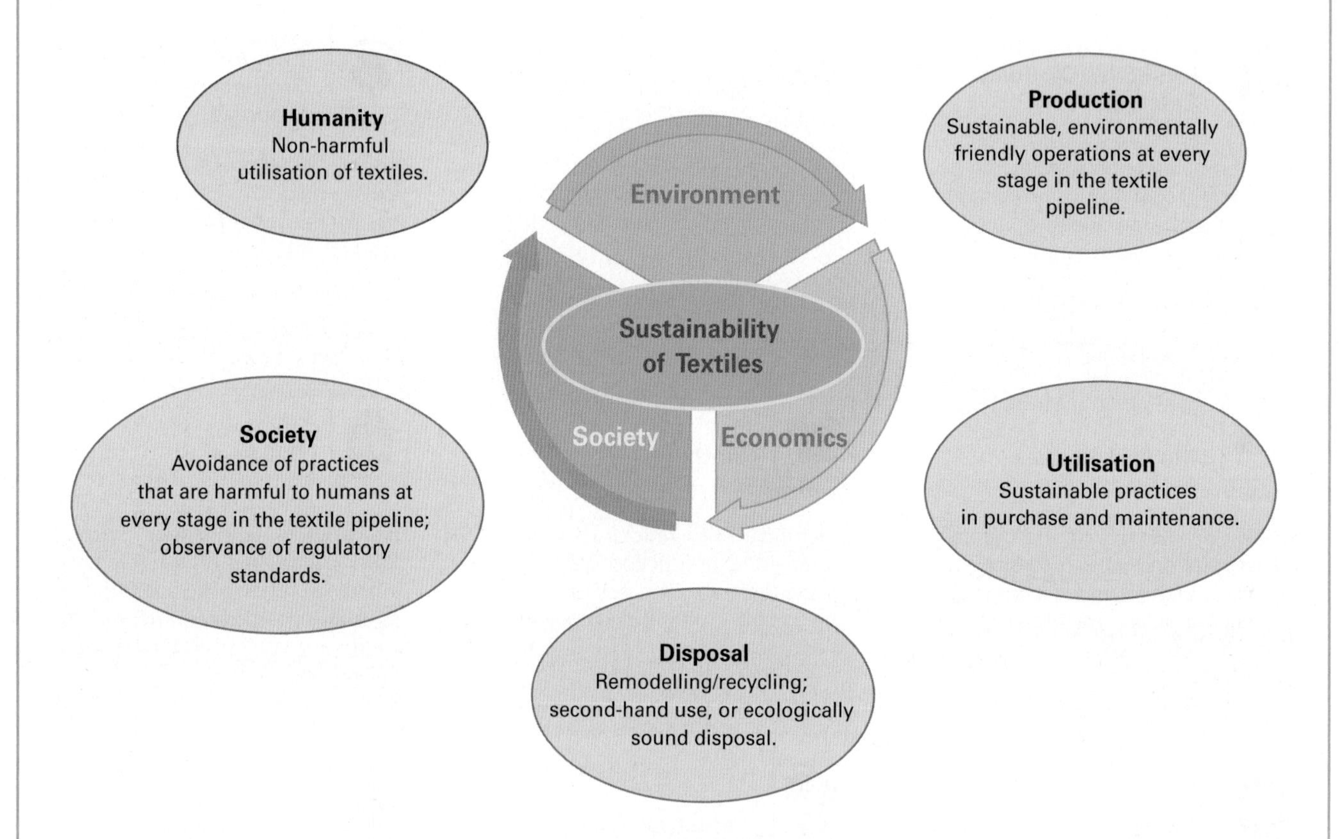

Ecology and Textile Production

This means sustainable, environmentally friendly operations at all stages of the textile chain, including natural and man-made fibre production, manufacture of yarns and fabrics, textile processing and garment making. Transportation distances between production stages and from end-product to end-user should be minimised.

Objectives

- Improving **added value** whilst reducing **environmental impact** and **consumption of resources** (high productivity and efficiency).
- Maintenance of **product quality.**
- Taking account of the broader concerns of **society.**

Fulfilment of these objectives yields active **Environmental Protection** which includes:

- **Control of emissions** Emissions should have minimum adverse impact on humans, animals, plants, water and land. Clear standards have to be fixed and adhered to.
- **Water conservation** Water effluent should be purified and recycled.
- **Energy efficiency** Energy consumption should be minimised and should emphasise renewable resources, such as waste heat recovery and utilisation of solar and wind power.
- **Waste management** Waste materials should be recycled or disposed of in an environmentally friendly manner.

1) ISO 14040 (2006): Life cycle assessment – Principles & framework
2) ISO 14044 (2006): Life cycle assessment – Requirements & guidelines

4.1.2 Ecology and Textile Production (2)
4.1.3 Social Considerations

Maize

Sugar beet

Wheat

Cane sugar

1: Raw materials for the production of biopolymers

Sustainability in Fibre Production

Economic production of **vegetable fibres,** predominantly **cotton,** requires fertilisation and irrigation of the land and protection of the plants against pests and diseases. Water consumption can be very high in some areas, so there is often scope for improved sustainability[1].The so-called Organic cotton, or Biocotton is grown from certified seed, using certified agronomic practices, fertilisers and pest control systems, on land that has been used for such practices for a given number of seasons.

Animal fibres, predominantly **wool,** may also require fertilisation of the land and pest control chemicals, some of which may persist on the fibres, in the wool grease. Silk worms are often treated with hormones, to increase the size of the cocoons. The degumming and weighting processes can be environmentally unfriendly.

The production of man-made fibres requires energy-intensive chemical processes. The two main classes of man-made fibres are:

- **Synthetic fibres,** derived from fossil fuels (oil and gas),
- **Cellulosic fibres,** derived from plant materials (mainly wood from beech, pine, eucalyptus and bamboo).

Recent developments include fibres derived from the so-called **biopolymers** whose source materials are plant sugars extracted from wheat, maize, rice, sugar beet, sugar cane, etc. (*Figure 1*). It is claimed that, compared to oil-based synthetic fibres, biopolymer fibres require 60% less fossil fuel and release 80% less greenhouse gases. Nevertheless, they require large resources in agriculture. Furthermore, land used to service biopolymer production replaces that used to grow food.

Examples of biopolymer fibres are:

Ingeo® an industrial fibre used for packaging and, increasingly, for clothing.

Seralit® an industrial fibre used as a substitute for aramids and asbestos.

Biophyl™ for beachwear and underwear.

Sustainability in Yarn and Fabric Production

In spinning, weaving and knitting, chemicals are required as lubricants and protectives. Some of these can be substituted by more ecologically sound materials and the quantities used can be reduced by more efficient processes or recycling.

Sustainability in Processing

Chemicals are indispensable in dyeing and finishing: for colouration and to enhance the fibre and fabric properties. Here also, some of them can be substituted by more ecologically sound materials and the quantities used can be reduced by more efficient processes. Cleaning and recycling of water is very important in this area.

Sustainability in Transportation

Large quantities of textile goods, together with their packaging, are moved around the world daily. The travelling distances need to be reduced and efficient recycling systems for large volumes of packaging need to be available.

Social Considerations

Recent years have seen the fashion industry responding to concerns, raised mainly by NGOs[2], regarding working conditions in the textile factories in developing countries, which are suppliers to European manufacturers and retailers. One result of these concerns is the "Fairtrade" and "Fairwear" movements in Europe.

The **Fair Wear Foundation** (FWF, www.fairwear.org), founded in 1999, is an association dedicated to the improvement of workplace conditions in the garment and textile industry. It is located in Amsterdam and is governed by labour unions, NGOs and business associations. Funding comes from EU social funds, government, trade unions and NGOs. In addition, member companies, which operate in the European market, pay a fee to use the FWF logo on their goods (*Figure 2*) and promise to promote the ideals of the FWF to their suppliers. These include: no compulsion or discrimination in the workplace; no employment of children; freedom of association and the right to collective bargaining; payment of a living wage; safe and healthy working conditions; a legally binding employment contract. FWF has established offices in several countries, where complaints about non-compliant activities can be reported.

2: Logo of the Fair Wear Foundation; an association for the improvement of working conditions

[1] See www.cottoninc.com for further information on sustainability of cotton production.
[2] NGO = Non-governmental organisation: large international charity and lobbying group

4.1.4 Human Ecology, Utilisation and Disposal

Human Ecology

The aim is to have clothing that is healthy to wear and causes no harm. Clothing should be free from damaging or carcinogenic substances. The health of the wearer should be protected against skin damage, allergies or other hazards. To this end, it is useful to enforce strict labelling which indicates all relevant components of a textile product and where all who have contributed to its manufacture can be identified – a so-called "transparent textile".

An optimally labelled product should indicate:

- Information on all materials, fibres, yarns, accessories.
- Country of origin and method of manufacture, e.g. the use of biological or genetically modified materials.
- Information on chemical residues and special treatments, e.g. pesticides, plasticisers, lubricants, resins.
- Aftercare and disposal or recycling advice.

Ecology and Utilisation

This embraces the utilisation of textiles from purchase to disposal and requires sustainable purchasing behaviour as well as environmentally friendly aftercare procedures that do not consume excessive resources. Here again, strict content labelling and product traceability (transparency) are very useful. Each consumer should be actively evaluating the following questions.

- Do I really need another item of clothing?
- Should I be buying a higher quality garment?
- Has this product been manufactured taking account of social and environmental concerns?
- Does it respect the balance of nature?
- Will the necessary aftercare be environmentally costly?
- Will the garment be hard-wearing and can it be recycled?

Ecology and Disposal

Recycling of Second-Hand Clothing

1. Collection
About 750,000 tonnes of used textiles are collected in Germany alone, each year.

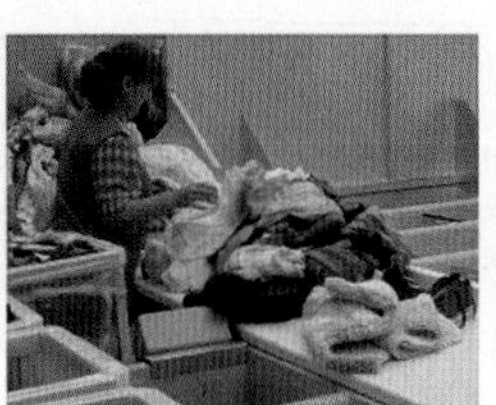

2. Sorting
The used clothes are sorted by hand in specialised operations.

3. Wholesaler
Second hand clothes are transported to Eastern Europe, the Middle East, and Africa for sale.

4. Small business
The clothes are repaired and re-modelled by small firms or individuals.

5. Consumer
There is an increasing demand for second-hand clothing in many countries.

1 to 5: Recycling of second-hand clothing

Collection, Sorting and Recycling

Clothing is **collected,** by house-to-house operations or from specially-provided local containers, and shipped off for upgrading on a well-established route. In Germany alone about 750,000 tonnes of discarded clothing is processed each year (*Figure 1*).

The textiles are sorted by hand in specialised facilities (*Figure 2*). About half of the collected garments can be **refurbished** for second-hand use.

- The collected clothing is sorted according to quality and baled up for distribution to wholesalers in the different markets: **Western Europe, Eastern Europe, Middle East** and **Africa** (*Figure 3*).
- In the importing countries, employment is provided for many small enterprises and individuals engaged in repairing and re-modelling second-hand clothing (*Figure 4*). In many countries, there is increasing demand for second-hand clothes (*Figure 5*).
- The **fibres can be recovered** from some materials by various techniques. They are classified as waste fibres and can be recycled into certain undemanding products, such as cleaning cloths, non-wovens, cardboard, and plastic containers.
- Textile materials that cannot be recycled may be used as feedstocks for furnaces in **energy generation.**

4.1.5 Eco-Labelling

There is a demand from some consumer lobbying groups that textile manufacturers and retailers should give information about any potentially harmful substances which could possibly be contained in their products. In various countries, governmental or private organisations have developed sets of criteria which can be embodied in a labelling scheme to satisfy these demands. In a competitive market, different labels have been developed to appeal to different segments. Typically, such labels guarantee one or more of the following.

- No potentially carcinogenic dyestuffs have been used.
- Heavy metals are absent, or are present in such small quantities that their concentration, when dissolved in perspiration, would be lower than the permitted levels for drinking water.
- Pesticides are absent, or are present in concentrations lower than those permitted for foodstuffs.
- Formaldehyde is absent, or does not exceed a certain concentration.
- The pH value is neutral or slightly acid (like human skin).
- Textiles intended for babies and small children shall not release any harmful chemicals on contact with saliva.

Manufacturers or distributors of textile products can apply to these organisations for the right to use promotional and marketing materials (labels, hang tags etc.) subject to their products being included in a stringent testing regime.

Logo	Description	Test Area				Raw Material			Issuing Body			Scope			Test Laboratory	
Examples of Eco-labels		Humanity	Production	Society	Disposal	Natural fibres	Cotton	All fibres	Company	Association	State	Global	National	Europe	Independent	In-house
	GLOBAL ORGANIC TEXTILE STANDARD (GOTS) global-standard.org	X	X	X				X		X		X			X	
	NATURTEXTIL BEST naturtextil.com	X	X	X	X	X				X				X	X	
	BLUESIGN SYSTEM bluesign.com	X	X	X	X			X		X		X			X	
	ECO-TEX STANDARD 100 oekotex100.com	X	X					X		X		X			X	
	TEXTILE EXCHANGE textileexchange.org	X	X		X		X			X		X				
	ECOLABEL European Eco-label (textiles) ecolabel.com	X	X					X			X			X	X	
	MEDICALLY TESTED koerpervertraegliche-textilien.com	X						X		X			X		X	
	EARTHPOSITIVE continentalclothing.de	X	X	X	X		X			X			X		X	
	GREEN COTTON Novotex novotex.dk	X	X	X	X		X		X				X			X
	PURE-WEAR OTTO-Versand otto.com	X					X		X				X		X	

5.1.1 Overview and Definitions

The word yarn (or thread) is used in common parlance to cover all of the linear textile structures given below. Thus a yarn is an assembly of fibres or filaments having a substantial length and relatively small cross-section, with or without twist, being the end-product of a spinning and winding process. Yarns can be either "single" or "folded (plied)".

Yarns can be made from either staple fibres or filaments. Distinction may be made between different types of yarn according to the intended end use, thus: warp yarns, weft yarns, knitting yarns, sewing threads, embroidery yarns, lace yarns.

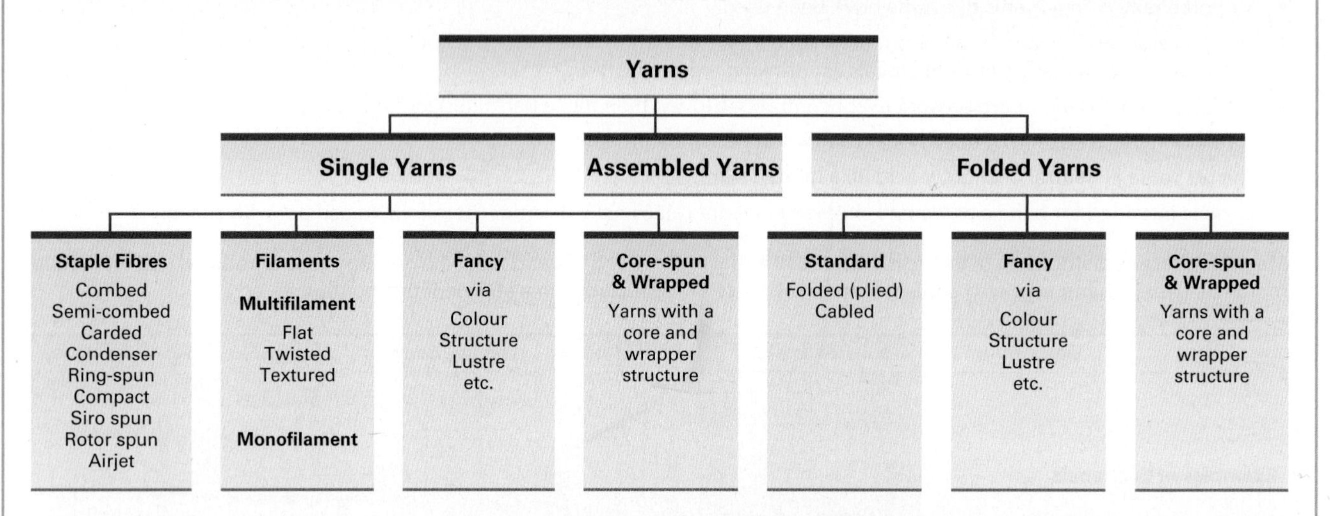

Terminology

Term	Schematic	Definition and Description
Spun Yarns		**Spun yarns** are made by mechanical assembly and twisting together (spinning) of staple fibres. Different spinning processes are used according to fibre type (wool, cotton, flax, silk, man-made) and fibre length (staple).
Filament Yarns		**Filament yarns** are made by the assembly of continuous filaments.
• **Flat**		The filaments can be harvested from nature (silk) or formed by extrusion of man-made chemicals through a spinneret.
• **Twisted**		A **multifilament yarn** is a filament yarn made from multiple filaments, assembled with or without twist.
• **Textured**		Filament yarns can be **textured** (made more voluminous) by introducing permanent crimp into the individual filaments.
• **Monofilament**		A **monofilament** yarn consists of only a single continuous filament, spun from a single-hole spinneret.
Assembled Yarns		Two or more yarns wound side by side onto the same package, but without twisting around each other, are called **assembled yarns.**
Folded (plied) Yarns		**Folded** or **Plied yarns** are made by twisting together two or more single (and/or folded) yarns of the same or different types.

Twist

The term twist stands for both the direction of twisting and the number of turns in a yarn.

If the direction of inclination of the fibres appearing at the surface of a yarn (or of the single yarn components of a folded yarn) is to the right, when the yarn is held vertically, then this is called **Z twist.**

If the direction of inclination of the fibres appearing at the surface of a yarn (or of the single yarn components of a folded yarn) is to the left, when the yarn is held vertically, then this is called **S twist.**

Twist level is the number of turns of twist per unit of length e.g. turns per metre. Yarns with the normal amount of twist are used for smooth and dense fabrics. Low twist yarns have greater volume and are used for softer, more open and thicker fabrics. Yarns with a significantly higher twist than normal are used for crêpe fabrics.

5.2.1 Basic Principles of Spun Yarn Production

Spun yarns are made by mechanical assembly and twisting together of staple fibres.

The basic principle can be applied to natural staple fibres, such as cotton wool and flax, as well as cut or broken filaments from silk or man-made fibres.

Different spinning systems are required for **short-staple spinning** (up to about 50 mm) and **long-staple spinning** (over about 60 mm).

Production of Spun Yarns (schematic)

Fibres from the compressed bales are first opened up and then assembled into a yarn in the following stages.

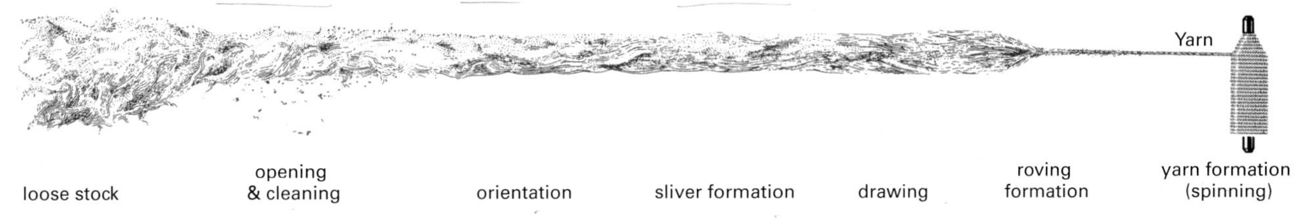

Formation of a Roving

There are two ways of forming a roving, depending on the fibre type and staple length.

Formation of a Roving (slubbing) by Partitioning a Web

After opening and cleaning, a fine web is formed on a carding machine. The web is folded on itself several times and then drawn out again to the original thickness at a second carding stage. The web is divided into narrow tapes, which are given some coherence by rubbing between reciprocating belts to form the slubbings. This is the basis for the **woollen** or **condenser** spinning system, for relatively short fibres.

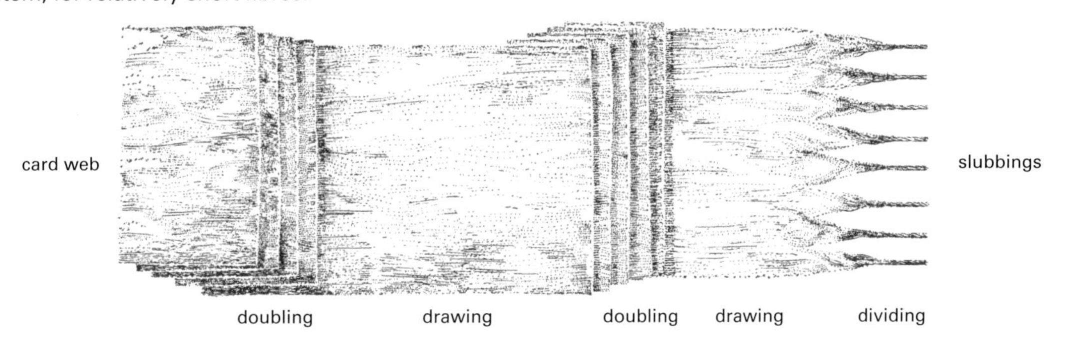

Formation of a Roving by Doubling and Drafting of Slivers

The card web is condensed into a sliver. Six or eight slivers are fed into a drawframe, where they are combined and drawn out to the original thickness. This doubling and drafting operation may be repeated once or twice more to improve the uniformity of the sliver and the orientation of the fibres. This method is used for the production of rotor- ring- and airjet-spun yarns.

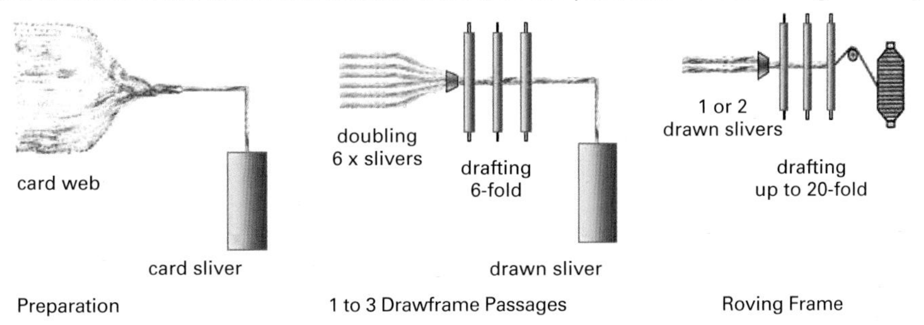

Spinning the Yarn (*see page 65*)

The final yarn is produced by drawing out the roving to the required fineness whilst inserting the required amount of twist. Several spinning systems are available, each with its own technical and market area. The most important are classical **ring spinning, compact ring spinning, Siro spinning, open-end rotor spinning and airjet spinning.**

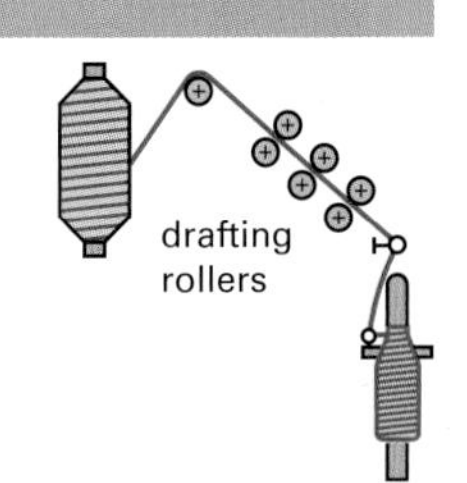

5.2.2 Manufacture of Spun Yarns (1)

Spinning Systems for Different Types of Fibres

Group	Spinning system	Fibre Type	Fibre Length
Long staple systems	Woollen system Semi-worsted system Worsted system Siro-spinning system	Wool wool-like man-made fibres (wool type)	18 ... 60 mm 60 ... 250 mm
Short staple systems	Condenser system (similar to woollen system) Cotton system (ring spinning) OE Rotor spinning Airjet spinning	Short cotton & waste Cotton and man-made fibres (cotton type)	10...20 mm 20...50 mm 10...100 mm
Bast fibre systems	Flax system Hemp system Jute system	Flax Hemp Jute	up to 1000 mm
Silk systems	Spun silk (schappe) Noil silk (bourette)	Silk	up to 250 mm up to 60 mm
Man-made fibre systems	Converter (cutting, breaking)	Cotton type Wool type Carpet type	40 mm 60 ... 80 mm 100 ... 250 mm

Woollen System

Almost any spinnable fibre can be processed on the woollen system but it is primarily used for short fibres and recovered waste. The starting material is usually compressed bales of sorted and washed raw wool, recovered wool, or other fibres. The material is taken from the bales in layers and fed to a carding willow (*stage 5, below*) for opening.

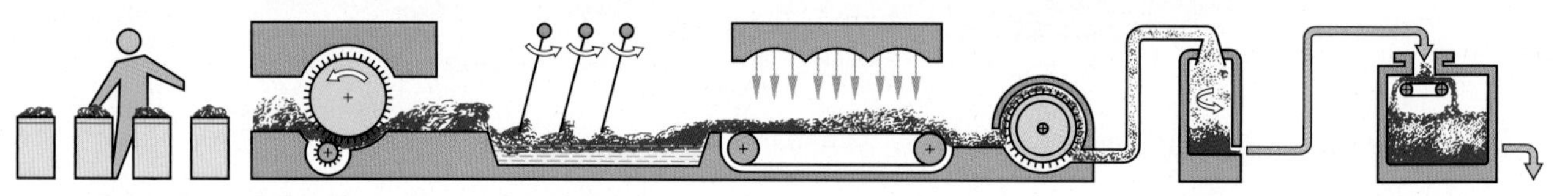

1: Sorting	2: Opening	3: Washing	4: Drying	5: Willowing	6: Mixing and Oiling
Sorting the fleece wool according to fibre quality.	Separating the stock into tufts and removal of coarse impurities.	Removal of dirt and grease with alkaline soap solution.	Drying with warm air.	Opening up and cleaning the loose stock.	Mixing fibre types and colours. Composing a spinning lot. Oiling to improve the processing characteristics.

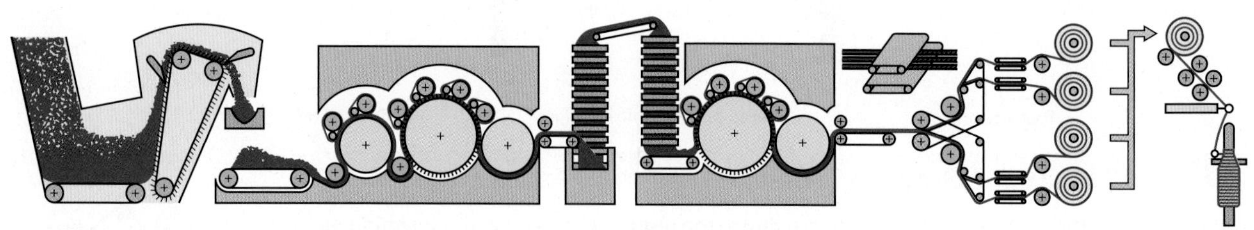

7: Weighing	8: Carding	9: Dividing the web and Rubbing	10: Spinning
Opening up the stock. Feeding portions of equal weights to the card.	Individualising the fibres. Improving fibre orientation. Removal of impurities. Formation of a web.	Dividing the web into ribbons. Rubbing the ribbons between reciprocating aprons to form the slubbing.	Drafting to the required fineness. Twisting. Winding.

5.2.2 Manufacture of Spun Yarns (2)

Worsted System

The worsted system is used to produce smooth, uniform yarns from the longer types of wool fibres. The raw wool is first prepared at the top-makers where it is washed, combed, and formed into a sliver. Six or eight slivers are combined (doubled) and then drawn (drafted) out to the original size. The unwanted short fibres are removed, in a complex machine called a comber, and the combed sliver is further drafted into a roving with a minimum amount of twist for cohesion. The final spinning machine draws the roving out to the required yarn fineness and inserts the necessary amount of twist to provide the required strength.

The original loose wool, or tops, can also be dyed for the production of coloured yarns.

Worsted Preparation

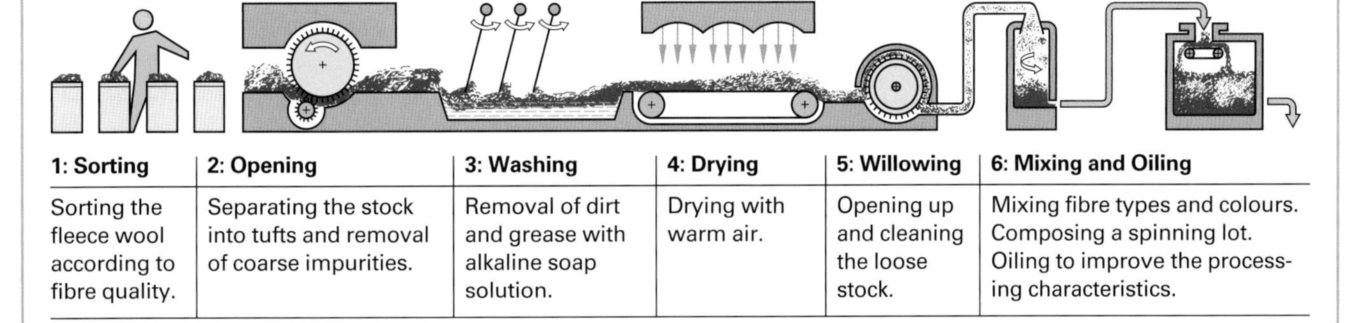

1: Sorting	2: Opening	3: Washing	4: Drying	5: Willowing	6: Mixing and Oiling
Sorting the fleece wool according to fibre quality.	Separating the stock into tufts and removal of coarse impurities.	Removal of dirt and grease with alkaline soap solution.	Drying with warm air.	Opening up and cleaning the loose stock.	Mixing fibre types and colours. Composing a spinning lot. Oiling to improve the processing characteristics.

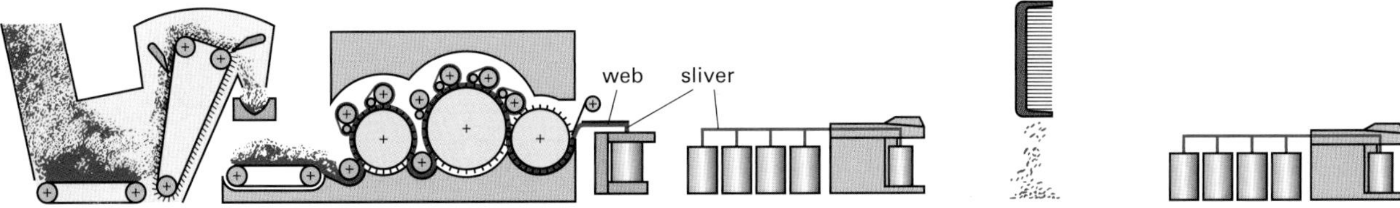

7: Weighing	8: Carding	9: Drawing	10: Combing	11: Drawing
Opening up the loose stock, feeding portions of equal weights to the card.	Individualising and orienting the fibres, removing impurities.	Doubling and drafting to improve regularity, mixing of fibre types and colours.	Combing out the short fibres and remaining impurities.	Further improvement of regularity. Contents of the final cans are compressed and these "bumped tops" delivered to the spinner.

Spinning

The bumped tops from the combing mill are fed to the worsted drawframes.

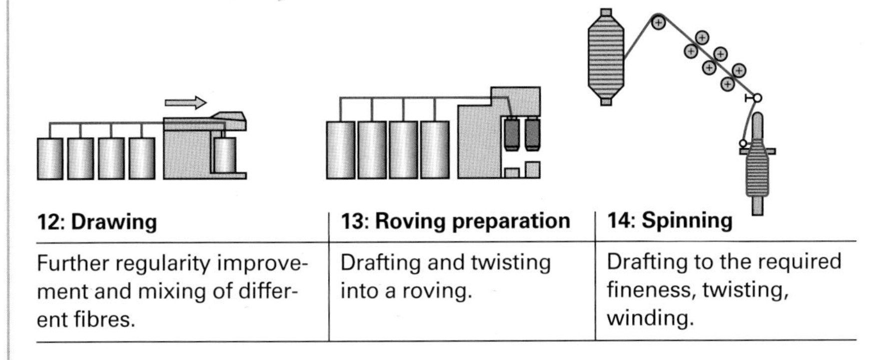

12: Drawing	13: Roving preparation	14: Spinning
Further regularity improvement and mixing of different fibres.	Drafting and twisting into a roving.	Drafting to the required fineness, twisting, winding.

Spinning is predominantly by the classical ring spinning system. Compact and Siro-spinning are also increasing in popularity.

Airjet spinning is also possible.

Semi-worsted Spinning

The designation semi-worsted means that the worsted process is followed with the exception that there is no combing stage. Instead of a combed top, the drawframes are fed with card sliver.

Semi-worsted yarns have a character between woollen and worsted yarns. Usually they are made from coarse fibres and are quite hairy but they are also quite regular, due to the doubling and drafting.

5.2.2 Manufacture of Spun Yarns (3)

Cotton Spinning

The cotton spinning system is sometimes known as the **three-cylinder system,** because the drafting zone of the ring spinning machine normally contains three pairs of drafting rollers (*Figure 10*).

At the drawframe six or eight slivers are laid together (doubled) and are drawn out by the effect of the different rotation speeds of successive pairs of rollers. For example if the surface speed of the delivery rollers is eight times that of the feed rollers, then the slivers will be drawn out (drafted) to eight times their original length.

The regularity of the final yarn depends on the number of drawframe passages and on whether a combing process is used (*Figures 6 to 8*).

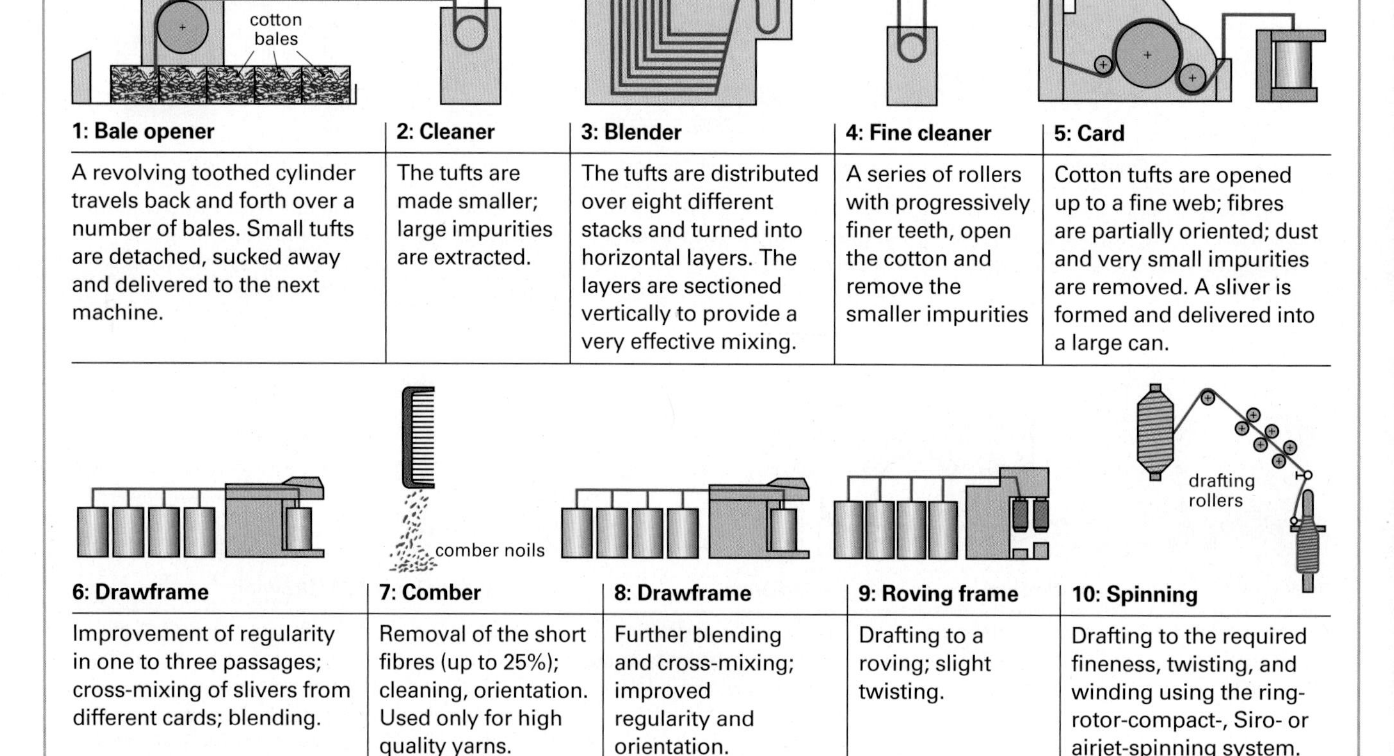

1: Bale opener	2: Cleaner	3: Blender	4: Fine cleaner	5: Card
A revolving toothed cylinder travels back and forth over a number of bales. Small tufts are detached, sucked away and delivered to the next machine.	The tufts are made smaller; large impurities are extracted.	The tufts are distributed over eight different stacks and turned into horizontal layers. The layers are sectioned vertically to provide a very effective mixing.	A series of rollers with progressively finer teeth, open the cotton and remove the smaller impurities	Cotton tufts are opened up to a fine web; fibres are partially oriented; dust and very small impurities are removed. A sliver is formed and delivered into a large can.

6: Drawframe	7: Comber	8: Drawframe	9: Roving frame	10: Spinning
Improvement of regularity in one to three passages; cross-mixing of slivers from different cards; blending.	Removal of the short fibres (up to 25%); cleaning, orientation. Used only for high quality yarns.	Further blending and cross-mixing; improved regularity and orientation.	Drafting to a roving; slight twisting.	Drafting to the required fineness, twisting, and winding using the ring-rotor-compact-, Siro- or airjet-spinning system.

Ring spun yarns are relatively smooth and regular. If the combing process is used to remove short fibres, then the regularity, and strength, is improved further and the end product is called a combed yarn. The compact-spinning process yields a smoother, less hairy, and a stronger yarn than the classic ring-spinning system (*see pages 65, 66*).

Bast Fibre Spinning Systems

The hackled flax or hemp is formed into a sliver on a spreading machine. This is then subjected to several passages of doubling and drawing on gill boxes to improve its regularity. A lightly twisted roving is then made on a flyer frame and the roving is converted into yarn either on a wet or a dry spinning frame. Wet spinning allows finer yarns to be made.

Silk Spinning

Spun silk yarns are made from the waste from the silk reeling process. The best waste is sorted, washed and degummed, then spun by a combed yarn process into high quality yarns, or **schappe** silk. Waste from the spun silk process, perhaps mixed with small quantities of fibres recovered from fabric waste, are spun into relatively coarse, irregular yarns on the condenser system, called **noil** or **bourette** silk.

Man-made Fibre Spinning

Man-made fibres can also be spun on short staple spinning machinery using the **Converter** system. The continuous filament tow is converted into a staple fibre top by breaking or cutting the filaments. The high degree of orientation of the fibres is preserved to a large extent but the regularity is improved by doubling and drawing. The resulting slivers can be spun, either alone or after mixing with other fibre types, by any of the spinning systems described above.

5.2.2 Manufacture of Spun Yarns (4)

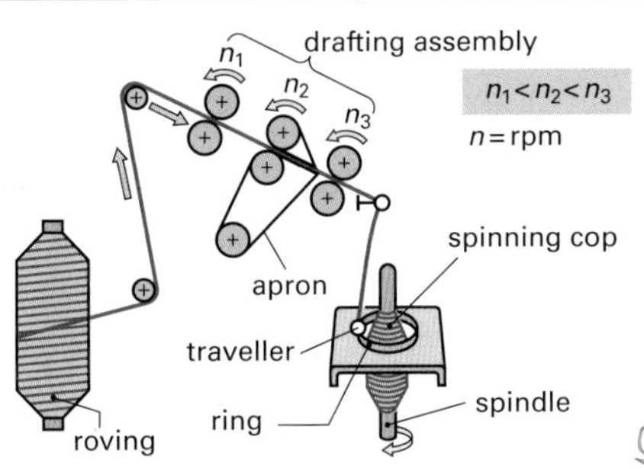

1: Principle of Ring Spinning

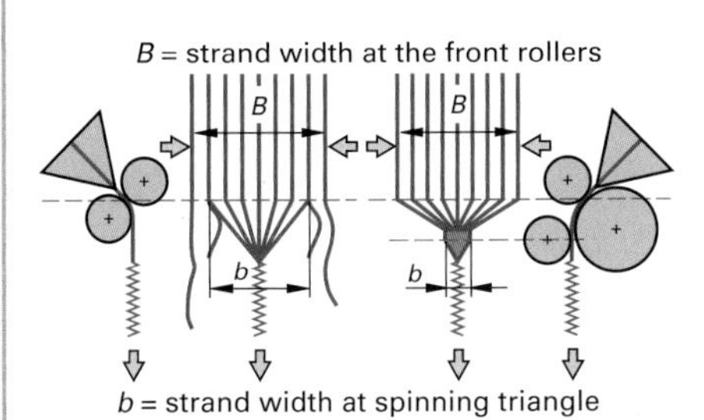

2: Standard front-roller geometry

3: Compact front-roller geometry

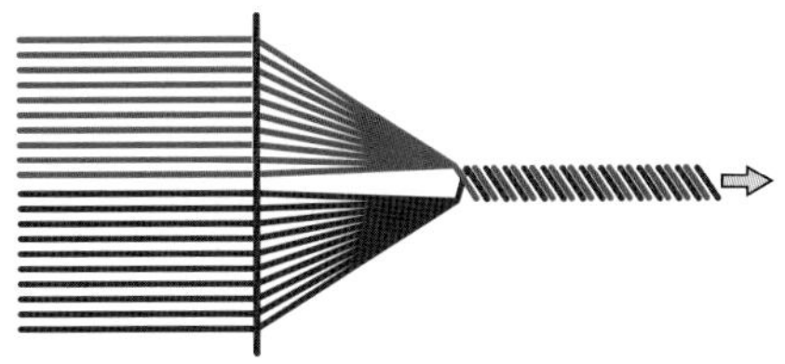

4: Principle of Siro spinning

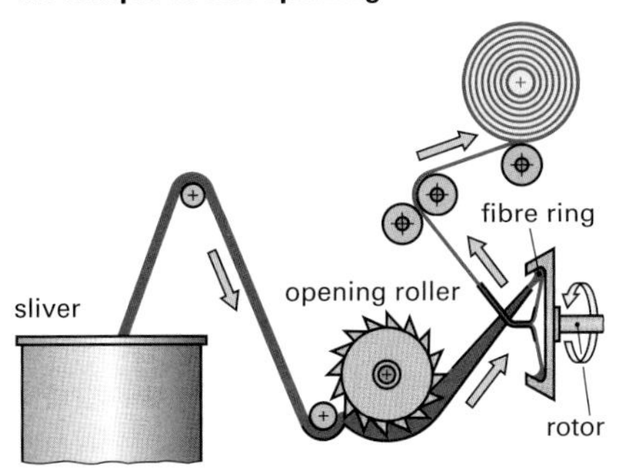

5: Principle of Rotor Spinning

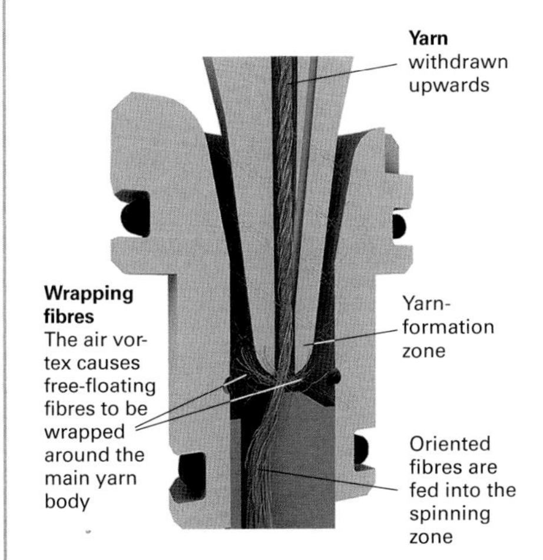

6: Principle of Airjet Spinning

The **spinning machine** is the last stage in the production of a spun yarn (though there may be further finishing processes carried out on the yarn). There are three main functions.

- Drafting the roving to the required fineness.
- Twisting to provide the required strength.
- Winding onto a suitable package.

Ring Spinning

In ring spinning (*Figure 1*) the relatively heavy, lightly-twisted roving is drafted to a thin strand and wound onto a spinning cop, which is driven by a spindle at the same surface speed as the strand is delivered. Twist is inserted into the strand by the rotation of the traveller, which runs on a circular guide – the ring – and is dragged around by the twisted strand. Thus the rotation of the spindle is transmitted to the yarn. The twist level of the yarn is controlled by the relationship between the rotational speed of the spindle and the delivery speed of the front rollers. The ring spinning system is capable of making very fine yarns.

Compact Spinning

Compact spinning is an improvement on the classical ringframe. Control of the fibre strand in the spinning triangle that emerges from the front drafting rollers, as the fibres are twisted in, is crucial to the quality of the yarn. The higher the draft (fine yarns) and the faster the spinning speed, the more difficult it is to control the spinning triangle and obtain uniform twisting-in of all of the fibres: fibres at the edges of the strand tend to fly loose (*Figure 2*). In the Compact system, suction is provided at the front rollers, to keep the strand together, and a supplementary roller helps to maintain the improved spinning geometry right up to the twisting-in point (*Figure 3*). This allows economic production of finer, stronger and smoother yarns at higher speeds.

The yarns are used for high quality underwear, shirts and blouses etc. Trade marks for such yarns are com4®, comforspin® and EliTe® (Rieter AG, Switzerland).

Siro Spinning

Siro spun yarn (*Figure 4*) is also made on an adapted ring-spinning machine. Two rovings are processed side-by-side on a specially adapted drafting assembly and are twisted together after the delivery rollers. This produces a yarn which has some of the characteristics of a two-fold yarn but is neither as regular nor as strong as a true two-fold.

Siro-spun yarns are usually used in worsted fabrics.

OE Rotor Spinning

The **rotor spinning** frame (*Figure 5*) is fed with card sliver or (more often) drawframe sliver. The sliver is opened up practically to single fibres and simultaneously cleaned. The fibres are deposited as a consolidated ring of the required thickness in a spinning rotor by the centrifugal effect. The open end of a seed yarn is used to withdraw the ring continuously whilst the rotor inserts twist into the strand as it is withdrawn. Spinning systems in which the yarn is assembled at such an open end are called **Open-End** or OE spinning systems.

OE rotor spinning is used mostly for cotton yarns in medium to heavy styles.

Airjet Spinning, Vortex Spinning

In **airjet spinning** (*Figure 6*) the roving is processed through a high-speed drafting assembly and the drafted strand is led into a vortex which applies a torque to the fibres. The vortex causes those fibres that are floating free at the edge of the spinning triangle (*Figure 2*) to be wrapped around the main body of the yarn. A second vortex, with opposite direction, untwists the core fibres and binds the wrappers more tightly. In the final yarn, the central core consists of fibres with little or no twist whilst the wrapping fibres give the yarn its strength and coherence. This kind of structure is called a **fasciated yarn.**

Airjet or vortex yarns are used mainly for medium count polyester/cotton yarns.

5.2.3 Properties and Applications of Spun Yarns

Yarn Properties

The performance of textile fabrics and clothing is strongly influenced by the properties of the yarns from which they are made. Sewing threads require particular yarn properties.

Regularity Smooth fabrics should be sewn only with very regular yarns. In spun yarns, this is achieved by repeated doubling and drafting, and by combing out the short fibres.

Strength Yarn strength depends on the quality of the fibres, the yarn regularity and the twist. Folding increases the strength.

Hardness/Twist The twist density affects the hardness of a yarn and hence the handle and the appearance of textiles.

Extensibility/ Elasticity Extensibility and elasticity are very important during yarn processing and utilisation. They are determined mainly by the fibre type and the spinning system.

Surface structure The surface structure of a yarn depends on the fibre type, the spinning system, and finishing. It is very important for the appearance and end-use performance of textiles and in the choice of sewing threads.

Handle The subjective softness or hardness of a yarn, and the textile into which it is made, depends on the fibre type, the twist, and finishing.

Specific Volume The specific volume of a yarn is largely a reflection of the amount of enclosed air, between the fibres. It is a key factor for the specific volume of the textile, and hence for the thermal insulation properties. It depends on the fibre type and the spinning system.

Spun Yarns	Yarn Type, Fibres	Features, Properties	Applications
	Worsted wool, fine hairs, mixtures; long-staple fibres	fine, smooth, regular; short fibres are combed out; harder twist, compact, strong	high quality smart suits, costumes and dressgoods, e.g. **gabardine, Cool Wool, mousseline,** fine knits
	Woollen wool, fine hairs, mixtures; mostly short-staple fibres	rough, irregular, hairy, coarse; less well-ordered yarn structure; softer twist, voluminous	rustic suitings and costume fabrics, bulky jacket and coat fabrics, e.g. **loden, fleece, Shetland, tweed,** heavy knits
	Ring spun, combed cotton and blends	fine, smooth, regular; short fibres are combed out; firm twist, compact, high quality	fine and superfine dresses, blouses and washable fabrics, e.g. **batiste, damask, satin, zephyr;** fine knits
	Ring spun, carded cotton and blends	medium to coarse, relative-ly regular; voluminous, softer twist; matt, less well-ordered yarn structure	medium to heavy weight washable fabrics, workwear, furnishings, e.g. **calico, cretonne, denim, drill;** knits
	OE Rotor spun cotton and blends	rougher surface due to less well-organised yarn structure; coarser, voluminous, matt	medium to coarse cotton fabrics, e.g. twills, **denim, drill**
	Spun silk (Schappe) longer waste from the silk reeling process (5–10 cm)	similar to worsted yarns: long staple fibres, regular, fine, lustrous, strong	fine to heavy silk fabrics for shirts, blouses, nightwear, underwear and bedsheets, e.g. **tulle,** sewing threads.
	Noil silk (Bourette) noils from the spun silk process	like woollen yarns: irregu-lar, rough, neppy, dull, voluminous	coarse and neppy silk fabrics for outerwear and furnishings, e.g. **bourette**
	Compact yarn Cotton and blends	smooth, soft, low hairiness; stronger than classical ring yarns	shirts, blouses, knits, underwear
	Siro spun yarn Long-staple wool, cotton, blends	compact, low hairiness; stronger than singles but weaker than two-fold yarns	substitutes some combed and worsted yarns
	Airjet, Vortex yarn polyester, combed cotton, blends	properties between ring and OE rotor yarns	similar to rotor yarns

5.3.1 Manufacture of Filament Yarns
5.3.2 Texturing

Manufacture of Filament Yarns

Filament yarns are composed of continuous[1] filaments, either natural (silk) or man-made.

- The silk worm extrudes a fibroin solution from a pair of spinnerets. On exposure to air, the solution solidifies to form the **silk filaments.** The silkworm uses the filaments to build its cocoon (*see page 21*).
- For **man-made fibres,** a polymer solution or melt is extruded through a machined spinneret (*see page 27*). The filament is solidified either by cooling (melt spinning), by evaporation of the solvent (dry spinning), or by precipitation in a bath of appropriate chemicals (wet spinning).

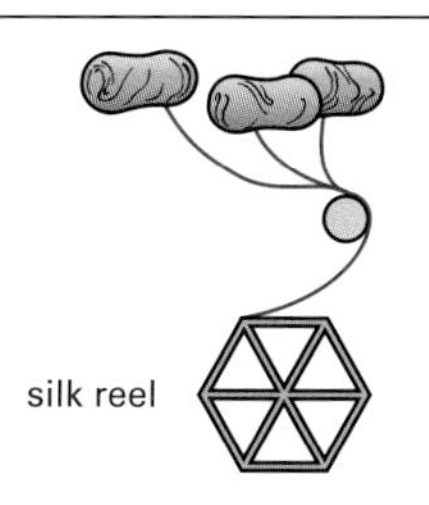

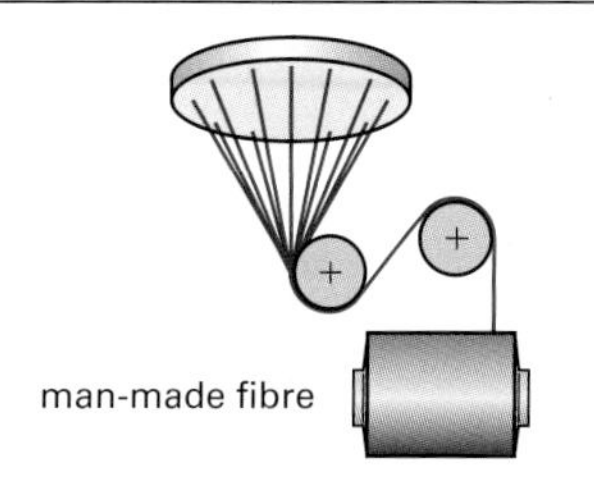

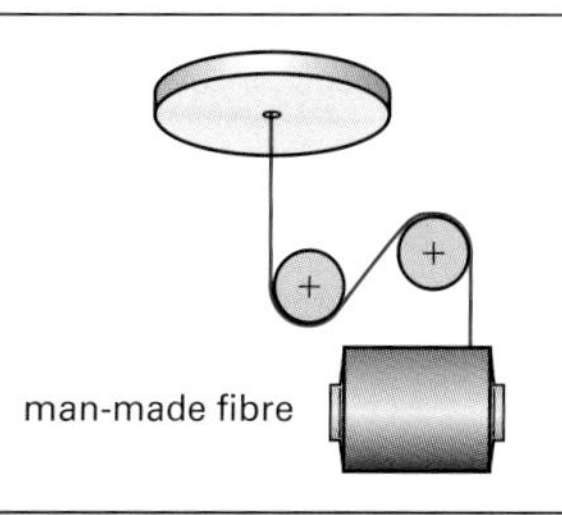

Reeled Silk	Multifilament	Monofilament
Reeled (Net) Silk is produced by unravelling the filaments from the cocoons and winding them over a silk reel.	For a **multifilament** yarn, multiple-hole spinnerets are used. A small amount of twist may be imparted.	For a **monofilament** yarn, a single-hole spinneret is used to extrude a single filament.

Texturing

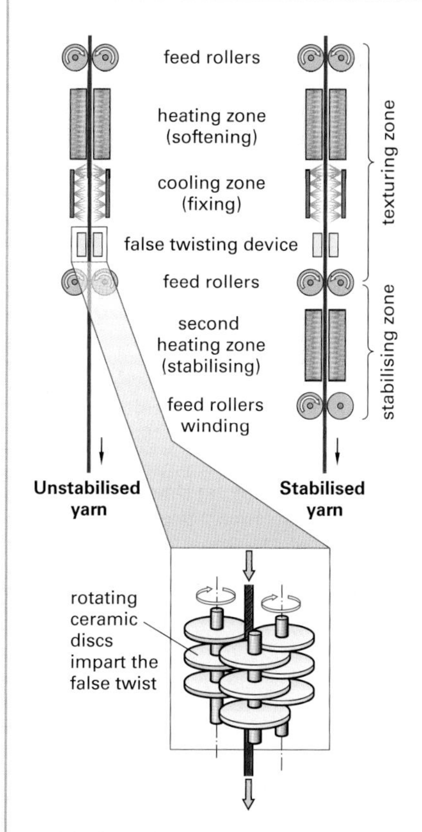

1: Principle of False-twist texturing

Texturing means the introduction of durable crimping to the filaments of a flat, multifilament yarn. Most, but not all texturing processes depend on exploiting the thermoplastic properties of synthetic filaments. By far the most important of these processes is **false-twist texturing.**

False-twist Texturing, Draw Texturing

For this process (*Figure 1*) the partially oriented yarn (POY) is fed through a heating zone which softens the filaments, followed by a cooling zone which re-hardens (sets) them. Meanwhile, a false-twisting unit, after the cooling zone, propagates twist backwards into the heating zone and removes it again further downstream. The effect of the twisting is to crimp the filaments. The intermediate feed rollers rotate somewhat faster to complete the drawing out of the filaments. The effect of the cooling zone is to set these twist-crimps into the filaments. The effect of untwisting is to open up the crimped filaments again to provide a more voluminous and highly extensible yarn. Normally, a second heating zone will be provided to stabilise the textured structure. The second heater is a little cooler than the first and the strand is slightly overfed to allow some contraction.

The following processes are of less importance commercially.

Airjet Texturing

The yarn is fed through a turbulent air stream, created by a jet. The air may be cold (for non-thermoplastic filaments) but usually hot air or steam is used. The air jet causes entangled loops to be formed in the filaments. The resulting textured yarn is very bulky with permanent crimps and loops.

Stuffer Box Texturing

The yarn is fed into a heated chamber where it is compressed. The zigzag deformations are permanently set by subsequent cooling.

Knit-de-knit Texturing

The yarn is knitted into a tube on a circular knitting machine. The knitted fabric is heat set and then unravelled. The shape of the knitted loops is set into the yarn.

[1] in the case of silk, "continuous" means up to about 1 km; in the case of man-made fibres, it means the length of the yarn on the wound package, i.e. several km.

5.3.3 Textured and Bicomponent Yarns
5.3.4 Properties and Applications of Filament Yarns

Textured and Bicomponent Yarns

Types of Draw Textured Yarns (DTY)

Stretch yarns Highly elastic yarns, with a crimp extension of 150 to 300%, achieved by high overfeeding to the second heater zone: for **stockings and tights** (pantyhose), **sportswear, swimwear.**

Stabilised yarns Yarns which have reduced elasticity and crimp extension, achieved by low overfeeding to the second heater zone: for **woven and knitted outerwear.**

Properties of Draw Textured Yarns

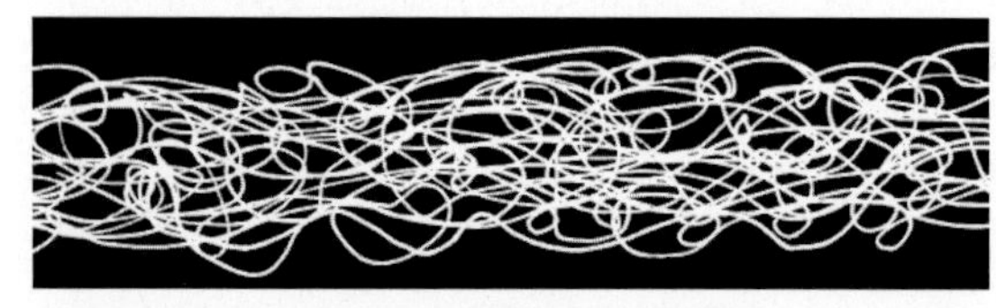

1: Crimping of a draw textured filament yarn

Compared to fabrics made from flat yarns, textured yarn fabrics have:

- Higher specific volume and bulk resilience,
- Higher extensibility and elasticity,
- Lower surface lustre,
- Good thermal insulation, due to entrapped air,
- Good moisture transport (with appropriate finish),
- Soft and pleasant handle.

Bicomponent Yarns

The textured effect can also be achieved by the use of yarns having two different components, one of which has a much higher shrinkage potential than the other. On suitable treatment, e.g. hot air or hot water, the high-shrinkage component contracts and forces the other to buckle and crimp.

Properties and Applications of Filament Yarns

Yarn Type	Features, Properties	Applications
Reeled silk, Net silk Continuous filament silk from the central part of the cocoons; several cocoons are reeled together (multi-filament)	Very fine, smooth, extremely regular, low twist (very lustrous) to high twist (matt); many fine filaments. The base material, fibroin, has good moisture absorption characteristics.	Fine, high quality fabrics for dresses, blouses, squares and ties; e.g. **pongee, organza, taffeta, satin, twill.** Folded yarns for embroidery and button-hole thread.
Monofilament A single filament, spun from a single-hole spinneret; mainly nylon, polyester, or elastomeric	Hard, stiff, smooth, fine to coarse (depending on spinneret size), lustrous, usually colourless (transparent) but can be dope-dyed.	Transparent **sewing threads,** mainly for technical textiles. Coarser filaments for mesh, bristles, nets, filter cloths, sieves.
Multifilament, flat A group of filaments spun from one multi-hole spinneret; cellulosic or synthetic man-made fibres	Smooth, compact, dense, regular, low twist (lustrous) to high twist (duller); many fine filaments. Woven fabrics have good surface cover with properties highly dependent on the fibre type and fineness.	Polyester and nylon microfilament yarns are used in all-weather clothing and **fleece.** Standard flat filament yarns for linings, dresses and blouses, ties, squares, lingerie, net drapes; e.g. **taffeta, satin, locknit, duchesse, twill, voile.**
Multifilament, textured Durably crimped filaments of synthetic man-made fibres, usually draw textured (*see Page 67*)	More or less highly crimped, bulky, voluminous, firm and elastic depending on the texturing process conditions; many fine filaments.	Stretch yarns for socks, stockings and tights (pantyhose), sportswear and swimwear, and as overedge sewing thread. Stabilised DTY for woven and knitted outerwear.

5.4.1 Folded Yarns and Cabled Yarns
5.4.2 Core Yarns

Folded (plied) and Cabled Yarns

1: Folded (plied) yarn

Folded or plied yarns are made by twisting together at least two single yarns, in order to:

- improve the strength and regularity,
- reduce or eliminate "twist liveliness",
- make heavier structures,
- achieve special effects.

The direction of twisting is designated as S or Z, just as in single yarns. Normally the folding twist is in the opposite direction to that of the single yarns. Folding twist may be soft, normal, or hard, according to the number of turns per metre compared to that in the single components. **Balanced twist** is when the folding twist is approximately equal and opposite to the singles. In single yarns, or in folded yarns with unbalanced twist, the yarn contains residual torque resulting from the twisting together of the fibres. This can cause yarns to snarl during processing, and garments to become distorted after laundering. Thus the highest quality knitted fabrics are made from two-fold yarns with balanced twist.

Folded Yarns

Folded yarns are made in a single process step, combining 2, 3 or more single yarns into one by twisting them together.

2: Two-fold or two-ply

3: Three-fold or three-ply

4: Four-fold or four-ply

Cabled Yarns

Cabled yarns require more than one twisting stage. Two or more folded yarns may be twisted together to form a cabled yarn.

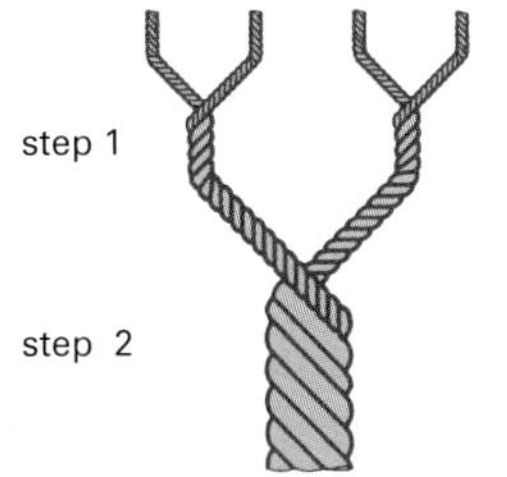

5: Two-fold, two-fold

6: Two-fold, three-fold

7: Three-fold, two-fold

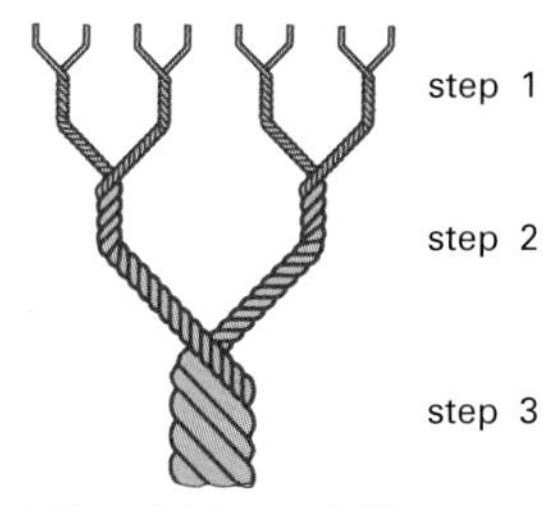

8: Two-fold, two-fold, two-fold

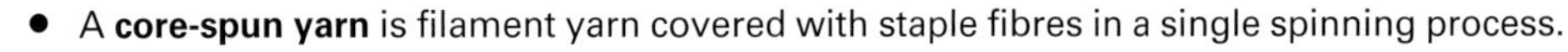

Core Yarns

Core yarns, or core-and-sheath yarns are multi-component yarns in which one of the components, the core, stays at the centre of the yarn whilst the others cover it. There are several types of **core-spun yarns.**

- A **core-spun yarn** is filament yarn covered with staple fibres in a single spinning process.
- A **core yarn** is a filament yarn covered with spun yarns in a yarn folding process.
- A **wrap yarn** has a twistless spun or filament core, which is provided with a protective yarn wrapping.

Core yarns have long been used for burnt-out effects in woven fabrics. (*see pages 99 and 109*) The covering component is made of a different material from the core and can be selectively removed, according to a printed pattern.

Twistless yarns can be made by dissolving away a soluble wrapping yarn, after weaving.

Stretch fabrics can be made from core yarns in which the core is an elastane filament and the covering is made from natural fibre, or textured filament yarn.

Sewing threads are often made from core yarns or core-spun yarns. The synthetic filament core gives high strength whilst the cover yarn or covering fibres prevent the needle from overheating and protect the core from softening or melting at the needle during high-speed sewing.

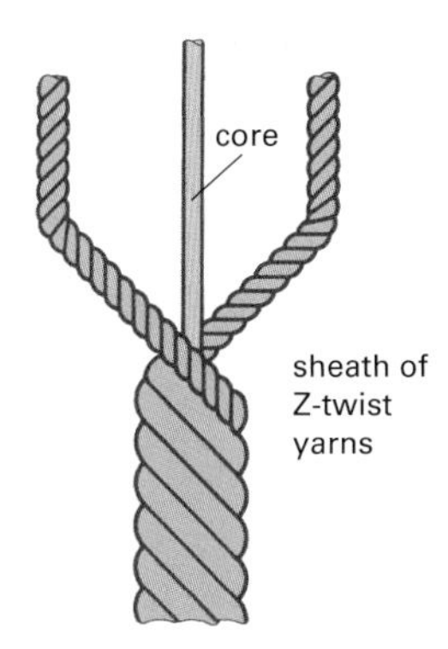

9: Core yarn

5.5.1 Properties and Applications of Fancy Yarns
5.5.2 Colour, Lustre and Structural Effects

Properties and Applications of Fancy Yarns

In the design of textile products, yarns are first selected on the basis of their **mechanical properties** such as strength, extensibility, elasticity, etc. Choices may also be made on the basis of the so-called **physiological properties** such as vapour permeability and moisture transport. Mechanical and physiological properties are governed mainly by the type of fibre, the fibre length, and the spinning system.

However, yarns may also be selected for their **appearance.** Special types of yarns, both single and folded, can be created to give particular optical effects, through **colour, lustre** and **structural** features.

Colour Effects

Mixture or **Ingrain** yarns are made by mixing fibres of different colours during spinning. This results in a heather effect. Fabric example: **marengo.**

Melange or **Vigoureux** yarns are spun from combed sliver or top which has been printed with stripes. The appearance is somewhat like mixture.

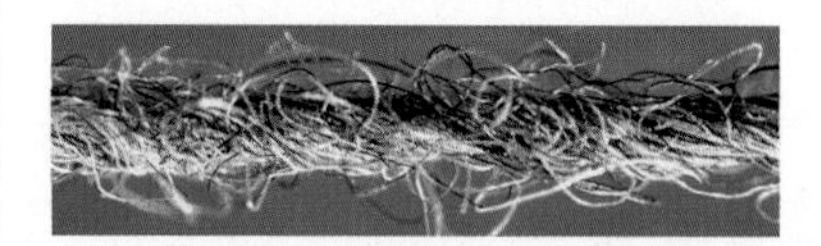

Mottle or **Marl** yarns are made by spinning from two-colour rovings, or from two rovings of different colours. The appearance is like mouliné but with less sharp contrast.

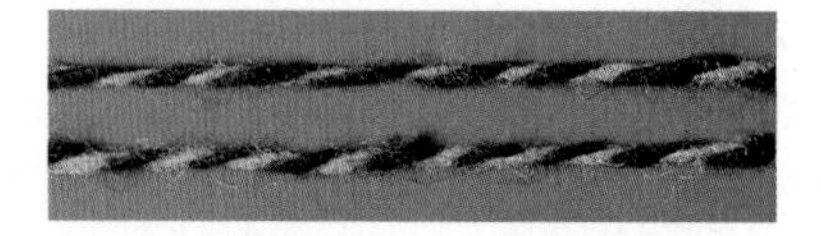

Jaspé or **Mouliné** yarns are made by folding two or more differently coloured yarns, or yarns made from different fibres with different dyeing behaviour. They give a mottled appearance. Fabric example: **fresco.**

Lustre Effects

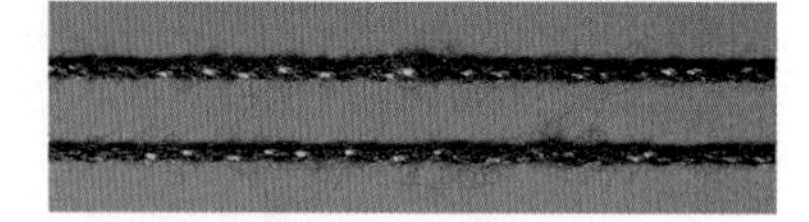

Matt/Lustre effects are obtained by mixing matt and bright fibres.

Lustre and Glitter effects can also be obtained by the use of metal fibres (uncommon today) or metallised plastic films such as Lurex®, or clear films, or man-made fibres with special cross-sections.

Fabric examples: **brocade, lamé.**

Structure Effects

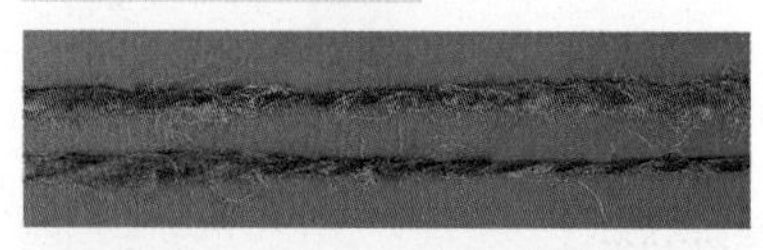

Slub yarns are single or folded yarns having long thick places, regularly or irregularly disposed. The slub effect is made either in spinning or in folding. Fabrics may have the character of linen or wild silk, which is favoured in furnishings. Fabric example: **flammé.**

Bourette or **Knop** yarns are folded yarns containing short, often coloured bunches of fibres or yarn at regular or irregular intervals. The knops may be formed during carding, during spinning, or during folding. Fabrics have a structured surface. Example: **Donegal, tweed.**

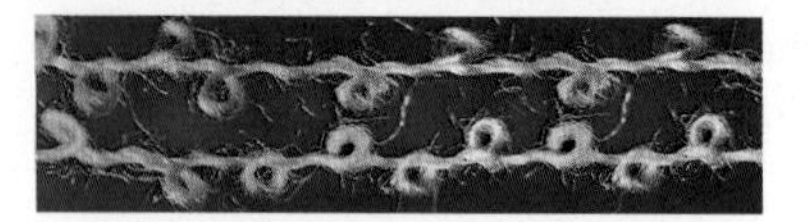

Bouclé or **Loop** yarns are compound yarns made by a special folding process which results in wavy or looped projections. Fabrics have a more or less grainy handle and a textured surface. Examples: **bouclé, frisé, frotté.**

Chenille is a cut pile yarn; it is soft and voluminous. These yarns are made by cutting special fabrics into strips. They are used in furnishing fabrics and knitwear.

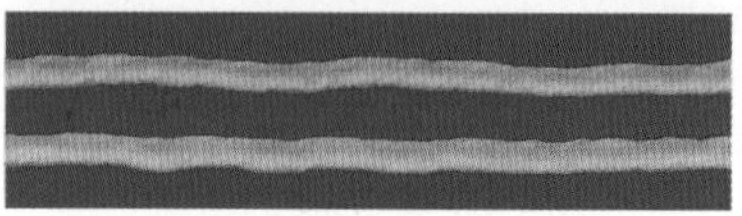

Crêpe yarns are used to make fabrics with a wrinkled surface and a granular handle. They are made from highly twisted yarns. Fabric examples: **chiffon, crêpe de chine, georgette, crepon, marocain.**

5.6.1 Overview and Packaging
5.6.2 Quality Requirements

Overview and Packaging

Yarn Type	Remarks	Applications
Cotton	Usually high quality, combed, ring spun, folded yarns; bleached, dyed, singed, mercerized and lubricated. Typically Ne 7...80 (7.4 ...84 tex).	Almost any sewings on cotton fabrics.
Silk	Doubled and folded silk filament yarns; dyed and lubricated. Nm 11...70 (14.3...91 tex).	Fancy button holes.
Spun silk	Folded spun silk yarns; dyed and lubricated. Nm 30...120 (8.3...33 tex).	Almost any sewings on wool and silk fabrics.
Polyester	Spun polyester folded yarns; heat set, dyed and lubricated. Nm 30...140 (7.1...33 tex).	Sewings on almost any fabric.
Monofilament	Usually transparent polyester. Nm 10...140 (7.1...100 tex).	Blind stitching.
Textured yarns	Textured multifilament yarns; dyed and lubricated. Nm 100...250 (4...10 tex).	Covering seams and cut fabric edges.
Core-spun yarns	Expensive threads with a core of continuous filament polyester wrapped by, or folded with cotton. The polyester is for strength whilst the cotton helps to keep the sewing needle cool. Nm 30...150 (6.7...33 tex).	All types of sewing, especially on high-speed machines.

1: Spools

2: Cross-wound cops

3: Cross-wound cones

4: Vicones

Quality Requirements

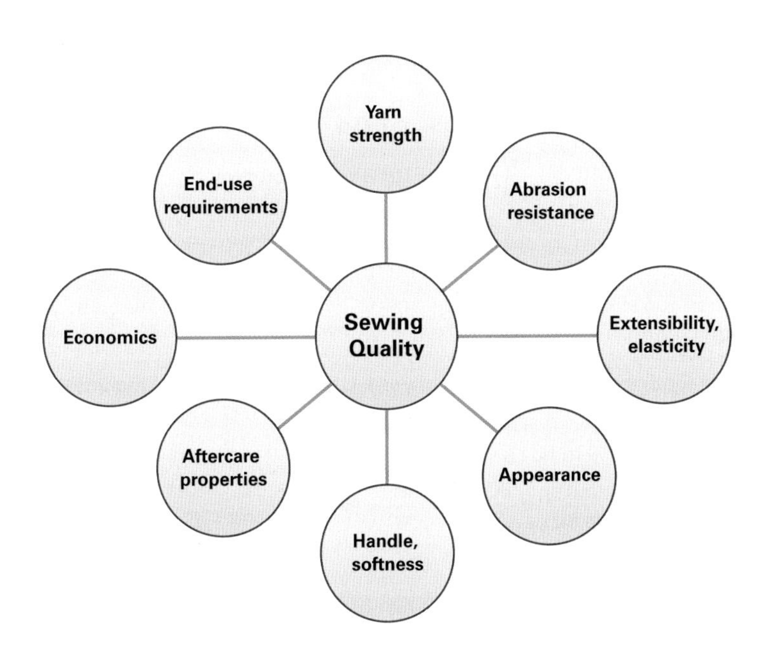

5: Influences on Sewing Quality

The quality of a sewing is strongly influenced by the characteristics of the sewing thread.

The **general requirements** for a sewing thread include, especially,

- tensile strength,
- abrasion resistance,
- extensibility and elasticity,
- good performance in washing, ironing and dry cleaning.

Special requirements for particular end-uses include

- high heat resistance (for heat-protective clothing),
- chemical resistance (for hazardous materials protective clothing),
- electrical conductivity (for conductive clothing),
- solubility (self-absorbing dressings and sutures in medical applications),
- extra-high strength (for airbags and safety belts).

5.7.1 Numbering Systems
5.7.2 Numbering of Single Yarns

In textile and clothing manufacture, a wide range of yarns is used, from coarse to very fine. The appearance and the properties of fabrics are influenced by the fineness of the yarns. Yarn fineness is indicated by a number which is based on the relationship between weight and length. This method of expressing fineness is called yarn numbering.

Numbering Systems

Direct Systems (linear density, titre)		**Indirect Systems** (number, count)	
Number of mass units per unit of length.		Number of length units per unit of mass.	
titre[1] tex Tt	**titre denier Td (den)**	**Metric Number (Nm)**	**English Cotton Count (Ne_c)**
mass unit = grams (g) length unit = **1 km**	mass unit = grams (g) length unit = **9 km**	length unit = metres (m) mass unit = **1 gram** (g)	length unit = hanks[2] mass unit = **1 pound** (lb)[3]
e.g. **20 tex** 1 km yarn weighs 20 g	e.g. **20 den** 9 km yarn weighs 20 g	e.g. **Nm 20** 20 m of yarn weigh 1 g	e.g. **Ne_c 20** 20 hanks of yarn weigh 1 lb
The unit is placed after the value		The unit is placed before the value	
Finer yarns have **smaller** values		**Finer** yarns have **larger** values	

Although all of the above yarn numbering systems (and many others) are used in certain areas, the tex system is the one which is internationally standardised.

[1] titre = linear density: mass per unit length
[2] 1 hank = 840 yards; 1 yard = 91.44 cm
[3] 1lb = 454 g

Numbering of Single Yarns

Tex System (Tt)

$$Tt\ (tex) = \frac{mass\ (g)}{length\ (km)}$$

Tex is the mass of a yarn per km of its length. The unit g/km has been given the name tex. For very fine or very coarse yarns, the prefixes **deci** or **kilo** can be used.

- for very fine yarns, decitex (dtex) is the weight of 10 km of yarn
- for very heavy yarns, kilotex (ktex) is the weight of 1 m of yarn

Yarns for clothing are normally in the dtex – tex range.

$$Tt\ [tex] = \frac{m\ [g]}{l\ [km]}$$

Example 1: A yarn with a length of 2.5 km has a weight of 40 g.

$$\mathbf{Tt\ (tex)} = \frac{mass\ (g)}{length\ (km)} = \frac{40}{2.5} = 16\ \frac{g}{km}\ \text{i.e. } \mathbf{16\ tex}$$

$$Tt\ [dtex] = 10 \cdot \frac{m\ [g]}{l\ [km]}$$

Example 2: A yarn with a length of 6 km has a weight of 150 g.

$$\mathbf{Tt\ (dtex)} = 10 \cdot \frac{mass\ (g)}{length\ (km)} = 10 \cdot \frac{150}{6} = \mathbf{250\ dtex}$$

Denier System (Td)

$$Td = 9 \cdot \frac{mass\ (g)}{length\ (km)}$$

Denier was originally used for silk yarn numbering and is now applied to all filament yarns. Td is the mass (g) of 9 km of yarn.

Metric Number (Nm)

The metric number is the length in metres of 1 gram of yarn. Used for spun yarns, including sewing threads.

$$Nm = \frac{length\ (m)}{mass\ (g)}$$

Example: A yarn with a length of 800 m has a weight of 20 g

$$\mathbf{Nm} = \frac{length\ (m)}{mass\ (g)} = \frac{800}{20} = 40\ \frac{m}{g} = \mathbf{Nm\ 40}$$

English Number, Cotton (Ne_c)

$$Ne_c = \frac{length\ (hanks)}{mass\ (pounds)}$$

The English cotton number is the number of hanks, each of 840 yards, per pound (lb) of yarn. Used for spun yarns, including sewing threads.

5.7.3 Numbering of Folded Yarns and Sewing Thread

Numbering of Folded Yarns

Direct (tex) System

For **folded and cabled** yarns, the individual yarns are indicated, followed by a multiplication sign and the number of components.
Examples:

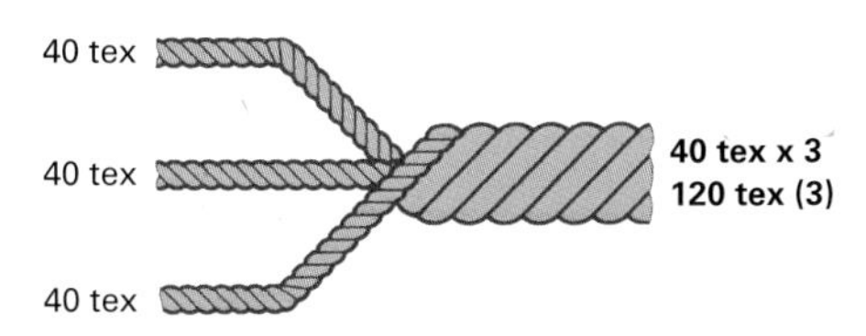

1: Three-ply yarn made from 40 tex singles

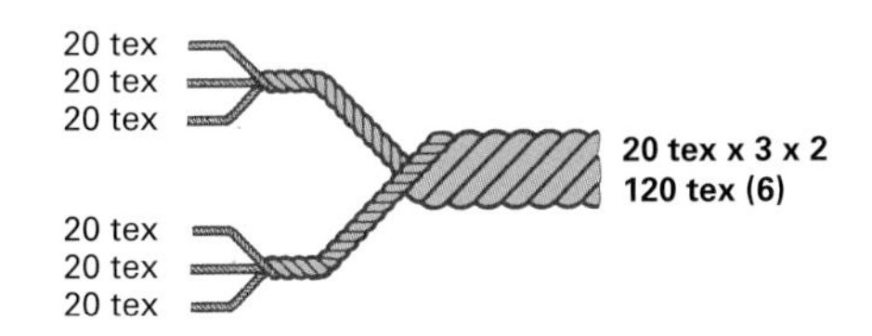

2: Cabled yarn made from six 20 tex singles

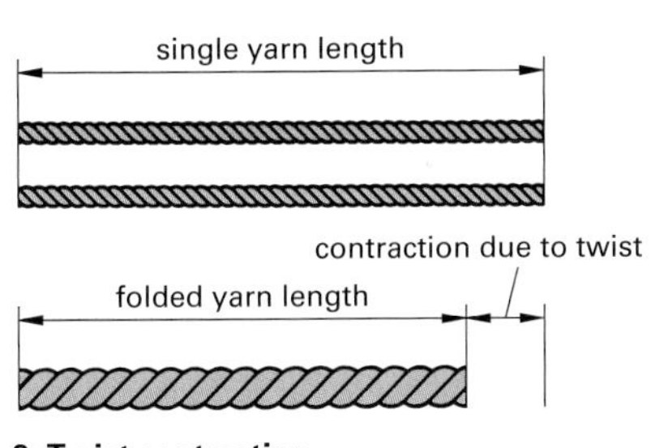

3: Twist contraction

In the second example, the final yarn count might be estimated as 20 tex x 3 x 2 = 120 tex. However this answer would not be correct because the cabled yarn is shorter than the individual single yarns due to the effect of twisting. Depending on the twist density, the actual yarn number could be e.g. 132 tex. This is called the **resultant** yarn number and is indicated by the letter R. In this example, the designation would be R 132 tex/3/2; 20 tex or, alternatively, 20 tex x 3 x 2; R 132.

The simple calculated tex, ignoring twist contraction, can be given with the number of components in parenthesis, thus **120 tex (6).**

Indirect (Nm, Ne) Systems

For folded yarns the single yarn number is usually given followed by a solidus (/) and the number of components. A simple, calculated result may be given with the number of components in parentheses.

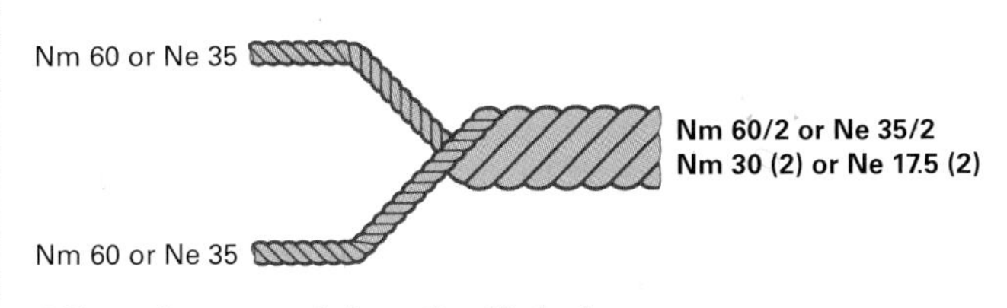

4: Two-ply yarn made from Nm 60 singles

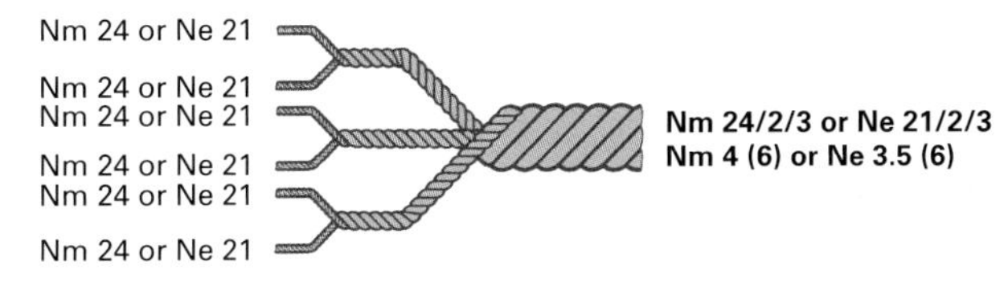

5: Cabled yarn made from six Nm 24 singles

Numbering of Sewing Threads

Unfortunately there is no coherent and rationalised system of numbering for sewing threads.

Threads made from silk, man-made fibres and wrapped yarns are usually designated by metric number (Nm 70/3; Nm 80/3; Nm 120/3; Nm 120/2). If the number of components is not given, then it is always the most common, three-ply yarn.

With cotton threads the English number is used (Ne_c 50/3; Ne_c 40/3). The number of components often is not given but usually is three. If it is not three, then the ticket number given is chosen so that division by three will give the number of the single yarn component.

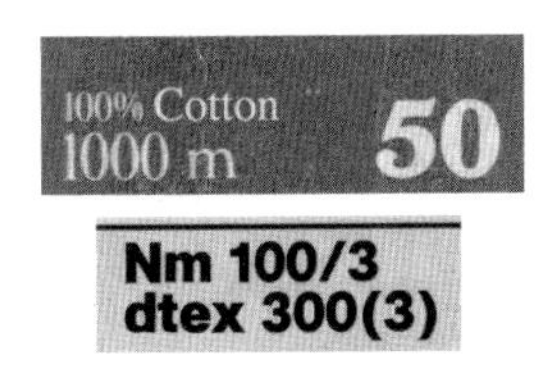

Ticket number	Yarn number	Component
No. 60	Ne_c 60/3	ca. Ne 20
No. 60/4	Ne_c 80/4	ca. Ne 20
No. 60/2	Ne_c 40/2	ca. Ne 20

6: Sewing thread tickets

6.1.1 Fabrics Overview
6.1.2 Wool Felts and Bonded Webs (1)

Textile fabrics are made from fibres and yarns by different manufacturing processes. The different types of fabrics can be classified according to the manufacturing process.

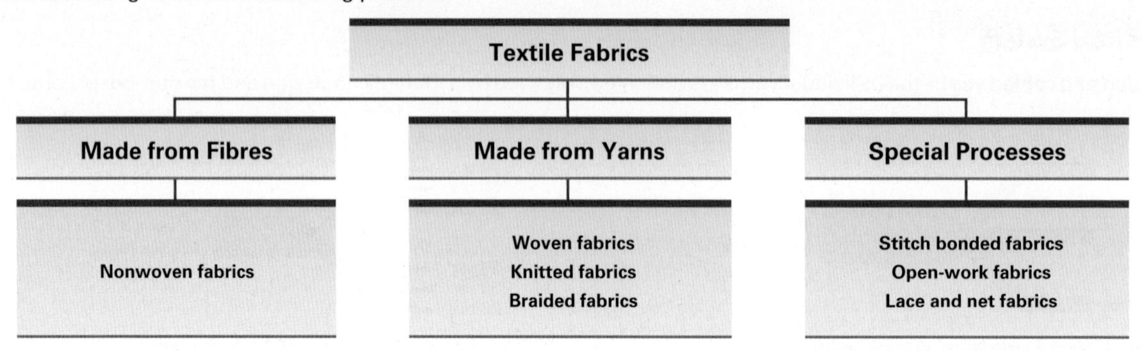

Nonwoven Fabrics

As the name implies, nonwoven fabrics are made directly from fibres, without the intermediate steps of yarn formation or weaving. Two groups may be distinguished according to the method of formation. The prerequisite for a nonwoven fabric is the production of a fibre web or batt using a carding machine. The web then has to be given strength by some form of fibre-bonding process. Following are the main methods of strengthening webs.

Nonwoven Fabrics	
Wool Felts	**Bonded Webs**
• Wool and hair fibres, or their blends • Mechanical entangling	• Staple fibres or filaments • Mechanical entanglement; thermal or chemical bonding; combinations of these

Production of Wool Felts

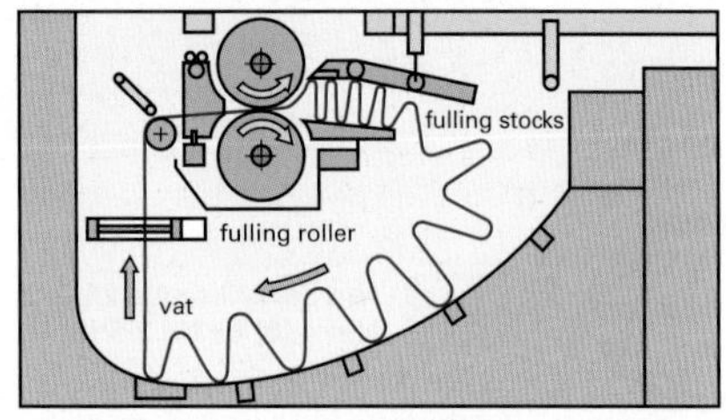

1: Principle of fulling (milling)

2: Collar-backing felt

3: Fulled loden

Wool and some other animal fibres will become progressively entangled, eventually into a **felt,** when a web is subjected to repeated mechanical action whilst immersed in hot, alkaline liquor.

Several fibre webs, from a carding machine, are superimposed, both lengthways and crossways, until the required thickness of batt is produced. The batt is steamed and wetted and is repeatedly compressed and vibrated by a heavy platen, so that the fibres become thoroughly entangled into a felt. The felt is squeezed, trimmed to shape and dried.

Felted (fulled, milled) woven fabrics, such as loden, are made by treating woven fabrics on the fulling (milling) machine (*Figure 1*), to develop fullness and to obscure the weave pattern. Milling of woven fabrics is often a precursor to a light raising, to produce a durable nap in fabrics such as **Loden, Melton, Woollen,** and **Velour** (*see pages 128, 129, 135*).

Properties and Applications of Wool Felts

The properties of a felt depend on the type of animal hair which is used – e.g. camel, goat, rabbit – and also on whether a proportion of non-felting fibres is mixed in.

Felts are **good insulators** and therefore can be made into warm garments but nowadays they are rather seldom used as such.

Main applications include: hats, collar backs for jackets and coats, furnishings, roller coverings, insulation materials, billiard cloths, conveyer bands in paper-making.

Production of Bonded Webs

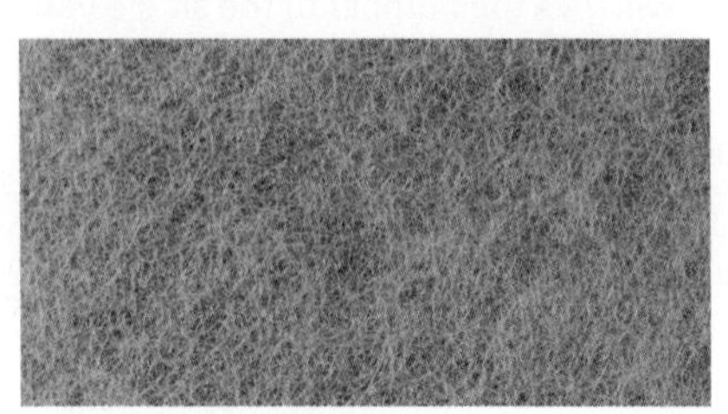

4: Random-laid web

Web Formation

- **Dry-laid** webs are made by carding (*see page 63*) or the fibres can be dispersed in an air current and condensed onto a suction drum. The fibres can be given a degree of orientation by drawing the web.
- **Wet-laid** webs are made by a process similar to paper making, in which fibres suspended in a liquid are filtered onto a sieve.
- **Spun-laid** webs are made by spinning synthetic fibre filaments directly onto a conveyor band.

6.1.2 Wool Felts and Bonded Webs (2)

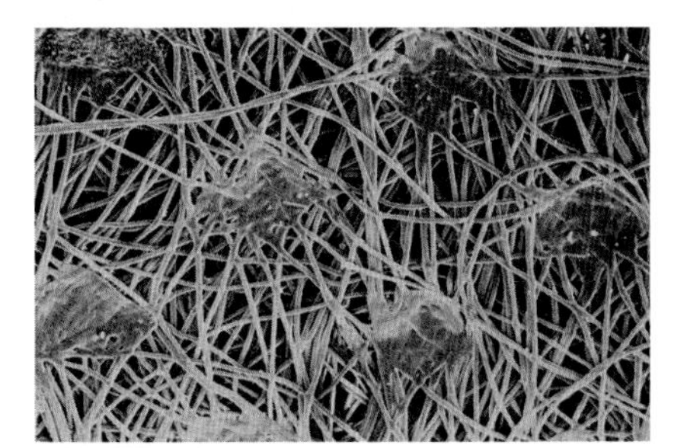
1: Point bonded web

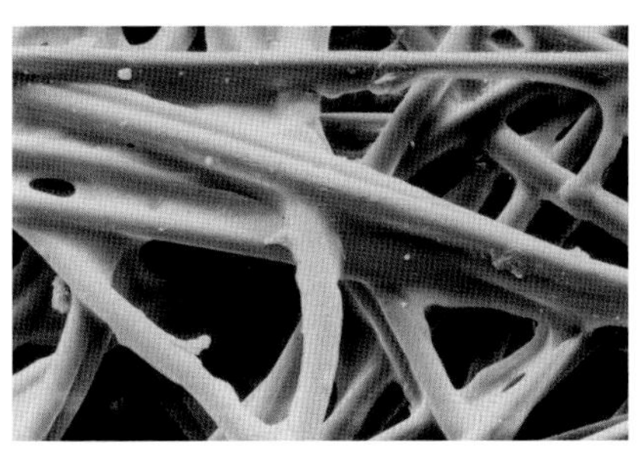
2: Adhesive bonded web

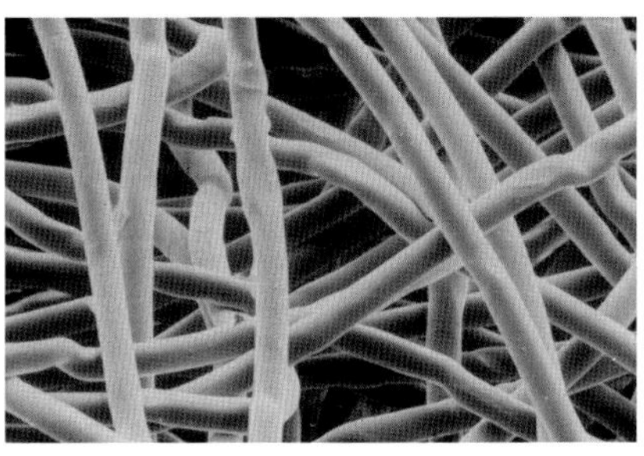
3: Web bonded by low-melting fibres

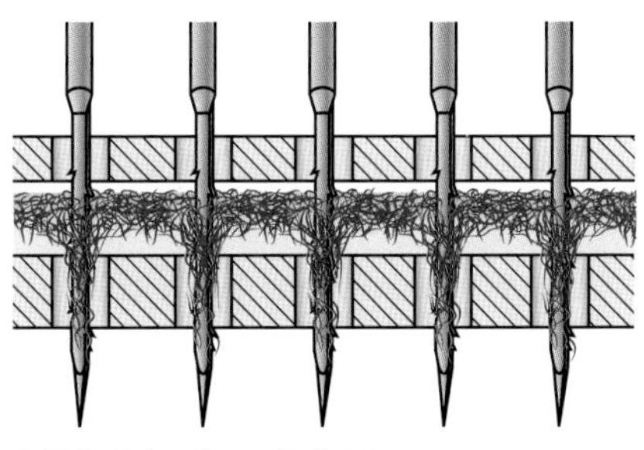
4: Principle of needle felting

5: Felting needle

Web Bonding Processes

The type of bonding process used depends on the fibre type and the end-use requirements.

- **Thermal bonding**

  A web made from thermoplastic fibres, such as polyamide or polyester, can be spot-welded, or point bonded, using heated, embossed calender rollers (*Figure 1*).

- **Adhesive bonding**

  The web is sprayed, saturated, or printed with adhesive solution, which thickens and sticks during drying (*Figure 2*).

- **Bonding fibres**

  A small proportion of the fibres may be of a special type, which can be melted or dissolved, or the fibres can be the bicomponent type, in which one component melts at a lower temperature so that they bond the other fibres (*Figure 3*).

- **Mechanical entanglement**

  Needle felting (*Figure 4*) is a way of introducing mechanical entanglement of the fibres. Almost any type of fibre can be used for the production of needle felts. In practice synthetic fibres are usually used. A bulky fibre web is repeatedly penetrated by a bank of barbed needles (*Figure 5*) fixed in a single needle board. At each stroke, every needle drags a certain number of fibres to the lower side of the web, forming loops in the fibres. Needle felts are normally given additional strength by supplementary fibre-bonding techniques.

  As an alternative to needle felting, fine, high-pressure jets of water can be used. This results in hydroentangled or spunlaced fabrics.

Properties and Applications of Nonwoven Fabrics

In clothing, bonded fibre webs are used mainly as interlinings. The most common types are thermally-bonded, dry-laid webs of polyamide and polyester. They are often provided with a fusible adhesive on one side, distributed in dots, diamonds, or stripes. The adhesive melts at temperatures between120 and 180 °C so that the interlining can be fused to the outer fabric on a special heated press.

Interlinings: end-use examples

- stabilising large parts, plackets
- small parts: collars, cuffs, pockets waistbands, trimmings
- stabilising edges
- mounting for lace

Interlinings: properties and requirements

- air permeability
- crease retention
- stability to washing and dry cleaning
- lightweight
- easy to work
- form stability
- strength
- good adhesion to the top cloth after fusing

Spun-laid nonwovens are used for disposable textiles, lightweight interlining, clean-room clothing, and specialised protective clothing such as for working with radioactive materials, in medicine, or in electronics. According to end-use, products may be lightweight, smooth, permeable, absorbent, insulating, machine-washable, crease-resistant, highly elastic and strong. Embossing, dyeing, or printing may be applied.

Microfibre spun-laid nonwovens are the basis for making faux leather cloths, such as Alcantara and Amaretta (*see page 118*).

Needle felts are resilient and can be lightweight. They are used mainly for floor coverings (underlay) and interlinings but also for mattress padding, filters and sieves.

6.2.1 Woven Fabric Manufacture

Woven Fabrics

Woven fabrics are made by the interlacing of (at least) two sets of yarns at right angles. Different types of woven fabrics are made with different yarn sets, different patterns of interlacing, and different optical characteristics.

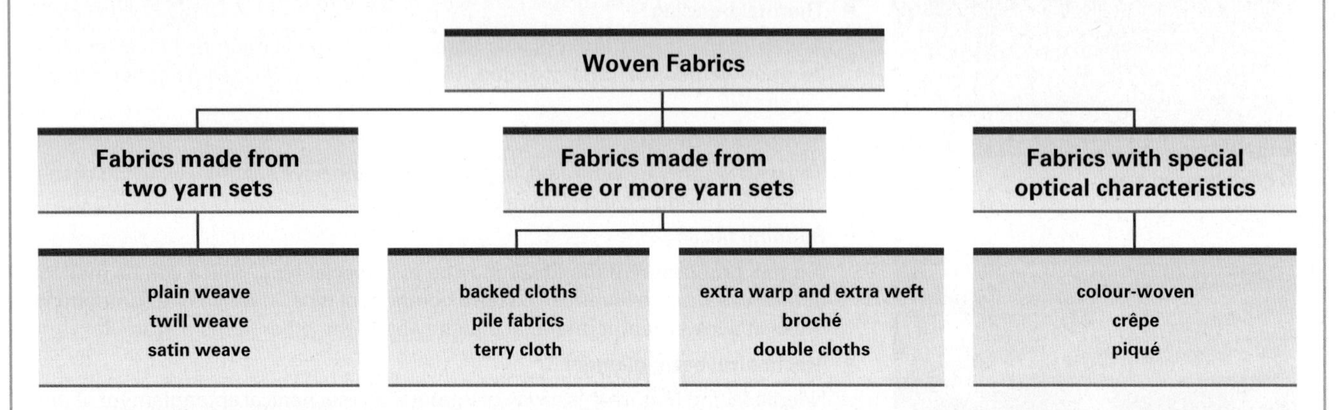

Principle of Weaving

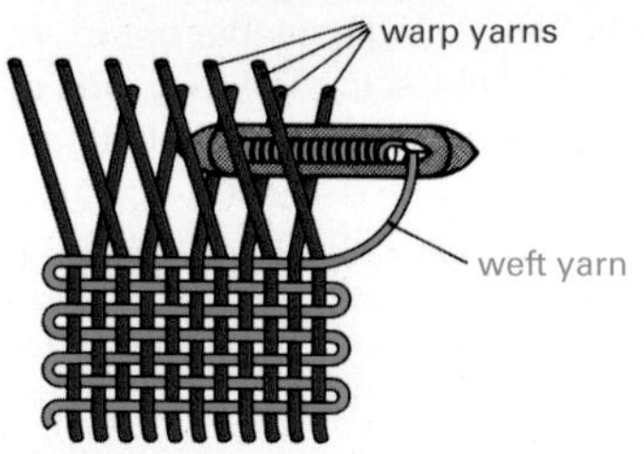

1: Principle of weaving

Weaving is the name given to the interlacing of two sets of yarns, warp and weft, at right angles (*Figure 1*).

The **warp** yarns are those which lie in the length direction of a fabric whilst it is being woven.

The **weft** or **filling** yarns are those which are introduced between the warp yarns, across the width direction of the fabric.

Warp yarns are usually stronger than weft because they have to sustain larger stresses during weaving.

Shaft and Jacquard Weaving

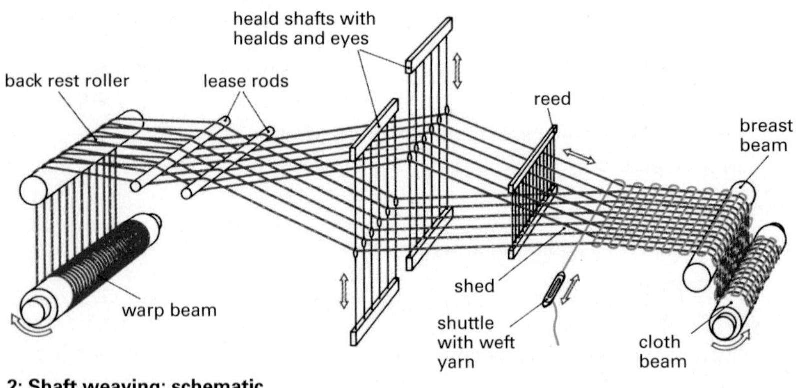

2: Shaft weaving: schematic

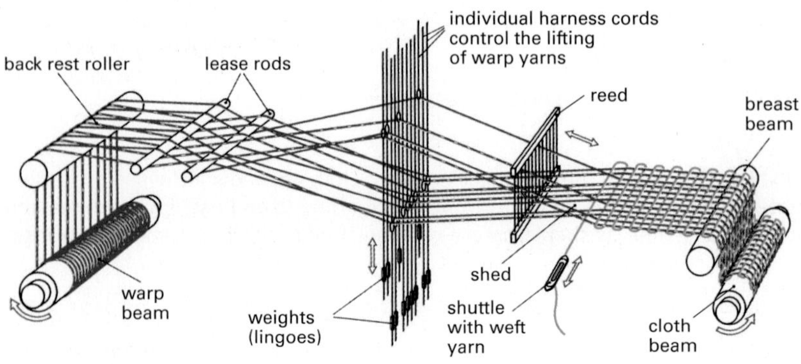

3: Jacquard weaving: schematic

In **shaft weaving** the warp sheet passes over the back rest roller and lease rods, through heald shafts and reed, and over the breast beam to the cloth roller. The heald eyes of each heald shaft are threaded in a set pattern (*Figure 2*) e.g. yarns 1, 3, 5, 7, etc. or 2, 4, 6, 8, etc.

By raising and lowering the heald shafts a shed is formed in the warp yarns, through which the weft yarn can be passed. For a plain weave at least two shafts (usually four) are needed. After the weft has been introduced the reed beats it up into the fell of the cloth. The range of patterns, which can be woven on a shaft loom, is limited by the number of shafts that can be accommodated in the machine.

In **Jacquard weaving,** the lifting of each warp yarn can be controlled individually. This is effected by either a punched card or an electronic control system, according to the required weaving pattern (*Figure 3*).

The technique is named after its inventor J.M. Jacquard (1755–1834), a silk weaver of Lyon. The name "jacquard pattern" is now used for any woven or knitted design with a large or intricate figured pattern.

6.2.2 Weaving Preparation

Before weaving, the warp and weft yarns are subjected to several preparation processes.

Winding

The first step (usually carried out by the spinner) is to wind the yarns onto large packages, suitable for the next process (*Figure 1*). Warp yarns, and weft yarns destined for shuttleless weaving machines, have to be wound onto large cross-wound packages called cones. Weft yarns destined for shuttle machines have to be wound onto small bobbins that can fit inside the shuttle.

An important additional function of the winding process is to remove faults (thick, thin, and weak places, knots) and replace them with smooth splicings. This improves the subsequent processing efficiency of the yarn, so as to minimise machine stoppages in warping, sizing, and weaving, as well as fabric faults. Clearing the faults can be done by mechanical or electronic mechanisms, or a combination.

1: Cone winding machine, detail

Warping

A definite number of warp yarns is wound onto a beam with a defined length, width and density. Warping may be carried out by direct beaming or by sectional warping.

Sectional Warping

A large number of yarn cones is mounted in a large creel and wound onto the sectional beam, one narrow section at a time (*Figure 2*). The sectional beam has a sloping edge. The first section is built up on this slope, so that it obtains a sloping side after winding on, ready for the next section. Each section comprises only a part of the total number of yarns required for the loom, but has the required length and yarn density. After the appropriate number of sections has been built up, all sections are off-wound together onto a single beam. Sectional beaming has to be used when warp stripes of different colours are required.

2: Sectional warping machine

Direct Beaming

Here again, the yarn cones are mounted in a large creel. Each yarn can be tensioned individually as they are led together to the beaming machine and wound onto a beam with parallel sides (*Figure 3*). Usually, the beams are not large enough to accommodate all of the yarns needed in the loom, so they have to be combined to form the final weaver's beam. This is usually done at the sizing machine.

Direct beaming is only economic for large runs of standard fabrics, and when all yarns are the same colour.

3: Direct beaming machine

Sizing, Slashing

Sizing (*Figure 4*) is used to protect the warp from the rigours of weaving. Unprotected yarns will give unacceptably large numbers of machine stoppages due to warp yarn breakages. The size is a film-forming polymer such as starch or poly(vinylalcohol) and is applied from a solution. The warp yarns are made smoother, stronger, and more resistant to abrasion.

For the best weaving efficiency, the size must be applied very uniformly and in just the right amount. Usually, the size has to be washed out of the yarn after weaving so it must be used in the minimum amount possible, to minimise the cost and environmental impact.

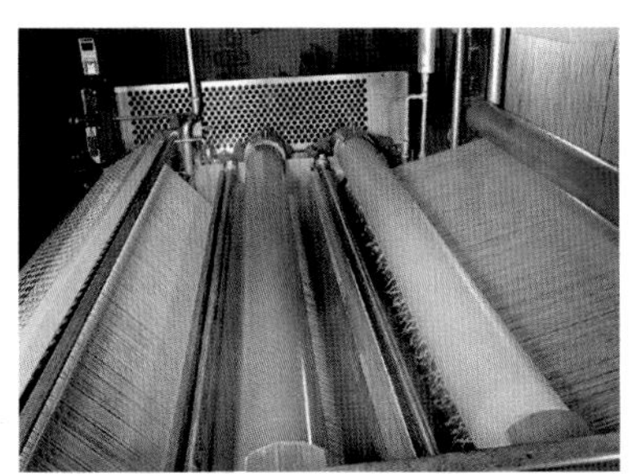

4: Impregnation zone in a sizing machine

Drawing-in

The warp yarns have to be drawn, in the correct order, through the heald eyes and then through the reed (*see page 76*). This is a very tedious operation and, in modern factories, it is done by automatic devices (*Figure 5*). If more than one warp of the same style is to be woven on the same loom, the new warp is knotted onto the old one. When a different style of warp has to be installed, the entire warp assembly, including the depleted weaver's beam, healds, and reed is lifted out and replaced with the ready-prepared new assembly together with the new beam.

5: Automated drawing in

6.2.3 Weft Insertion Devices

The weft (filling) yarn can be introduced into the shed by means of a shuttle, a projectile, a gripper, an air jet or a water jet. Shuttles were used from the early days of mechanisation but, since the middle of the 20th century, they are being replaced by the newer methods. Shuttleless looms offer higher production speed, wider fabrics, and fewer machine stoppages. With shuttleless looms, the weft is fed from large packages, so there is no need to stop, or delay the machine for bobbin changes.

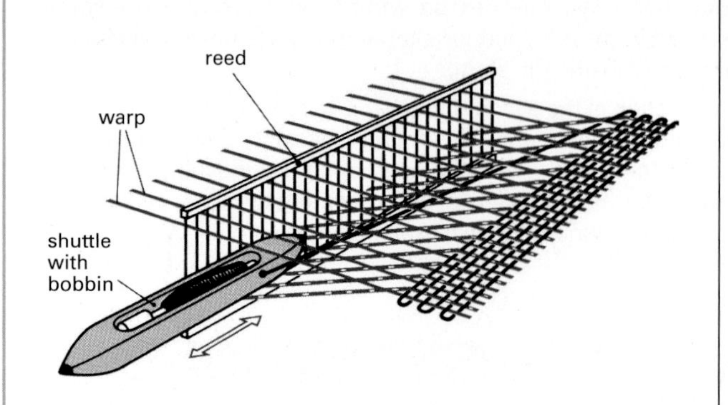

Weft Insertion by Shuttle

The weft yarn is wound on a small bobbin which fits inside the shuttle. The shuttle is repeatedly driven across the loom, travelling over a smooth surface (race) in front of the reed, and then driven back again, trailing the weft behind it. This forms solid edges to the fabric. To accommodate the shuttle, a relatively large shed is needed at each lifting cycle, which enforces a relatively large power requirement. This means that the maximum speed of the system is limited. Empty weft bobbins are normally replaced automatically but, even so, the bobbin change frequently results in a machine stoppage. Very few shuttle looms are manufactured nowadays.

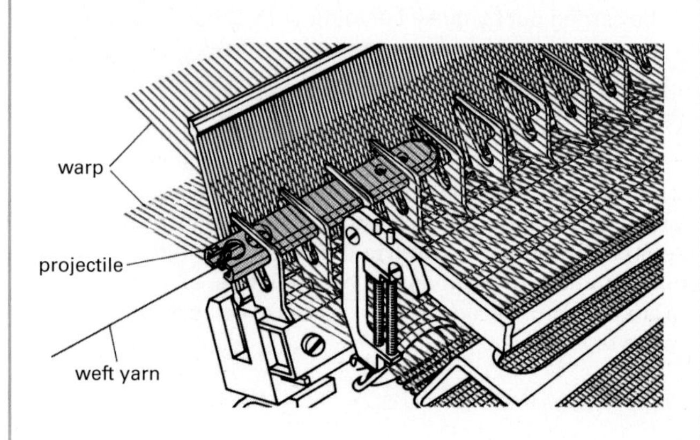

Weft Insertion by Projectile

The small gripper-projectile is supplied with weft yarn from a large cone and carries it through the shed, always in the same direction. The low mass of the projectile means it needs little power for its acceleration. Several projectiles are provided, together with an external return mechanism, so that the next is always ready for launching without delay. The smaller shed and the lower mass allow much wider fabrics and higher production speeds to be attained. However, the weft has to be cut and separately secured at the fabric edges.

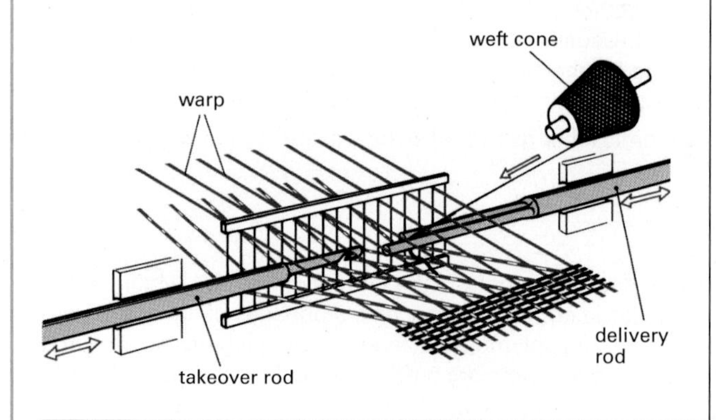

Weft Insertion by Rapier

The illustration shows rigid gripper rods (rapiers) on both sides of the loom, but single-sided and flexible-rapier designs are also available. A delivery rapier takes the yarn from the weft cone and transports it to the centre of the shed where it is accepted by a take-over rapier and drawn to the opposite side. The initial acceleration of the rapier is quite modest, which is very useful for handling weak or tension-sensitive materials such as woollen or textured yarns. The small shed and relatively low masses allow high production speeds but, here again, the weft has to be cut and separately secured at the fabric edges.

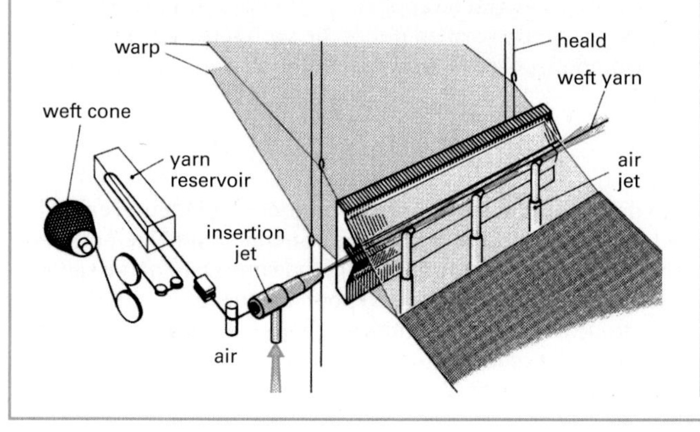

Weft Insertion by Jets

In this system the required length of weft yarn is held loosely in a reservoir and is projected through the shed by a jet of air or water. With air jet machines, there are several booster jets along the yarn path. The air jet principle is gentle and is especially suitable for sensitive materials such as textured yarns.

With the water jet system, the fabric becomes wet and has to be dried directly after weaving. The system is suitable only for yarns made of fibres that absorb very little water, such as polyester.

6.2.4 Principles of Cloth Construction

The pattern of interlacings of the warp and weft yarns is called the cloth **construction.**

The diagrammatic representation of a construction is called a **pattern draft** or **point paper design.** It is marked and read from bottom left to top right. The vertical columns represent the warp yarns; horizontal rows represent the weft. A mark placed in any cell indicates that the warp is lifted over the weft at that intersection. Absence of a mark indicates the reverse (warp remains below weft).

Each cell represents one **interlacing** of warp and weft.

The smallest number of cells that can specify a given construction is called the **repeat.** A pattern draft usually contains several repeats.

The interlacing of the yarns may also be represented by a **fabric section.**

When a yarn is not interlaced over several cells, it forms a **float.**

Basic Weave Constructions

	Plain Weave	**Twill Weave**	**Satin Weave**
	Each warp yarn is lifted over alternate weft yarns. Neighbouring warp yarns lift in the opposite sense.	This construction makes a pattern of diagonal lines. Each warp yarn lifts over (and/or remains under) more than one weft. Adjacent warp yarns make the same lifting pattern, but displaced by one cell.	The warp floats over four or more wefts and remains under only one. Adjacent warps have their floats arranged as randomly as possible, so no twill line is generated.
Interlacings	weft 1 2 3 4 5 6 7 8 9; 1 2 3 4 5 6 7 8 warp		
Pattern Draft	warp lifted; warp under; inter-lacings; repeat; repeat	twill line; weft yarns; cloth section; warp yarns	float
Condensed Notation	10 - 01 01 - 01 - 00	20 -01 02 - 01 - 01	30 - 04 01 - 01 - 03

Condensed Notation after DIN 61101 (suitable for EDP)

Pattern drafts can also be represented numerically. A system of notation used in Germany codifies information on the weave type, warp lifting pattern, number of ends lifting together, and move number.

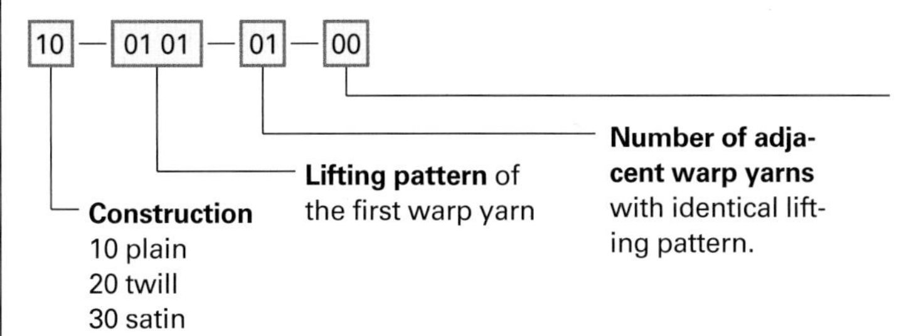

Move number. The number of weft yarns by which the lifting pattern of each subsequent warp yarn must be displaced, always reading from bottom left to top right.

00 means weaving oppositely.

6.2.5 Plain Weave and its Elaborations

Plain Weave

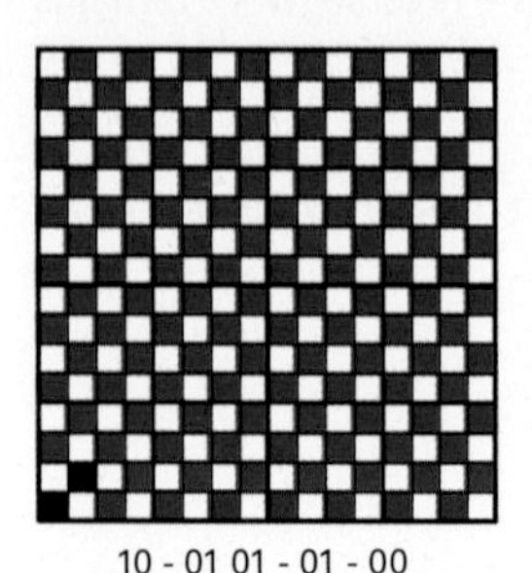

10 - 01 01 - 01 - 00

1: Pattern draft

2: Plain weave fabric

Plain weave is the simplest and the tightest method of interlacing warp and weft. Each warp yarn passes alternately over and under each weft. The interlacing is opposite in all neighbouring cells. The repeat is over two ends and two picks. Opposite sides of the fabric are the same (*Figures 1 and 2*).

Plain weave allows the highest possible number of interlacings which, depending on the fibre and yarn type, the thread density and the finishing, can yield fabrics with high abrasion resistance and resistance to yarn slippage. **Batiste, cambric, Donegal, fresco, Honan, muslin, taffeta,** and **voile** are all plain weave fabrics.

Elaborations of Plain Weave

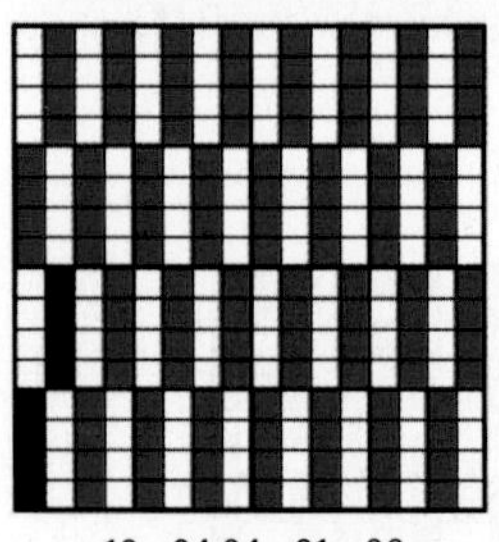

10 - 04 04 - 01 - 00

3: Pattern draft

4: Warp rib

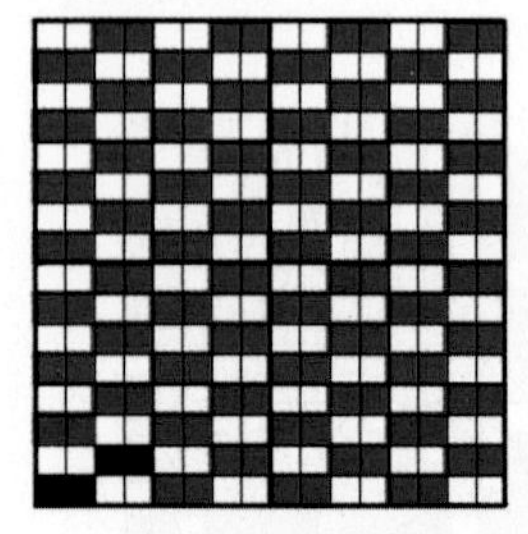

10 - 01 01 - 02 - 00

5: Pattern draft

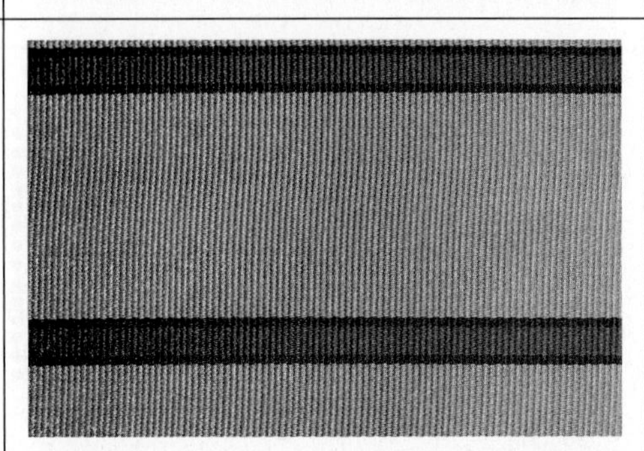

6: Weft rib

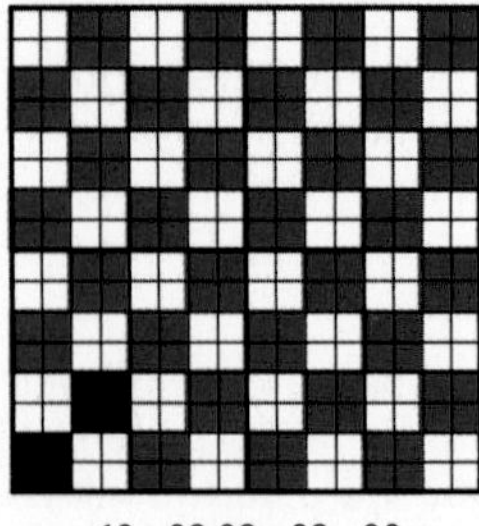

10 - 02 02 - 02 - 00

7: Pattern draft

8: Hopsack, Basket

Ribs

A rib fabric is one whose surface shows raised lines or ridges.

Warp Rib

A rib running across the fabric width is obtained with a high density of warp ends, when two or more weft picks are placed in each shed (*Figure 3*). The warp yarn is usually finer than the weft and covers the surface of the fabric. Hence the name warp rib (*Figure 4*).

The properties and the appearance are determined by the fibre and yarn qualities used in the warp, since this predominates on both sides of the fabric.

Commercial styles: **Ottoman, rib.**

A ribbed appearance can also be obtained in plain weave by using coarse weft and fine warp yarns, e.g. **poplin.**

Weft Rib

Ribs running the length of the cloth are obtained with a high weft density, by alternately raising and lowering two or more warp ends over and under the weft picks, with the same number of adjacent ends doing the opposite (*Figure 5*). The high density of weft results in a lower weaving production rate, so these fabrics are not very common.

The properties and appearance depend primarily on the nature of the weft yarns (*Figure 6*).

Hopsacks, Matt, Basket Weave

Hopsacks have a chequered appearance, made by alternately raising and lowering two or more warp ends over and under the same number of weft picks, with the same number of adjacent ends doing the opposite (*Figures 7 and 8*).

Commercial styles: **hopsack, matt, basket.**

6.2.6 Twill Weave and its Elaborations (1)

Twill Weave

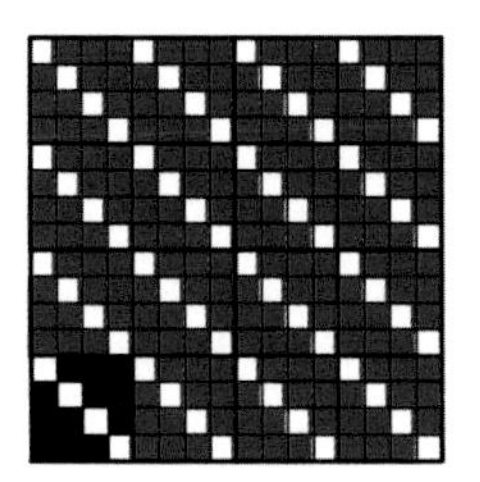

20 - 03 01 - 01 - 03

1: Pattern draft

2: Warp faced twill

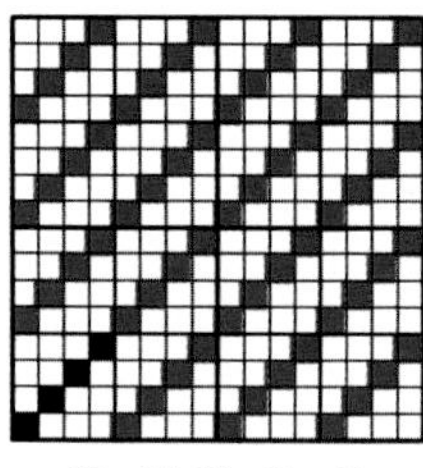

20 - 01 03 - 01 - 01

3: Pattern draft

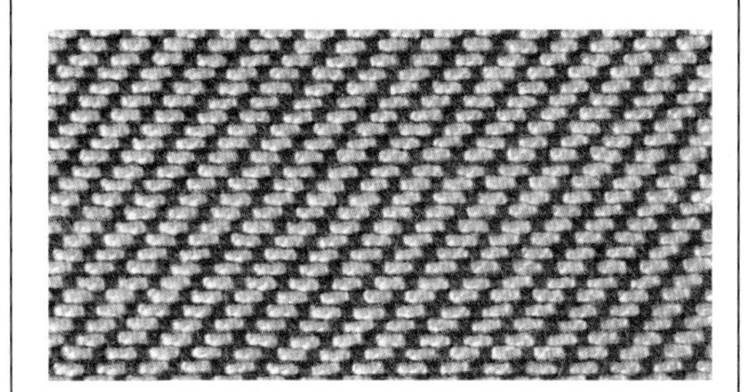

4: Weft faced twill

The **twill order** of interlacing causes diagonal lines to appear in the fabric. The lines may run to the right (Z direction) or to the left (S direction). On the back of the fabric the twill line runs in the opposite direction and may be less distinct.

The smallest repeat size for twill weave is three warp and three weft threads. The twill line is created by floats between interlacing points, which move one cell upwards (or downwards) on adjacent threads.

Warp faced twills show a predominance of warp yarns on the face (*Figures 1 and 2*).

Weft faced twills (twillette) have more weft than warp showing on the face (*Figures 3 and 4*).

Twill fabrics can be made soft and loose or smooth, dense, and durable depending on the fabric construction and thread density.

Typical twill fabrics are **cavalry, denim, diagonal, drill, gabardine, serge, tweed, tricotine, and whipcord.**

Elaborations of Twill Weave

20 - 02 02 - 01 - 01

5: Pattern draft

6: Balanced twill

Balanced Twills

In balanced twills, the warp and weft floats are of equal sizes and the face and back of the cloth look the same, apart from the direction of the twill line (*Figures 5 and 6*).

Commercial styles: **twill, sheeting.**

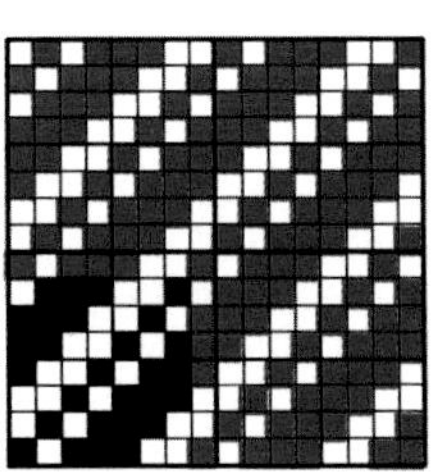

20 - 01 02 03 01 - 01 - 01

7: Pattern draft

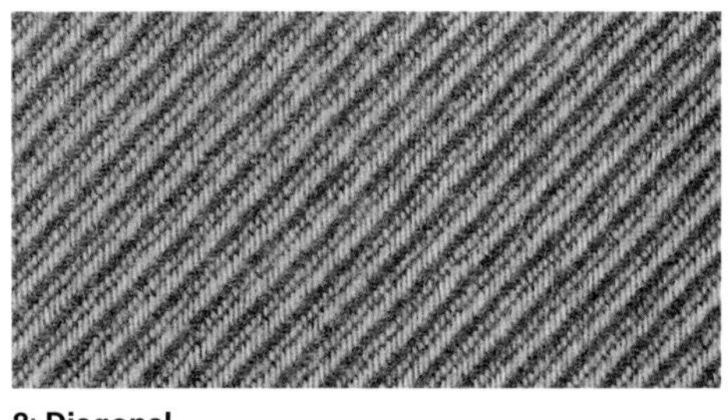

8: Diagonal

Diagonals

Diagonals are larger twills with two or more twill lines of differing widths. They can be warp faced, weft faced, or balanced (*Figures 7 and 8*).

Commercial styles: **diagonal, cavalry.**

20 - 04 02 - 01 - 01

9: Pattern draft

10: Broad twill

Broad Twills

Broad twills show a very broad twill line. Warp floats usually cover more than two cells and weft floats at least two. They can be balanced or unbalanced (*Figures 9 and 10*).

Commercial styles: **diagonal.**

6.2.6 Twill Weave and its Elaborations (2)

Developments of Twill Weave

The basic twill weave is capable of far broader and richer development than plain weave. The form of the twill line can be extensively modified not only by variations in construction but also by colour and material effects.

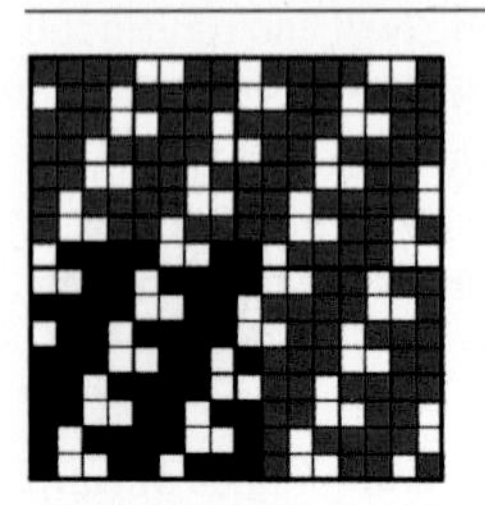
20 - 05 01 01 02 - 01 - 02

1: Pattern draft

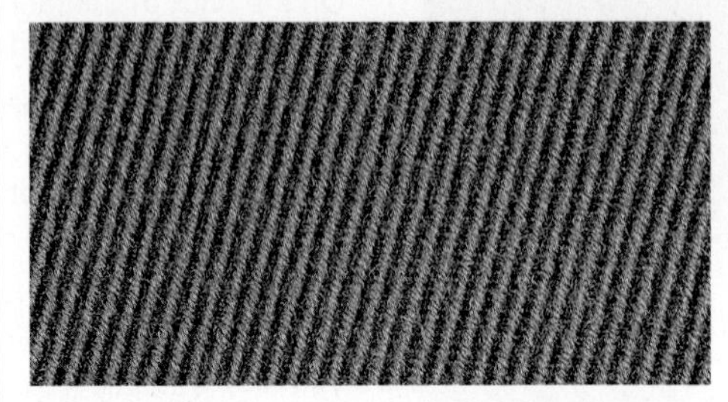

2: Steep twill

Steep Twill

With equal densities of warp and weft, the simple twills display a twill line of about 45°. A steeper twill line can be obtained either by increasing the relative density of the warp or by using a move number of two in the pattern, or by special constructions.

Commercial styles: **gabardine, tricotine**

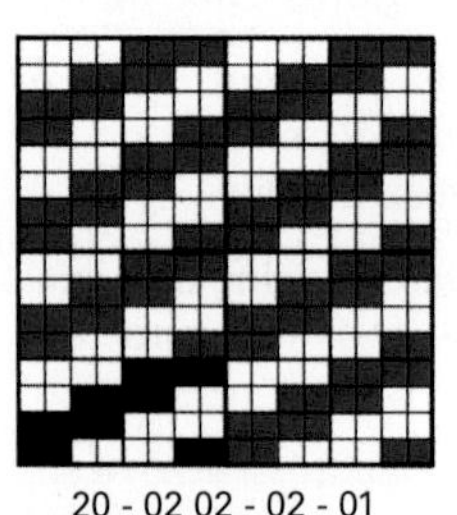
20 - 02 02 - 02 - 01

3: Pattern draft

4: Flattened twill

Flattened Twill

In flattened twills, the angle of the twill line is less than 45°. They are usually weft-faced, which means that the twill line is formed by the weft yarn and the warp is mainly on the back of the fabric. Usually, the weft floats are longer than the move number which, in turn, is greater than one.

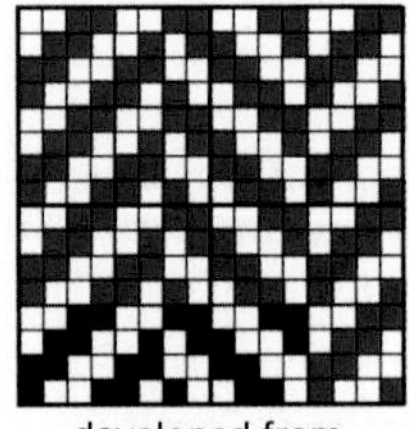
developed from
20 - 02 02 - 01 - 01

5: Pattern draft

6: Herringbone

Herringbone

This is made by reversing the direction of the twill at regular intervals. At the reversal, the pattern is displaced by one or more cells, so that the twill lines do not meet in a point. The pattern can be emphasised by using different colours for warp and weft.

Commercial styles: **herringbone, chevron**

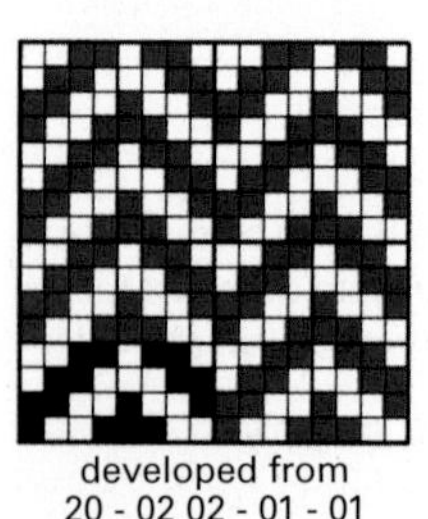
developed from
20 - 02 02 - 01 - 01

7: Pattern draft

8: Waved twill

Waved Twill

By changing the direction of the twill line at regular intervals a wave, or zigzag effect can be created either across the fabric or along its length. Diamond checks can also be made. The twill lines come to a point at the reversals.

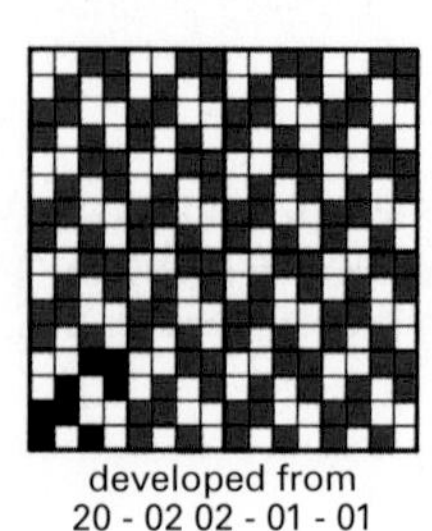
developed from
20 - 02 02 - 01 - 01

9: Pattern draft

10: Broken twill

Broken Twill

Broken twills are formed by reversing the pattern part way through the repeat. Usually the break will be at the centre of the repeat, with only one reversal, but more complicated breaks can be made. The pattern can be broken either in the warp or in the weft direction and no twill line will be generated.

6.2.7 Satin Weave and its Elaborations

Satin and Sateen

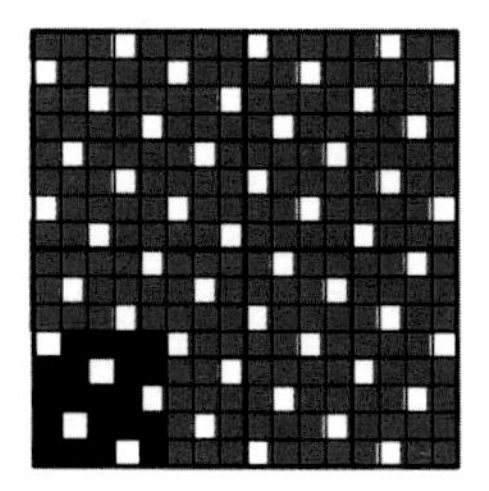
30 - 04 01 - 01 - 02

1: Pattern draft

2: Satin

30 - 01 04 - 01 - 02

3: Pattern draft

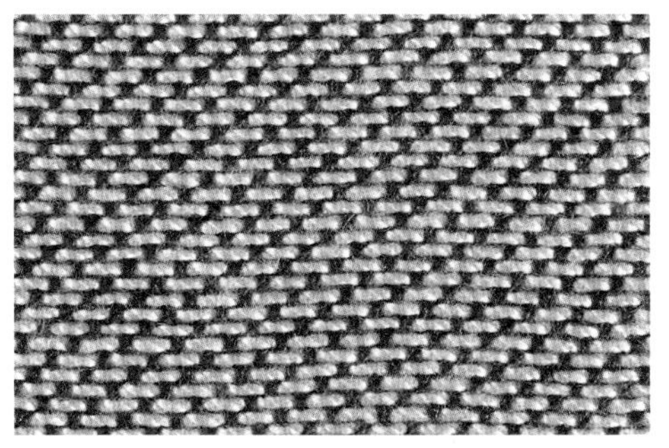

4: Sateen

The feature of the satin and sateen weaves is a uniform distribution of the interlacings, which are never adjacent to one another. Satin and sateen repeat over at least 5 ends and 5 picks but the warp ends interlace only once per repeat. This results in the long floats which determine the appearance and the properties of these fabrics. The face and back of the fabric look quite different.

Warp satins have a predominance of warp on the face side (*Figures 1 and 2*).

The less popular **weft sateens** have the weft on the face (*Figures 3 and 4*). They are often brushed and cropped for a suede or mock-velvet style, e.g. duvetine (duvetyn).

Satins and sateens are smooth, uniform, and lustrous due to the scarcity of interlacings and the density of threads. A soft and supple handle and drape can be obtained with relatively loose constructions.

Commercial styles: **duchesse, doeskin, satin, sateen, venetian.**

Developments of Satin Weave

Variations on the satin weave are few because the interlacings must not be allowed to come close together. Patterning can be achieved by arranging for **interchanging areas** of satin and sateen, or by having areas of satin or sateen on a plain or twill background. Typical examples are **façonné, damask, satin stripe,** and many **figured jacquard** fabrics (*see pages 116 ff Commercial Terminology*).

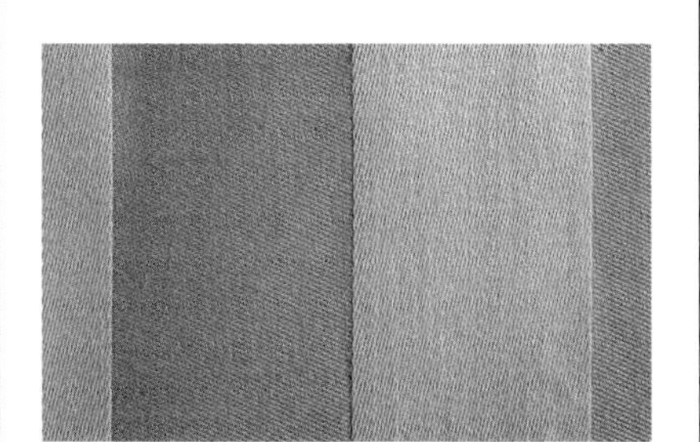

5: Satin stripe

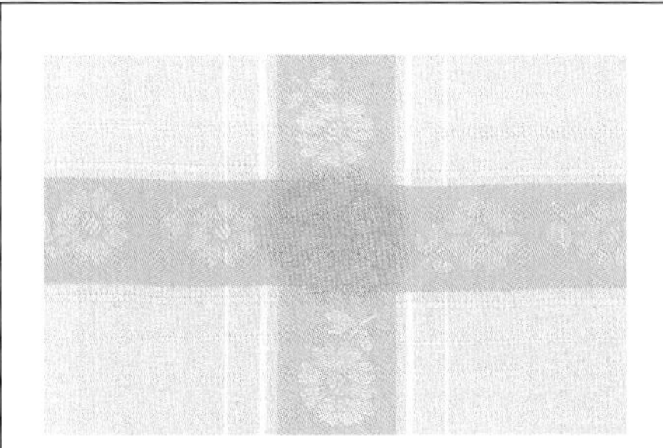

6: Coloured satin stripe

7: Damask

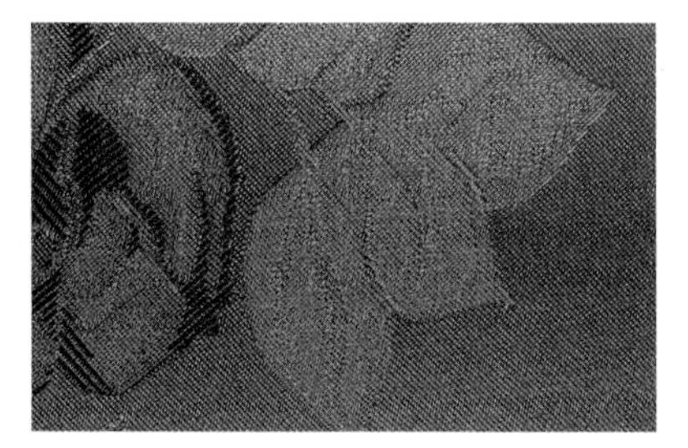

8: Figured jacquard, changeant

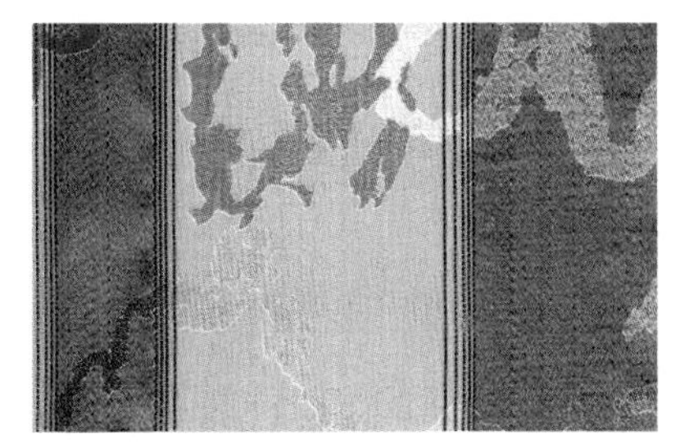

9: Chiffon with satin stripes

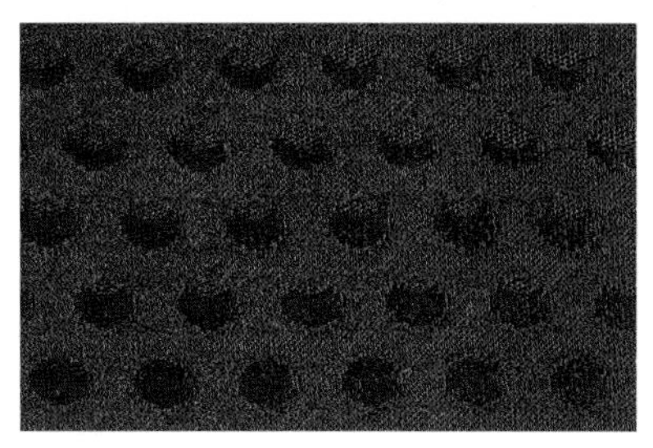

10: Satin façonné

6.2.8 Colour Woven Fabrics

Colour woven fabrics achieve their patterning effects by using dyed warp and weft yarns in various combinations. **Stripes** across the width are obtained by using two or more colours in the weft; length-way stripes by using multi-coloured warps. **Checks** and **small figures** use colours in both directions.

1: Changeant, Chambray

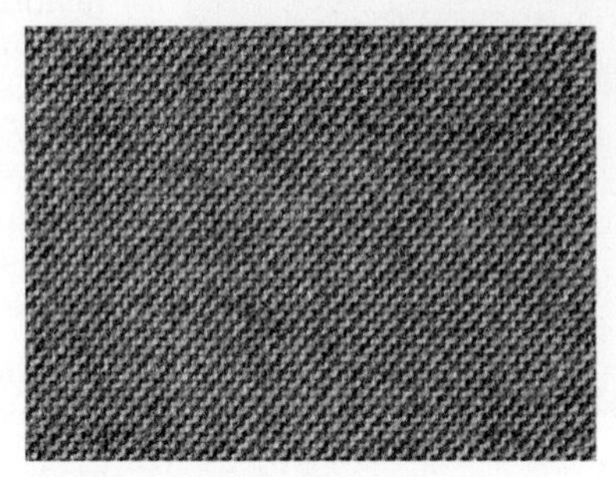

2: Fil-à-fil (end-on-end)

Changeant, Chambray

The whole warp is a different colour from the weft. A shimmering effect can be obtained by using filament yarns (shot silk). Chambray has a white weft.

Fil-à-fil (end-on-end)

Dark and light yarns alternate in both warp and weft. With a 2/2 twill construction a miniature staircase effect results.

3: Pin stripe

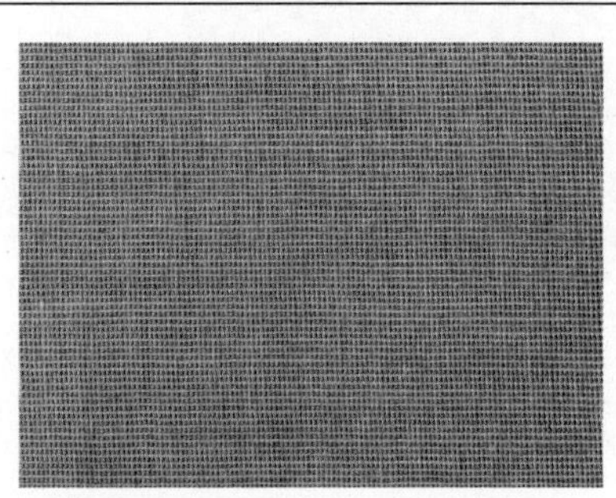

4: Oxford

Pin Stripe

Fine lines are formed by the use of individual light-coloured ends on a darker monotone background.

Oxford

A plain weave base but with two ends weaving as one and with different colours in warp and weft. Gives a tiny chequered appearance.

5: Tartan, Plaid

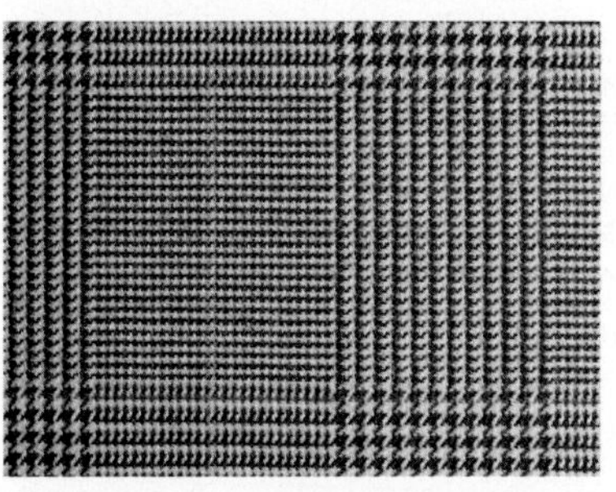

6: Glen check

Tartan

Large squares of colour overlaid by warp and weft stripes, from coloured warp and weft. The patterns and colours derive from traditional Scottish dress.

Glen Check

Glen check is made on a 2/2 twill base by having dark and white threads and a colouring order of n sets of 4:4 followed by 2n sets of 2:2 in both directions.

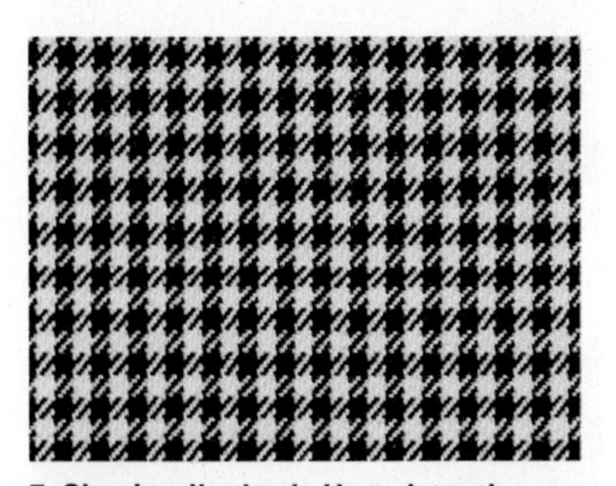

7: Shepherd's check, Houndstooth, Pepita

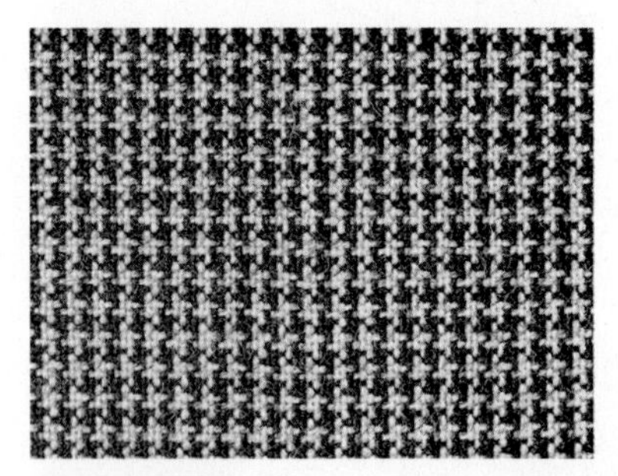

8: Spot effects

Shepherd's Check

Small checks in contrasting colours, usually on a 2/2 twill base with 4:4, 6:6 or 8:8 colouring. **Houndstooth** is a particular type based on 2/2 twill with 4:4 colouring. Also known as **Pepita** in Austria/Germany.

Spot effects

Also made from alternating contrasting colours in warp and weft. There are many possibilities, including **Birdseye** (*see page 136*). Most common are 2:2 or 4:4 colouring on plain weave and 2/2 or 3/1 twills.

6.2.9 Crêpe Fabrics

Crêpe fabrics have a **granular, irregular surface texture** which is obtained by various means, including high twist yarns, special weave constructions, special finishing processes or combinations of these.

Crêpe-Yarn Fabrics

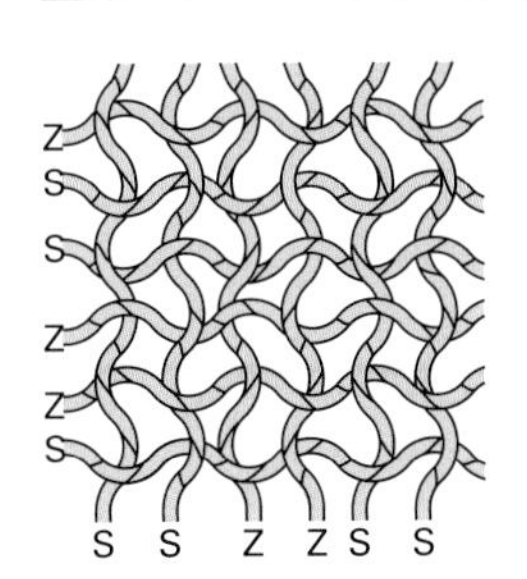

1: Yarn arrangement in a full crêpe

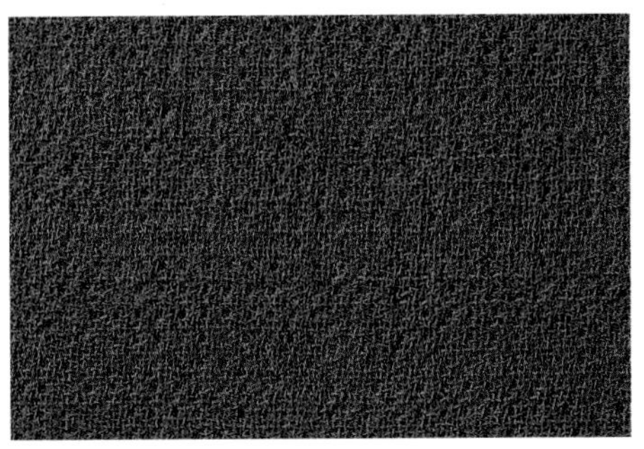

2: Crêpe georgette

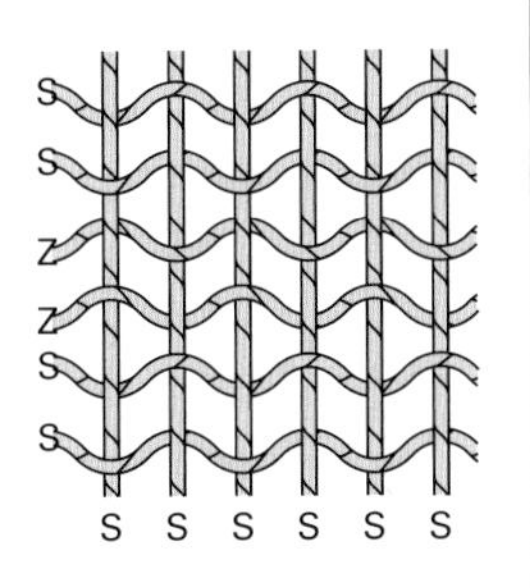

3: Yarn arrangement in a half-crêpe

4: Crêpe marocain

Crêpe-yarn fabrics are made from highly twisted yarns (crêpe yarns). The fabric is light and soft with an irregular and finely textured surface and a sandy handle.

Full crêpe is made with crêpe yarns in both directions (*Figure 1*). The weave is either a plain or crêpe construction. Commercial styles: **crêpe georgette** (*Figure 2*), **chiffon.**

Half crêpe has crêpe yarns in only one direction, usually the weft.

A crêpe with a fine rib effect in the weft direction is made with a 2:2 pattern of alternating S and Z twist crêpe yarns in the weft (*Figure 3*). Commercial styles: **crêpe de chine, crêpe marocain** (*Figure 4*).

A crêpe with a granular texture in the warp direction is made with weft crêpe yarns all having the same twist direction. Commercial styles: **crêpon, crêpe suzette, bark crêpe.**

Alternating flat and crinkled stripes are made by inserting groups of crêpe yarns in the warp, woven at different tension to the normal warp yarns. A similar effect can be obtained using yarns with high shrinkage.

Commercial style: **seersucker.**

Crêpe Weaves

5: Example of a crêpe weave

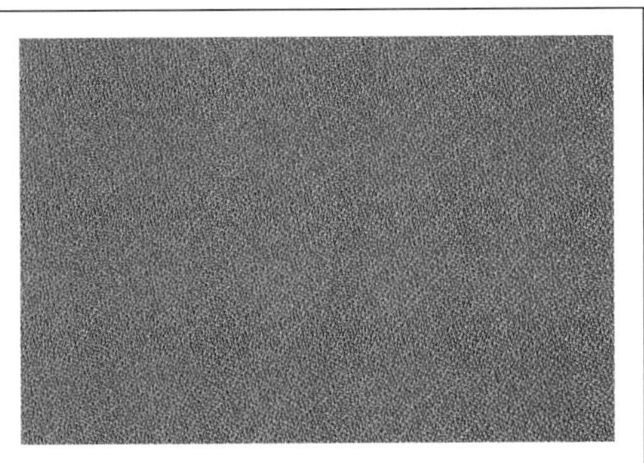

6: Sand crêpe

Crêpe weave fabrics have a granular, irregular appearance. It is achieved by special weave construction techniques. Almost any weave can be rearranged, modified, or combined with another to make a crêpe weave. There should be no stripes, twill lines or long floats; the repeat is difficult to discern (*Figure 5*).

Commercial styles: **sand crêpe, moss crêpe, oatmeal crêpe.**

Crêpe Finish

7: Bark crêpe

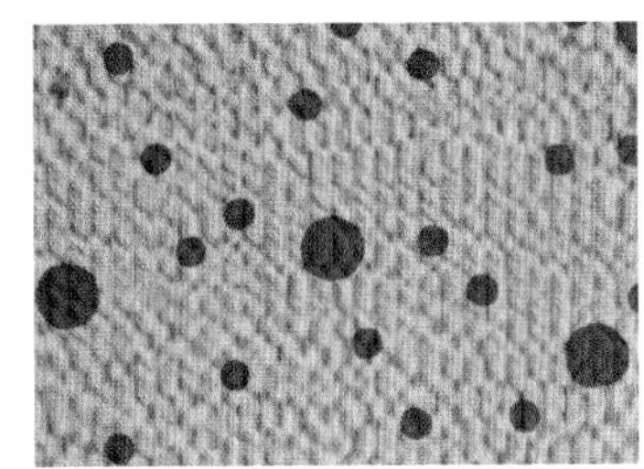

8: Plissé

Crêpe effects can also be achieved in finishing. Caustic soda solution may be printed onto cotton fabrics in a stripe or other pattern. The printed portions shrink and cause the fabric to cockle. Commercial styles: **plissé, blister, bark crêpe, seersucker.**

Crêpe effects can also be obtained using an embossing calender (*see page 111*).

Commercial types: **honeycomb, embossed seersucker.**

6.2.10 Fabrics with Three or more Yarn Systems (1)

By providing a third set of yarns, fabrics can be produced with higher strength and durability, greater weight and substance, additional patterning, or a special surface texture.

1: Reversible, face and back

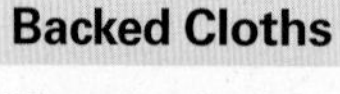

Backed Cloths

Warp-backed fabrics have an additional set of warp threads which do not appear on the face. The two sides of the fabric can have a different appearance.

Commercial styles: **reversible** (*Figure 1*), **backed fabric.**

Weft-backed fabrics have an additional set of weft yarns. The binding points for the backing weft are invisible on the face. For raised fabrics, soft, low-twist, voluminous yarns are used for the backing.

Commercial styles: **molleton, charmante.**

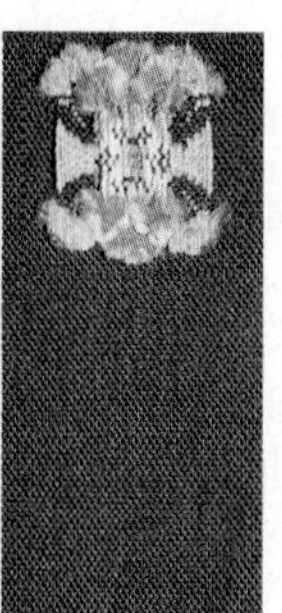

2: Lancé, face and back

Extra Warp and Extra Weft

Extra warp or extra weft yarns can be used on a plain, twill, or satin ground to produce small figured designs, somewhat like trimmings or embroidery. The extra yarn stands out from the ground due to its figured pattern of interlacing and it usually has a distinctive colour, fibre type, or lustre.

Extra weft yields figures across the width. Extra warp gives figures along the length. Both effects can be combined.

The extra yarn produces the figure on the face side but it may float unbound on the back, depending on the yarn and fabric properties and the end-use requirements. If there are large spaces between the figures, then the extra yarn can be bound in at intervals or, if the long extra yarn floats would show through, they can be cut away from the back (*Figure 2*).

Commercial styles: **lancé, clip-spot.**

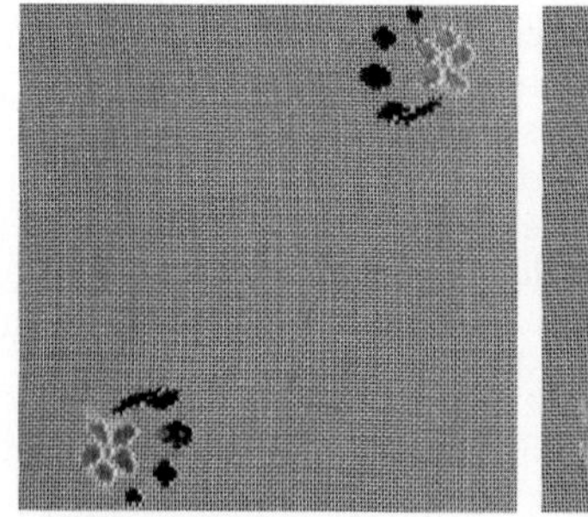

3: Broché, face and back

Broché (swivel) Fabrics

Broché is an extra weft figured fabric made on a swivel loom. The figuring yarn is supplied from a series of small shuttles mounted over the weaving surface. The effect is like small embroidery patterns (*Figure 3*). This is a very expensive technique and is seldom used; usually fabrics are actually embroidered.

Commercial styles: **broché.**

4: Terry cloth

Terry Fabrics

Terry or loop-pile fabrics (*Figure 4*) are made from two warps. The ground warp is normally or tightly tensioned, the pile warp is looser. Two or three weft yarns are introduced but are not fully beaten up into the cloth. With the next weft yarn all three or four threads are beaten up together. They slide over the tensioned ground warp but the pile warp is simultaneously slackened off so that it is bent up into a loop whose size corresponds to the final beating-up distance. Loops can be formed on one or both sides of the fabric. Pattern effects are achieved by introducing colour into the pile warp, and by having loops of different sizes.

The pile yarns can be singles or two-fold. Two-fold yarns produce a more durable product and make very efficient towelling. Singles-yarn fabrics can be made more dense and durable by a fulling process.

Terry velour is produced by cropping and brushing the loops to give a velvet-like appearance.

Loop yarn fabric has the appearance of terry but is made from only two sets of yarns, with a loop yarn in the weft.

6.2.10 Fabrics with Three or more Yarn Systems (2)

Cut Pile Fabrics

Cut pile fabrics are made by using the third yarn system to form a cut fibre pile on the face of the fabric. Fabrics with a short pile are called **velvet** or **velveteen,** long-pile fabrics are called **plush.**

Cut pile fabrics can be made either with an additional warp or with an additional weft. The former are velvets, the latter are velveteens.

The quality is determined by the density of the ground weave and by the height and density of the pile. There are different ways of binding the pile into the ground fabric, according to end-use requirements.

Mock velvets, such as **duvetine,** have a surface pile which is created by raising and brushing.

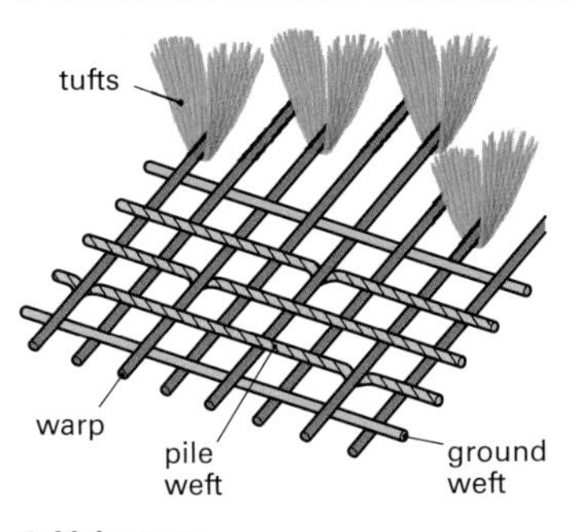

1: Velveteen

2: Plain velveteen

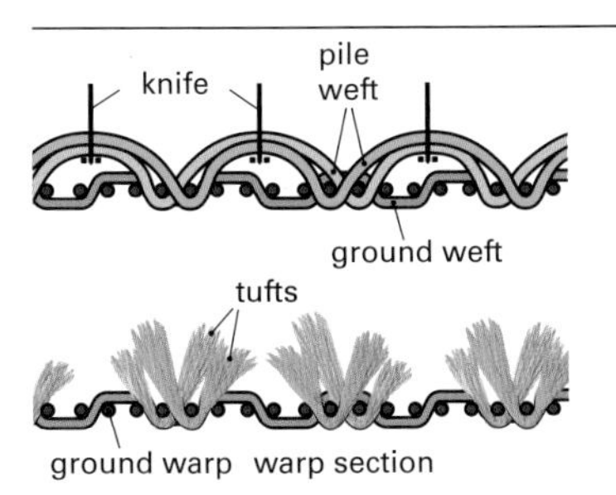

3: Corded velveteen

4: Corded velveteen; grey fabric partially cut

Velveteens are constructed so that the pile weft floats largely on the surface of the fabric. After cutting, the tufts are held by the warp yarns (*Figure 1*).

The density of the fabric and the pile height are determined by the interlacing pattern of ground and pile. The pile is cut in a special separate operation. It is then brushed open and cropped to a uniform height.

If the binding points for the pile yarn are uniformly distributed, then a **plain velveteen** results (*Figure 2*).

Commercial styles: **velveteen.**

If the pile yarns always float between the same warp yarns, then **corded velveteens** are produced after cutting (*Figure 3 and 4*).

The cords may be of various widths, from under 5 **(jumbo cord)** to more than 16 **(needle cord, pincord)** wales per inch. Cord widths can be mixed in the same fabric.

Commercial styles: **needlecord** (very fine cords), **corduroy.**

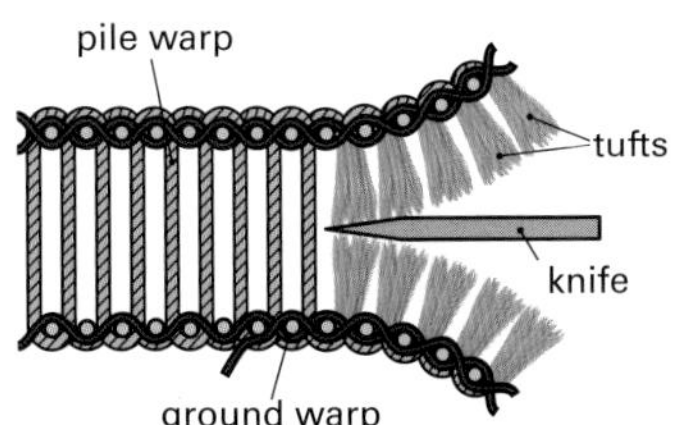

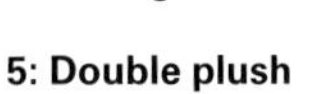

5: Double plush

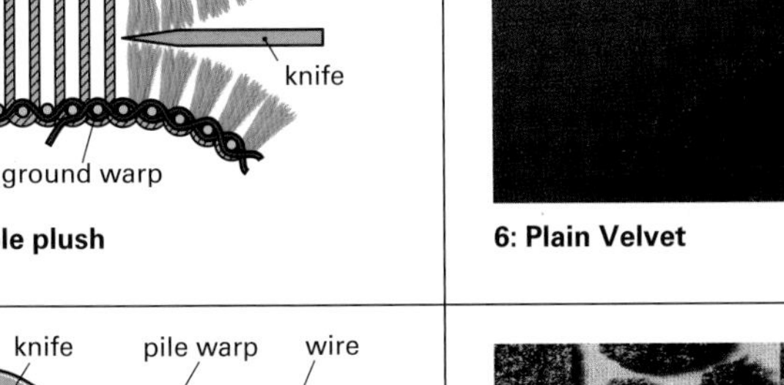

6: Plain Velvet

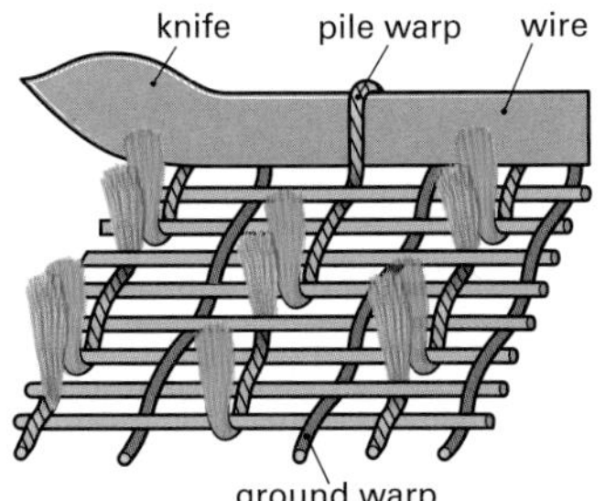

7: Wire velvet

8: Burn-out velvet

Velvets are made with an additional warp and the cut fibre tufts are bound into the ground fabric by the weft.

The two main production techniques are **wire weaving** and **double plush** weaving. The latter is more economical but less uniform. Two fabrics are woven together on a special loom. The ground fabrics are independent but they share a single pile warp. The pile yarns are subsequently cut through the middle by a reciprocating knife. Thus five sets of yarns make two fabrics, each with three yarn sets (*Figure 5 and 6*).

In **wire weaving,** the pile warp is led over either looping wires or cutting wires. When the wires are withdrawn the pile either forms loops or is cut (*Figure 7*). The pile may be cropped, to make it level then brushed and steamed.

Burn-out velvets are made by printing a pattern onto the pile using a chemical which dissolves or destroys it (*Figure 8*).

Commercial styles: **velvet, crushed velvet** (embossed patterns), **chiffon velvet** (very light), **panne velvet** (flattened pile).

6.2.10 Fabrics with Three or more Yarn Systems (3)

Four or more yarn systems are used to make **double cloths.** These are effectively two fabrics woven one on top of the other, which are linked to each other at intervals by various techniques. Double cloths are used for **greater strength, weight, and volume** or to have **different appearances on face and back,** or for **surface relief effects.**

1: Double cloth, face

2: Double cloth, back

Self-stitched Double Cloths

Four yarn systems are used. **Warp stitching** or tying is when the backing warp interlaces with the face weft. **Weft stitching** is when the backing weft interlaces with the face warp. The stitching is so close that the two fabrics cannot be separated. The technique is often used to produce jacket and coat fabrics with an integral lining. Usually the two sides look quite different.

3: Centre warp-stitched double cloth

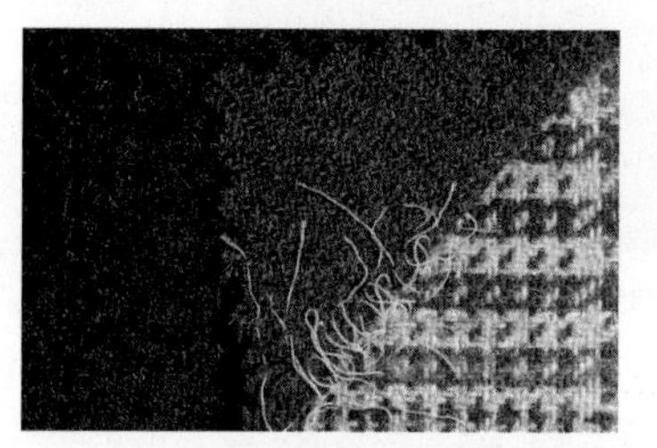
4: Centre weft-stitched double cloth

Centre-stitched Double Cloths

In this case, the two fabrics are stitched together by a fifth yarn system. They are softer and fuller but are less firmly united and can be pulled apart. The fabrics are suitable for making reversible garments.

5: Double plain, face

6: Double plain, back

Interchanging Double Cloths

These are double cloths in which the face and back fabrics interchange according to a specified design. The fabrics may be unstitched between the interchanges, leaving holes between the two. The pattern is the same on both sides, though they may be oppositely coloured. The fabrics may be used reversibly. They can be used for cloaks, shawls, and tablecloths.

7: Cloqué, face

8: Cloqué, back

Cloqué

These are double cloths with a figured blister effect. The face fabric is made from fine yarns with normal twist. The back has crêpe yarns which are stitched to the face fabric according to a certain pattern. During wet processing, the crêpe backing fabric shrinks and causes the face fabric to crinkle. The same effect can be obtained by using high-shrink fibres in the backing fabric.

9: Matelassé, face

10: Matelassé, back

Matelassé

Double fabrics with a figured relief effect on the face side are called Matelassé. The back cloth may be coarse. The designs are formed by floating threads or by areas of different weaves and by the stitching pattern of back to face cloth. The pattern can be emphasised by the use of additional wadding picks.

6.2.11 Piqué Fabrics

Piqué, fabrics have a **textured quilt-like surface.**

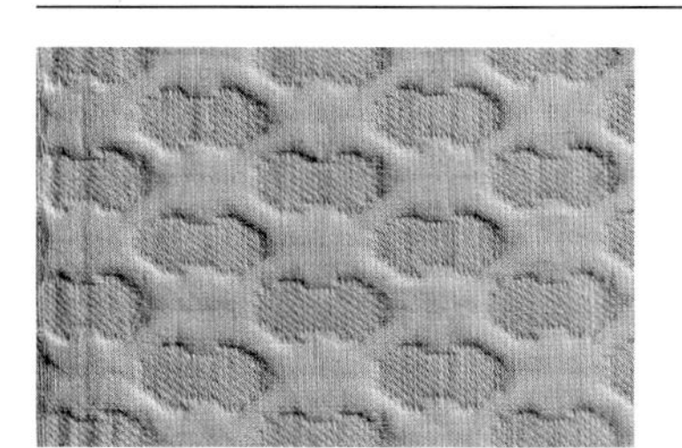

1: Piqué, face

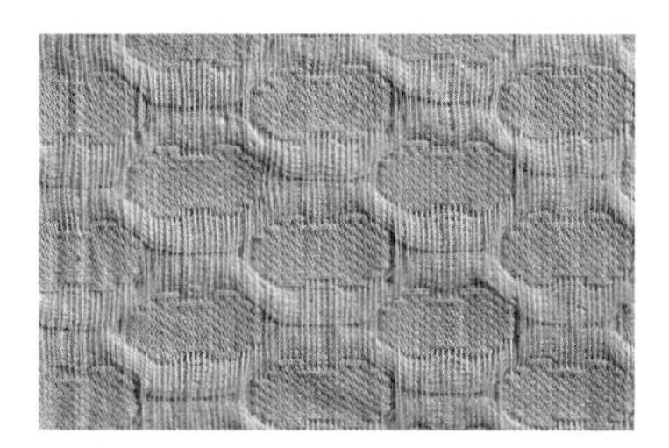

2: Piqué, back

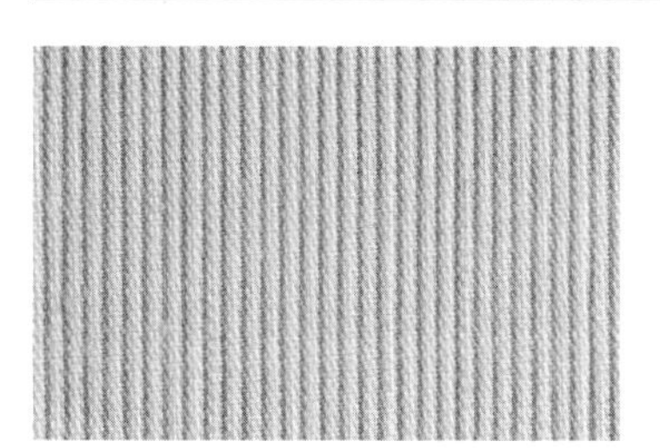

3: Piqué cord; double cloth, face

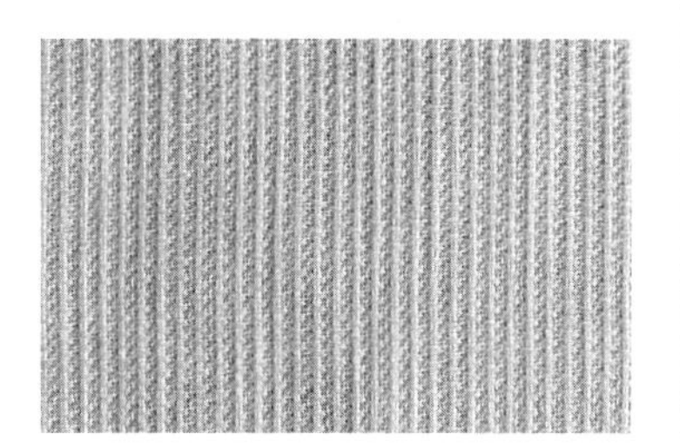

4: Piqué cord; double cloth, back

Piqué

Nowadays, the term piqué is frequently applied to a wide range of fabrics, woven or knitted, which display a regular, prominent textured surface. The texture may be in the form of straight or wavy welts (widthways ribs), cords (lengthways ribs), or honeycomb structures.

A true piqué is a double cloth with a fine face fabric and a coarser back. The pattern of stitching is arranged to produce waved welts, welts, or small figures which can look like quilting. Extra weft, laid unbound between the two fabrics, can be used to provide a relief effect on the face. The fine stitching warp is highly tensioned to outline the pattern and press the wadding picks against the face fabric (*Figures 1 and 2*).

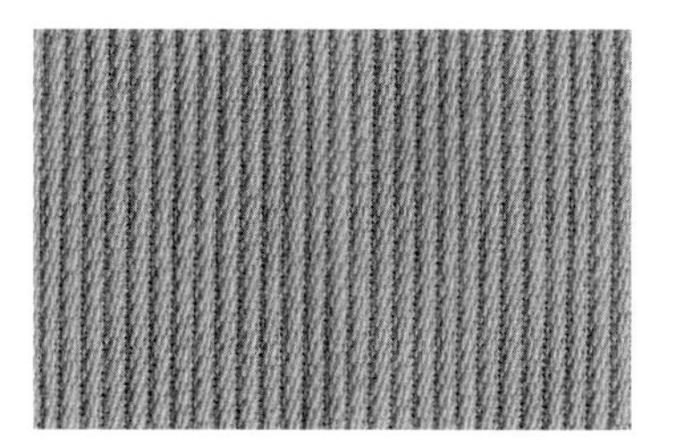

5: Piqué cord; single cloth, face

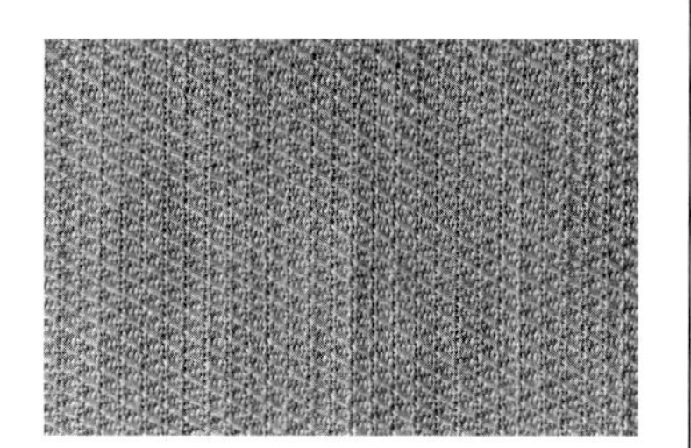

6: Piqué cord; single cloth, back

Piqué Cord

These fabrics have fine cords on the face in the length direction.

They can be made either as double cloths or single fabrics. The double cloths have a fine face fabric with a coarse wadding warp and a stitching weft on the back (*Figures 3 and 4*).

The cords in the single fabric are made by regular weft floats on the back of the fabric (*Figures 5 and 6*). They are developments of the basic Bedford cord.

7: Honeycomb, face

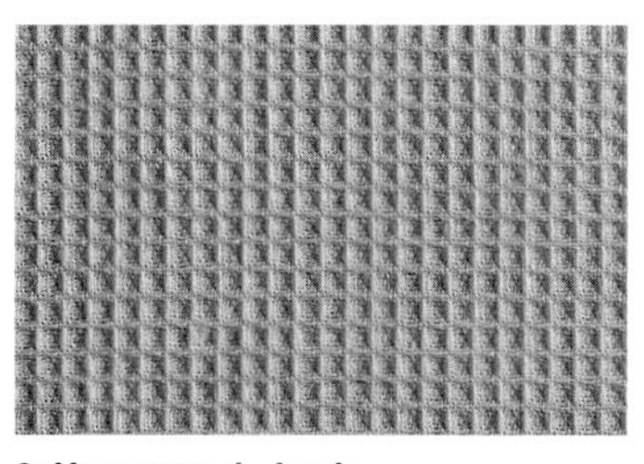

8: Honeycomb, back

Honeycomb

Usually single cloths made by progressively lengthening and shortening both warp and weft floats to form ridges and hollows on a square pattern, to give a cellular appearance (*Figures 7 and 8*). Both sides of the fabric look the same. Sometimes called waffle or waffle piqué.

9: Bedford cord, face

10: Bedford cord, back

Bedford Cord

The basic cord weave allows a raised warp rib effect without using an extra thread system. The warp is more dense and firm so that it predominates on the face. A proportion of the weft floats on the back in a regular formation which causes the face to buckle slightly into ribs (*Figures 9 and 10*). Can also be made with wadding ends laid freely between the face cords and the back weft floats.

6.3.1 Classification of Knitted Fabrics

Classification after ISO 7839: 2005

Knitted fabrics are made from interlocking loops, formed from a single yarn or from many.
They are classified into weft knitted and warp knitted fabrics.

Knitted Fabrics

Weft Knitted	Warp Knitted

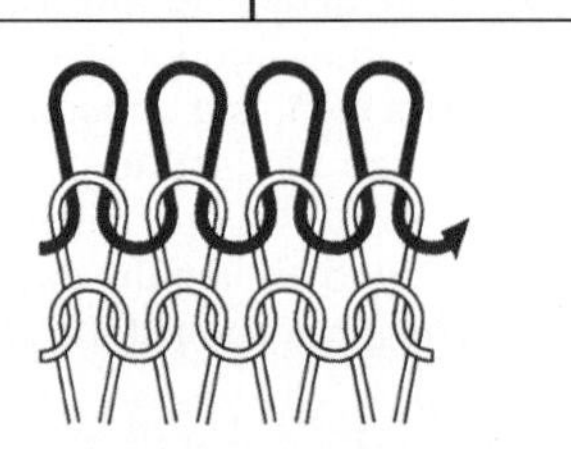

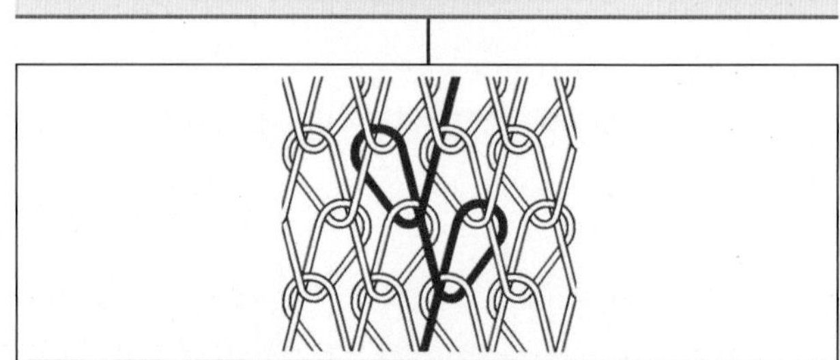

Characteristics (Weft Knitted)

- May be made from a single yarn.
- The yarn is fed crosswise to the length of the fabric.
- Can be unravelled; may ladder.
- Knitting needles can work sequentially or all together.

Characteristics (Warp Knitted)

- Requires a full warp sheet.
- The loop-forming yarns are fed in the direction of the length of the fabric.
- Can not be unravelled, usually does not ladder.
- Knitting needles always work together as a unit.

Classification by Production Method

Weft Knitted Fabrics		Warp Knitted Fabrics
Sequential needles: Loops are formed in sequence across the width of the fabric. Machines can be flat or circular. Needles are usually of the latch type.	**Simultaneous needles:** All of the needles are moved together or the needles are stationary and the fabric is moved. Machines can be flat or circular. Needles are usually of the bearded type.	**Warp knitting:** Warp knitting uses one or more warp sheets. Each yarn is looped around a needle and the needles are all moved together. The needles may be of the bearded, latch, or compound type. Warp knitting machines with latch or compound needles are called raschel machines and the material they make is called raschel fabric.
1: Sequential loop formation on a flat machine	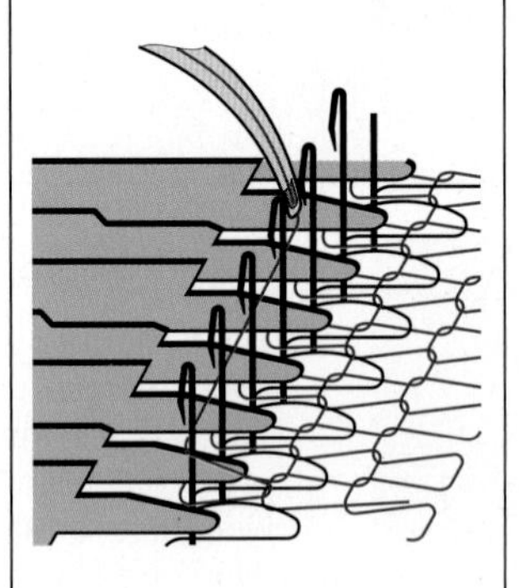 2: Simultaneous loop formation	 3: Loop formation on a warp knitting machine

6.3.2 Weft Knitted Fabrics (1)

Loop Formation

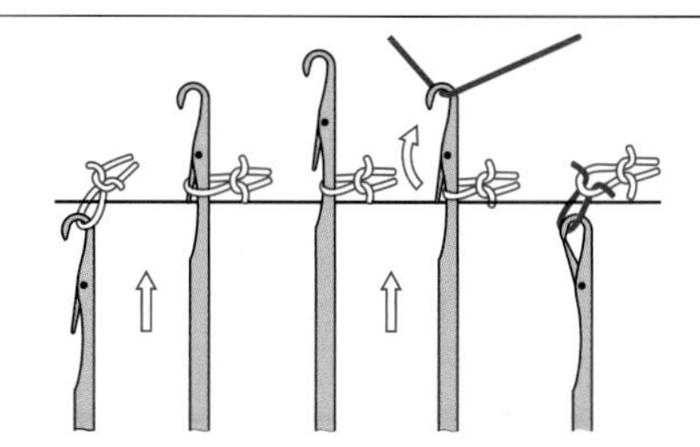
1: Latch needles

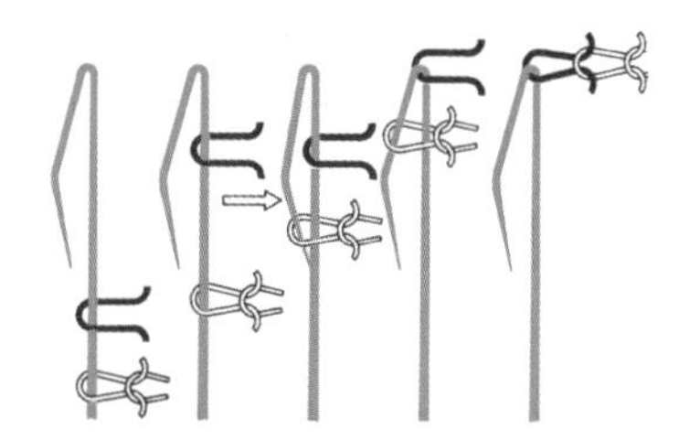
2: Bearded needles

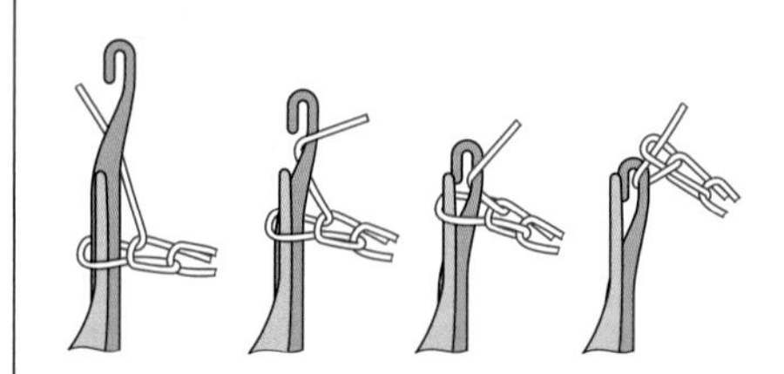
3: Compound needles

Terminology in Weft Knitting

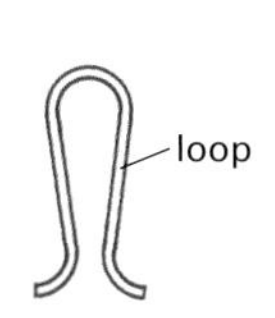

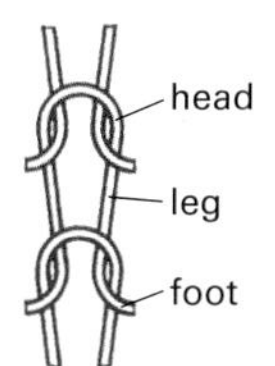

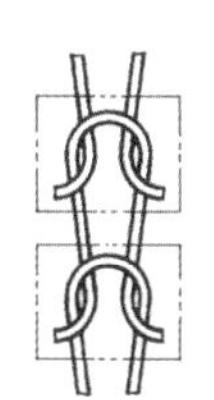

4: Loop characteristics

The Intermeshing of Loops

The loop is the basic construction element. It comprises a **head** (the **needle loop**), **two legs,** and **two feet.** The feet joining two adjacent loops form the **sinker loop.**

Fabric is formed by intermeshing loops. Each loop has four **intermeshing points** in two pairs. The legs within one pair must always mesh in the same sense; both legs lying either under or over the head of the preceding loop. The upper pair may intermesh in the opposite sense to the lower pair, depending on the construction.

5: Back loop

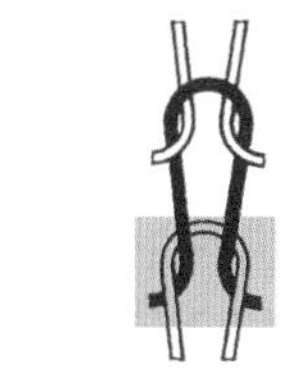
6: Face loop

Face and Back of Knitted Loops

The lower pair of meshing points determines whether the loop is a face loop or a back loop.

A **back loop** is formed when the loop is drawn through the previous loop in a direction away from the viewer: the legs of the loop lie under the head of the preceding loop.

A **face loop** is formed when the loop is drawn through the previous loop in a direction towards the viewer: the legs of the loop lie over the head of the preceding loop.

7: A course

8: A wale

Courses and Wales

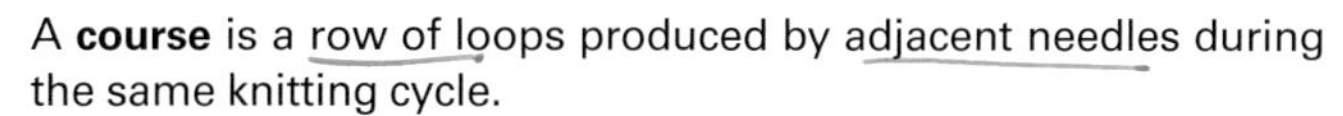

A **course** is a row of loops produced by adjacent needles during the same knitting cycle.

A **wale** is a column of loops produced by the same needle on successive knitting cycles.

The size of the loop and the fineness of the yarn determine the density of courses and wales. The number of wales determines the width of the fabric, the number of courses determines its length; their product determines the weight per unit area.

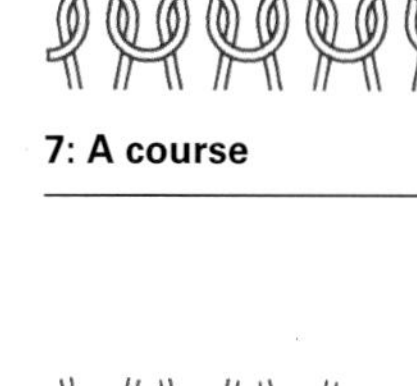
9: A tuck stitch

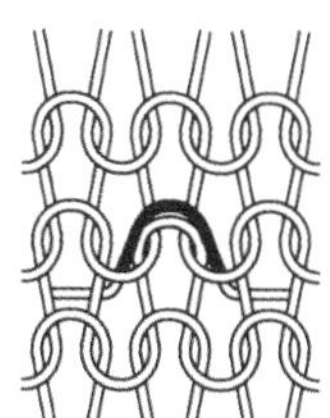
10: A tuck loop

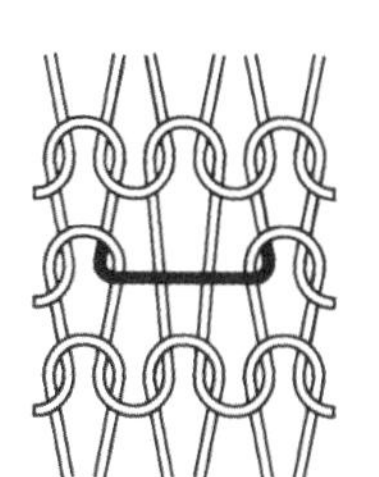
11: A float (miss) loop

Tuck and Float (Miss) Loops

A **tuck stitch** comprises a held loop, a tuck loop, and knitted loops intermeshing over two or more courses (*Figure 9*).

Held loop: a loop pulled through the loop of the previous course and retained by the needle over one or more courses (*Figures 9 and 11*).

Tuck loop: a length of yarn received by a needle but not pulled through the loop of the previous course (*Figures 9 and 10*).

Float (miss) loop, a length of yarn not received by a needle and connecting two loops of the same course that are not in adjacent wales (*Figure 11*).

6.3.2 Weft Knitted Fabrics (2)

Basic Weft Knitted Structures

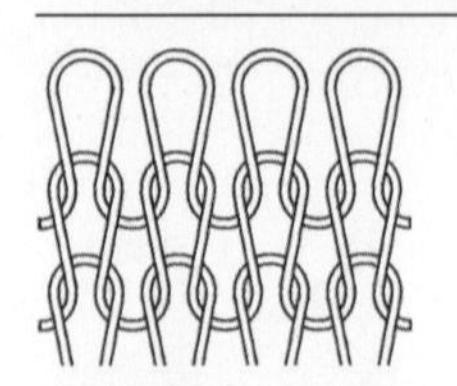

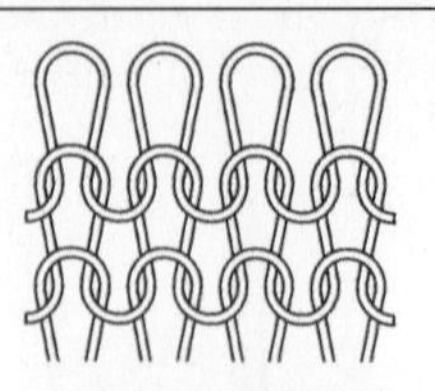

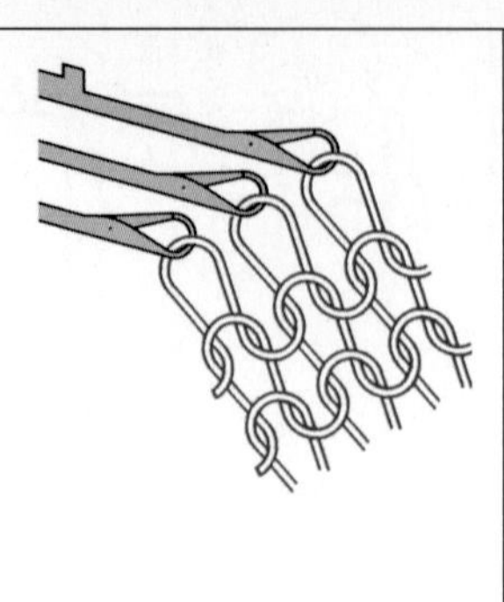

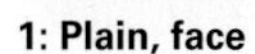

1: Plain, face — back — formation

Plain, Single Jersey

This structure is made with only a single set of needles. It is called single face, plain or **single jersey**[1].

The two sides of the fabric have a different appearance. One side shows only face loops, the other side only back loops.

It has relatively low extensibility in the width and tends to curl at the edges.

Plain jersey is used in different weights for shirts, sweaters, blouses, dresses, T-shirts, and underwear.

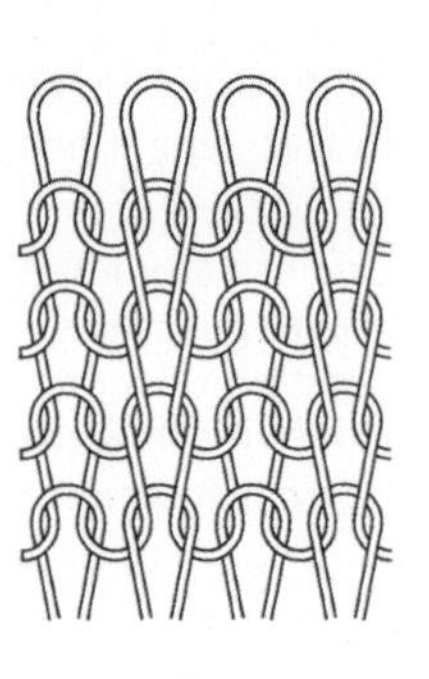

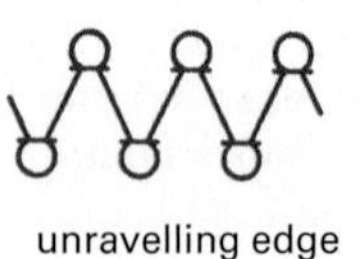

2: Rib fabric — formation

Rib Fabric

Rib fabrics are made on two needle beds with the needles in a staggered formation. The loops are drawn in opposite directions so that face and back loops alternate in each course. Both sides of the fabric show only the face loops. The back loops are exposed only when the fabric is extended in the width direction. **Rib** fabrics are very extensible in the width.

Applications include pullovers, waistcoats, underwear, and socks.

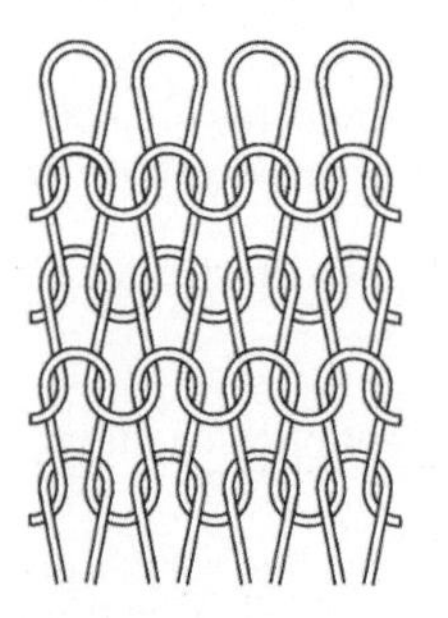

3: Purl fabric — formation

Purl Fabric

Purl is usually made with double-ended latch needles, which can slide between two opposed needle beds. In 1x1 purl, single courses of face and back loops alternate. Both sides of the fabric look the same, with prominent course-way ribs. These are formed by the juxtaposition of the needle loops of the face course and the sinker loops of the back course.

Purl fabric has high extensibility in the length.

Applications include romper suits, pullovers and cardigans.

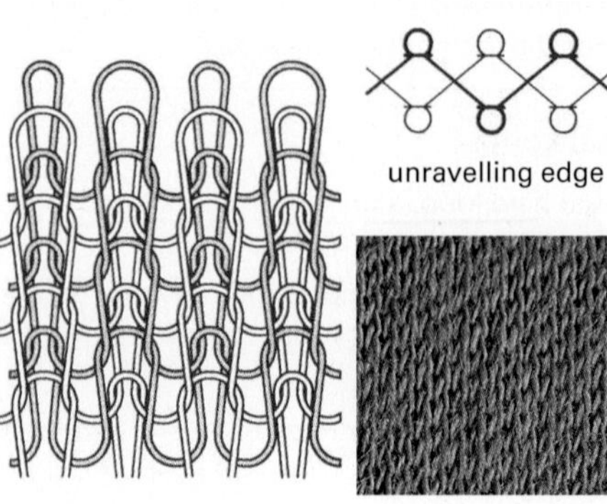

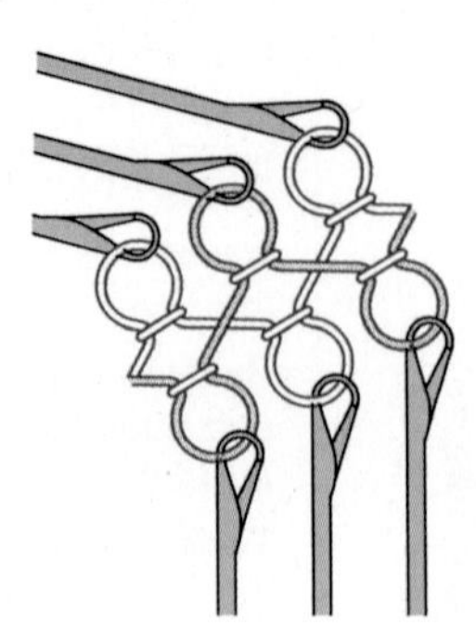

4: Interlock fabric — formation

Interlock

Interlock is made on two needle beds in which the needles are directly opposed and work alternately. In the fabric, the loops on one side are directly opposite those on the other. It takes two courses to make one row of loops on the face and back. Neighbouring loops in a row are displaced by half a course.

Interlock has a close surface structure. Both sides show only face loops and look identical. The fabric is extensible, but not very elastic.

It is used for T-shirts, blouses, underwear, sports and leisure wear.

[1] Jersey is a general name for knitted fabrics. It is not restricted to any particular structure.

6.3.3 Developments of the Single Jersey Structure

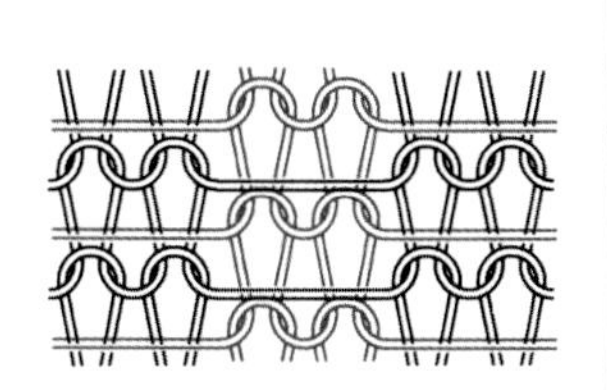
1: Jacquard, schematic

face

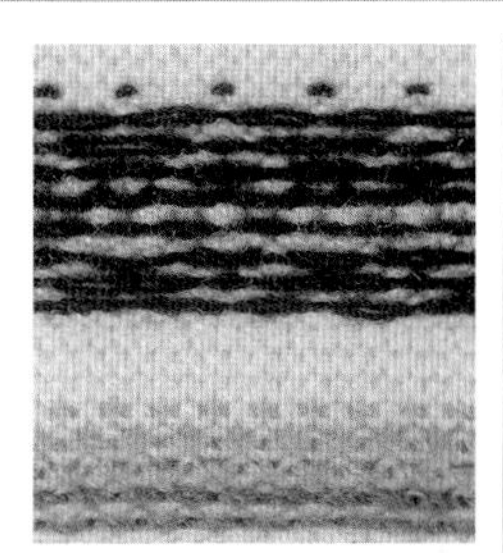
back

Jacquard

Patterns are created by selecting needles to knit with coloured yarns. Colours and needle selections are changed on each course to build up the pattern. When a colour is not required on the face, the yarn floats on the back of the fabric. A wide range of designs can be created. The fabric is not very extensible, because of the large number of floats. Applications include fashion pullovers and waistcoats.

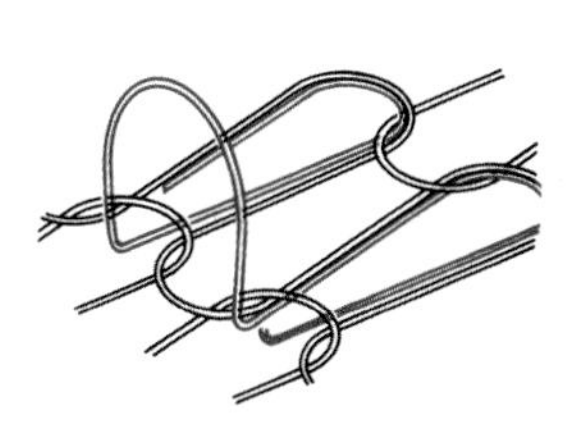
2: Plush or terry, schematic

Plush or terry

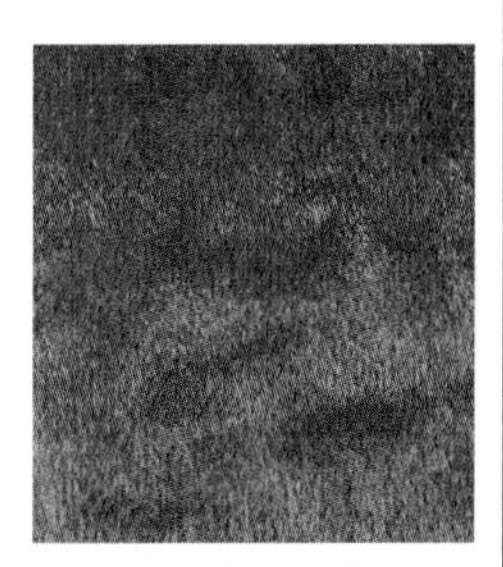
Cut plush (velour)

Plush or Terry

Plush, or knitted terry fabric, is made by including (plating) an extra yarn which is made to form extended sinker loops. The plated yarn can be knitted at every needle or on selected needles to form a pattern.

Cut plush, or knitted velour is made by cutting the plated yarn loops. The fabric surface then resembles velvet (velour). Applications include leisure and children's wear and socks.

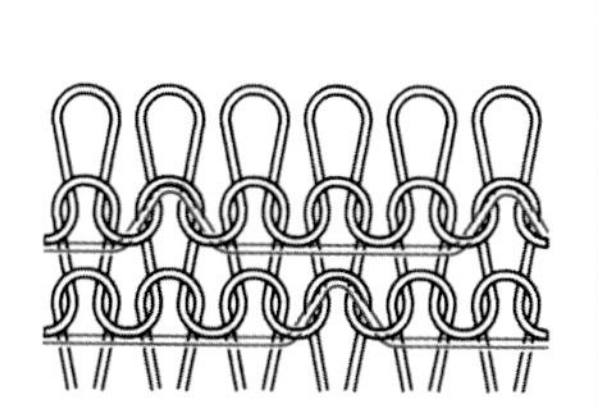
3: Inlay or loopback, schematic

face

back (not raised)

Inlay (loopback)

An extra (inlay) yarn is floated on the technical back, tucking at regular intervals. Usually the inlay yarn is much coarser than the ground yarn. These fabrics have a fine face and a bulky looped back which is often brushed or raised, when it is known as **two-thread fleece.** Either side of the fabric can be used as the face side for garment making. Applications include leisure and children's wear, track suits and sweatshirts.

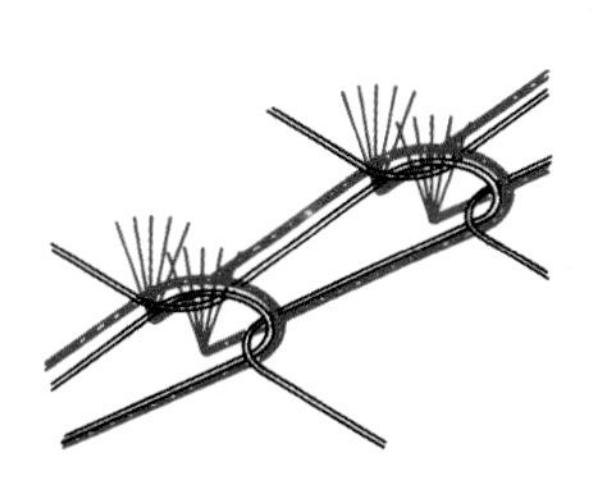
4: Sliver knit, schematic

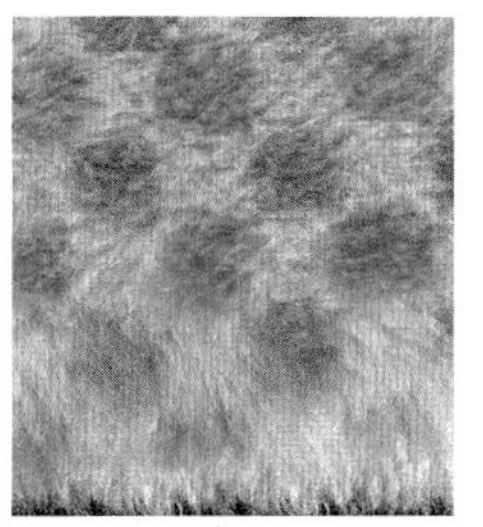
Sliver knit (fake fur), face

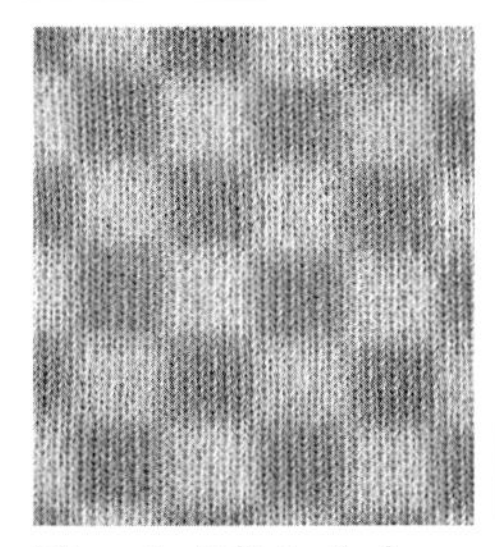
Sliver knit (fake fur), back

Sliver Knit (fake fur)

A sliver is fed to the needles and bound in by the intermeshing. A pile or fleecy effect is formed on the technical back.

If the fabric is printed, especially with an animal hide pattern, then it is called fake fur.

Applications include fur coats and winter lining (fleece lining) for coats and shoes.

5: Cross-tuck (piqué), face

Cross-tuck (piqué), back

Cross-tuck (piqué)

Piqué-style relief patterning can be made on single or double jersey base structures. The single jersey base is more common because of its lighter weight. The pattern is formed by alternating plain and tuck loops within one course and between one course and another. A complete course of knitted loops can be interspaced between the courses containing knit and tuck loops. Applications include sports and leisure shirts.

6.3.4 Developments of the Rib Structure

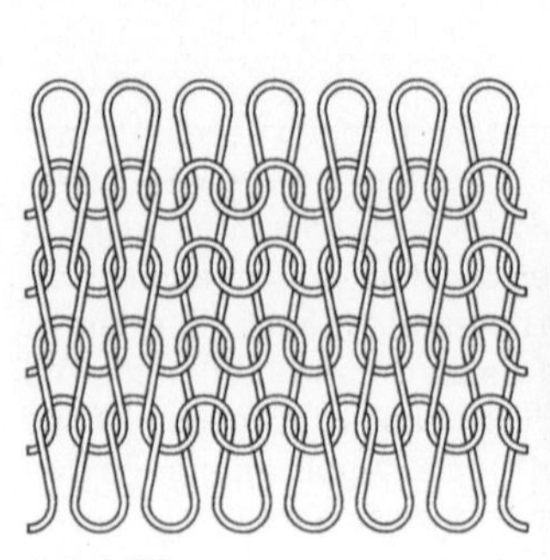

unravelling edge

1: 2x2 Rib

2x2 Rib (broad ribs)

A wide range of rib fabrics can be produced, depending on the set-out of the needles. The most popular is 2x2 rib, which is made by taking every third needle out of action in each needle bed (2:1 needle set-out).

The two sides of the 2x2 rib fabric look the same. If the fabric is stretched in the width, the two rib loops are exposed between the two face loops. It is very elastic in the width direction.

Applications include cuffs and welts, pullovers and dresses.

2: Half milano, face

back

Half Milano (ripple)

In half milano a course of 1x1 rib is followed by a course in which only the back needle bed knits plain. The loops in the front bed are held over and are extended. The extensibility in the width is reduced by the plain course.

If more than one course of plain loops is knitted, either on the front or back needle beds, the result is a ripple fabric. The plain courses are thrown into relief (without special patterning).

These fabrics are used for pullovers and waistcoats.

3: Cardigan

Half-cardigan

Cardigan Stitch

In cardigan stitch, the first course knits tuck loops on the front bed and plain loops on the back. The next course is the opposite. The tuck stitches emphasise the plain loops. Cardigan is heavier and wider than 1x1 rib. In half-cardigan (Royal rib) a course of 1x1 rib is followed by one with plain loops on the front bed and tuck loops on the back. The face side shows prominent wale ribs whilst the back looks like cardigan. The voluminous cardigan and half-cardigan structures are used mainly for thick winter pullovers, scarves, and berets.

4: Double piqué, face

back

Double Piqué

Double piqué is made on rib machines by a selection of knitted loops and floats. The floats greatly reduce the width extensibility. This allows the fabric to be processed like a woven material without losing the comfortable wearing characteristics of a knit. Unlined fabrics have a tendency to bulge.

Also known as **wevenit, rodier,** and **overknit.**

Applications include women's coats, trousers, skirts, costumes.

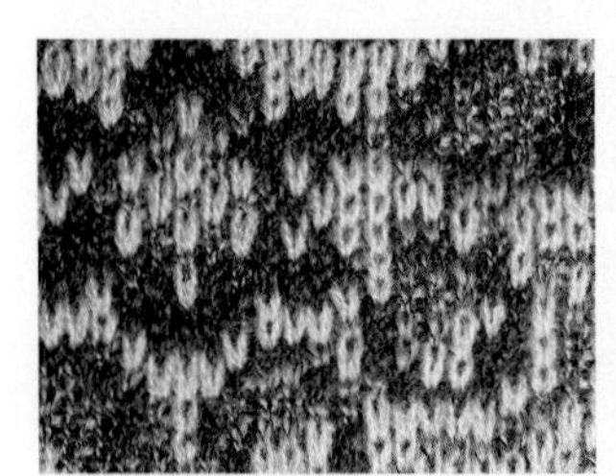

5: Jacquard, face

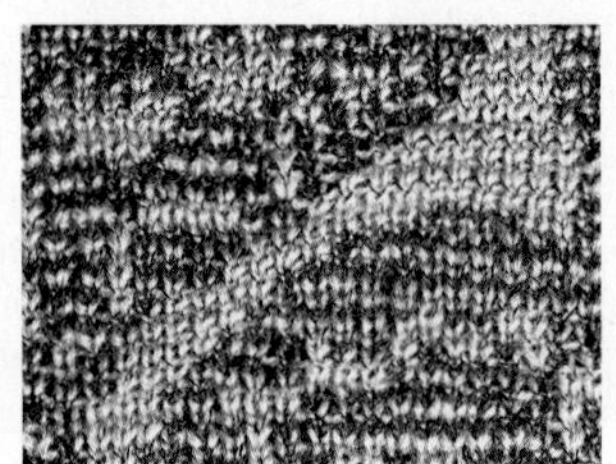

back

Rib Jacquard

In double jersey jacquard machines, the needles in the two needle beds (cylinder and dial) can be selected either to knit or miss. The pattern is created by selecting cylinder needles to knit or miss each coloured yarn in sequence. When the yarn is not knitting on the cylinder needles it is knitted by the dial needles to form the back of the fabric. The number of feeders required to complete one course depends on the number of colours in the design.

These fabrics are used for pullovers, dresses and jackets.

6.3.5 Developments of Purl and Interlock
6.3.6 Spreading, Cutting and Sewing of Knitted Fabrics

Developments of Purl Stitch

1: Figured purl

Purl fabrics are characterised by mixtures of face and back loops in the wale direction. Patterns are realised by controlled selection of double-headed needles to knit either face or back loops at a given point. On each course, the needles are divided over the front and back needle beds, according to the required pattern. A wide variety of patterns can be produced, mainly for women's pullovers and cardigans.

Developments of Interlock Stitch

2: Double faced interlock
Cotton side Polypropylene side

Interlock fabrics are usually very fine and are often printed. Nevertheless the interlock structure is capable of development. An example is the production of double faced interlock for sportswear. In these fabrics, the outer side is predominantly of cotton whereas the inner side is a synthetic fibre such as polypropylene. The cotton absorbs sweat whilst the synthetic fibre stays dry. This avoids the "wet cling" effect during intense physical exertion (*see page 52*).

Spreading, Cutting and Sewing of Knitted Fabrics

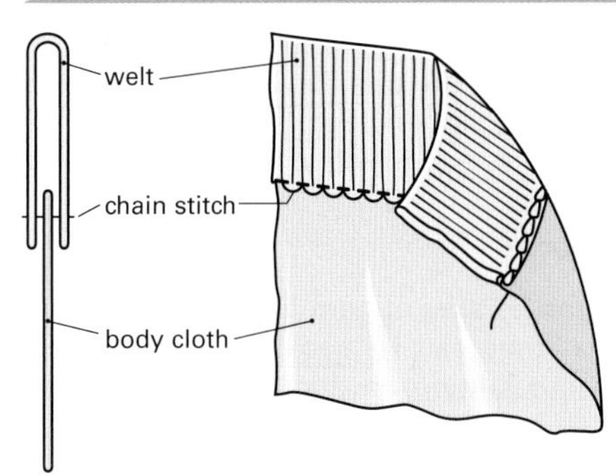

3: Linking a welt

When making weft knitted fabrics into garments, more care has to be taken than with wovens because of the higher extensibility of knits and the danger of stitching damage.

Spreading and Cutting

Whether spreading is done by hand or by machine, the highly extensible fabric has to be kept under minimum tension.

Cutting may be done with circular or band cutters but also die cutting machines are used (*see page 158*).

Sewing and Linking

Weft knits are usually sewn with chainstitch.

Linking or looping is the precise, loop-for-loop joining of two pieces of fabric, on a special linking machine (*see page 165*). First the two fabric pieces are placed in register on the needles of the linking machine and then the machine joins them using chainstitch (*Figure 3*). Linking is a very labour intensive operation but it gives a clean, flat seam. Linking is used to attach collars, cuffs and welts for high quality garments.

Flat seam stitches are used for attaching lace trimmings, rubber tapes, neckbands, waistbands and other ornamentation.

Overedge stitch types are used to make clean and covered joining seams, but some simple neatening operations are also carried out.

4: Damaged stitches

Stitching Damage

During sewing, it is possible to damage the fabrics if the yarn is not able to move out of the path of the sewing needle. Damaged stitches (*Figure 4*) can lead to holes or ladders at the garment seams. There are four main causes of stitching damage:

- inappropriate fabric finishing (most common)
- worn or damaged needle point
- needle too large
- inappropriate needle point

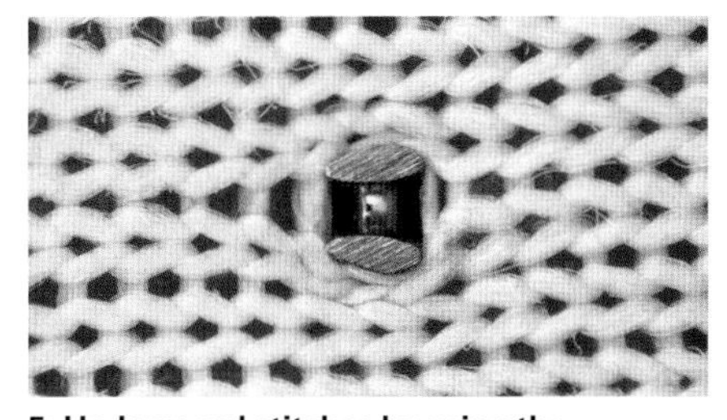

5: Undamaged stitches by using the correct needle

6.3.7 Circular Knits, Flat Knits

Circular Knitted Fabrics

1: Circular knitting machine

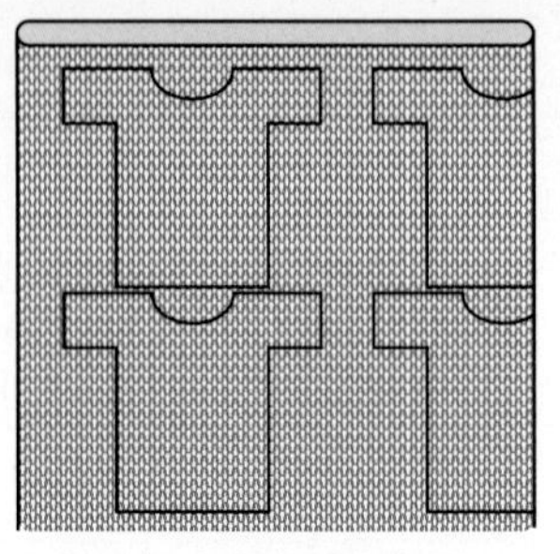
2: Circular knitted fabric

Garments such as T-shirts, sweatshirts, underwear, nightwear, polo shirts and jogging suits are cut from circular knitted fabrics. The fabric is manufactured on **circular machines** (*Figure 1*) as long lengths in the form of a tube (*Figure 2*). The fabric can be maintained in its tubular form throughout processing or, after the preparation and dyeing operations, it can be cut open for final finishing and garment making. Circular knitting is used mainly for highly efficient and economical production of **piece goods** in standard fabric types. Circular knits are almost always finer, lighter fabrics than those made on flat bed machinery.

Flat Knitted Fabrics

3: Flat knitting machine

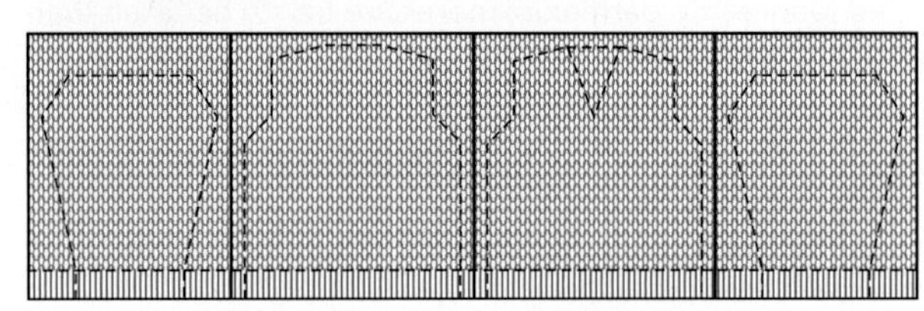

4: Panel knitting

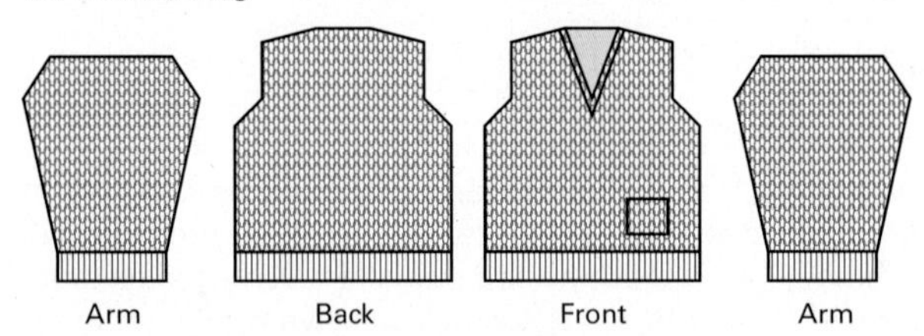

5: Fully fashioned parts

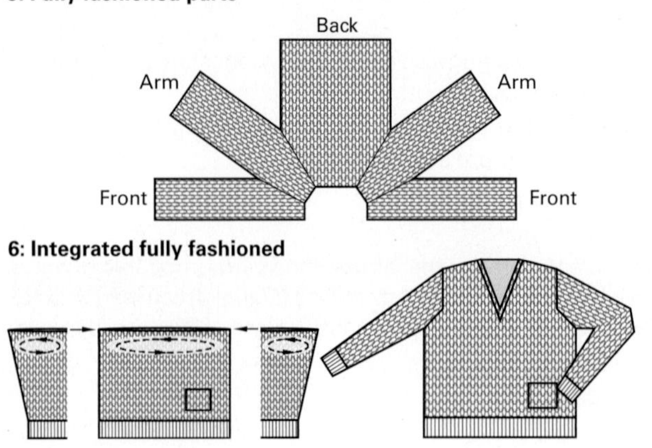

6: Integrated fully fashioned

7: Whole garment knitting

Garments such as knitted jumpers, sweaters, cardigans and dresses are usually made on **flatbed machinery** (*Figure 3*). The manufacture of flat-knitted garments has changed greatly in recent years. This is partly because of the high cost of garment making but also because of radical technical developments in flat knitting machinery. The following development stages can be distinguished.

Panel Knitting (pieces with integral welts)

Garment parts are knitted to the appropriate length and width, including an integral welt for the cuff or waistband (*Figure 4*). The parts are cut to shape and assembled into the garment. Pockets and neckbands are knitted separately and attached by linking.

Fully Fashioned

Fashioning is the knitting of garment parts which are shaped so that they can be sewn directly into the garment, without cutting. In addition to the welts, pockets and the front neckband are knitted integrally (*Figure 5*). After garment assembly, the back neckband is linked in.

Integrated Fully Fashioned

In this case all of the garment parts are knitted together as a single piece. Welts, pockets and collars are all included. Very little sewing is required to assemble the final garment (*Figure 6*).

Whole Garment Knitting

The complete, fully fashioned garment is made as a complex tube directly on the knitting machine (*Figure 7*). In the first stage, the body of the garment is knitted either as a fully fashioned tube or as front and back parts joined at the shoulders. In the second stage, the fully fashioned arm parts are attached either by sewing or by linking and the side seams are closed if necessary. All pockets welts and neckbands are integrated and all of the necessary closings, i.e. side seams, shoulders and arms, are made by the knitting machine. There are no visible seams.

6.3.8 Warp Knitted Fabrics (1)

Production and Terminology

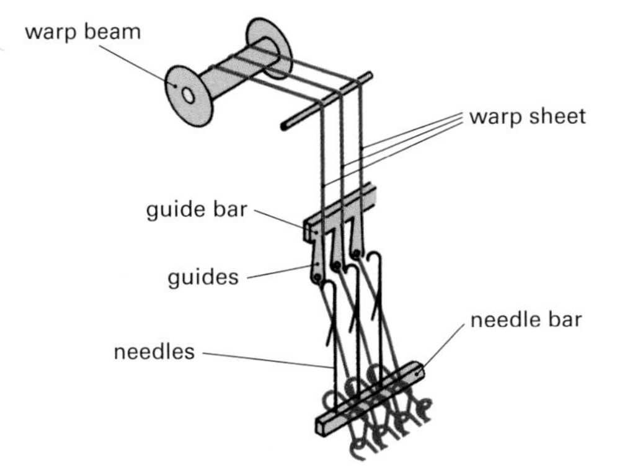

1: Principle of warp knitting

Warp knitted fabrics are made with at least one sheet of warp yarns. Usually there are at least two warps, each on its own beam.

Each individual warp yarn is drawn through a guide, which is mounted on a guide bar. Movements of the guide bar (lapping) cause the thread to be lapped around the needle, which may be a bearded, latch, or compound needle. After the yarns are lapped, the needle bar is moved so as to cause loops to be formed simultaneously at all needles, resulting in a whole knitted course.

Finally, the guide bar is displaced sideways (shogged) by one or more needles before the next cycle produces another course. The shogging of the guide bar determines the structure of the fabric.

Open lap: the feet of the loop do not cross.

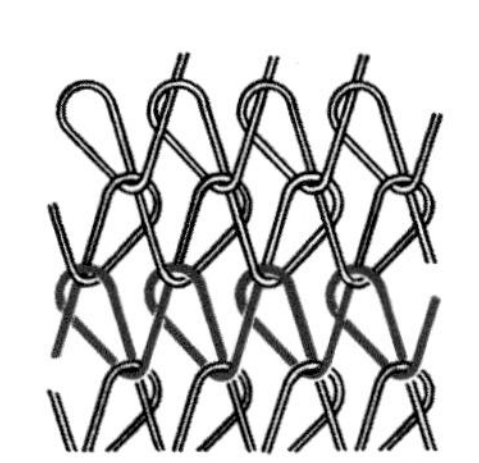

Course: a row of loops across the fabric width.

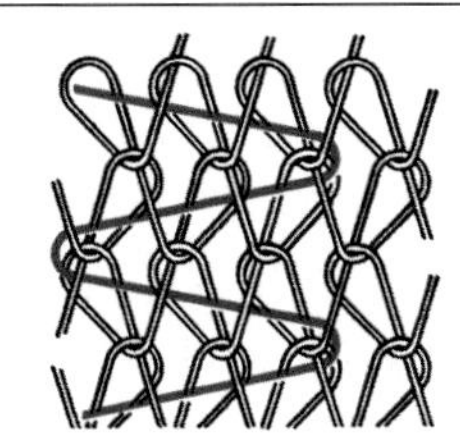

Inlay: a yarn laid between the loops and the underlaps across the width.

Closed lap: the feet of the loop are crossed.

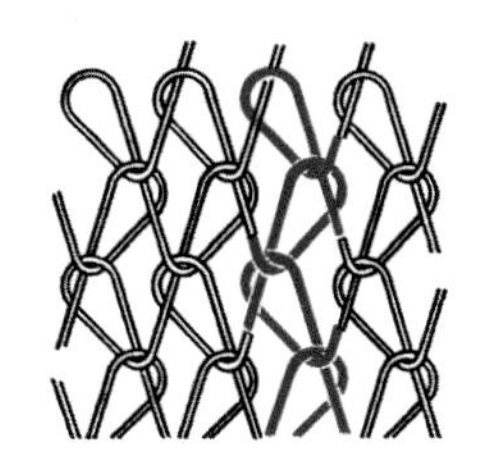

Wale: a column of loops in the length direction.

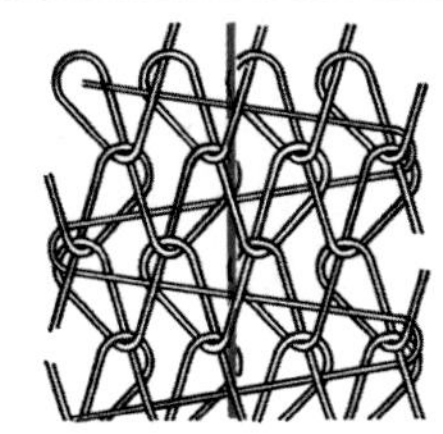

Vertical inlay: a yarn laid between the loops and the underlaps in the length direction.

Selected Single Guide Bar Structures

Pillar (chain) stitch	Plain (tricot) stitch	2x1 Plain	Atlas
Chains of loops in unconnected wales are produced. They must be connected together by yarns supplied from a second guide bar.	Each yarn works in a zig-zag fashion lapping between two neighbouring wales. All laps are closed.	This stitch is the same as tricot except that each yarn laps over to the next but one wale.	The guide bar laps progressively in the same direction for at least two courses, followed by an identical lapping sequence in the opposite direction. Laps at the turning points are closed; intermediate laps are open.

6.3.8 Warp Knitted Fabrics (2)
6.3.9 Stitch-bonded Fabrics

Multiple Guide Bar Fabrics

For most warp knitted fabrics, the basic lapping structures are used in combination. This means that more than one warp sheet and guide bar must be used.

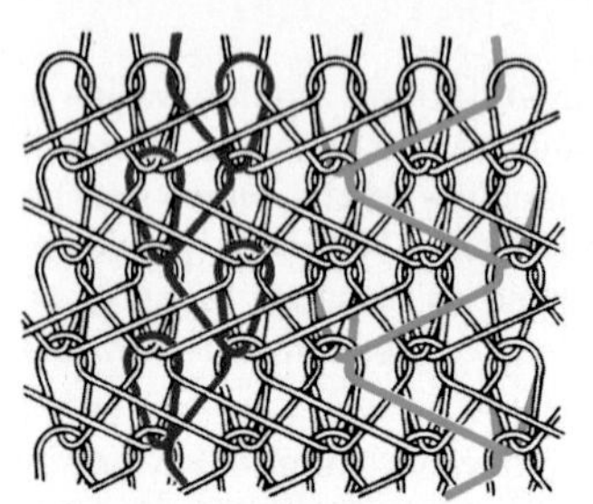
1: Locknit, schematic

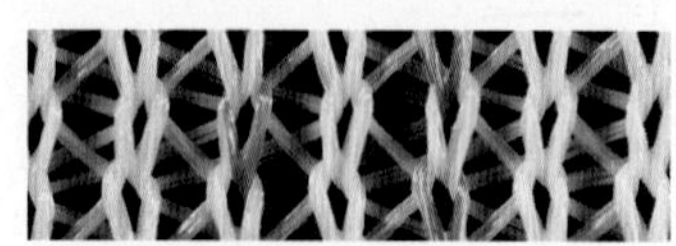
2: Locknit, face

3: Locknit, back

4: Warp knitted terry

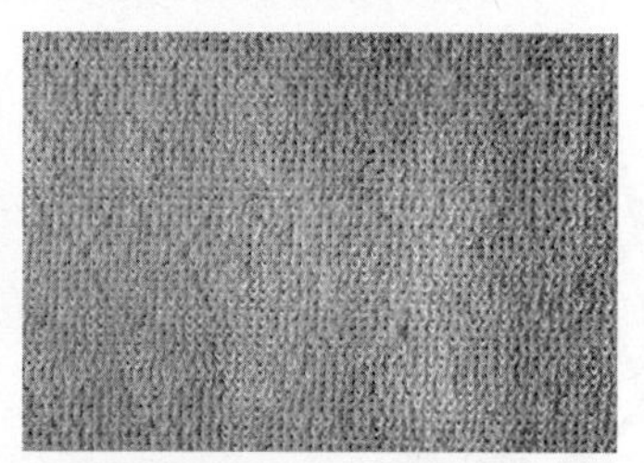
5: Warp knitted plush, velour

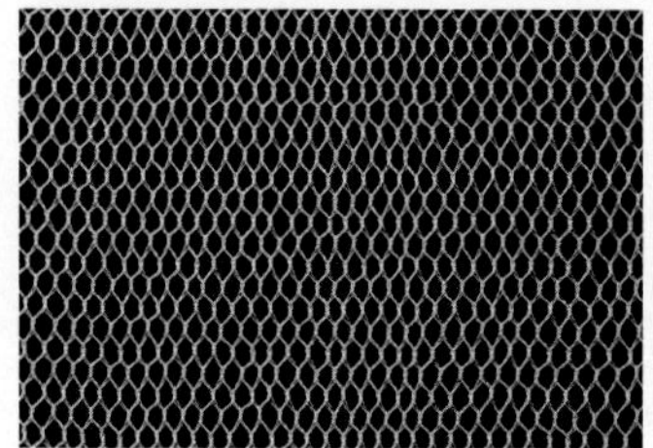
6: Raschel net

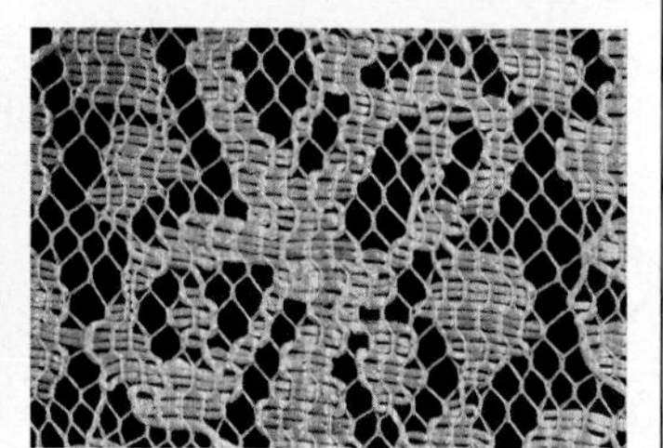
7: Raschel lace

Locknit (*Figures 1, 2, 3*)

Locknit (charmeuse) is a combination of tricot and 2x1 plain stitches. On one side the fabric displays distinct wales of small face loops; the other side shows the zig-zag formation of the underlaps. It is made from filament yarns which give the characteristic lustre. Applications: linings, interlinings, lingerie.

Warp Knitted Terry (*Figure 4*)

This is made with an extra warp sheet of pile yarns which are caused to form loops, bound into a ground fabric. Applications include furnishings and bed sheets

Warp Knitted Plush, Velour (*Figure 5*)

In this case, the pile loops are cut to give a fleecy or velvet-like surface. Applications include beach, leisure and sportswear, ladies outerwear.

Raschel Net (*Figure 6*)

Nowadays, net fabric is almost always made on raschel machines. It is a combination of pillar and tricot stitches. Raschel net is most popular in bridal wear.

Raschel Lace (*Figure 7*)

Raschel lace fabrics are often made on a base of net fabric with a pattern formed from inlay yarns. They are used for foundation and lingerie, bridal and formal wear, and as trimmings

Stitch-bonded Fabrics

In these fabrics a **fibre batt** or a series of **laid yarns** is bonded together by sewing or stitching along the length direction. The stitching resembles the formation of loops on a warp knitting machine using chain stitch or plain tricot stitch. The great advantage of stitch-bonded fabrics is that they can be manufactured at a high production rate with low capital investment. Applications are mainly fleecy filling materials (*Figure 9*), knit-like materials with stitched yarns (*Figure 10*) low-cost furnishings (*Figure 11*) and cleaning cloths.

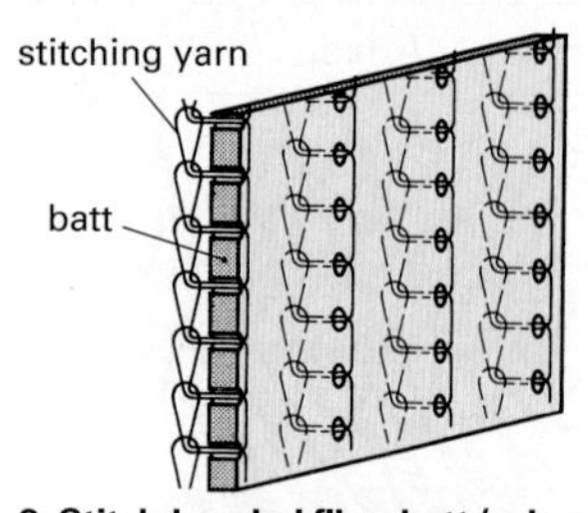

8: Stitch-bonded fibre batt (schematic)

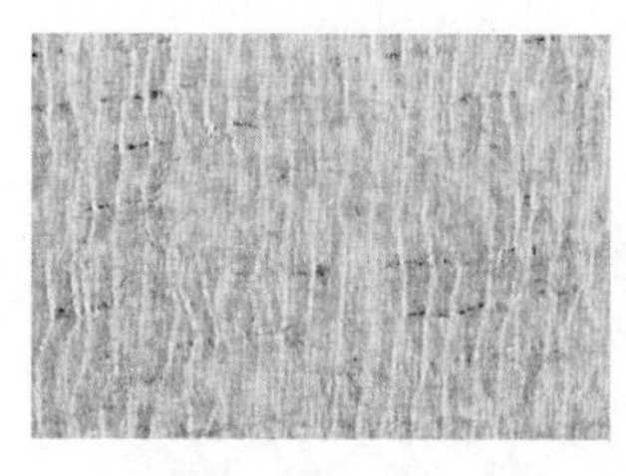
9: Stitch-bonded fibre batt

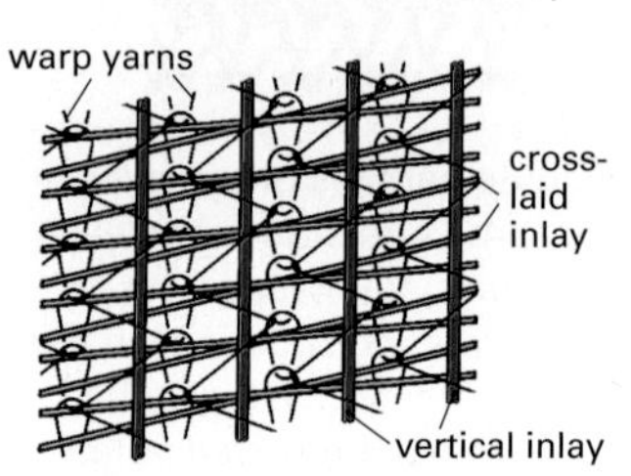

10: Stitch-bonded yarns (schematic)

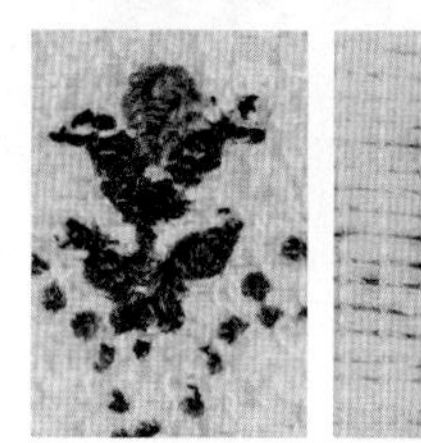
11: Stitch bonding with effect yarns

Stitch-bonded Batts (*Figure 8, 9*)

Stitch-bonded batts (Arachne, Maliwatt) are warm and voluminous. They can be used as filling materials for winter clothing

Stitch-bonded Yarns (*Figure 10*)

Stitch bonded yarns (Malimo) can be made with only cross-laid inlay yarns, or both cross-laid and vertical inlays. The inlay yarns are laid under tension side-by-side; there is no interlacing or intermeshing. It is the stitching that binds the structure together.

Stitch Bonding of Effect Yarns (*Figure 11*)

Length-wise effect yarns can be stitched onto one side of a carrier material to give furnishing-type fabrics, including loop-pile effects.

6.4.1 Transparent and Open-work Fabrics

Transparency and openwork effects can be achieved by yarn and fabric construction, by finishing processes, or by combinations of these. Applications are in dresses and blouses, lingerie, squares, drapes, tablecloths and napkins.

Fine, Lightweight Fabrics

Fine yarns woven with low thread densities yield semi-transparent fabrics, such as **chiffon** (*see page 120*) and **mull** (*see page 130*). To improve the strength and abrasion resistance at low thread density, a higher twist or folded yarns can be used, e.g. **Voile** (*see page 136*). Transparency can also be achieved using the parchmentising process, e.g. **batiste glacé** (*see page 126*) and **organdy** (*see page 131*)

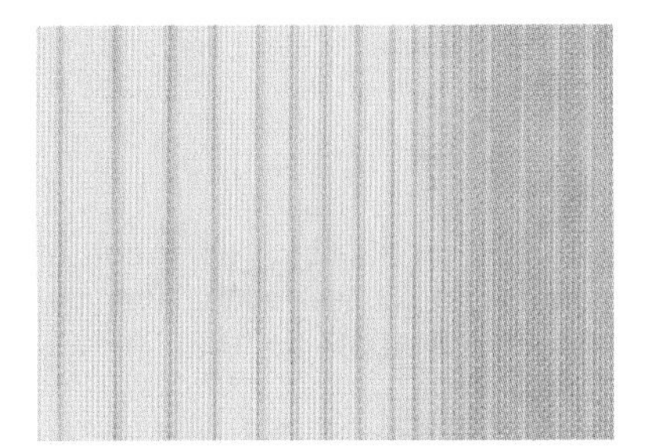

1: Voile rayé ombré

Varying Thread Density

Lengthways stripes with varying transparency can be introduced by varying the density of the warp threads in a regular pattern across the width of the fabric to yield ombré and degradé effects e.g. **shadow stripe, voile rayé ombré** (*Figure 1*) and **georgette rayé dégradé** (*see page 116*).

2: Satin-batiste with leno effect

Varying Weave Construction

By changing the weave, from a dense to a relatively open construction, a semi-transparent effect can be obtained, especially at the changeover points. Often a striped or chequered pattern will be produced, e.g. **satin-batiste carré** (*Figure 2*), **satin stripe chiffon** (*see page 83*).

Openwork Fabrics

In openwork fabrics, the weave or knit structure is such as to produce holes, often in a striped arrangement. Openwork includes e.g. **ajour** (*see page 118*) leno and mock leno. In knits, the effect is produced by including multiple tuck stitches (*Figure 3*).

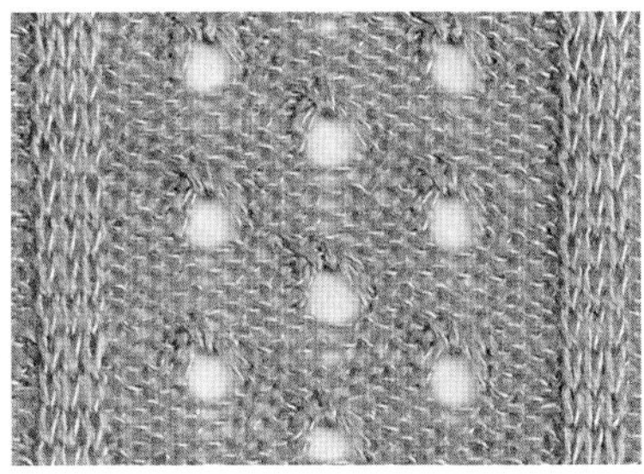

3: Open-work knit

Mock Leno

Groups of closely associated warp and weft yarns are woven in plain or basket weave so that holes appear between the groups. Examples are **aida** and **natté** (*see page 130*) although these terms are also applied to true leno fabrics, especially in continental Europe.

Gauze, Leno

In gauze and leno weaving (*Figures 4 and 5*) certain of the warp threads (crossing ends) are passed from side to side of one or more neighbouring warp threads (standard ends) and are bound into these positions by the weft. Open areas are created either all over the fabric or in a pattern. In spite of their low yarn density, the fabrics have good abrasion resistance.

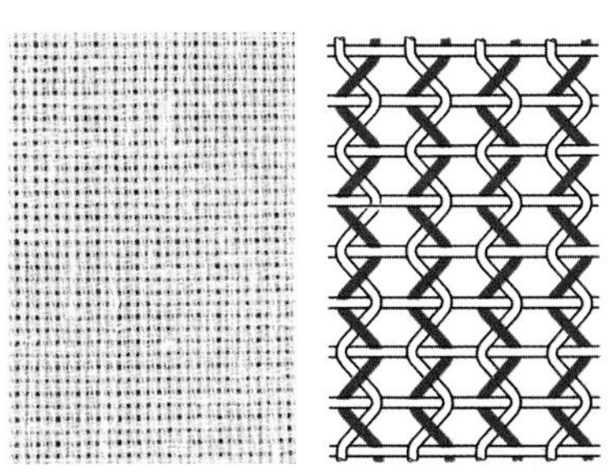

4: Gauze or Leno **5: Leno, schematic**

Burn-out (dévoré) and Burn-out Velvet

Fabrics made from at least two different fibres, having differing solubility, or chemical resistance characteristics can be used for producing burn-out effects.

Burn-out fabrics can be produced with cotton/polyester or rayon/polyester fabrics by printing with strong acid to selectively dissolve away the cellulosic fibre (*see page 118*).

Burn-out velvet is made by selectively dissolving the velvet pile, e.g. a velvet with a silk ground cloth and a viscose pile can be selectively burnt out with an acid paste (*see page 118*).

Lancé, Clip Spot, Découpé

Extra warp or extra weft yarns can be selectively bound into a transparent ground fabric to form small figured designs. The extra yarn may float on the back or the face of the fabrics, where it is not interlacing, and these long floats can be cut away (*Figure 6*).

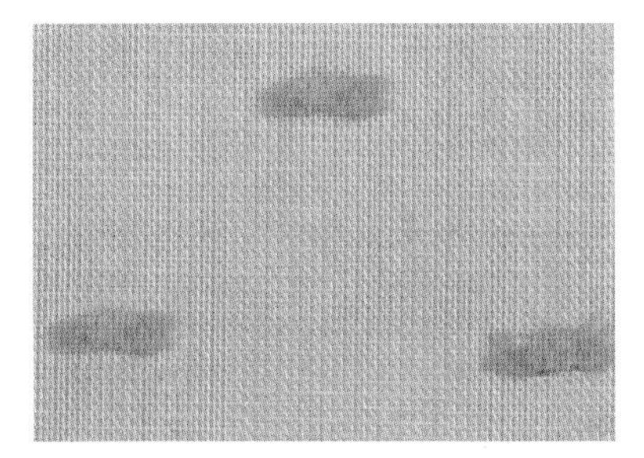

6: Voile découpé (clip-spot)

6.4.2 Laces and Nets

Lace has been used for a long time as a decorative element in clothing. Hand-made lace materials, developed rapidly in the 15th and 16th centuries AD but, nowadays, most laces are made by machines. Traditionally, nets were made on the bobbinet machine but today the raschel warp knitting machine predominates. The raschel machine can imitate lace, crochet and macramé.

Lace trimmings are used in blouses, dresses, lingerie, bed clothes, napkins, pillow covers, handkerchiefs etc. Lace and net fabrics are made up into blouses, dresses, wedding and formal wear, bodices, tablecloths, curtains, hatbands etc.

1: Embroidery lace (burn-out, wash-away)

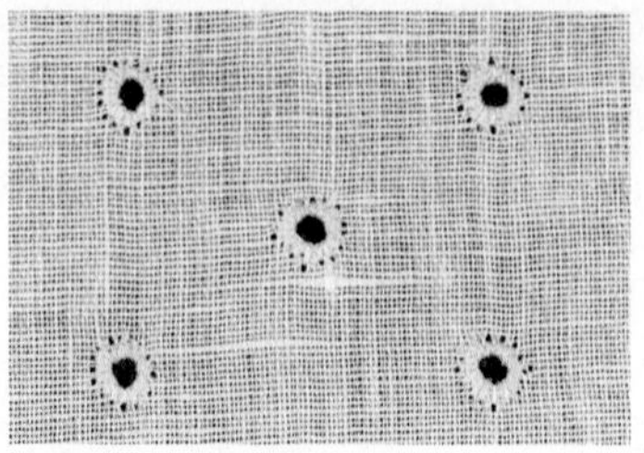

2: Broderie anglaise

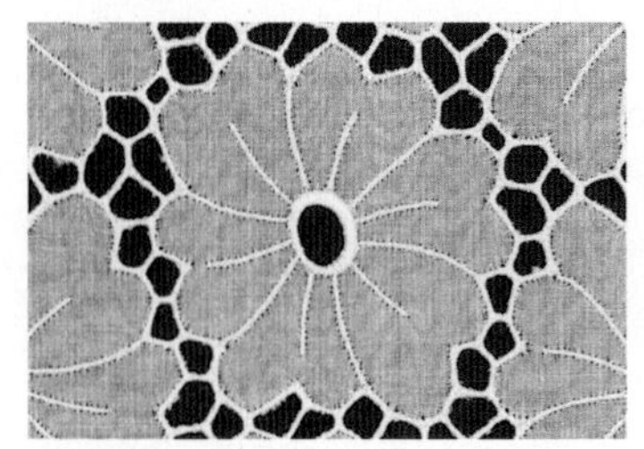

3: Madeira lace

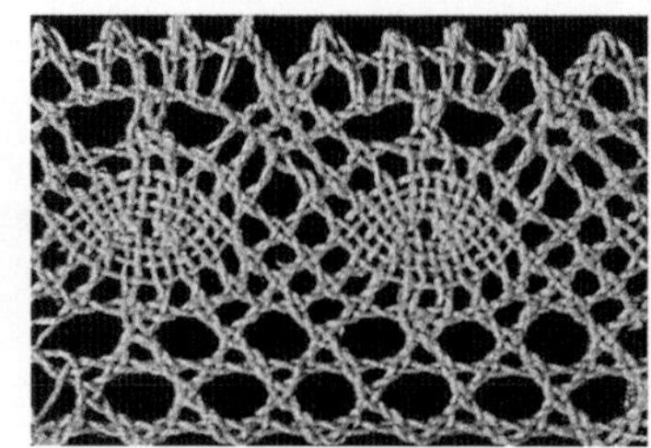

4: Bobbin lace

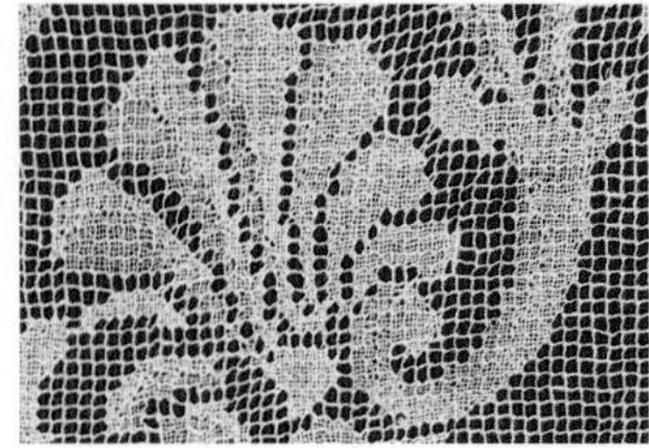

5: Filet lace

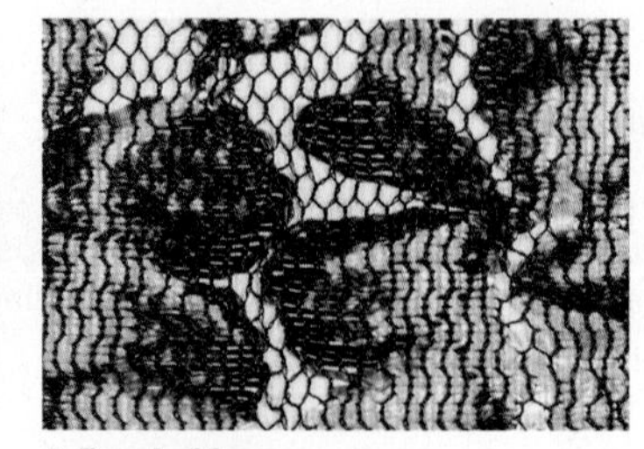

6: Raschel lace

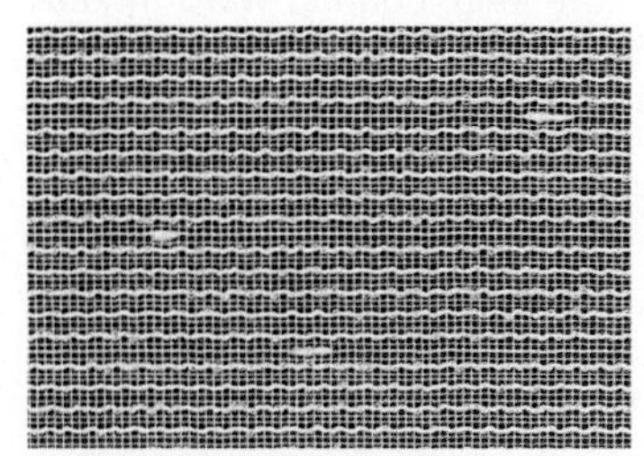

7: Marquisette (leno fabric)

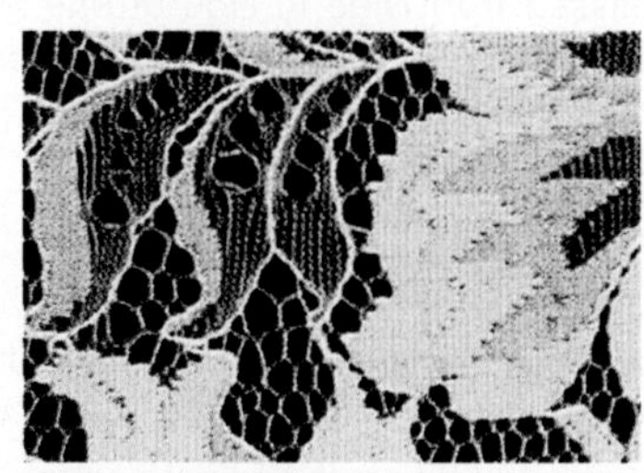

8: Raschel lace, embroidered lace

9: Florentine lace (embroidered net)

10: Plain net (bobbinet) with knops

Embroidery Lace

This is made by hand or machine application of embroidered patterns to a base fabric. After the pattern has been embroidered, the base fabric is wholly or partly removed.

For **Wash-away** lace, the embroidery is made on paper or a soluble base, which is later washed away. The same effect is obtained as with **burn-out** lace (*Figure 1*).

Cutwork lace is where a pattern is cut in the base cloth, to provide a framework for embroidery, or the base cloth is first embroidered and the material in-between is cut away.

With **broderie anglaise** (*Figure 2*), holes are stamped out and their edges are embroidered.

Madeira lace (*Figure 3*) is a type of broderie anglaise where the pattern is made from larger cut-outs.

Bobbin Lace

Bobbin lace (*Figure 4*) is a kind of plaited or braided structure produced on the bobbin lace machine. Hand-made bobbin lace is made using from 4 to 400 bobbin yarns. The yarns are worked into a pattern by twisting and crossing the threads. The pattern is outlined by pins stuck in a pillow. Also known as **pillow lace.**

Filet lace (*Figure 5*) is made on a base of a square, knotted net (filet). The pattern is formed by filling in the chosen squares. Also known as **darned lace.**

Raschel Net and Lace

These are made on a warp knitting machine with latch needles. Raschel net (*see page 98*) is made with a combination of chain stitch and tricot. **Raschel lace** (*Figure 6*) is developed on a net background. Heavy curtain nets, e.g. **Marquisette** (*Figure 7*) are similar to leno fabrics (*cf. page 99*).

Heavily worked Raschel laces, with an appearance like embroidery, showing more-or-less high relief and gimp-yarn emphasis are imitating **Embroidered lace** (*Figure 8*). Florentine lace (*Figure 9*) is an embroidered hexagonal net.

Plain Net (bobbinet)

On the plain net or bobbinet machine a series of pairs of thread carriers (bobbins) swing backwards and forwards through the warp sheet whilst progressing from one side of the machine to the other, and back again. The bobbin yarns are thus looped around the warp yarns in a spiral formation leaving a regular series of holes in the fabric, in a honeycomb effect (*Figure 10*). The machines can be provided with jacquard mechanisms for figuring, and pattern threads can be provided in the warp.

6.5.1 Properties and Applications of Textile Fabrics

Type	Production	Basic Characteristics	Applications
	Woven Two sets of yarns, warp and weft (length and width), interlaced at right angles.	Firm, stable, dense, low extensibility and elasticity, cut edges will fray.	Jackets and coats, suits, costumes, dresses, shirts and blouses, linings and interlinings, bed clothes, table cloths, household textiles, drapes and coverings.
	Weft Knits At least one yarn running cross-wise and forming rows of loops (courses). The loops on each row are intermeshed with loops on the previous row.	Soft, supple, voluminous, very extensible and elastic, crease resistant, may ladder.	Underwear, nightwear, babywear, socks and stockings, pullovers, cardigans, caps and scarves, sports and leisure wear.
	Warp Knits At least one warp sheet is formed into length-wise columns of loops, with columns connected laterally in a zigzag fashion.	Firm, stable, smooth, moderate extensibility and elasticity, crease resistant, will not ladder.	Lingerie, lace, net, trimmings, elastic linings and interlinings, swimwear, sportswear, foundation garments, curtains, bed clothes, technical textiles.
	Braids Zigzag, diagonal interlacing of at least three sets of warp yarns.	Extensible, supple, formable, cut edges fray strongly.	Trimmings (braids, cords) ribbons, laces, hats.
	Wool Felt A random assembly of wool or other animal fibres closely interlocked as a result of the felting action of heat, moisture, and mechanical working.	Stable, formable by heat plus moisture, good insulator, hygroscopic, cut edge will not fray.	Hats, collar backs, decoration, slippers, insulation material.
	Bonded-fibre A random or more or less oriented batt of fibres entangled by needling and/or bonded by adhesives, solvent fusing or thermal fusing.	Moderately stable, light weight, porous, cut edges will not fray.	Interlinings, disposables (table cloths, serviettes, briefs, wipes), cleaning cloths.

[1] Only basic aspects are compared because, for any given fabric type, the properties are strongly dependent on the fibre type, the structure, the density, and finishing.

7.1.1 Definition and Objectives
7.1.2 Finishing Processes: Overview

Dyeing and finishing includes all processes that are intended to upgrade the appearance or the end-use properties of a raw material.

- The general character of the fabric can be enhanced by coloration, pressing, embossing, etc.
- The performance in garment-making can be improved, e.g. sewability, seam stability and seam strength.
- The handle and drape can be modified and the easy-care performance can be improved.
- The wearing comfort can be improved by providing enhanced extensibility and moisture management (wicking away of perspiration, water repellency of outerwear).
- The aftercare characteristics can be improved by stain-release and anti-felting finishes.
- Protection can be provided against insects or sunburn.

Textile Dyeing and Finishing

Preparation & Ancillary Processes	Coloration			
	Dyeing	**Printing**		
		Techniques	**Styles**	
Singeing, Washing, Mercerizing, Bleaching, Optical brightening, Carbonising, Dye fixation, De-watering, Drying	Fibre Yarn Fabric Garment	Block, Roller Screen Digital Transfer	Direct Discharge Resist Pigment	Lacquer Flock Warp print Burn-out

Finishing				Coating & Laminating
Mechanical	**Thermo-mechanical**	**Chemical**		
Raising Ratiné Emerising Shearing	Felting Milling Crabbing Decating Shrinking Pressing Calendering Embossing Heat-setting	Antistatic Anti-pilling Bacteriostatic Anti-felting Flame-resistant Stain-release Functional finishing Handle modification	Easy-care Hydrophilic Hydrophobic Moth-proofing Anti-slipping Parchmentising Insect-repellent "Wellness"	Coating Bonding Laminating Combining

Finishing is always a combination of various **chemical or mechanical processing** stages. Examples are:

- **Chemical Processes:** Bleaching, Dyeing, Carbonising, Mercerizing, Stain-release, Anti-felting, Easy-care, Parchmentising.
- **Mechanical Processes:** Raising, Emerising, Ratiné, Shearing, Calendering, Drying.
- **Combinations:** Felting, Milling, Embossing and Chintzing (cotton).

Many processes, e.g. raising, may be independent of the type of raw material but, more often, processes are tailored for the particular chemical constitution and surface characteristics of particular fibre types.

Finishing at Different Stages in Textile Production

Finishing is most efficiently carried out on **piece goods.** However, there are times when a finishing process must be performed at some other stage. For example:

- **Stock (loose fibre) dyeing,** e.g. for production of mixture yarns
- **Yarn dyeing,** e.g. for production of colour-woven fabrics, and for sewing threads.
- **Garment processing,** e.g. pre-shrunk or faded jeans, printed t-shirts.

Environmental Protection

The question of **environmental conservation** has a large impact on the finishing sector (*see page 56*). Liquors used for coloration and finishing cannot be discharged to waste without some purification. The same is true of discharge gasses, such as solvent vapours. Energy is recovered and re-used wherever possible.

Regulations governing discharge of waste liquids and gasses, as well as health and safety measures for the protection of factory workers are currently the responsibility of local, state, and national government. There are no universal, world-wide regulations.

7.2.1 Singeing, Desizing, Scouring, Washing, Mercerizing

Preparation means getting the fabric ready for dyeing, printing, or finishing. Any processing aids which may have been applied during spinning, weaving, or knitting must be removed. These might be spinning oils, waxes, sizes, etc. Any natural or adventitious contaminants must also be removed so that the fabric has the required purity for the following processes. Thorough preparation is a prerequisite for good results in dyeing and finishing.

After dyeing, printing, or other preparatory processes, the fabric may need to undergo various other treatments in order to make it suitable for the final finishing stages.

Following are the most important processes.

Singeing

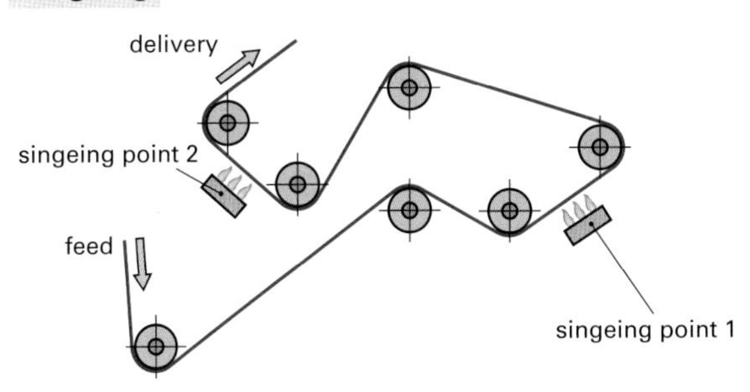

1: Gas singeing, schematic

Singeing is used mainly, but not exclusively for cotton woven fabrics. Projecting fibre ends are burned away using one or more banks of gas flames or other heat sources. The fabric surface is made smoother and the weave is revealed more clearly. Development of hairiness and pilling during processing is reduced. Reduction of pilling can be especially important for staple fibre polyester blend fabrics (*see page 112*).

In a gas singer (*Figure 1*) the gas jet housings are water-cooled and, in the event of a machine stoppage, the flames are rapidly swung away from the fabric surface to prevent damage to it.

For many fabrics, both sides of the fabric are singed but for some only the face is treated.

Scouring, Washing

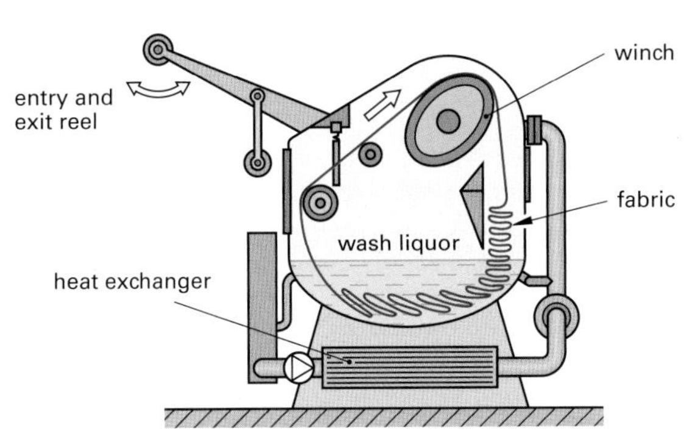

2: Rope washing machine

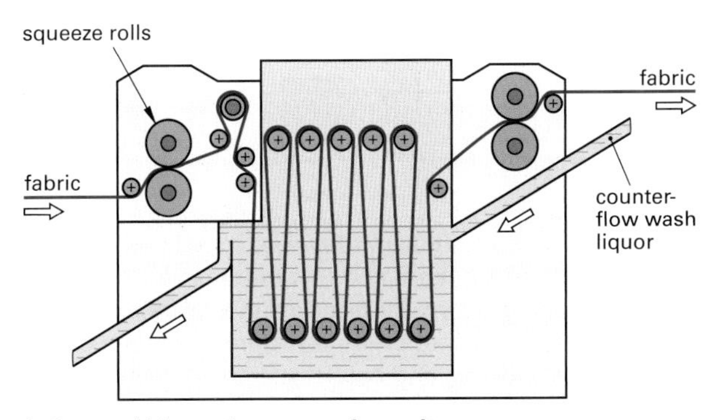

3: Open-width continuous washer unit

Desizing is the removal of sizes and other substances applied as weaving aids (*see page 77*), using enzymes, oxidising agents or hot washing, depending on the type of size.

Scouring is the removal of natural or adventitious impurities, or processing aids (waxes, lubricants, marker dyes) applied during yarn and fabric formation. Cotton requires high temperature, alkaline detergent liquors. Man-made fibres may need only a mild detergent scour. The natural wool grease, if still present, is removed by a gentle washing in mild alkaline detergent. Silk is de-gummed in a hot, mildly alkaline detergent.

Washing treatments are used at all stages in preparation, dyeing and finishing for the removal of impurities, oils, sizes, etc. In addition, any unfixed dyestuff, or printing auxiliaries, or other chemicals must be washed out. Various types of washing machine are available, depending on the type of material to be washed and the process technology in place (*Figures 2 and 3*). Total water and energy consumption is minimised by the use of counter-flow and recycling systems.

Modern factories will normally carry out all of the wet processing, including preparation, bleaching and dyeing either in a single, batch processing machine (e.g. a jet dyer, *see page 106*), or a single long line of separate machines that process the fabric continuously, or a combination, e.g. continuous scouring and bleaching followed by separate dyeing.

Knitted fabrics and delicate wovens will normally undergo low-tension batch processing, whereas continuous, high-speed processing is used for robust woven fabrics.

Mercerizing

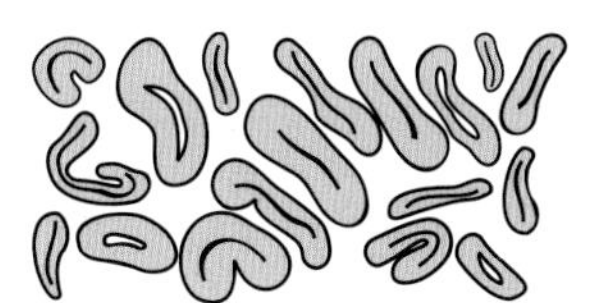

4: Cotton fibre sections, raw

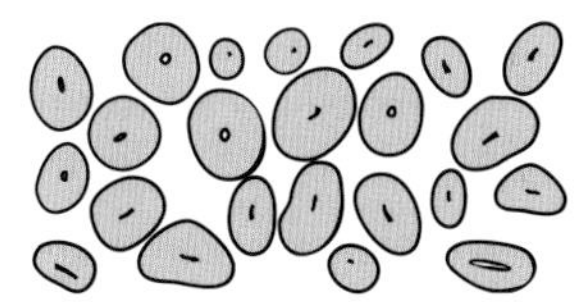

5: Cotton fibre sections, mercerized

Mercerizing is the treatment of cotton yarn or fabric, under tension, in a concentrated solution of caustic soda. Mercerizing causes the fibre cross section to become swollen and more rounded. Yarns and fabrics are made stronger, more lustrous, and capable of being dyed or printed to a much deeper shade for a given amount of dyestuff.

7.2.2 Bleaching, Optical Brightening, Carbonising, Heat Setting, Drying, Fixation

Bleaching and Optical Brightening

If a pure white is required in the finished textile, or if it is to be dyed to a clear pastel shade, then bleaching will undoubtedly be necessary. In natural fibres the natural colouring is destroyed; in man-made fibres the whiteness can be enhanced.

Cotton fabrics are almost always bleached. The exception is when a good white fibre is to be dyed to a deep shade with a dark colour. Bleaching is an oxidation process and hydrogen peroxide is by far the most common bleaching agent. Sodium hypochlorite (once very common) and sodium chlorite are also used. Oxidation converts the naturally coloured substances into colourless, water-soluble compounds, which can then be rinsed away. **Wool** is only very lightly bleached; a pure white is never obtained. **Silk** is whitened during the degumming process. **Linen** has to be severely bleached, because of the high concentration of coloured pectins and, therefore, can suffer a loss in weight of up to 40%. **Man-made fibres** usually need only a gentle bleach.

Optical brightening is the treatment of fibres with a chemical that can absorb UV radiation and re-emit the energy at the blue end of the visible spectrum. The extra blue light counteracts any residual yellowness in the fibres. The effect is usually greater on natural fibres.

Carbonising

Carbonising is the destruction of cellulosic impurities in wool by treatment with sulphuric acid. After the acid treatment, the degraded cellulose can be blown out with compressed air. Cellulosic impurities in virgin wool are vegetable matter such as burrs, hay and straw (*see page 16*). In recovered wool, they may be cellulosic fibres.

Heat Setting

Heat setting is one of the most important processes for synthetic fibres. During all of the processes from fibre manufacture through to dyed fabric, the material has been subjected to various tensions which have resulted in stresses being stored within the fibres. If these stresses are not relieved, they will result in an irregular fabric appearance and dimensional instability. With synthetic fibres, especially polyester, they can be relieved only by heat treatment, followed by controlled cooling at the required fabric dimensions, usually on the stenter frame.

Dewatering and Drying

Evaporation of water using heat is very expensive. Therefore, before any drying process an attempt will be made to reduce the fabric's water content to a minimum by mechanical means. These include centrifuging, suction, and squeezing. Drying machinery varies, depending on the fabric type and the processing stage. For woven fabrics, and for open-width knits, the most common final drying machine is the stenter, or tenter frame (*Figure 1*). For tubular knits, a variety of machinery is available but the modern trend is to use the so-called relax dryers, in which the fabric is transported between two endless mesh belts whilst hot air is blown from above and below. In either case, the fabric will first be squeezed, to remove excess water, and then it will be stretched by a pre-determined amount in width. On the stenter frame, the fabric is gripped at the edges by pins or clips mounted on two endless chains. On the relax dryer the flat fabric tube will pass around an expander device which stretches it from the inside. The hot exhaust air is used to pre-heat fresh air entering the machine, to recover some of the energy.

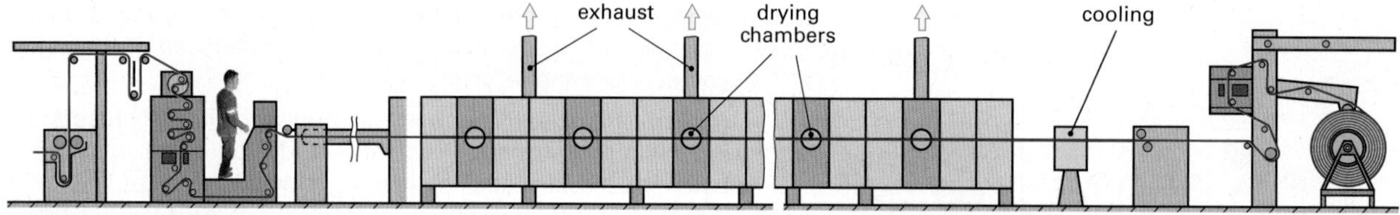

1: Stenter drying frame

Fixation

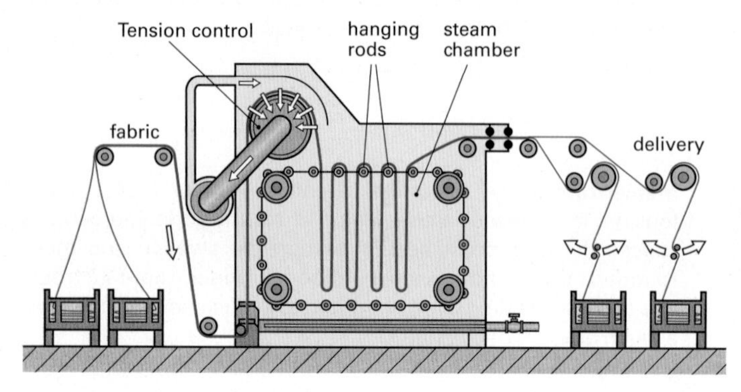

2: Festoon (loop) steamer

The dyed or printed colour may need to be **fixed** (durably bound) within the fibre and this often is accomplished with the aid of steam, for example in a festoon steamer (*Figure 2*). Condensation of steam onto the fabric provides rapid heating and accelerates the diffusion of the dyestuff into the fibres. Cotton, viscose, silk, wool and nylon fabrics will be fixed using saturated steam[1] at about 102 °C. Disperse dyes on polyester can be fixed with dry steam[2] at about 180 to 200 °C in the festoon steamer, or on the stenter frame with dry air, at the same time as heat setting.

Pigment/binder systems are fixed by curing the polymer binder in dry air at about 150 °C.

[1] saturated steam: water vapour, usually at about 100 °C, which is in equilibrium with liquid water.
[2] dry steam: water vapour, usually at more than 100 °C, where no liquid water is present.

7.3.1 Dyeing: Fundamentals

The desire to colour textiles is as old as spinning and weaving. **Natural colouring materials** have been used for thousands of years: **mineral pigments** such as yellow and red ochre, cinnabar; **vegetable dyes** such as indigo, litmus, logwood, madder and saffron; **animal dyes** such as cochineal and Tyrian purple. **Synthetic dyes** were first produced in the 19th century and have now almost completely replaced the natural colours.

The basic requirements of a dyeing process are:

- Uniformity of coloration
- Optimal depth and purity of shade
- Minimal fibre degradation
- Conservation of resources
- Economy
- Health and safety

In addition to the dyestuff, a **dyebath** will contain auxiliary chemicals, such as solvents, dispersants, emulsifiers, wetting agents, levelling agents, accelerants, salts, acids or alkalis. Additional chemicals may be required for after-washing and after-treatments.

- With man-made fibres, **dope-dyeing** can be used, where a pigment is included in the spinning dope.
- **Stock dyeing** is when the raw fibres are prepared and dyed before spinning. This is used for the preparation of mixture or melange yarns.
- **Yarn dyeing** can be carried out either on cross-wound spools, or in hank form, or as continuous ropes, or as a warp sheet (in the sizing machine).
- **Piece dyeing** is the most common process. This is the most economical method of colouring woven and knitted fabrics, since it enables just-in-time processing and minimises warehousing costs.
- **Garment dyeing** allows the most rapid reaction to market trends for particular product types, and can permit certain special effects to be achieved.

Dyestuff Classes

With the exception of pigment/binder systems the type of dyestuff has to be chosen to suit the fibre substrate, because the formation of a physical or chemical bond between dye and fibre depends on the chemical and physical structures of both dye and fibre. A broad spectrum of colours is available in countless shades and a wide range of fastness for the different fibre types and blends. Dyestuffs are classified according to the way that they interact with the fibre. Three of the most important classes are given below.

Dyestuff Class/ Applications	Dye-Fibre interaction	Schematic
Reactive Dyes Cellulosic fibres particularly but also wool & silk	The dyestuff molecules form chemical bonds at or near the surfaces of the fibre microfibrils or micro crystals (*see pages 10 and 25*).	micro-fibril → reaction
Vat Dyes Cellulosic fibres; mainly for heavy-weight woven fabrics	The insoluble dyestuff is made soluble in a reducing vat[1] so that it can diffuse into the fibre. After diffusion is complete, it is then re-oxidised into its insoluble form.	fibre → reduction → oxidation
Disperse Dyes Polyester mainly	Water insoluble pigments which can diffuse into the fibre at high temperature (over 100 °C). They are dispersed in water and dyeing is carried out in a pressure vessel, to obtain the required temperature.	fibre → dyeing temperature over100° C

[1] vat: dyeing vessel, dyebath

Colour Fastness

Colour fastness means the resistance of the colour to various insults which textiles may suffer during manufacture and use. Fastness depends on the type of dyestuff and the fibre substrate; there is no universal colour with the same fastness on all substrates. Moreover, different end uses have different fastness requirements; underwear has different requirements from furnishings. There are standardised methods (ISO 105) for evaluating the different types of fastness. The most important are:

- Resistance of the colour to **rubbing,** either wet or dry. Even the best dyeings, in a very deep shade, may lose some colour in wet rubbing.
- The fastness to **washing** determines the wash program which must be used by the consumer. Nowadays, fastness to a strong wash at 60 °C is expected.
- Resistance to the effects of **perspiration** is important for underwear, outerwear, and sportswear.

Colours may also be required to be fast to **sunlight, weather, seawater, solvents, saliva** and **ironing.**

7.3.2 Dyeing Processes

The choice of dyeing equipment depends on the type of material to be dyed. Following are the main criteria.

- **Nature of the goods** (fibres, yarns, woven, knitted, or nonwoven fabrics, garments);
- **Fibre type;**
- **Strength and robustness** of the material;
- **Economics.**

The dyeing process may be **discontinuous** (batch), **continuous,** or **semi-continuous.**

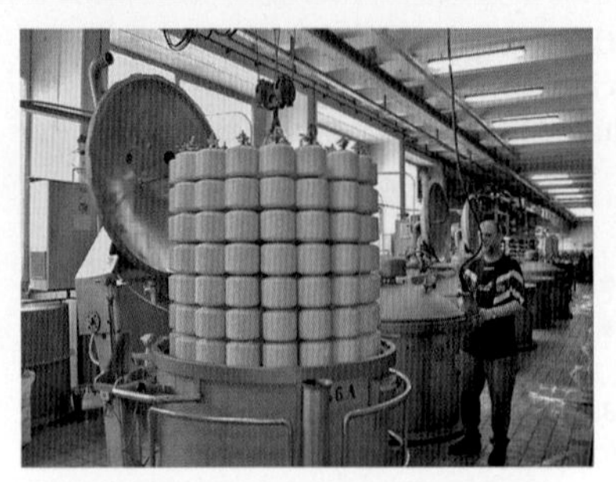
1: Yarn (package) dyeing machinery

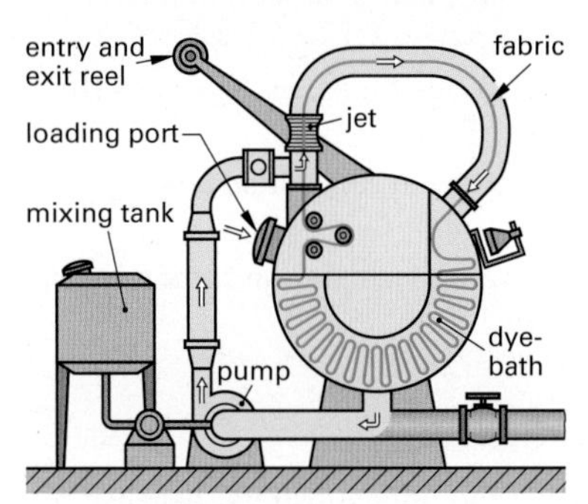

2: Jet dyeing machine

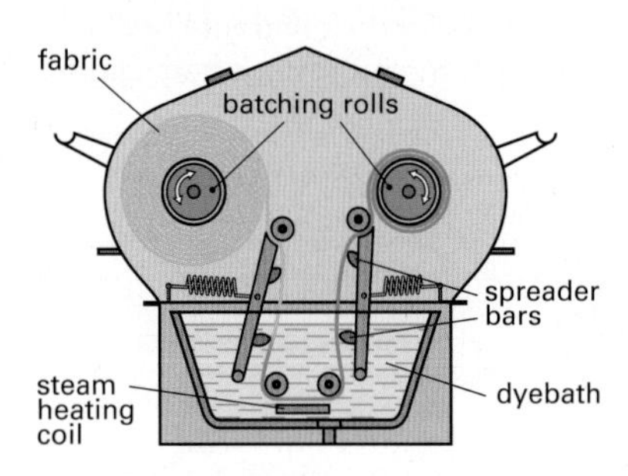

3: Jig dyeing principle

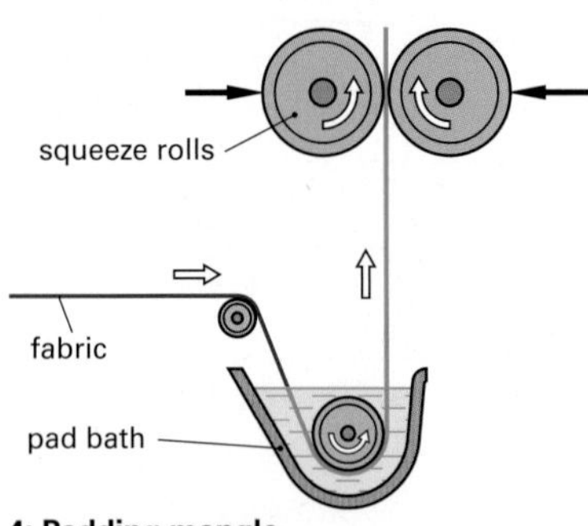

4: Padding mangle

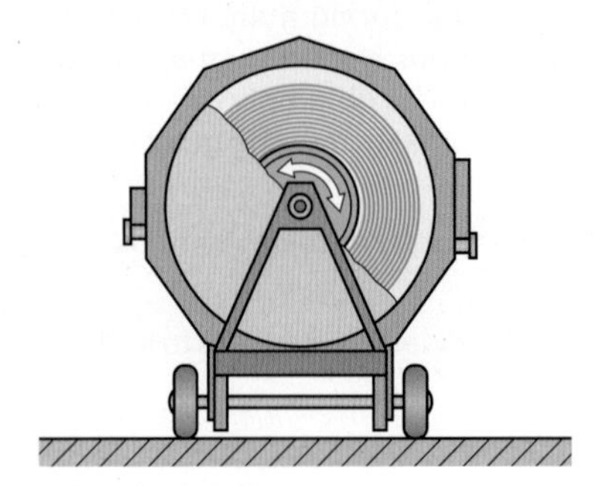
5: Docking station

Batch Dyeing Processes

Batch processing machinery of various types is used for dyeing **fibre stock, yarn hanks** (skeins), **yarn packages, knitted fabrics** and **sensitive wovens.**

In a batch process, a defined weight of material is treated in a dyebath[1] contained in a machine that is designed either to circulate the dye liquor through the material, or the material through the liquor, until the transfer of dye to material has proceeded to an equilibrium. The size of the batch (volume, number of packages, weight or length of fabric) depends on the machine, the material, and the job in hand. Most batch processing machines can also be used to carry out the preparation processes **(scouring, bleaching, optical brightening)** before dyeing as well as the after-washing and any after-treatments (fixation, softening) that may be required.

Figure 1 shows the unloading of a batch of yarn packages from a yarn dyeing machine.

Knitted fabrics and sensitive wovens are usually dyed in a **jet dyeing machine.** The required length of cloth is sewn into a loop and circulated through the dye liquor. Transport of the fabric through the liquor is effected either by a high-pressure liquor jet (*Figure 2*) or, more commonly, by a combination of low-pressure liquor jet and winch reel. The latest machines also inject air into the low-pressure jet and use a much reduced liquor ratio[2]. Synthetic fibres can be dyed in a **pressurised jet** at temperatures over 100 °C.

In a **jig dyeing** machine (jigger), the smoothly spread fabric is led backwards and forwards through the dyebath (*Figure 3*). Jiggers are used mainly for medium to heavy weight wovens and they use a low liquor ratio[2].

Continuous Dyeing

In continuous or pad dyeing the open-width fabric is passed through a relatively small, continuously replenished pad bath, containing the dyestuff and auxiliaries, and is then squeezed between rubber-covered rollers. The squeeze rollers ensure that a defined quantity of the liquor is uniformly penetrated and distributed within and across the fabric. After the padding station there will be some form of continuous dye fixation machinery, depending on the fibre and the dyestuff type.

The **pad mangle** (*Figure 4*) is a component of all continuous processes, whenever there is a requirement to handle fabric in the open width and to apply a dyebath or other concentrated chemical liquor in a uniform manner.

Continuous processing allows a faster changeover time between lots and reduced water consumption, compared to batch processes. However, it requires very long batches (e.g. 10,000 metres).

Semi-continuous Dyeing

The dyebath is applied to the fabric on a **pad mangle** and the impregnated fabric is wound up onto a **batching roller** (*Figure 5*) which can hold a very long length. Fixation of the dyestuff can be carried out on the batching roller, which may be slowly rotated at a docking station for several hours at a certain temperature, or the batch may be taken and used as the feed for a separate fixation process.

[1] dyebath: finite volume of liquor containing a defined weight of dyestuff plus auxiliary chemicals.
[2] liquor ratio: proportion by weight of liquor to fabric.

7.3.3 Printing (1)

Printing can be described as the controlled placing of defined areas of colour onto a substrate. The colorant must first be brought to the fabric surface, usually in the form of a printing paste. If it is a soluble dyestuff it must be diffused into the fibres. The colorant must then be fixed in place and, finally, excess unfixed colour has to be washed out.

1: Printing block

2: Block print

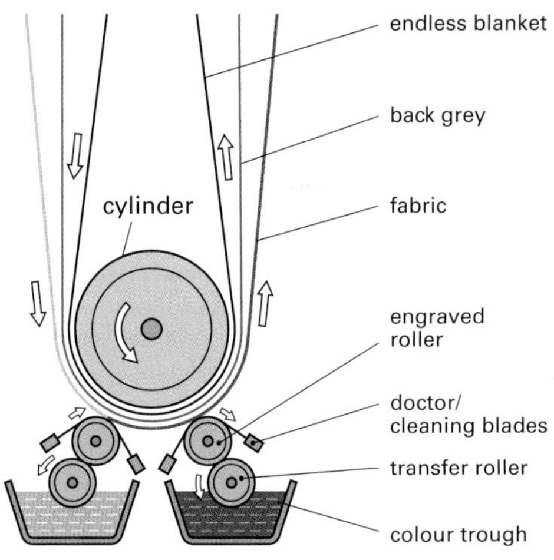

3: Principle of roller printing

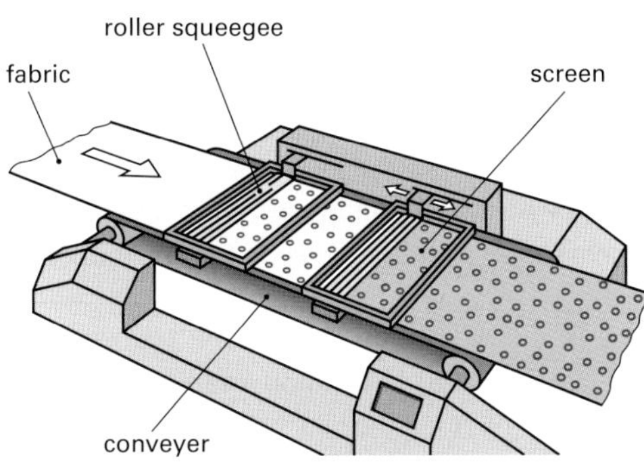

4: Principle of flat screen printing

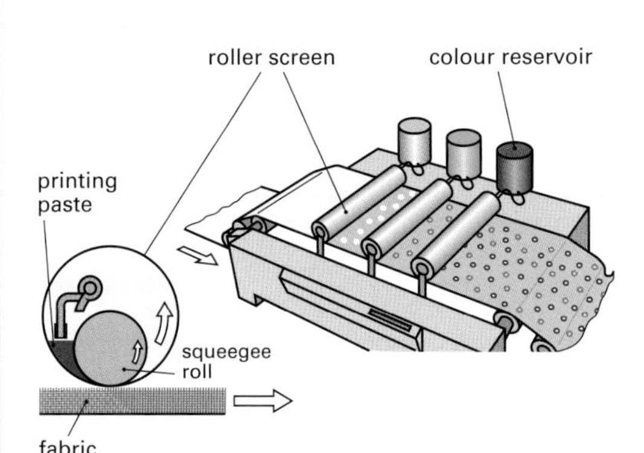

5: Principle of rotary screen printing

Hand Printing

This is the oldest method of printing but is now used mainly for traditional work in Asia and Africa. The printing paste is applied by means of a wooden block, which carries the design in relief (*Figures 1 and 2*), or by a stencil.

Roller Printing

The oldest mechanised method for continuous printing represents less than 10% of print production today, and is declining. Roller printing (*Figure 3*) is capable of producing very sharp outlines to the printed pattern which is especially important for small figures and intricate designs e.g. for cravats and squares. The maximum design repeat is the circumference of the engraved roller.

The design is engraved onto copper rollers, one roller for each colour, which are then chromium plated. The rollers are mounted against the large main cylinder, around which the fabric travels together with a resilient blanket and a protective back grey. The printing paste is located in a trough. A transfer roller runs partly immersed in the paste and in contact with the engraved roller. A doctor blade scrapes away all of the paste except for that contained in the engraving. A cleaning blade on the other side scrapes away any lint picked up from the fabric. The pressure of the engraved roller against the fabric causes the design to be transferred. Any excess paste which is squeezed through the fabric is taken up by the back grey. This protects the blanket and prevents the design from being smeared.

Screen Printing

Screen printing (flat and rotary) is the most important printing method with more than 80% of total production.

The design is formed on a screen by blocking off those parts of the screen where no printing is to occur. The screen is coated with a light-sensitive polymer and then selectively exposed through a stencil. Exposed areas are made insoluble; unexposed areas are washed away. A modern alternative is to coat the screen with an insoluble polymer which is then selectively etched away by a computer-driven laser beam.

A separate screen is required for each colour. The maximum design repeat is the size of the screen, which can be much larger than an engraved roller.

Flat Screen Printing

The fabric is held firm and flat on a conveyer blanket by a tacky adhesive. The conveyer moves intermittently over the printing table, one screen width at a time. When the fabric stops, the screens are lowered onto the printing table, printing paste is supplied to the screens and forced through the patterned areas by a squeegee blade or roller. The screens are lifted and the next cycle begins with the fabric moving forward one further screen width (*Figure 4*).

Rotary Screen Printing

The rotary screen system is a further development which allows continuous production. The printing paste is pumped at a defined rate from the reservoirs to the insides of the cylindrical screens, from where it is continuously squeezed through onto the moving fabric by a blade or roller squeegee (*Figure 5*). Rotary printing has more than 60% of the market.

7.3.3 Printing (2)

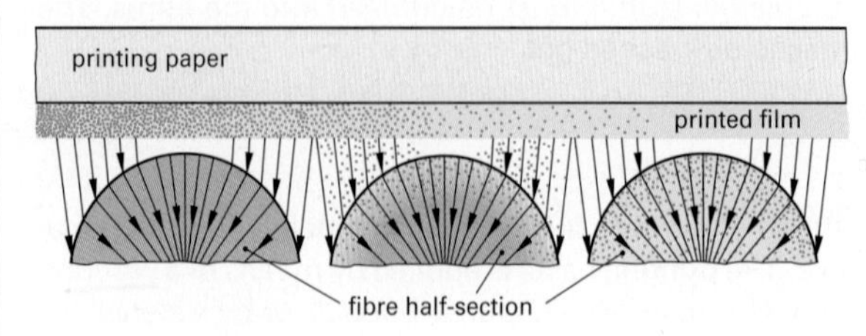

1: Transfer printing, schematic

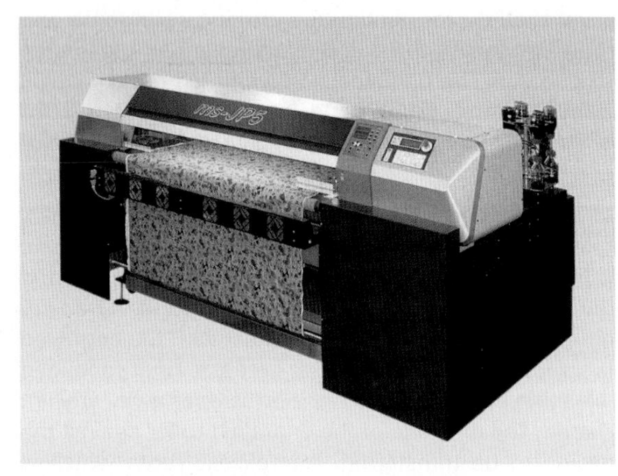
2: Digital printing machine

3: Digitally printed sample

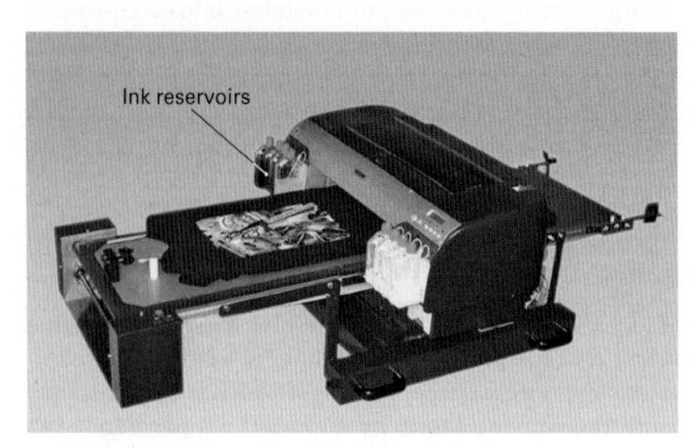

4: Garment printing machine

Transfer Printing

The design is first printed onto a special type of paper with certain types of dyestuffs. These papers are prepared by specialist suppliers. The pattern is transferred to the fabric with the aid of a heated calender (*Figure 1*). The temperature is high enough to cause the dyestuffs to pass into the vapour phase (sublime). Since it is held in close proximity to the paper, under pressure, some of the dye vapour finds its way onto the fabric and diffuses into the surface fibres. Penetration into the interior of the fabric is not very good (deliberately – so as to have a good colour yield at the surface) so the reverse side is often almost uncoloured.

The process represents about 5% of print production and finds its most direct and simple application on synthetic fibre fabrics, especially polyester. Special techniques, papers, and fabric preparations have been developed for natural fibres and blends, and for lacquer-effect printing.

Digital Printing

The principle is similar to that of inkjet printing on paper. The design is held in digital form on a computer and is transferred directly to the printer (*Figure 2*). The printer head (or multiple printer heads) can deliver up to eight different colours, from a set of large reservoirs, and make any desired combinations on the fabric. Theoretically, any colour can be generated from just four basic components – yellow, cyan, magenta, and black – but, in practice, supplementary colours are required for some shades, e.g. bright orange.

Printing inks are based on one of four dye types: reactive, acid, disperse, or pigment/binder. Depending on the fibre type, and the ink type, fabrics may need to be prepared for digital printing by impregnation with various chemicals that regulate the absorption and localisation of the ink, or promote bonding of the ink to the fibre. After printing the ink will need to be fixed, e.g. by steaming or curing, and any unfixed ink and other chemicals may need to be washed out.

By appropriate choice of inks and machine, almost any textile structure can be printed digitally, from the finest silks to the heaviest carpets.

Some of the advantages of digital printing are as follows.

- No need for the expensive preparation and storage of printing screens;
- Very large designs, including non-repeating patterns can be used;
- Unlimited design possibilities, including merging or overlapping colours (*Figure 3*);
- Start-up and changeover between lots is extremely fast;
- Small lots are possible and economic, compared to screen printing;
- Very rapid translation of design ideas to printed fabric.

Development of digital textile printing machinery has been quite rapid over the last two decades. Early machines were rather slow and were used mainly for sampling and small items. Modern machines are much faster and can be used for medium-scale production. Current market share is only about 1% but is growing.

Garment Printing

Whole garments, or garment components can be printed using either screen or digital techniques using specialised machinery. *Figure 4* shows a typical digital, inkjet type garment printer. Garment screen printers are often arranged as a circular carousel of eight or ten stations and use mainly pigment-binder systems.

7.3.3 Printing (3)

1: Discharge print (face & back)

2: Resist print (face & back)

3: Gold pigment print

4: Lacquer print

5: Flock print

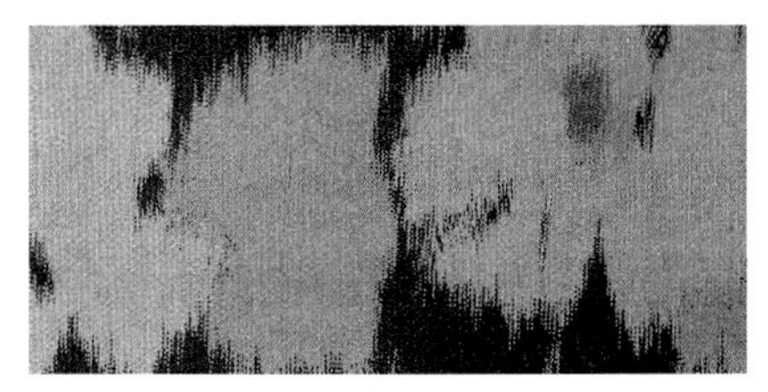

6: Warp print (chiné)

7: Burn-out

Regardless of the printing process, there are several different **printing techniques,** yielding various combinations of colour and tactile effects on the fabric.

Direct Printing, Overprinting

The printing paste is applied directly to the prepared fabric surface. Overprinting indicates that a plain dyed fabric is printed with a pattern in a darker colour.

Discharge Printing

A plain dyed fabric is overprinted with a discharge paste which destroys, or decolourises, or changes the colour of the dye. A white discharge is when the original white is restored to the printed area. A colour discharge is when a separate colour is applied at the same time as the discharge paste. The background colour intensity is the same on both sides but the printed pattern is much stronger on the face side (*Figure 1*). Discharge printing is expensive so it is used only for high-quality goods.

Resist Printing

This is when a white fabric is printed with a resist paste. On subsequent dyeing the printed area is not coloured. Resist areas can also be white or coloured. The background colour intensity is the same on both sides but the printed pattern is much stronger on the face side (*Figure 2*).

Pigment Printing

Pigments are colours which do not dissolve and penetrate into the fibres. They have to be applied together with a film-forming binder; usually an acrylic polymer, which, with heavy applications, can more or less obscure the fabric structure (*Figure 3*). Pigment-binder systems are relatively economical and give good rubbing fastness, but the fabric handle may suffer. The majority of all printing colours are pigment types.

Lacquer Printing, Effect, Lustre, Glitter and Pearl Print

A pattern is formed by printing the fabric with a pigment-coloured resin, such as coating grade pvc, which forms a matt or shiny film or three-dimensional effect (*Figure 4*). Base fabrics are usually synthetic warp knits. To avoid cracking of the resin over time, it is formulated with a very soft binder to promote flexibility.

Flock Printing

The fabric is printed with adhesive and cut fibre snippets are applied, which stick where the adhesive is present (*Figure 5*). A velvet-like appearance to the print can be obtained by electrostatic flocking, in which the fibre snippets are caused to stand upright in an electrostatic field as they are being applied. The fibre snippets can be relatively fine or coarse, short or long according to requirements.

Warp Printing

Before weaving, a pattern is printed onto the warp sheet. After weaving the design is subdued and shadowy, without a distinct outline (*Figure 6*). Also called **chiné** or **shadow print.**

Ikat fabric is made by a similar process involving tie-dyeing the warp threads.

Burn-out Printing

A fabric that is composed of two fibre types is printed with a chemical that will dissolve or degrade one of the components. Thus if a polyester-cotton blend is printed with an acid-generating paste, the cotton will be severely degraded and can subsequently be washed out, leaving the printed pattern as an opaque design on a transparent base (or vice-versa) (*Figure 7*).

7.4.1 Mechanical Finishing

The term **finishing** covers a wide range of processes. In general it means making the fabric suitable for its intended end use. Therefore, it is usually the last stage of fabric processing and a fabric is often said to have a certain "finish". Originally, finishing was simply the weighting (starching) and calendering of cotton or linen fabrics and the milling and pressing of wool. Nowadays a much wider range of options is available.

- Modification of sensory properties (handle, appearance, aroma, etc.)
- Modification of the surface (raising, smoothing, embossing, etc.)
- Modification of performance in garment making (surface friction, sewing efficiency, etc.)
- Modification of the wearing properties (staining, creasing, draping, etc.)
- Modification of aftercare characteristics (ironing, shrinking, etc.)
- Modification of bulk properties (flame resistance, crease resistance, etc.)
- Modification of functional characteristics (water transport, water resistance, etc.)

In **mechanical finishing,** a desired effect is achieved by a mechanical process. In **chemical finishing,** a desired effect is achieved by a chemical reaction. Final finishing can sometimes require a combination of processes which are not very compatible. For example a stiffening finish and a crease resistant finish have mutually contradictory effects. The requirements of the market, in terms of end uses and consumer preferences are constantly changing and this places great demands on the ingenuity of the finisher.

Mechanical Finishing

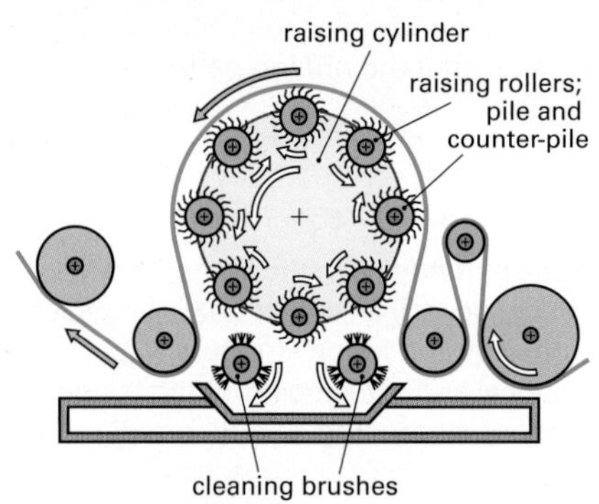

1: Principle of Raising

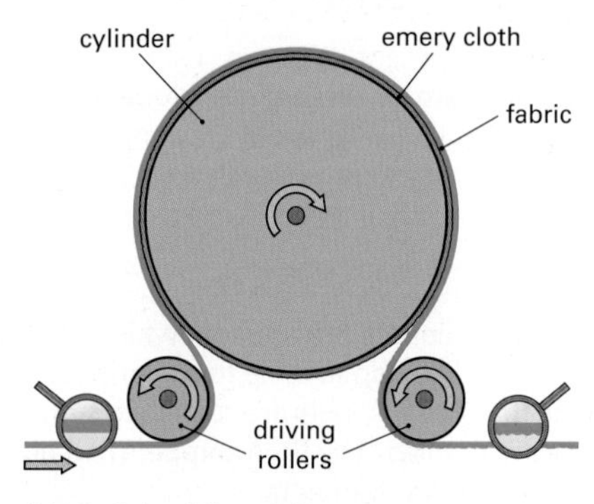

2: Principle of Emerizing

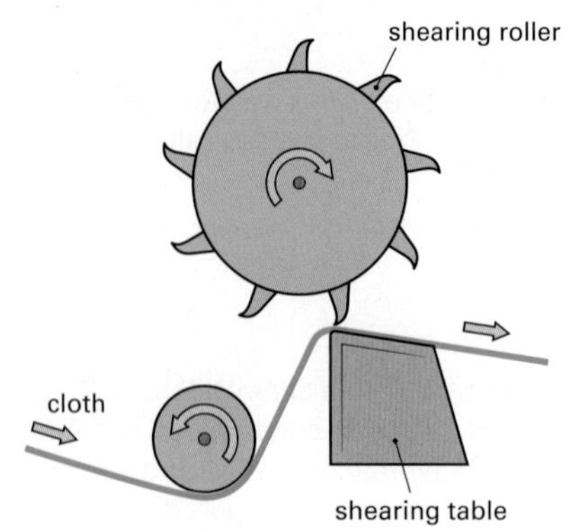

3: Principle of Shearing

Raising, Brushing

On the raising machine (*Figure 1*), fibre ends are teased from the fabric to form a fibre pile which can more or less obscure the fabric weave. This is accomplished by the action of fine wire-clad rollers which hook into the fabric surface as they rotate. The raising action must not be too strong or the fabric can be weakened.

Most textile fabrics made from spun yarns can be raised or brushed, including loop pile fabrics and felted or milled fabrics. Raised fabrics have a soft and fluffy handle. They are also very warm, due to the increased volume of enclosed air.

Commercial styles: **velour, flannel**

Rateening

Ratiné (curled), and similar effects, are produced on raised fabrics by special brushing or rubbing devices working to a predetermined pattern.

Commercial style: **ratiné**

Sanding, Sueding, Emerizing

Sanding or sueding (*Figure 2*) is a variant of raising. It is achieved by the use of emery cloth of various grades, according to the fabric quality and the desired effect.

Instead of lifting fibre ends out of the fabric, the fibre surfaces are lightly abraded, resulting in a soft, warm, peach-skin effect. There is usually a loss in strength of about 10%.

Many textile fabrics can be emerized, including synthetic filament fabrics but excluding wool fabrics.

Commercial styles: **duvetyn, moleskin**

Shearing, Cropping

The fabric is led over the edge of a cutting table and under a rotating, spiral-bladed shearing roller, which is set at the required distance from the fabric surface (*Figure 3*).

Cropping produces a level and uniform pile on raised, velvet, or plush fabrics: knitted terry is converted to knitted plush

Commercial styles: **velvet, velour, knitted plush**

Shearing is cleaning the surface of a smooth (e.g. worsted) fabric by cutting away the projecting surface hairs to reveal a more clearly-defined weave pattern. Shearing can be an alternative to singeing (*see page 103*).

Commercial styles: **gabardine**

7.4.2 Thermo-Mechanical Finishing

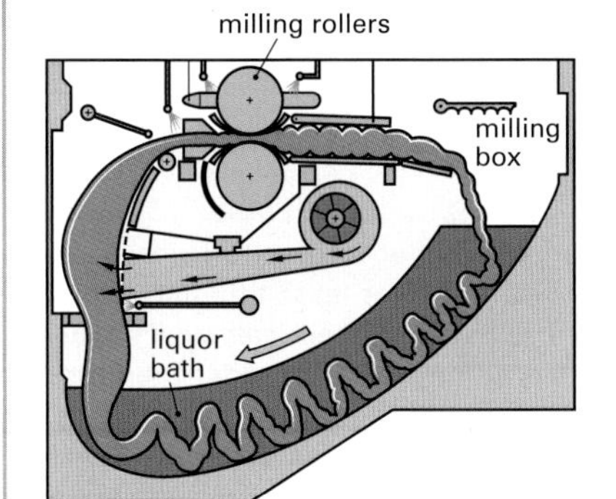

1: Principle of Milling

Milling, Fulling, Felting

Wool fibres exhibit a property called differential friction, due to the scaly surface structure. This property can be exploited in feltmaking (*see page 74*) and in the mechanical finishing of wool fabrics.

In **fulling** (*Figure 1*) the fabric is subjected to repeated extension and compression cycles in a warm alkaline liquor. The fabric shrinks (felts) progressively, so the treatment time and the severity of the conditions are adjusted according to the density of felting required. The fabric becomes fuller and denser, the weave pattern is obscured, and there are improvements in tensile and tear strength as well as abrasion resistance and weatherproofing.

Milling is a lighter treatment, after which the fabric is somewhat consolidated but the weave pattern is still fairly clear. It is applied to high quality fabrics such as **worsted flannel.**

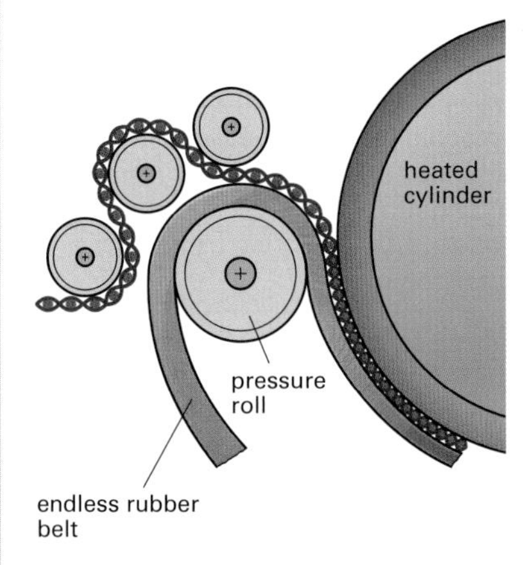

2: Principle of Compressive Shrinking

Shrinking

During all previous processes, the fabric has suffered greater or lesser stretching forces. Tensions are built into the material, which tend to be relieved during subsequent (tensionless) washing. The resulting shrinkage is facilitated (in cellulosic fabrics) by swelling in water or (in synthetic fabrics) by heat. This potential dimensional instability must be anticipated in the finishing by a controlled induced shrinking of the fabric.

Cotton fabrics and blends are usually processed in a so-called "compactor" (*Figure 2*), which forces the fabric to shrink in the length direction by compressive forces. The fabric is passed through a steam box, to adjust the moisture content, and is then led over a thick rubber belt between a pressure roll and a heated cylinder. At the point where the fabric arrives, the surface of the belt is stretched, due to the curvature of the pressure roll. After passing onto the cylinder, the curvature reverses so a longitudinal compression force is generated at the surface of the belt. Due to the confined space, the fabric is forced to shrink in length under the action of this compression. The (nominal) amount of compressive shrinkage can be adjusted, from zero up to about 15%.

Many variations in machine design are available, but the original and best-known process is **Sanforizing®**.

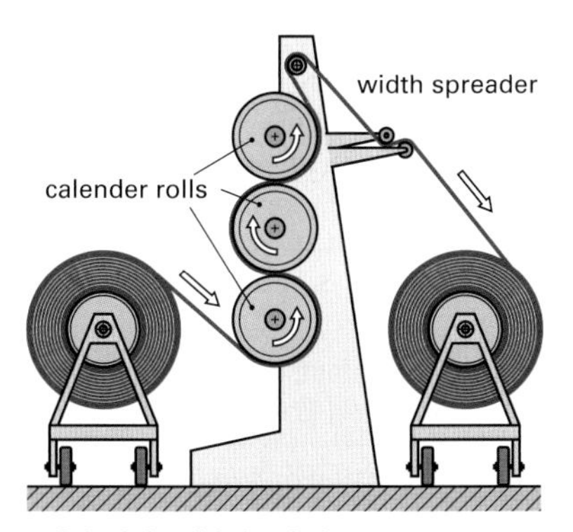

3: Principle of Calendering

Decatizing, Decating

Treatment of wool fabrics with heat, steam, and pressure, either in a batch or continuous process to provide a smooth surface and a softer handle together with some lustre and dimensional stability. In the continuous process, the fabric is moistened and led between a heated drum and an endless felt blanket. Steam is generated in the fabric which provides the setting effect.

Calendering

The fabric is passed between pressure rollers (*Figure 3*). Various effects can be achieved depending on the nature of the roller surfaces, the roller temperatures, the roller clothing and relative speeds of the rollers (slippage gives polishing).

The effects of calendering usually are not permanent but can be made durable: for synthetic fibres by raising the bulk fabric temperature to around the glass transition[1], or for cellulosic fibres by the inclusion of a resin which can later be cured.

Particular forms of calendering are **embossing, moiré,** and **glazing.**

With **embossing,** the fabric is fed between a relatively soft roller and a heated engraved steel roller, under heavy pressure, to produce a relief pattern on the fabric. A special case is **schreinering,** in which the engraved roller is provided with very fine diagonal lines. The very fine pattern embossed on the fabric cannot be seen with the naked eye but results in a pleasing lustre.

Moiré engraved calender rolls are also available but the original moiré watermark pattern is produced when two moistened ribbed fabrics are calendered together (*see page 130*).

The polished, lustrous finish of chintz fabrics is produced by **glazing,** or **friction calendering.** The fabric is pre-treated with a polymer or resin and then run between heated rollers running at slightly different speeds. Often one of the rollers will be made from relatively softer, dull material whilst the other is hard, polished steel.

[1] glass transition temperature, Tg: the temperature at which a synthetic polymer begins to soften.

7.4.3 Chemical Finishing (1)

A **chemical finishing** process aims to effect a change in the basic fibre or fabric properties, in order to improve some aspect of its behaviour (*see page 102*). Textile chemists are continually developing new or improved processes to better satisfy the demands of consumers and environmental pressure groups.

1: Clothes moth

2: Fabric with poor slipping resistance

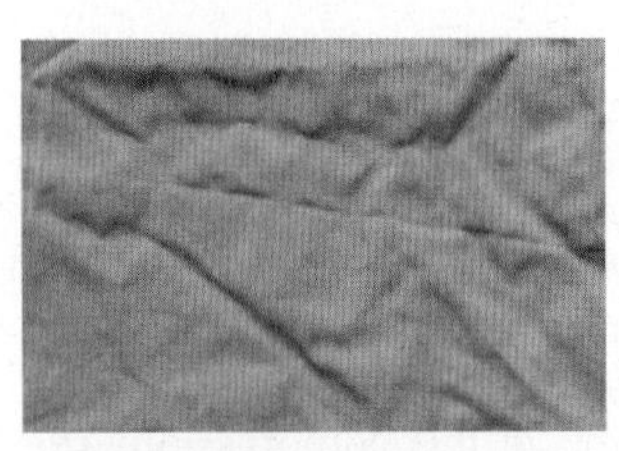

3: Fabric without easy-care finish

4: Fabric with easy-care finish

5: Effect of anti-pilling finish on knitted fabric

6: Stain-resistant fabric

Process/Application	Description
Parchmentising cotton batiste	A range of processes giving a variety of effects ranging from transparency to opalescence, together with more or less stiffening. Often there is a high degree of lustre. Use is made of chemicals which have a very severe swelling or partial degrading effect to render the fibres almost gelatinous. The fabric is calendered and the chemicals removed before the fibres can be degraded. Commercial styles: **organdy (Swiss finish), organdie**
Flame resistance all textile materials	Application and fixation of e.g. phosphorous/nitrogen-based substances which render the textiles non-flammable or difficult to ignite. The release of inflammable volatiles is suppressed so that, instead of flaming, the materials will degrade and char. Flameproof materials are mandatory for public buildings.
Anti-felting wool textiles	Wool fabrics cannot normally be machine washed because of felting. Felting can be largely eliminated by softening, eroding, or masking the scale tips on the fibre surface. The most common treatment is to prepare the fibre surface, by oxidation with a chlorine treatment, and then to apply a thin layer of a flexible polymer.
Moth proofing wool	Wool textiles are susceptible to attack by clothes moth (*Figure 1*) or carpet beetle larvae. To prevent this, the textiles can be treated with insecticides, or with chemicals that render wool inedible or to which the larvae are averse.
Slipping resistance linings, furnishings	Loosely-woven fabrics containing smooth filament yarns tend to suffer distortion by mutual slippage of the warp and weft (filling) yarns under shear stress (*Figure 2*). This can be especially problematic at a seam (seam slippage). Friction between the yarns can be increased by the application of a thin polymer film containing microcrystalline material, such as aluminium oxide or silicate.
Easy-care cotton, rayon, linen	Fabrics made from cellulosic fibres are susceptible to creasing during wearing and laundering. This can be markedly reduced by the application and fixation of chemicals which reduce the sensitivity of the fibre to moisture and to creasing. Reduction of inter-yarn friction is also helpful. Treated fabrics become more resistant to wrinkling, do not shrink, and will dry faster but their strength is reduced (*Figures 3 and 4*). Dyed and printed colours are made more washfast, calender glaze and emboss effects are made permanent, and pilling is eliminated.
Anti-pilling apparel and upholstery fabrics made from synthetic fibres and blends	Pilling is the formation of tiny pills, made from one or two fibres, on the surface of the cloth caused by constant chafing. Each pill is anchored by one or two fibres embedded in the fabric interior. The problem is normally ameliorated by the use of low-pill (i.e. weak) synthetic fibres, and by singeing (*see page 103*) so there is no specific anti-pilling chemical treatment as such. However, many polymer treatments, used primarily for other purposes will reduce pill formation (*Figure 5*). If the anchor fibres are cellulosic, then an enzyme treatment or an easy-care treatment will reduce pilling.
Stain resistance Apparel and household textiles	Application of stain-resistant substances based on special types of silicone, fluorocarbon, or acrylic polymers, depending on the fibre and end use. The surface energy of the fibres is changed so as to discourage stain particles from clinging. Usually, a degree of oil and water repellency is also imparted, so that the stain-carrying medium is prevented from wetting the surface and depositing the stain (*Figure 6*).

7.4.3 Chemical Finishing (2)

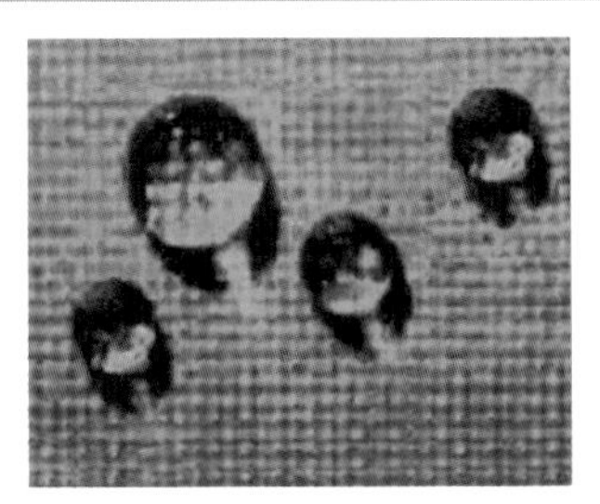
1: Hydrophobic finish

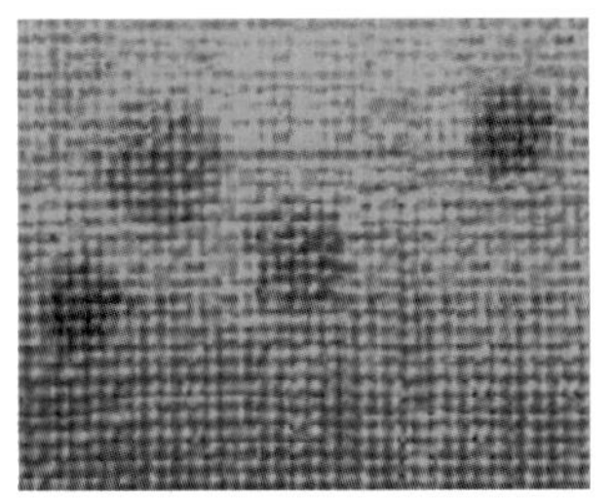
2: Hydrophilic finish

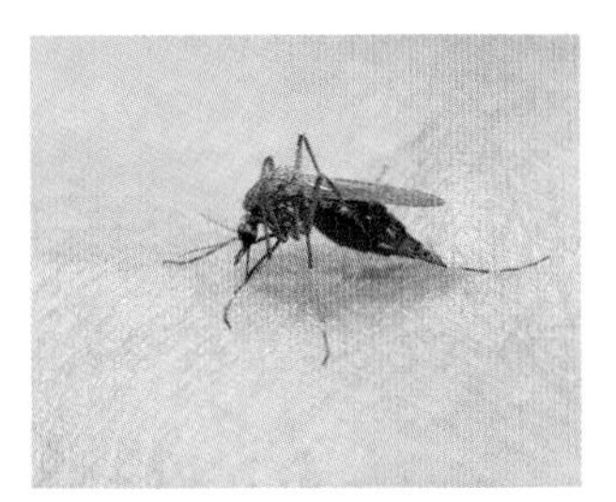
3: Gnat

4: Fibres with silver particles

5: Aloe vera leaf

6: Honey bees

Process/Application	Description
Antistatic apparel and carpets made from synthetic fibres	Synthetic fibres are poor conductors so they are susceptible to the build-up of electrostatic charge as a result of rubbing, especially in a dry atmosphere. This can result in uncomfortable clinging to the body, crackling when dressing or undressing, or even an electrical discharge after walking over a carpet. In addition, dust particles are attracted. **Conductivity** can be improved by applying a hygroscopic chemical or by a treatment that renders the surface hydrophilic. Such finishes can be either a temporary dressing or a durable surface coating. Stain-release finishes usually have an antistatic effect.
Modification of Handle all textile materials	A fabric can be made to feel stiffer or softer and more or less resilient, but the most common treatment is to apply **softening agents,** either as a temporary dressing or as a durable polymer finish. Partly this is to provide a more pleasing first impression for the consumer, but also it is to improve the sewing performance in garment making, including some antistatic benefit.
Functional finishing sportswear	Many sportswear fabrics incorporate elastomeric yarns, to provide high extensibility together with good elastic recovery. Easy **stretching and recovery** can be aided by finishing with certain silicone-elastomer polymers which, after curing, form a smooth, continuous, low-friction film over the yarn surfaces. The same silicone polymers are used as handle modifiers.
Hydrophobic finishing weatherproof clothing	Many textile fibres are hydrophilic i.e. they have high surface energy, so they are easily wet by water. This is an advantage in many areas, but not in weatherproof clothing. For such clothing to provide protection against rain and snow, it has to be provided with a hydrophobic **(low surface energy)** finish (*Figure 1*). Traditional water-resistant finishes included waxes or oils but modern processes use fluorocarbon or silicone polymers.
Hydrophilic finishing sportswear	Synthetic fibres are hydrophobic i.e. they have low surface energy. This is a problem for clothing comfort, whenever it is necessary to facilitate **wetting and capillary transport** of liquid water, e.g. perspiration. A hydrophobic surface is also stained easily by oily materials. The solution is to provide a hydrophilic surface (*Figure 2*). The same treatments as are used for antistatic finishing generally help with wetting and capillary transport, as well as the rejection of oily stains.
Insect resistance; vector protection military, forestry, tropical and trekking clothing, mosquito nets	Vectors, in the biological sense, are insects that can transmit diseases (*Figure 3*). Finishing processes are available that can provide the textile with a durable coating of **insect repellent and insecticide.**
Bacterial resistance workwear, sportswear, underwear	Many fabrics, especially those made from synthetic fibres, tend to generate body odours after a short time. The odour is caused by a build-up of bacteria that thrive on the constituents of sweat. Silver ions are known to **limit the growth of bacterial colonies** so processes have been developed which deposit silver on the fibres (*Figure 4*).
"Wellness" finishing Wellness textiles	"Wellness" literally is a state of health and wellbeing. In the marketing of textiles the term is used as a metaphor, to embody the concept that provision of cosmetic products on apparel fabrics will **promote a feeling of health and wellbeing.** Wellness fabrics are mainly made from natural fibres and the dressings applied include products such as essential oils, e.g. aloe vera, and beeswax (*Figures 5 and 6*). Usually, a soft handle and a pleasant aroma are achieved. These dressings are not very durable.

7.4.4 Garment Processing: Jeans

Denim jeans have been used as work clothes in the USA for more than a hundred years, but they began to become popular as a fashion item in the early 1950s by association with Hollywood movie stars. Originally, the denim fabrics received no finishing before making up into jeans, not even desizing.

1: Ring-dyed warp yarns

2: Tools for manual treatments

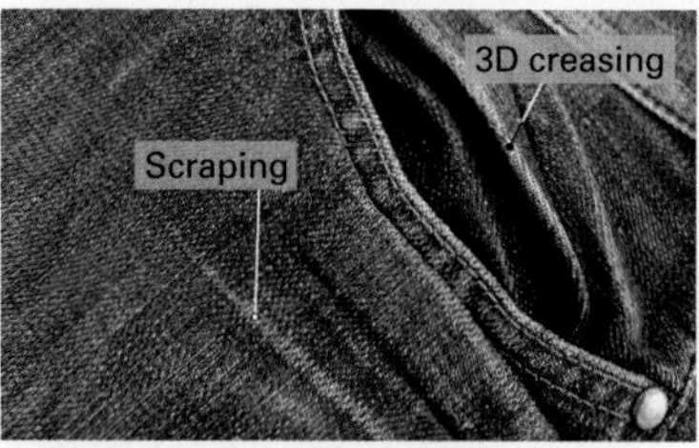

3: Scraping and 3-D creasing

4: Different shades from various bleaches

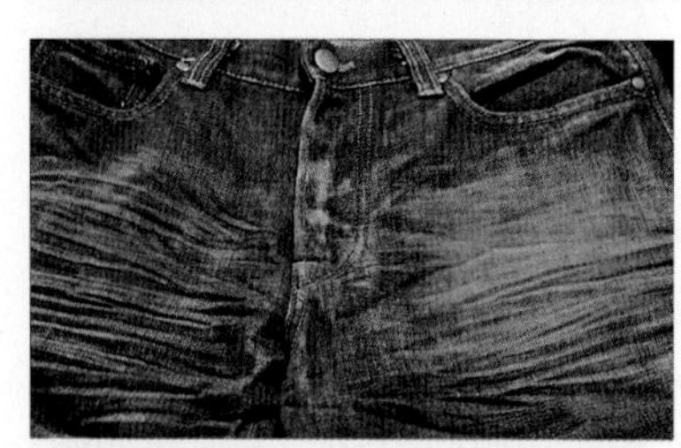

5: Vintage look

6: Speckled look

This was not a problem for miners and cowboys but fashion consumers had to "break in" the jeans by dint of hard wear and many launderings before a comfortable and highly appealing product was obtained. Seizing the obvious opportunity, the fashion industry made a new market in **pre-washed and pre-aged jeans** which has become highly developed and diversified, so that designer jeans are now very expensive items.

The presence of **size** in raw denim fabric does have advantages in garment making. The fabric is very stable and does not slip, so laying-up and cutting it is made much easier. However, the new garment finishing processes demand that materials such as sewing threads and pocketings have to be compatible with any bleaches, dyes, acids, and enzymes that may be used.

Denim is a **3/1 twill weave with an indigo-dyed warp and an undyed weft.** The blue warp appears on the face and the white weft on the back. **Indigo** is a type of vat dye (*see page 105*). The traditional indigo warp dyeing process is long and expensive. The warps are passed through 6 to 12 separate baths of reduced (solubilised) indigo, which is yellow. Between each bath they are skied (exposed to the air) to oxidise the indigo back to the insoluble blue form. The more baths, the deeper the dyeing. The result is a **ring-dyed yarn** (*Figure 1*). Nowadays, the traditional indigo dyeing can be supplemented, by using additional dyestuffs (e.g. sulphur black) in one or more of the baths, or even completely replaced, by a simultaneous yarn sizing and sulphur dyeing process.

Garment processing of jeans is an area of high creativity. A wide range of techniques has been developed, using e.g. sprays, brushes, shaving, painting and grinding tools (*Figure 2*). Following are a few of the more important variants.

Stonewashed was one of the earliest pre-aged variants. The garments were loaded into a large industrial drum washer along with a quantity of **pumice stones** and were tumbled until the required degree of "distress" had been achieved. Abrasion takes place preferentially at the seams and creases, giving a more-or-less authentic worn look. Later variants had the pumice soaked in chlorine or permanganate bleach for a more rapid fading. Pumice stone has now largely been replaced by **enzymes**[1] which achieve fading by partially degrading the cellulose fibres at the fabric surface.

Scraping at particular areas of the garment, especially the seams and cuffs and creases is done with hand tools (*Figure 3*) or sandpaper or mechanical grinding or sanding tools. The jeans can be stretched over a board containing ridges that mimic the natural creases in a pair of trousers, so the abrasion can be located realistically. Subsequent bleaching accentuates the effect.

3-D Creasing is introduced by first impregnating the garment with a resin or polymer, then manually introducing creases at the required positions, drying in the creases and finally curing the resin to set the creases.

Bleaching can be overall or localised. Overall bleaching is done in a large industrial washing machine. Localised bleaching is achieved with a spray-gun or a sponge, or by splashing the bleach liquor. Additional effects, such as stripes, can be achieved by use of stencils. Different formulations and concentrations of bleaches can give different final shades, from sky blue to grey-blue (*Figure 4*).

With **tinting** the pre-aged jeans are dyed in a dyebath of low concentration to give a so-called "vintage" look (*Figure 5*). The dyeing conditions can be arranged such that it is the worn areas that are preferentially dyed.

Impregnating the garments with acrylic or polyurethane polymers, followed by curing, can result in a **speckled, worn-out or oil-stained** appearance (*Figure 6*).

[1] enzyme: a catalyst that promotes a specific biochemical reaction, in this case the hydrolysis (breakdown) of cellulose.

7.5.1 Coating, Bonding, Laminating

Coating

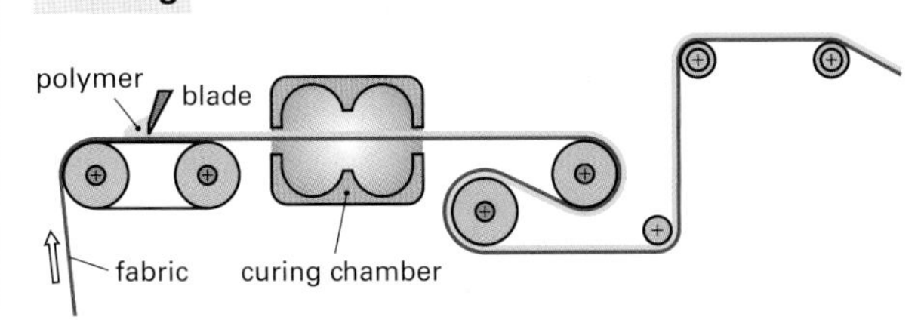

1: Principle of direct coating

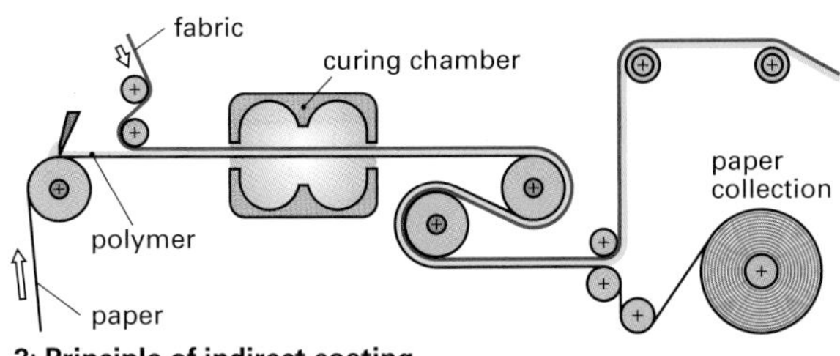

2: Principle of indirect coating

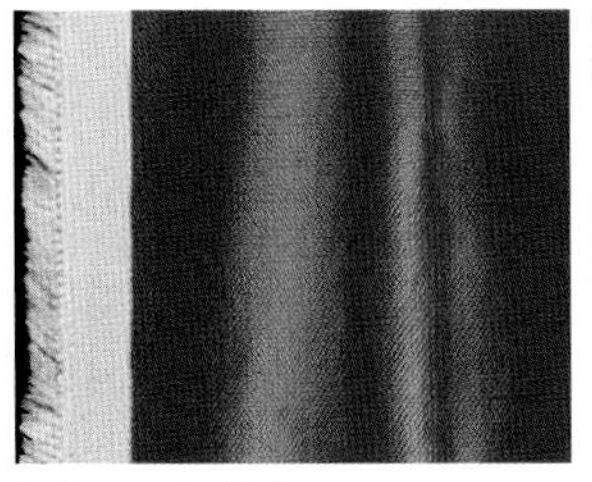

3: Coated fabric

4: Coated and embossed fabric

Coating is the application of a layer of natural or synthetic polymer to one side of the fabric, followed by fixation in a curing oven.

The polymer film can be applied directly to the fabric (*Figure 1*). However, if the fabric is an open one, or the material to be applied has a low viscosity, the liquid will first be applied to a carrier paper and then transferred from there to the target fabric (*Figure 2*).

The coating imparts **new properties** to the fabric, which are a combination of the original material (woven, knitted, nonwoven) and the coating (polyurethane, polyvinylchloride).

Coated textiles (*Figures 3 and 4*) have a wide range of uses from clothing to technical fabrics. In some cases, the primary objective is **functional,** e.g. waterproof materials. In others it is **aesthetic,** e.g. imitation leather. For clothing uses, it is advantageous if the coating is permeable to air and moisture vapour.

Clothing applications:

- Imitation leather jackets, coats, shoe uppers, handbags, and belts.
- Sportswear, protective clothing, high-visibility (fluorescent) workwear.

Household and technical textiles

- Upholstery, window blinds, shower curtains, table cloths, floor and wall coverings.
- Automobile furnishings, conveyor belts, tarpaulins, awnings, air-supported structures, inflatable dinghies, textile roofing, etc.

Lamination

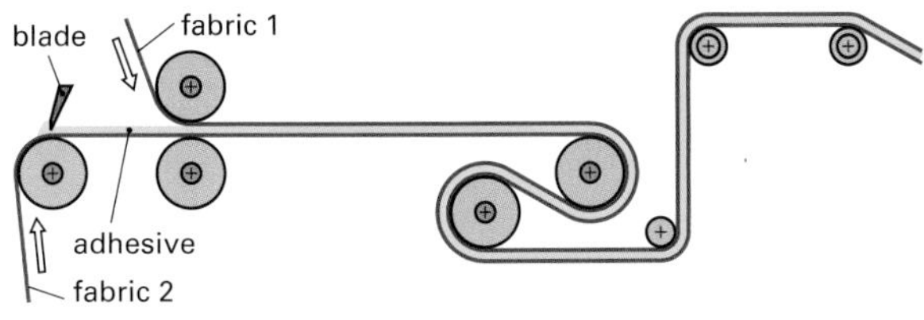

5: Adhesive lamination

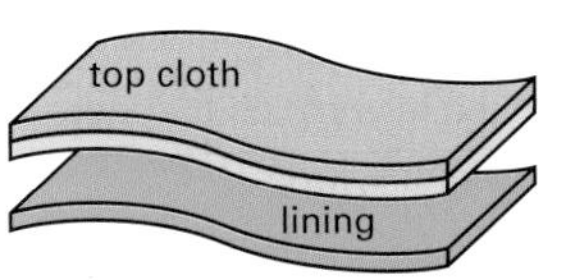

6: Combination top cloth

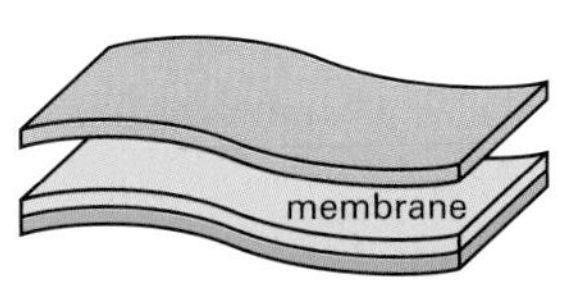

7: Combination lining

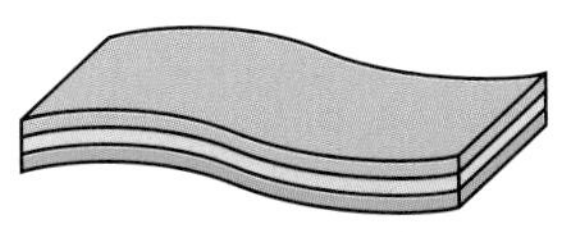

8: Three-ply combination

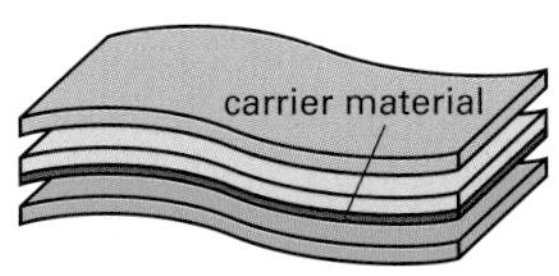

9: Bonded membrane

10: Bonded fabrics – Imitation suede & fur

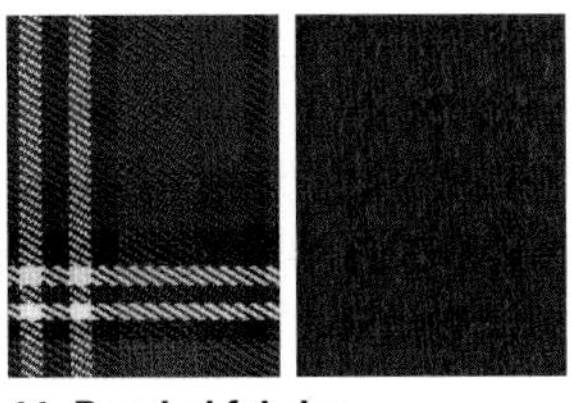

11: Bonded fabrics – Tartan & Fleece

Lamination or **combining** or **bonding** is the superimposition and bonding of two or more fabrics, or a fabric with paper, film, or foam. The resultant product is often called a **combined fabric** or a **bonded fabric.**

The bonding can be achieved with an adhesive (*Figure 5*), or by heat, whereby a polymer film or foam is melted onto the surface of one fabric and then the other fabric is pressed onto it **(flame lamination).**

Combined fabrics are often used in the manufacture of all-weather clothing (*see page 50*), where an air-permeable but water-resistant, and rather delicate membrane is inserted.

The combination can be made in several ways.

- **Combination top cloth** – the membrane is bonded to the top cloth before assembly (*Figure 6*).
- **Combination lining** – the membrane is bonded to the lining material (*Figure 7*).
- **Three-ply combination** – the membrane is bonded to both top cloth and lining (*Figure 8*).
- **Bonded membrane** – the membrane is bonded to a carrier material (usually a warp knit) and is assembled loosely between top cloth and lining (*Figure 9*).

Combined fabrics can be substantial and can have completely different characters on the two sides (*Figures 10 and 11*) or they can be made much lighter. For example, a **foam laminate** makes a lightweight but stable and highly insulating material.

8.1.1 Technical Terms for Particular Effects (1)

Commercial descriptions imply information about the general appearance, properties and applications of fabrics. These names have not been standardised and therefore do not always give unambiguous information. Nevertheless, certain names have become accepted in the trade for certain types of fabrics.

A given fabric is defined by its **fibre type, yarn type, structure,** and **finishing.** The two main sets of characteristics are its **surface appearance,** e.g. patterning, lustre, surface texture, and its **bulk properties,** e.g. drape, wrinkle resistance, thermal insulation.

Commercial names are usually derived from some particular characteristic of the fabric, e.g. the **raw material** (cheviot), the **yarn type** (bouclé), the **weave** (herringbone), the **production system** (velvet), the **finishing** (moiré), the **application** (lining), the **place of origin** (Shetland), the **patterning** (check), the **surface structure** (cloqué), the **colouring** (changeant). The latest fashion developments may be called **novelty** fabrics, if no existing term is available.

Technical Terms for Particular Effects

Most of the terms are taken from French, and can be used either as a modifier, e.g. Satin-Batiste rayé (satin stripe) or as a main descriptor, e.g. Rayé (striped cloth).

Satin-rib barré
Barré

barre (fr) = bar

Satin carré,
Carré

carré (fr) = square

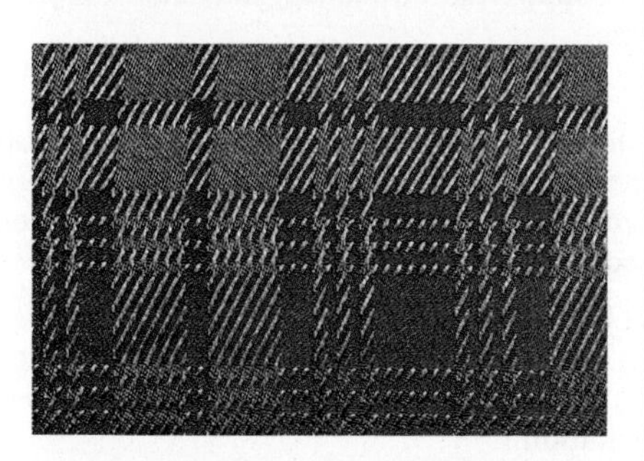

Georgette rayé degradé,
Dégradé

dégradé (fr) = shading off

Soielaine-Satin figuré,
Figuré

soie (fr) = silk
laine (fr) = wool
figuré (fr) = patterned

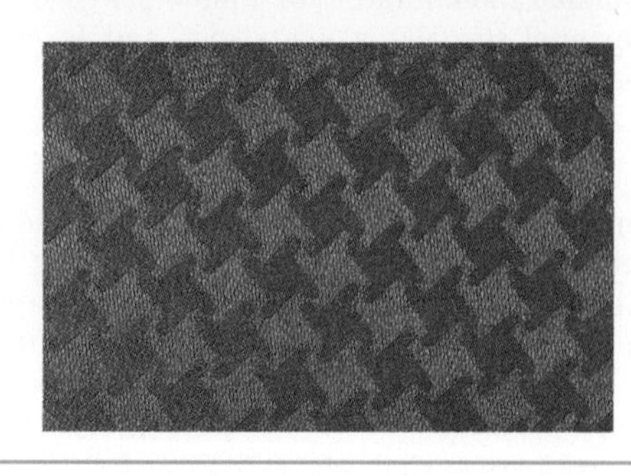

Pattern Effects

ajour:	light, openwork
all-over:	a pattern that covers the whole surface
barré:	crosswise bars, woven or printed
broché:	small extra weft motifs
brodé:	embroidered
carré:	chequered
chiné:	warp printed (shadow print)
cravattes:	patterns used for neckties & cravats
découpé:	extra yarn patterns from which the long floats have been cut out
dégradé:	reductions in tonal strength of a colour
dévoré:	patterning by selective removal of material (burn-out)
façonné:	allover weave pattern of small motifs
faux uni:	giving the illusion of a single colour, though made with multi-coloured yarns
figuré:	larger weave patterns, figured
lancé:	patterns made with extra warp or extra weft
mille fleurs	allover pattern of small flowers
mille point:	tiny allover dot pattern
mille rayé:	fine lengthways stripes
minimals:	very small pattern motif
navajo:	ethnic pattern or motif
ombré:	gradual changes in colour tone or hue (shaded)
paisley:	printed pattern of stylised Indian pine cones
patchwork:	combination of various designs; figured, printed, or appliqué
pointillé:	pattern of points, usually printed
quadrillé:	small chequered pattern
rayé:	lengthways stripes, woven or printed
travers	crossways stripes, woven or printed

8.1.1 Technical Terms for Particular Effects (2)

Flammé bicolore, Bicolore

flammé (fr) slub yarn
bicolore (fr) = of two colours

Taft ombré, Ombré

ombré (fr) shadowed

Satin quadrillé, Quadrillé

quadrillé (fr) squared

Satin rayé, Rayé

rayé (fr) = striped

Toile travers, Travers

travers (fr) across

Lustre Effects

ciré:	strong lustre and lacquer effect through finishing
glacé:	shimmering surface lustre through yarn and weave effects
lamé:	metallic lustre through yarn and weave effects

Structure Effects

bouclé:	looped, buckled
boutonné:	knobbly surface produced by knop yarns
cloqué:	wrinkled relief pattern caused by shrinkage effects
côtelé:	ribbed
crash:	lengthways creases introduced in finishing
flammé:	irregular appearance produced by slub yarns
floconné:	flock-like
frisé:	surface with curls or fine loops, made from bouclé yarns
frotté:	imitation terry made with loop yarns
gaufré	embossed pattern
matelassé:	quilted
moiré:	watermark pattern
natté:	braided, plaited, basket-weave patterns
noppé:	knobbly surface produced by knop yarns
ondé:	wave-like ribs
perlé:	pearl-like knobs produced by a fancy yarn
piqué:	woven double cloth with relief pattern, or knitted crosstuck fabric
plissé:	pleats or creases
ratiné:	curly or otherwise disturbed napped surface
relief:	pattern made of raised and lowered areas
structuré:	similar to relief
welliné:	wavy fibre pile

Colour Effects

bicolore:	modest shading effects using yarns of two different colours
changeant:	shimmering colour changes using different colours in warp and weft
imprimé:	printed patterning
jaspé:	modest colour effects using fancy (jaspé) yarns
melange	subtle colouring using mixture yarns
mouliné:	speckled, mottled
multicolor:	bright, more than two colours
uni(color):	no pattern, a single colour

Some of the most important types are illustrated, with short descriptions, on the following pages. Others may be found by reference to the index. Note that the order of presentation is the alphabetical order of the *original* German.

8.1.2 Top Cloths (1)

Afghalaine

Plain weave, medium weight, all wool woven fabric for dressgoods. A lightly pearled appearance due to the use of pairs of S and Z yarns alternately in both warp and weft.

Ajour,

à jour (fr) = open-work

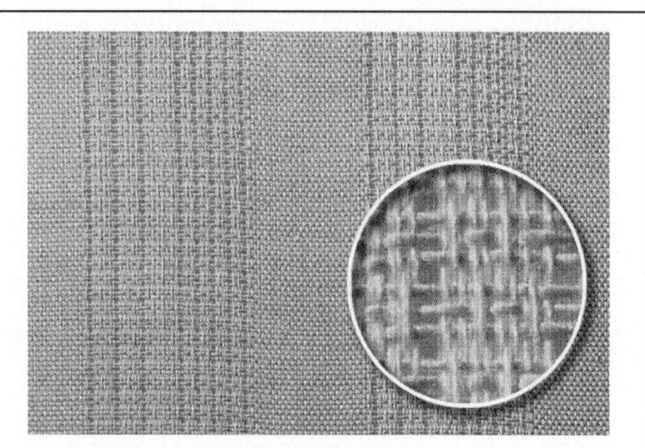

Ajour is a collective term for open-work fabrics, woven or knitted. The open-work areas are produced by the structure e.g. leno, basket weave, missing warp or weft threads (*see page 99*).

Alcantara®
Amaretta®
Leather cloth

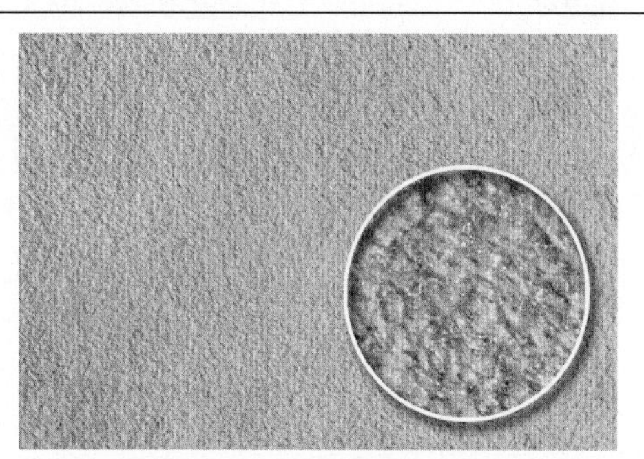

Nonwoven imitation suede made from a microfibre batt impregnated with polyurethane. It handles like fine leather but is lightweight and easy-care. For jackets, skirts and coats.

Burn-out Velvet

Velvet with a short, dense, tightly bound pile on which a pattern is created by selective removal of the pile, allowing the ground weave to show through. Used in dresses, blouses and formal wear.

Embroidery lace

Heavy relief lace fabric made by machine embroidering on a base fabric which is subsequently dissolved out or cut away.

Burn-out,
Dévoré

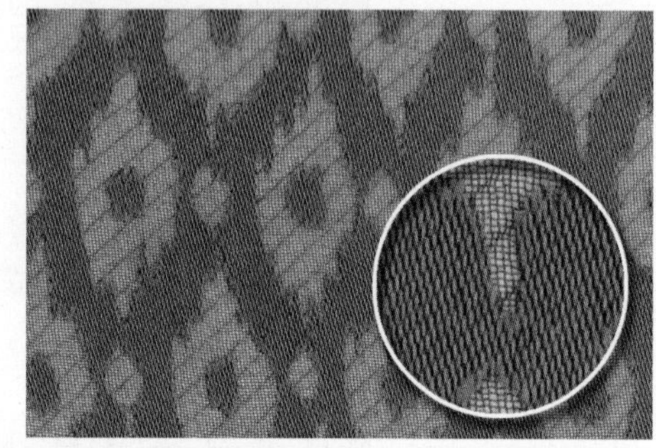

General term for fabrics of all types, made from fibre blends, in which one of the fibres has been selectively removed according to a pattern. The design appears opaque on a transparent ground (*see page 109*).

Babycord
Millrayé

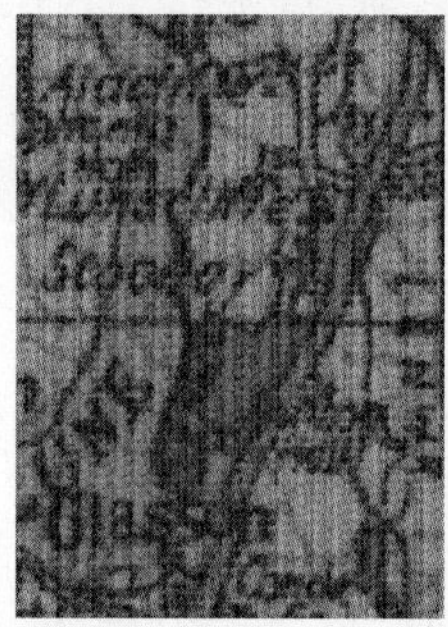

Babycord (left) is a lightweight, soft, fine cord, often printed, for children's wear, shirts, and lightweight jackets.

Milleraýe (right) is a general term for styles with fine, lengthways stripes, ribs or cords, including the finest corded velvets (corduroys).

Batiste

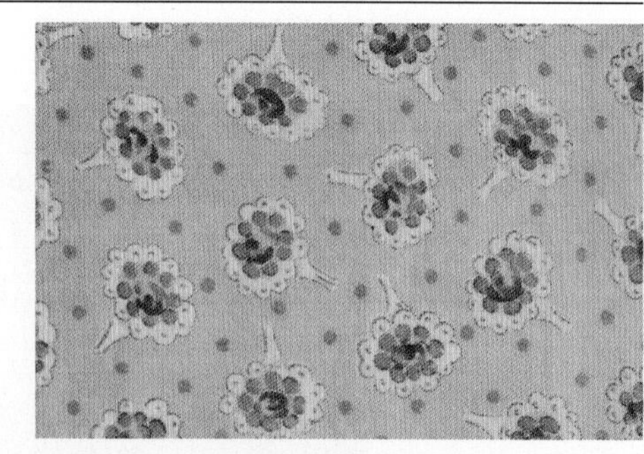

Fine plain weave fabric in cotton, linen, wool, or cotton/polyester. Used for dresses, blouses, lingerie, and interlinings. Swiss batiste has an embroidery pattern, usually as edging.

8.1.2 Top Cloths (2)

Bark crêpe

The bark-like surface texture may be achieved by alkali treatment, by embossing, or by the use of crêpe yarns in the weft. Applications include blouses, dresses and shirts (*see page 85*).

Bouclé

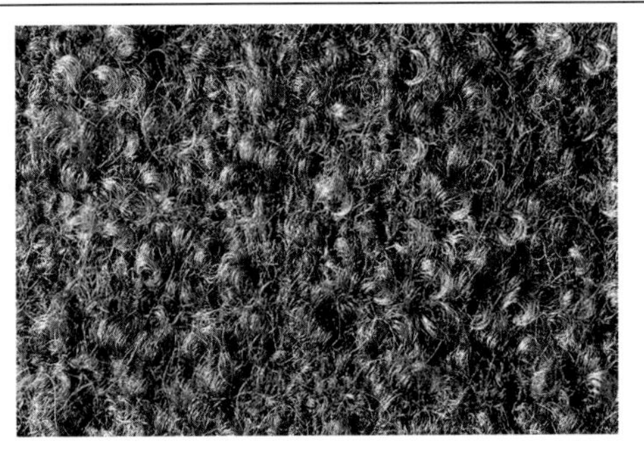

Fabrics with a knoppy, knotty surface texture made with loop or bouclé yarns. Used in dresses, costumes and coats.

Bourette

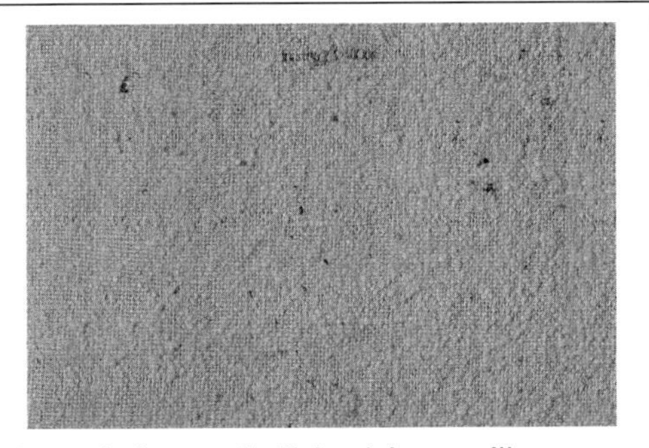

Dull neppy fabric made from noil silk in plain or twill weave. Used for women's outerwear and furnishings.

Broché

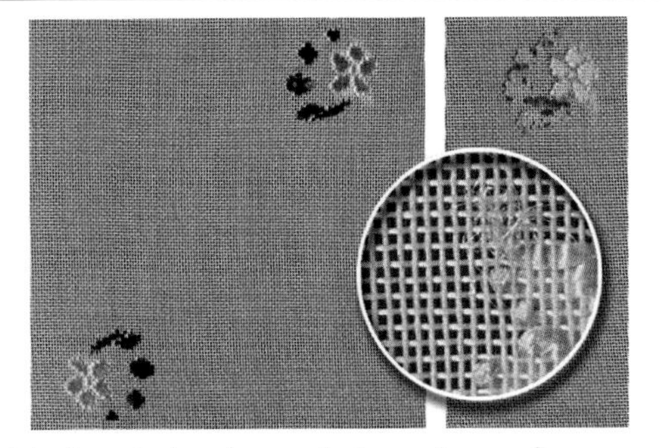

Fabrics in which the design is made by extra weft on a swivel weaving loom. The figuring threads are present only at the figured motif. Used in traditional costume, ribbons and trimmings.

Brodé

Collective term for fabrics that have been decorated by embroidery. The patterning is usually applied by machine using zigzag lockstitch or chain stitch. Used in blouses, dresses and evening wear.

Brocade

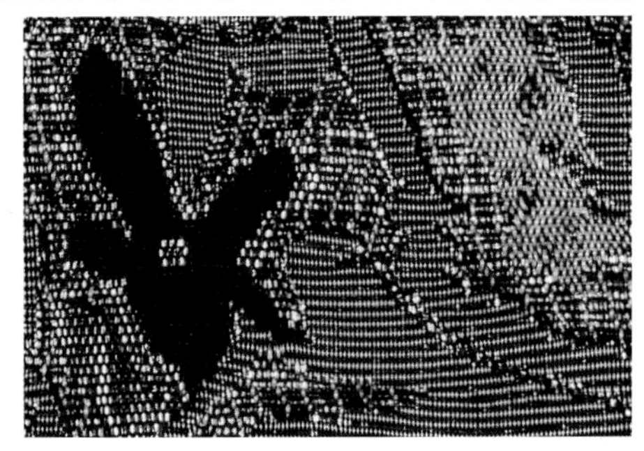

Heavily figured jacquard fabric, often with lustre yarn effects. Used in formal wear and furnishings

Canvas

Strong, durable, heavy cotton fabric in plain or double-end plain weave. Also known as **sailcloth.** Used for trousers, jackets, pockets and shoes in leisurewear.

Changeant
changeable, shot

An iridescent effect produced by different colours in warp and weft. Usually made from filament yarns (shot silk) and employed in dresses, blouses, and linings.

8.1.2 Top Cloths (3)

Charmelaine

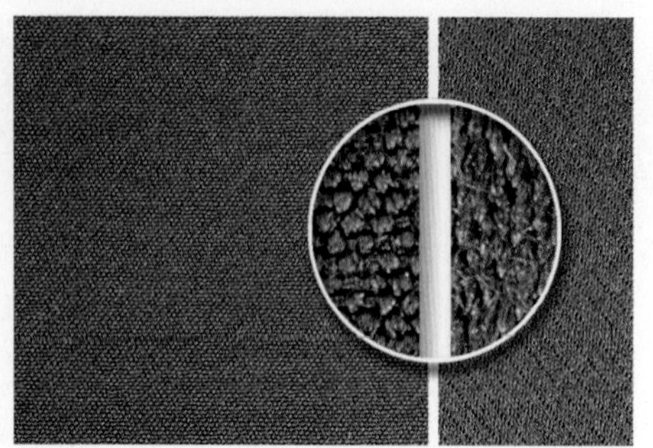

A soft worsted fabric in twill or satin weave with a lustrous face and matt reverse. The lustre is developed by shearing and pressing. Used in women's outerwear.

Chiffon

Delicate, sheer, open fabrics originally of silk in plain weave using crêpe yarns; may be embossed. Used for blouses, dresses, squares, and evening wear.

Charmeuse
Locknit

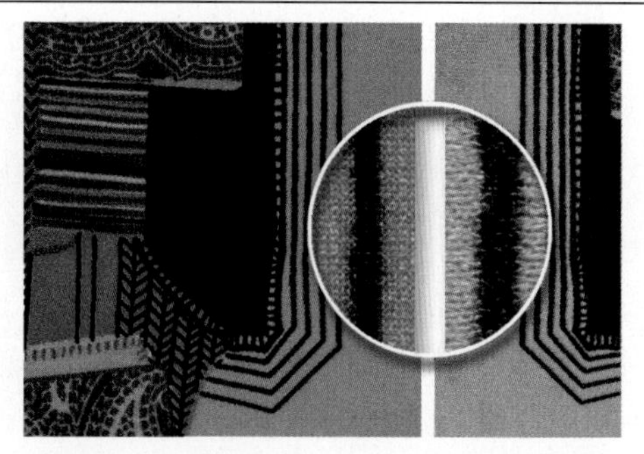

Light weight, smooth, non-laddering warp knitted fabric made from filament yarns. Used for linings, lingerie, and blouses (*see page 98*).

Chiné
shadow print

chiné (fr) = clouded, shadowed

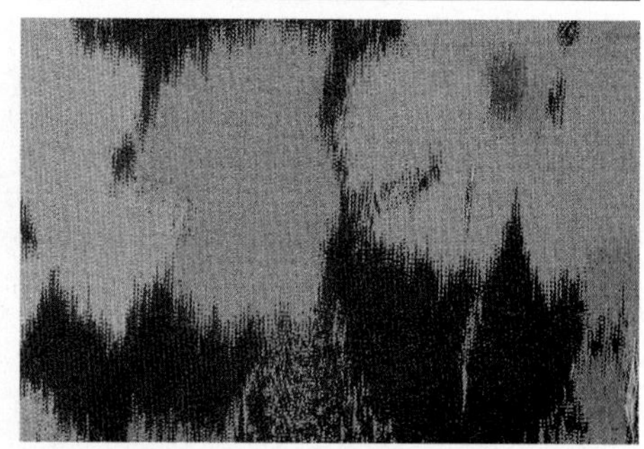

Fabric woven from a printed warp. After weaving the design appears shadowy and indistinct. Often made from filament yarns for dresses and furnishings.

Chenille

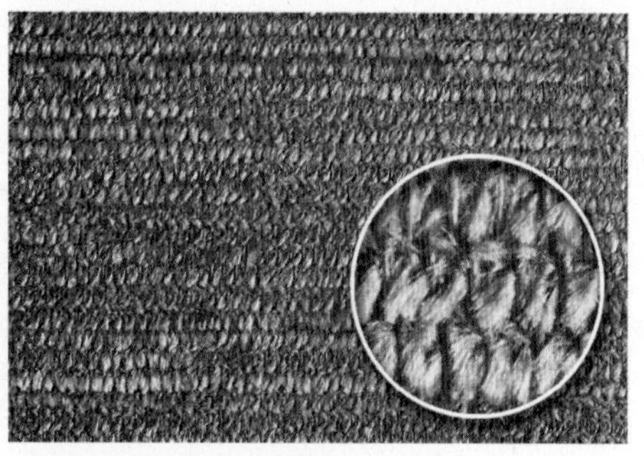

Soft velvet-like fabric, made with chenille yarns in the weft. Can also be made in circular knitted fabric. Used for pullovers, jackets, furnishings, shawls and caps.

Chintz

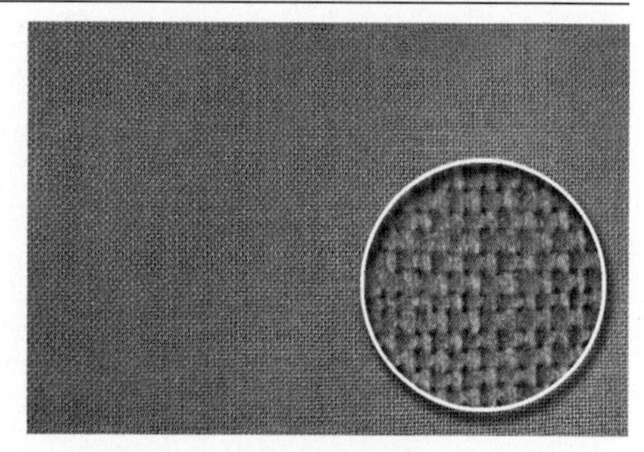

Strongly lustrous cotton fabrics, usually printed; surface appears almost as if waxed. Finished for stain and water repellence by impregnation and calendering. Used mainly in furnishings.

Cheviot

Cheviot: a breed of sheep from the Cheviot hills (Anglo-Scottish borders)

Heavy, durable, smooth-finished worsted or woollen tweed fabrics in twill weaves. May or may not be made from cheviot wool. Used for jackets, suits, costumes and coats.

Ciré

ciré (fr) = waxed, polished

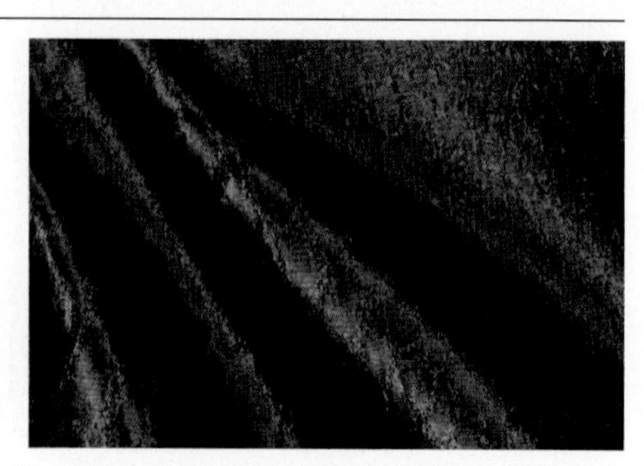

Finish obtained by impregnation with wax followed by hot calendering. Can also be made by hot embossing of synthetic fabrics or by lacquer printing to form a pattern of shiny areas. For jackets, coats and ladies outerwear.

8.1.2 Top Cloths (4)

Cloqué
blister

Double fabric with a figured blister effect on the face and a crêpe back. Some or all of the yarns used on the back have high shrinkage potential. The face cloth blisters according to the stitching pattern between face and back (*see page 88*). Used in women's outerwear.

Corduroy
corded velvet

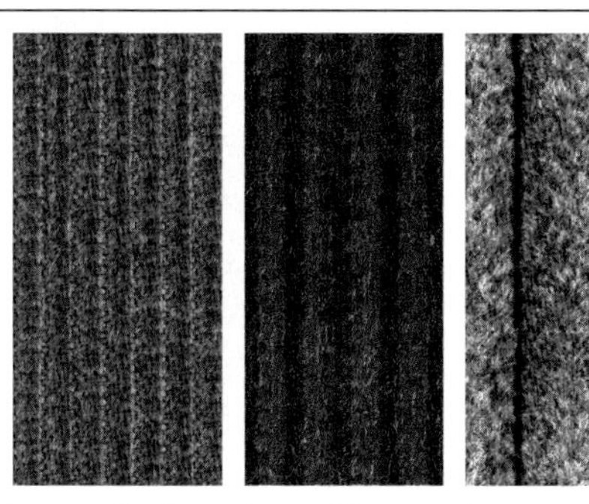

A cut pile cord, usually in cotton. The cords may be of various widths, from under 5 **(elephant cord)** to more than 16 **(needle cord, pincord)** wales per inch (*see page 87*). Used mainly in leisure and business wear.

Côtelé
Bedford Cord

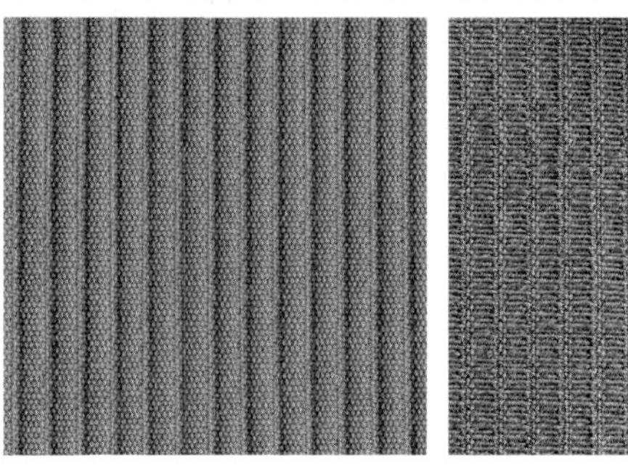

Hollow or wadded, length-wise cords. Light weight qualities for women's outerwear, heavier weights for trousers and furnishings (*see page 89*).

Crash,
Crinkle

Crash was originally unbleached, rough, coarse, plain weave linen fabric made with irregular yarns. Nowadays often deliberately creased by pressing and fixing creases during finishing **(Crinkle)**. Fashionable outerwear.

Crêpe
de Chine

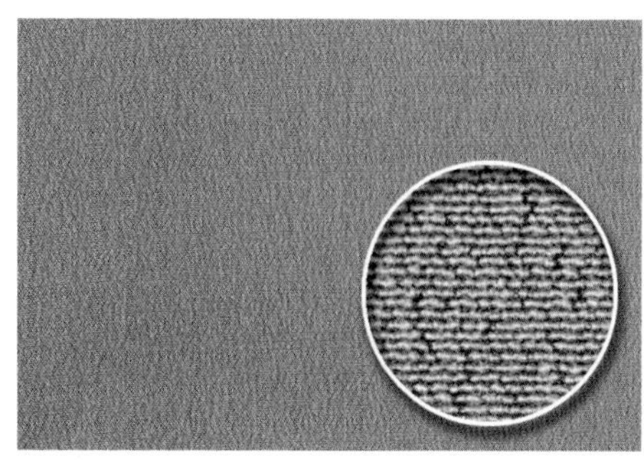

Light weight, supple, plain weave silk fabric with S and Z crêpe yarns in the weft and lightly twisted warp. Used for dresses and blouses.

Crêpe
Georgette

Plain weave in silk, polyester, wool, cotton, or viscose with S and Z crêpe yarns in both warp and weft; has a grainy, sandy handle. Women's outerwear (*see page 85*).

Crêpe
lavable
warp crêpe

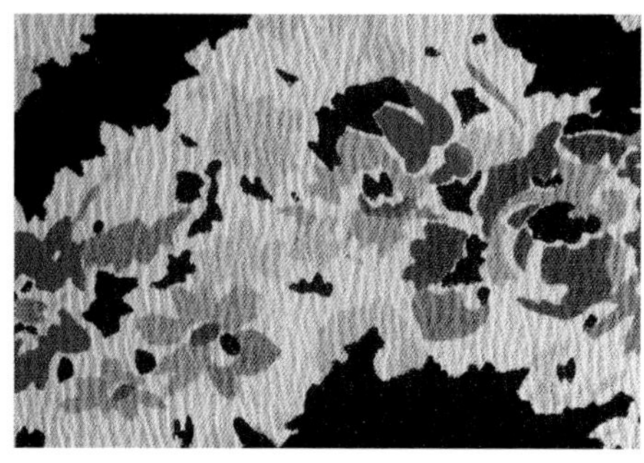

Plain woven, filament crêpe fabrics with crêpe yarns in the warp and normal yarns in the weft. Used for dresses and blouses.

Crêpe
Marocain

Plain woven, filament yarn fabric with crêpe yarns in the weft (*see page 85*). The rib effect can be strengthened by embossing. Used for dresses and blouses.

8.1.2 Top Cloths (5)

Crêpe Satin
satin crêpe

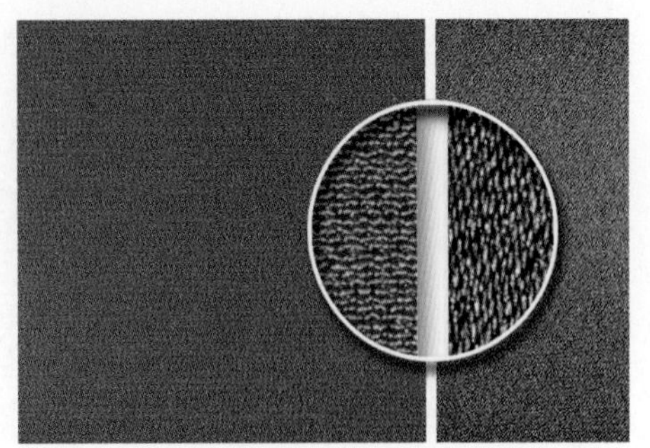

Softly draping, supple satin or sateen weave filament yarn fabrics with crêpe yarns in the weft and normal yarns in the warp. One side is lustrous; the other is matt. Either side can serve as the face. Used for dresses and blouses.

Croisé
twill

croisé (fr) = crossed

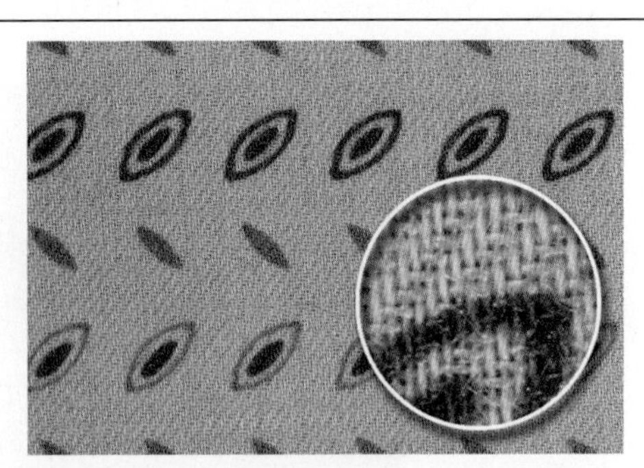

Regular, two-sided twill weave fabrics with a soft handle and drape. Twills from cotton and blends are used for shirts and nightwear. Lining twills are used in menswear for waistcoats and sleeve linings.

Damassé

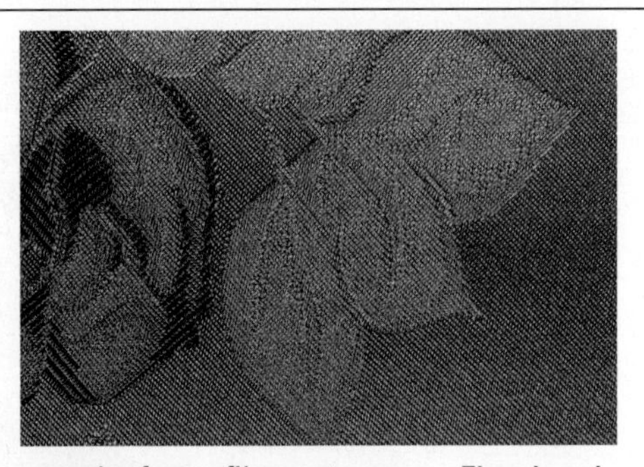

Damask fabrics made from filament yarns. Figuring is achieved by interchange of satin and sateen weaves, often with a changeant effect. Used for blouses and formal wear.

Damask

Figured jacquard woven fabrics, originally made from expensive mercerized cotton for bed linen and table cloths. The figured design may be made by interchanging satin and sateen weaves.

Denim

de Nîmes (fr) = from Nîmes

Durable woven cotton twill, originally with an indigo dyed warp and white weft (blue denim). For jeans, leisure wear and workwear.

Diagonal

A weave that produces a steep diagonal twill line, often emphasised by colouring. Women's outerwear, men's and boy's wear in woollen or worsted fabrics.

Donegal

Donegal: a County in N.W. Ireland

Coarse, woollen, plain woven tweed fabrics with differently coloured warp and weft yarns having random flecks of other colours. For sports jackets, suits, costumes and coats.

Double Rib, Swiss Rib
Rib 2x2

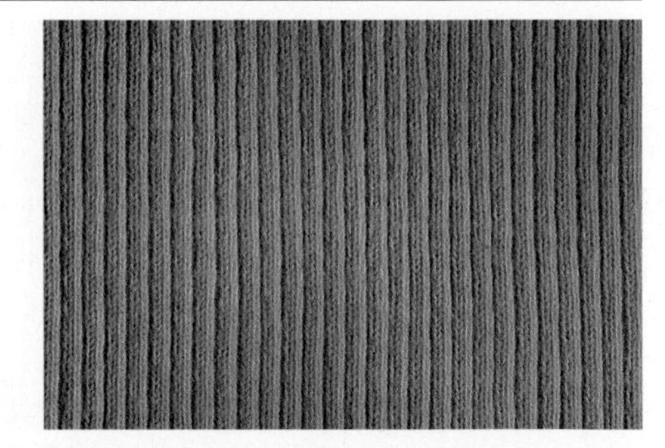

Weft knitted rib fabric with high width extensibility (*see page 94*). Used for welts and cuffs, cardigans and tops.

8.1.2 Top Cloths (6)

Double face

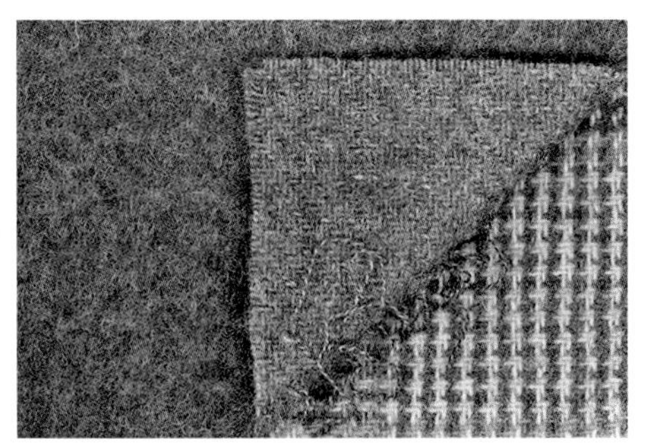

General term for reversible double cloths, usually with contrasting colours; either side can serve as the face. Used for jackets, coats, dresses, and furnishings.

Duvetine
duvetyn

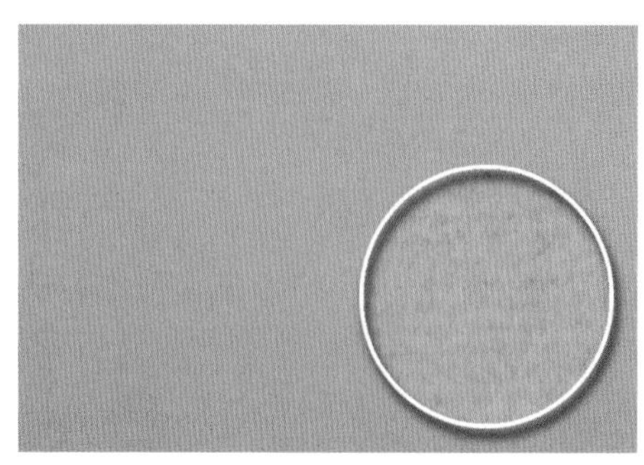

Cotton sateen with a dull, suede type surface made by emerising or raising (brushing) and cropping. Used for jackets and trousers.

Doupion, Doupioni

Plain woven fabric made from rough irregular silk yarns. Doupion means a double cocoon. Silk strands reeled from such cocoons are very irregular. Used for women's outerwear and furnishings, often with net silk filament warp.

Etamine Gauze

Light weight, open weave, gauze fabric (*see page 99*) made from wool, silk or polyester, sometimes with slub yarns. Used in dresses, blouses and shirts, accessories and furnishings.

Drapé
amazon,
venetian

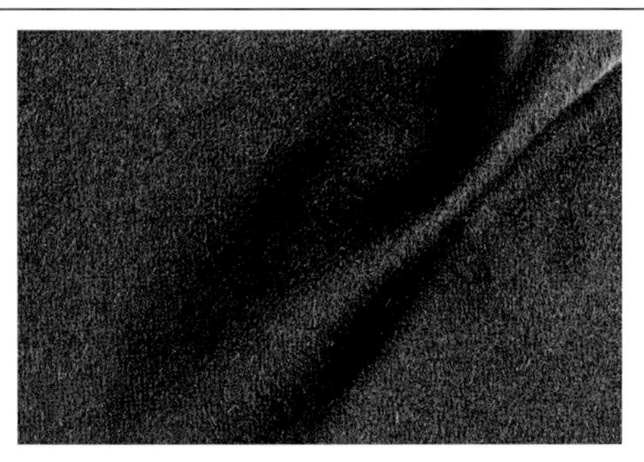

Very fine, satin weave for business suitings with fine worsted warp yarns and woollen weft. A light milling or raising finish may be given.

Façonné

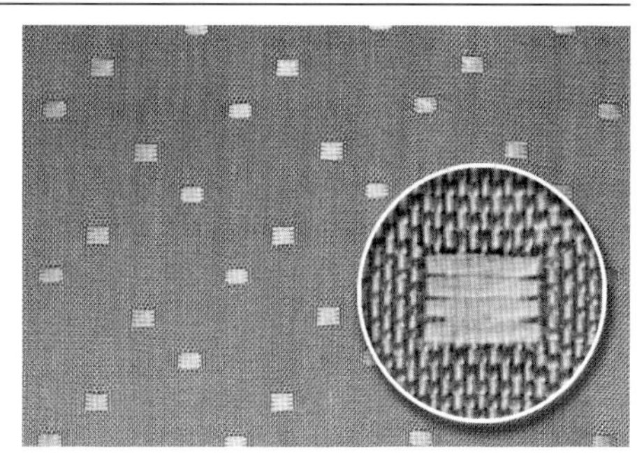

General term for small figured pattern effects, usually made on dobby or jacquard looms. The pattern is made by local changes in weave structure. Used for dresses, blouses and linings.

Duchesse

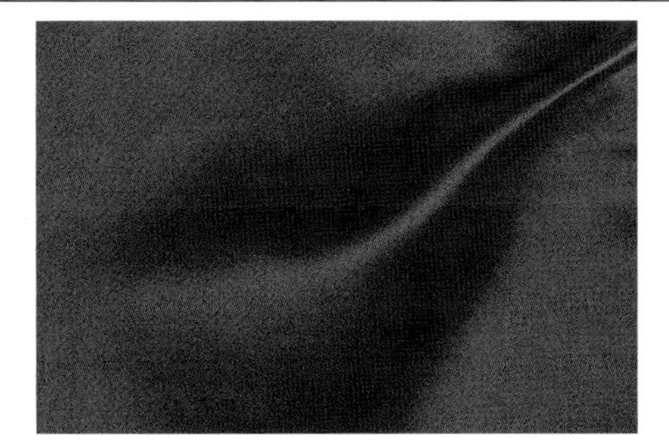

Densely woven, highly lustrous, filament satin cloth. Used for ornamental and formal wear; satin linings for jackets and coats.

Faille

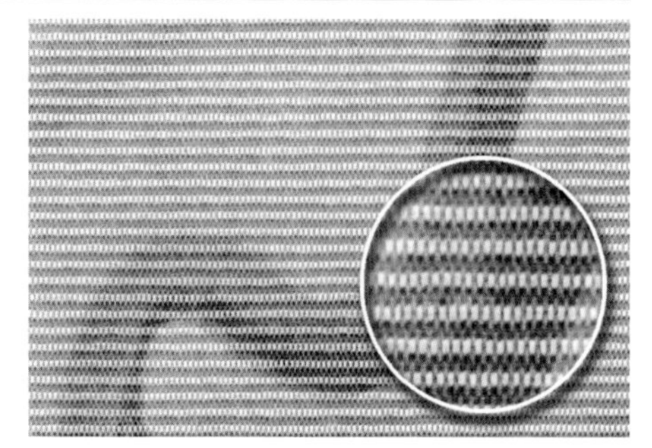

Fine, soft plain woven fabric made from filament warp and soft-spun weft. The rib is formed by using a fine, close-set warp with a coarser weft. Used for dresses and costumes.

8.1.2 Top Cloths (7)

Fine Rib
Rib 1x1

Fine to medium weight extensible and elastic weft knitted cotton fabrics used for underwear and ladies tops (*see page 92*).

Flannel

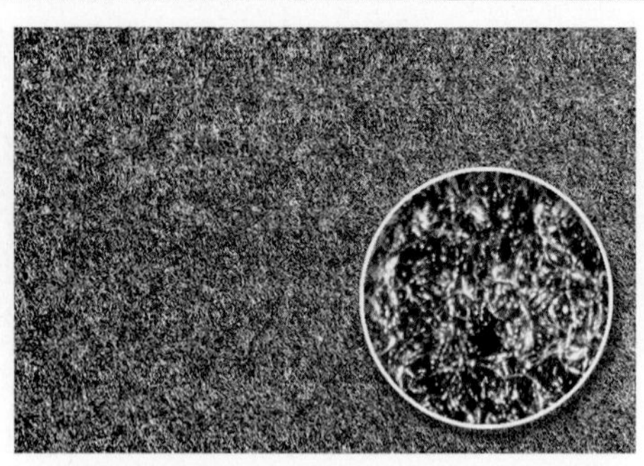

Light or medium weight plain or twill weave fabrics, originally in wool, often in mixture yarns, raised on one or both sides by varying degrees. Cotton flannel is used for shirts, nightwear and bed clothing; wool flannel is for outerwear.

Fil-à-fil
end-on-end

fil (fr) = yarn

2/2 twill weave fabrics in which light and dark colours alternate in both warp and weft, making a miniature staircase pattern. Used for suits and costumes.

Fleece

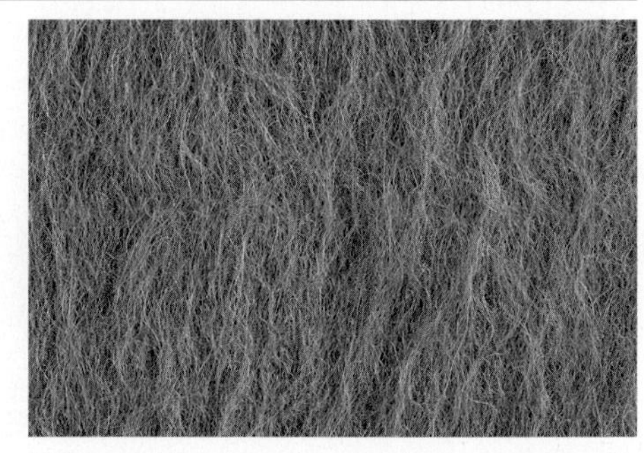

Heavy woollen fabrics with a long brushed pile, made with three to five yarn systems. Used for jackets and coats.

Finette
brushed twill

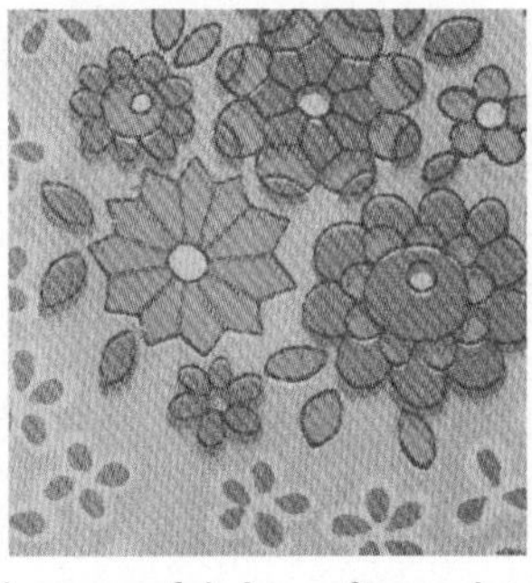

Cotton 2/2 twill weave fabrics, often printed, raised and brushed on the back. Used for shirts and nightwear.

Polar Fleece

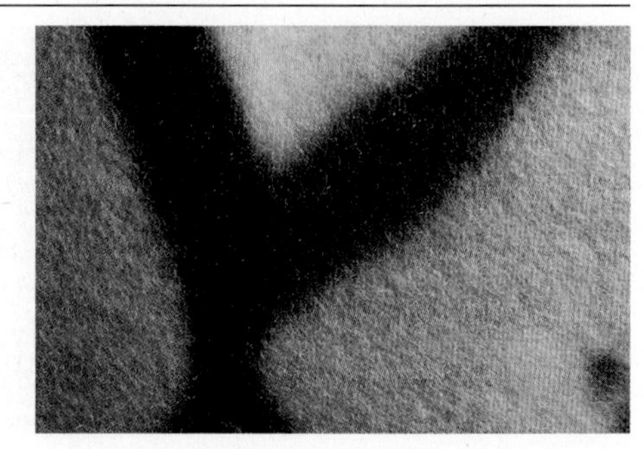

Soft medium to heavy weft knitted fabric intensively raised on one or both sides. Made from nylon or polyester, plain dyed or printed. Used for jackets, pullovers, caps, gloves and scarves.

Fishbone, Herringbone

General term for reversed twills, where the reversal point is offset (*see page 82*). Made from wool, cotton, polyester or blends, often with contrasting colours in warp and weft. Used in jackets, suits, costumes, coats, shirts and blouses.

Flock Print

The velvet-like relief pattern is obtained by printing the design with adhesive and then flocking with small snippets of fibres (*see page 109*). Used for dresses and blouses.

8.1.2 Top Cloths (8)

Foulé, Milled

fouler (fr) = to mill

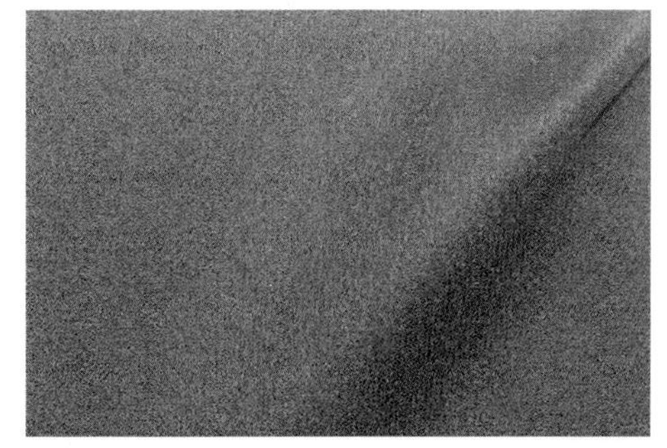

Fine wool fabric, usually with a worsted warp and woollen weft. Typically the face side will be lightly brushed and milled. Used for smart costumes and suits.

Fresco Suiting

Firm, durable, worsted, plain woven fabric with hard twisted, multi-ply yarns in unicolour or marl (*see page 134*). Used for men's suitings.

Frisé
loop fabric

friser (fr) = to curl, wave

Fabrics woven from fine, hard-twist loop (bouclé) yarns, having a granular surface (*see page 70*). Porous and wrinkle resistant, finer than frotté and a more subtle surface texture. Used for dresses, jackets, costumes.

Frotté
imitation terry

A woven fabric with loop yarns in the weft, made to imitate terry cloth, with an uneven, knobbly surface and a granular handle. Used for dresses, jackets, costumes, beachwear.

Inlay
(loopback, fleece)

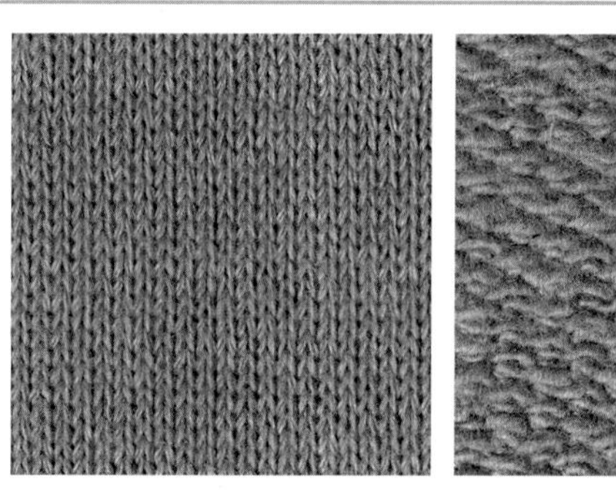

Weft knitted fabric with a fine, smooth single jersey face and bulky, coarser back of tucked inlay yarns. The back is often raised (*see page 93*). Used for sweatshirts, jogging suits, children's wear.

Gabardine

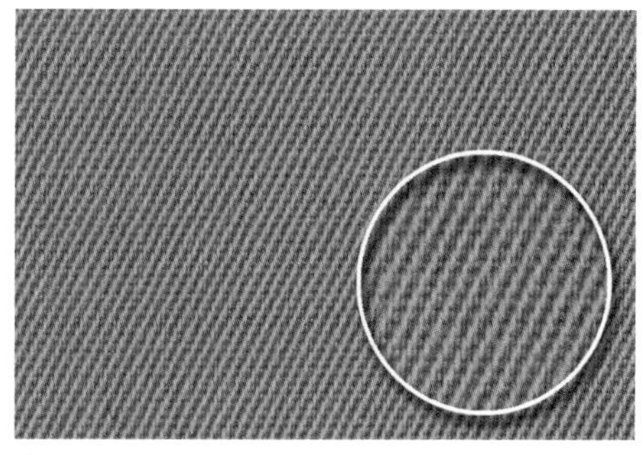

Densely woven fabric with a distinct steep twill line made from wool, cotton, polyester, or blends. The face is made smooth and clear by shearing and pressing. Used for suits, costumes, and coats.

Gaufré
embossed

Fine to medium weight plain woven fabric with relief patterns impressed by an embossing calender during finishing (*see page 111*). Subtle pattern emphasis in reflected light. Used in ladies outerwear.

Glacé

glacé (fr) = glazed

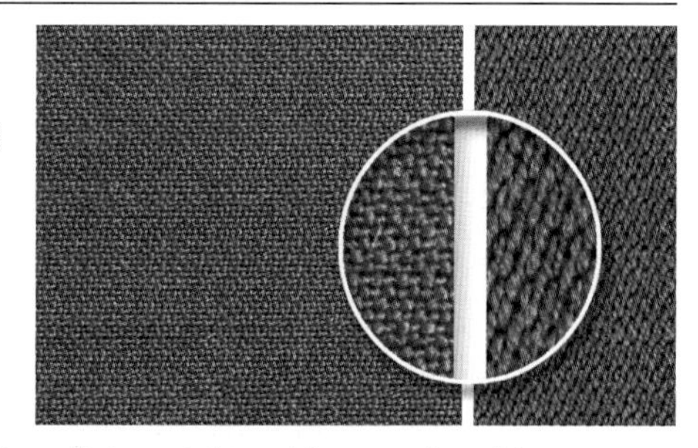

Originally a fine, lightweight suiting made with a cotton warp and mohair weft. Also, a fine worsted cloth in twill or satin made smooth and flat by shearing and pressing. No obvious surface structure but with a lustrous back. Used for costumes, suits and blazers.

8.1.2 Top Cloths (9)

Glazed Batiste

Fine, plain woven cotton made lustrous, semi-transparent, and stiff by parchmentising (*see page 112*). Used for blouses, trimmings, and evening wear.

Harris Tweed

Protected name for hard-wearing, hand woven twill fabrics made from melange yarns in the Scottish Hebrides. Lightly milled, with a firm handle for jackets, coats, and costumes.

Glen Check

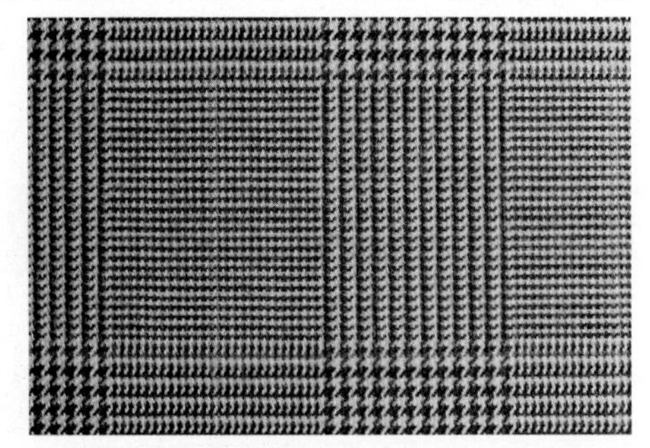

Colour woven with overlaid checks of different sizes, in tone on tone or contrasting colours. Used for suits and costumes.

Knitted Plush
knitted terry

Weft knitted loop pile fabric with an extra plated yarn which forms a uniform surface of loops on one side of the fabric (*see page 93*). Used for babywear, bed sheets, beach wear and leisure wear.

Granité, Granite Weave
momie cloth

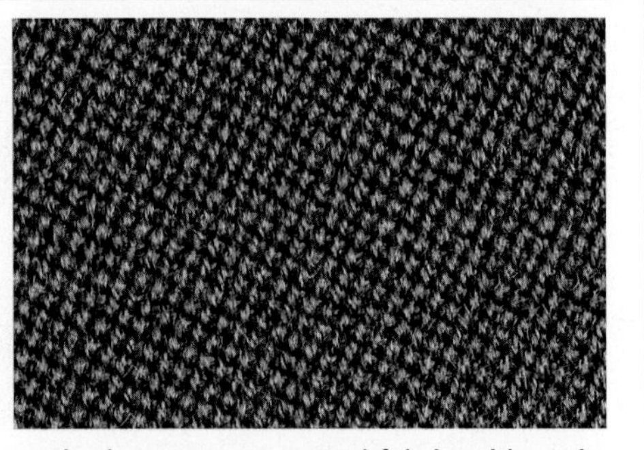

Tightly woven combed cotton or worsted fabric with an irregular, pebbled surface, like crêpe. Usually it is a development of satin or twill but showing no twill line. For suits and costumes.

Homespun

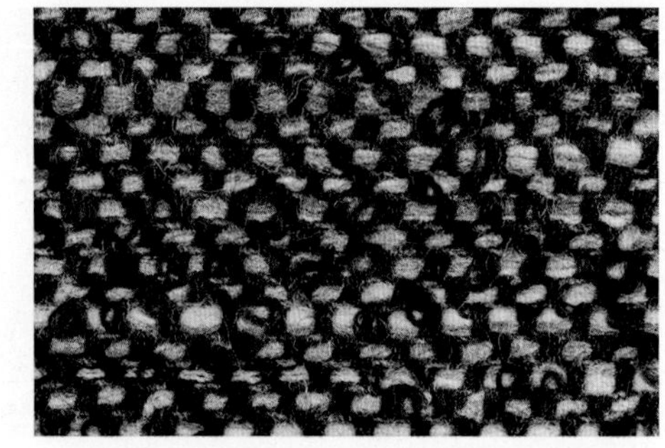

Originally indicated fabrics made from homespun yarns and hand woven. Usually plain weave, loosely constructed and made from coarse, irregular woollen yarns. For sporty jackets and costumes.

Colour-woven spot effect

2:2 colouring on a plain, basket, or 3/1 twill results in a small spot effect. See also **Birdseye** (*see page 136*). Used in suits and costumes.

Honan silk

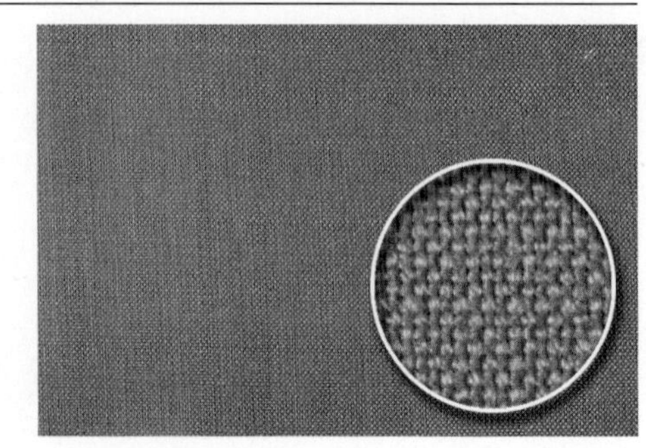

Fine to medium weight, plain woven fabric, with a scroopy handle made from wild silk. Usually somewhat irregular in warp and weft, plain dyed or printed. For dresses, blouses and furnishings.

8.1.2 Top Cloths (10)

Interlock

Fine but compact surface; extensible, but easily deformed; double sided, combed cotton weft knitted fabric in interlock structure (*see page 92*). Used for dresses, blouses, T-shirts, underwear.

Jacquard, woven

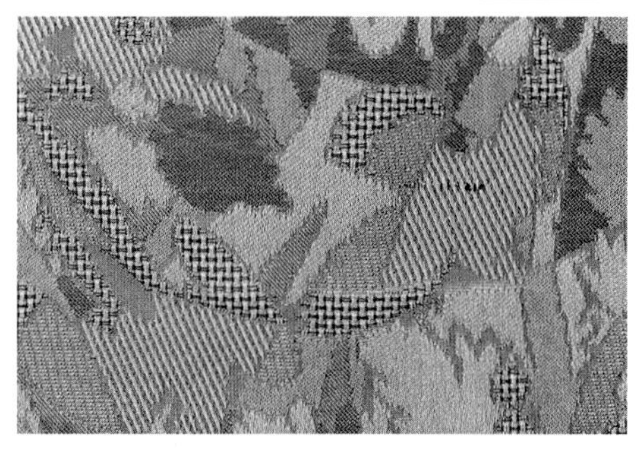

Fabric with a complicated figured design. Figuring is commonly by interchanging satin, sateen, plain, and twill weaves. Colour and yarn effects may be used to accentuate the design. Mainly for furnishing fabrics and formal wear.

Jacquard, knitted

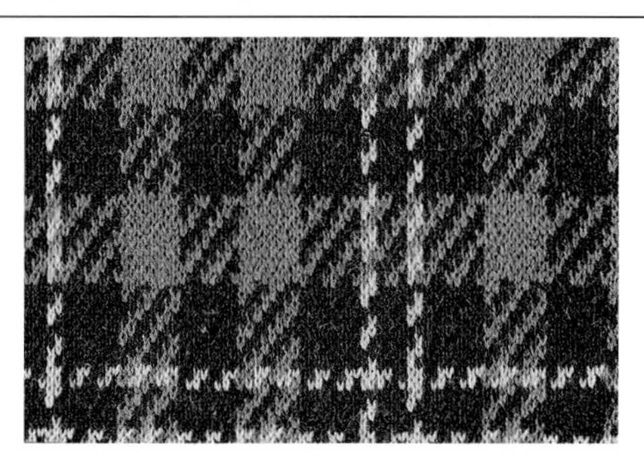

Numerous designs made by selecting coloured yarns to knit on the face in the required pattern (*see page 94*). Used in knitted outerwear such as jackets, skirts, pullovers and cardigans.

Jägerleinen
Bavarian linen
Strawcloth

Jäger (ger) = hunter

Plain woven, green-brown fabrics from linen, half linen, or cotton. Used for suits and costumes.

Javanese

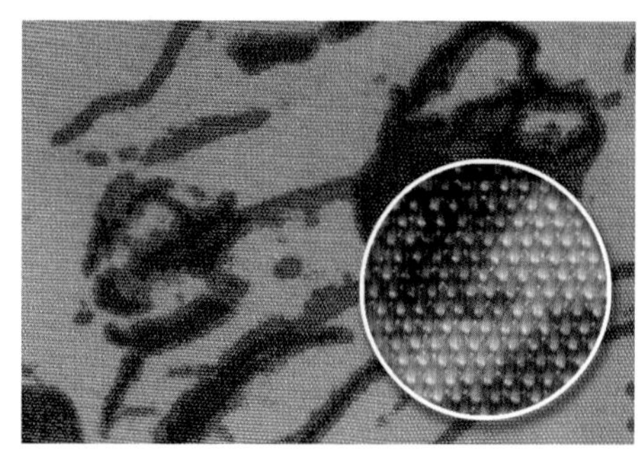

Smooth, soft plain weave viscose fabric with fluid drape; usually printed. Filament warp and spun weft, giving a lightly ribbed appearance.

Cheese cloth

Soft, light weight, plain woven carded cotton fabric with low thread density. Fashion styles may mix yarns with opposite twist for a light crêpe effect. Used for dresses, blouses, squares.

Calico

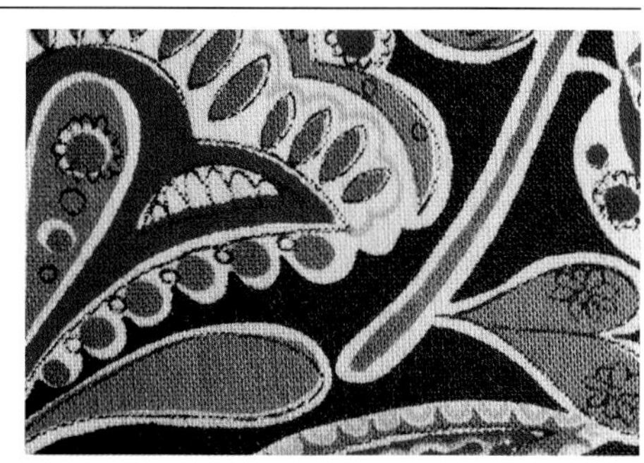

Basic, medium weight, plain woven cotton fabric; usually printed for bed sheets, table cloths, aprons and light Summer clothing – shirts, blouses, dresses. Used in raw (unbleached) form as modelling material for garment design.

Plissé

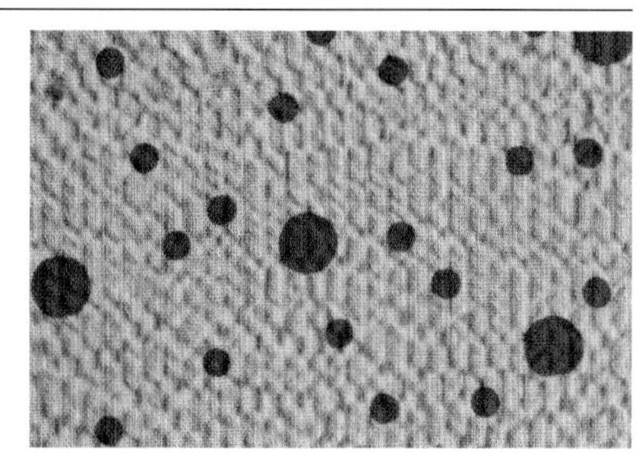

Cotton fabrics with a puckered or crinkled effect produced by the action of caustic soda applied in stripes (*see page 85*). Used for dresses and blouses. Also known as crinkle or blister.

8.1.2 Top Cloths (11)

Chalk Stripe

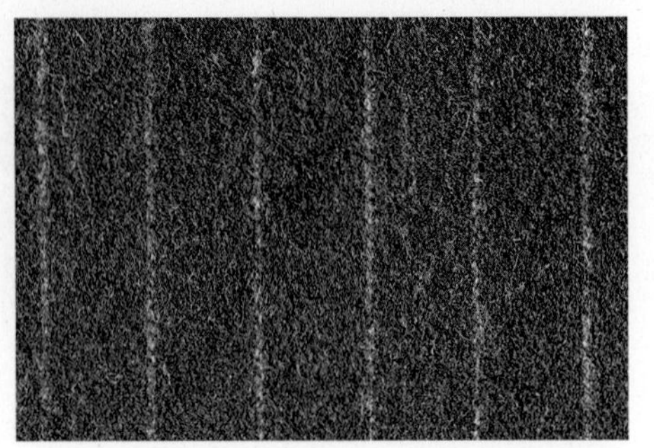

White stripes, broader than pin stripes, on a dark background. Usually woven wool fabrics for suits and costumes. Stripes may be partially obscured by raising. Can also be printed.

Lancé
Clip-spot

lancer (fr) = to throw

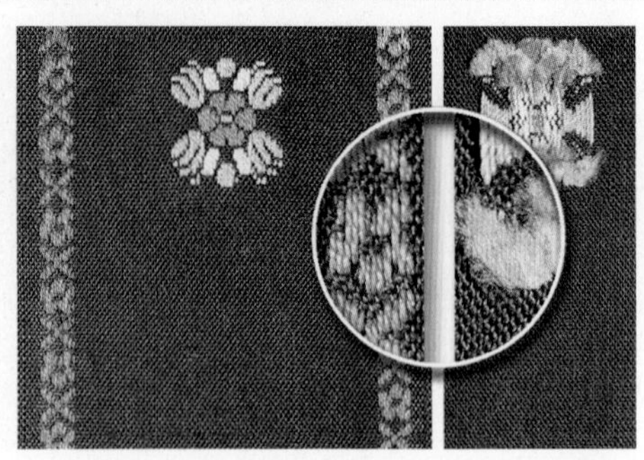

Woven fabrics in which the design is provided by an extra warp or extra weft, which is interlaced only in the pattern area. With **clip-spot** the surplus patterning yarn is cut away. Used for dresses, blouses and furnishings.

Cretonne

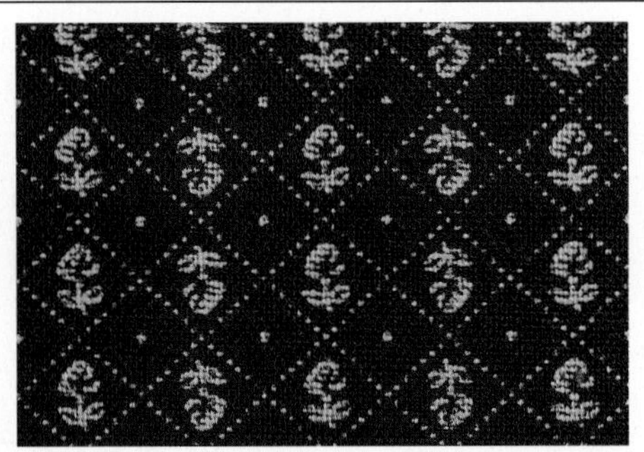

Medium to heavy weight cotton plain woven printed fabric. Used for aprons and Summer clothing. Used in raw (unbleached) form as interlinings and as modelling material for garment design.

Linen
Mock Linen

Usually plain weave in linen and linen blends (*see page 14*). Mock linen can be made from various fibre blends using rough, irregular yarns to give a linen-like appearance with a subdued lustre. Used for dresses, jackets, blouses, skirts.

Mock Astrakhan

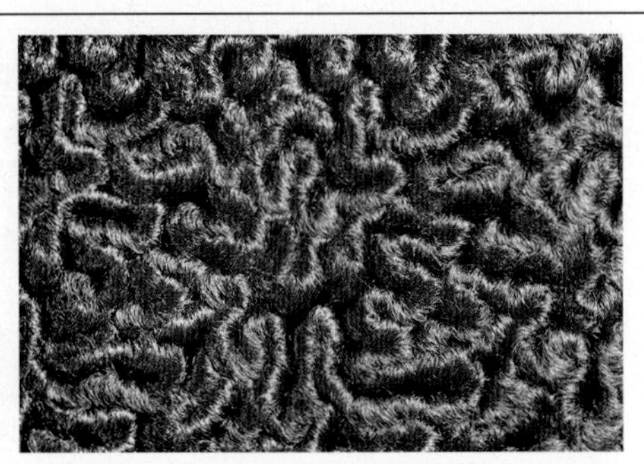

Woven curled-pile fabric, with cut or uncut loops, made to imitate the fleece of a new-born Astrakhan lamb. Used for coats, jackets and trimmings e.g. for cuffs and lapels.

Liberty Print Lawn

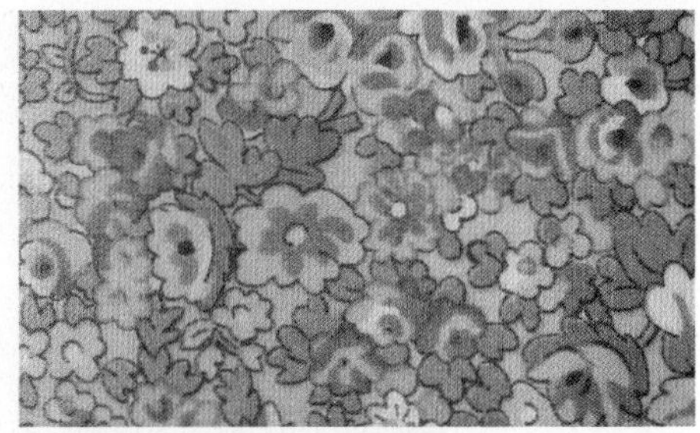

Originally a Trademark of Liberty of London. High quality, light weight, plain woven combed cotton fabrics made with fine or very fine yarns and decorated with floral prints. Originally hand block printed and lightly stiffened for dresses and blouses.

Lamé

lamé (fr) = spangled, worked with gold or silver

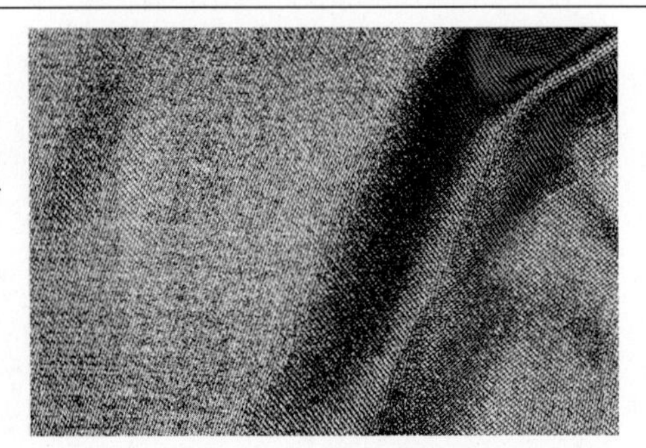

General term for woven fabrics in which metal threads are featured, usually in the weft, providing a glitter effect. The warp is usually silk or cotton. Used for women's formal evening wear.

Loden

Medium to heavy woollen fabric, often made from mixture yarns. Heavily milled to make it dense and durable; may also be raised. Used for suits, costumes and, especially, overcoats.

8.1.2 Top Cloths (12)

Loop

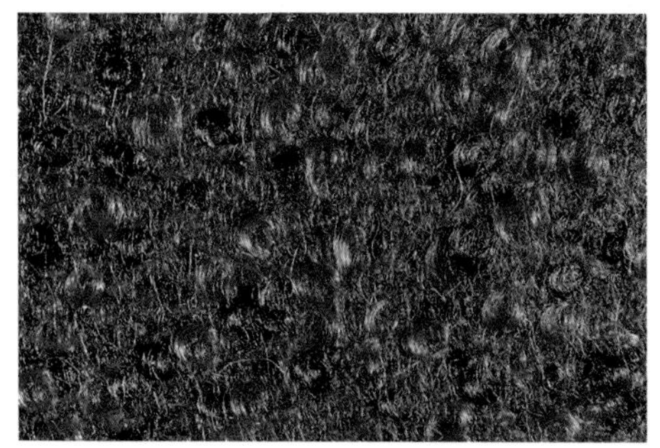

Loose, plain woven fabric with large rounded loops on the surface, made by weaving with loop yarns in the weft (*see page 70*). Used for jackets and costumes.

Lustre

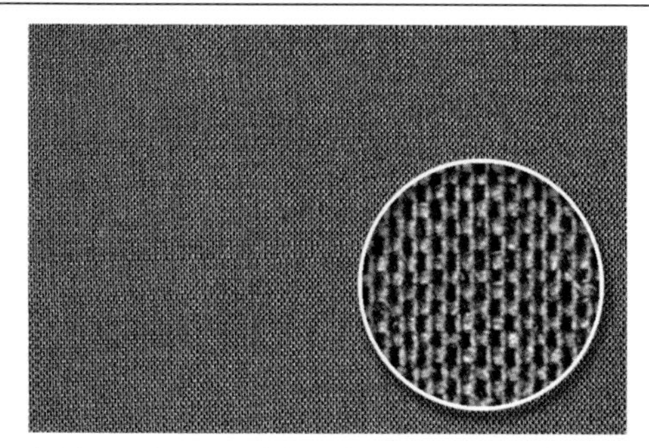

Light weight, wrinkle-resistant, plain woven worsted fabric, including e.g. mohair or alpaca fibres for lustre. Used for summer suits and nun's habits.

Madras

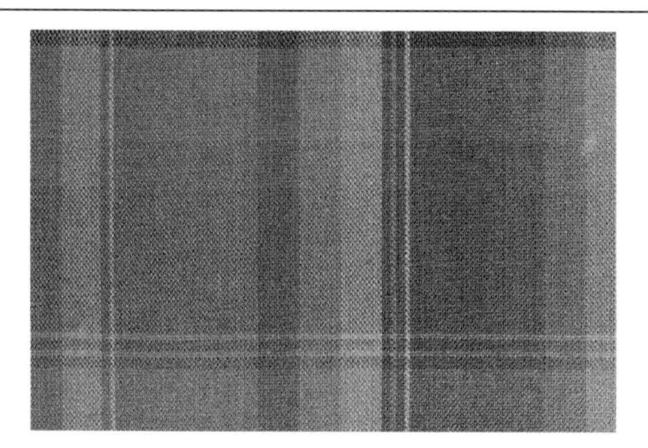

Light weight, fine, plain weave cotton fabric with a large colour-woven check pattern in darkish tones with bright accents. Used for shirts, blouses and dresses.

Marengo

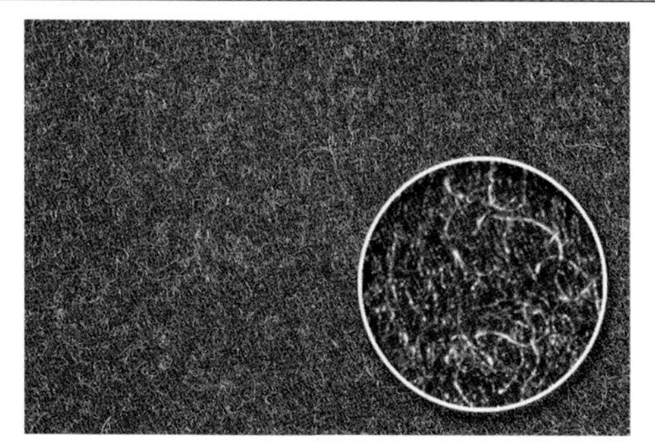

Dark wool fabric with 2 to 5% of white fibres mixed in, so that fluff will not show up. Used for overcoats, suits and costumes

Matelassé

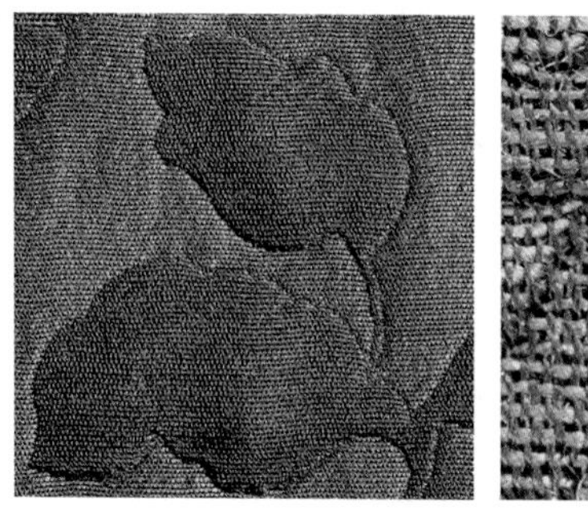

Double cloth with large figured designs which are given a quilted effect by wadding (*see page 88*). Used for women's coats, evening wear and furnishings

Melton

Strongly fulled and lightly raised, tightly woven woollen fabric, sometimes with a cotton warp. The short, smooth surface nap completely obscures the weave. Used for overcoats and uniforms.

Microfibre fabric

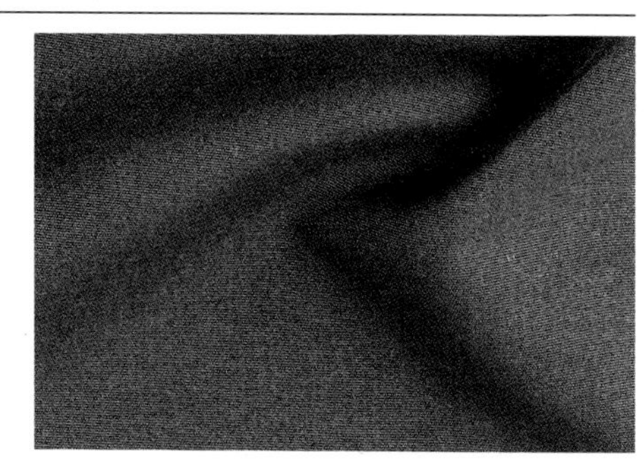

Tightly woven but light and soft fabric made from microfibre polyester or nylon. Relatively wind and water resistant but breathable. Used for jackets and coats. Brands are e.g. Tactel®, Trevira Finesse®, Belseta®.

Mille fleurs

mille fleurs (fr) = thousand flowers

All-over printed design of small flowers. Used for dresses and blouses.

8.1.2 Top Cloths (13)

Moiré

moiré (fr) = water marked

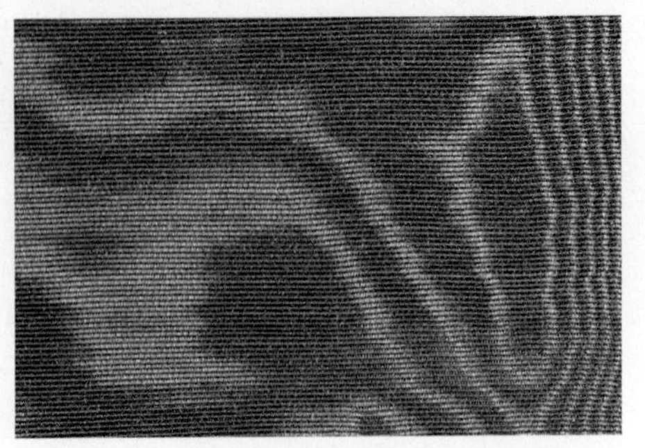

The wavy watermark effect is obtained by calendering or pressing together two superimposed warp ribbed fabrics, or by embossing (*see page 111*). Used for dresses, blouses and linings.

Mouliné

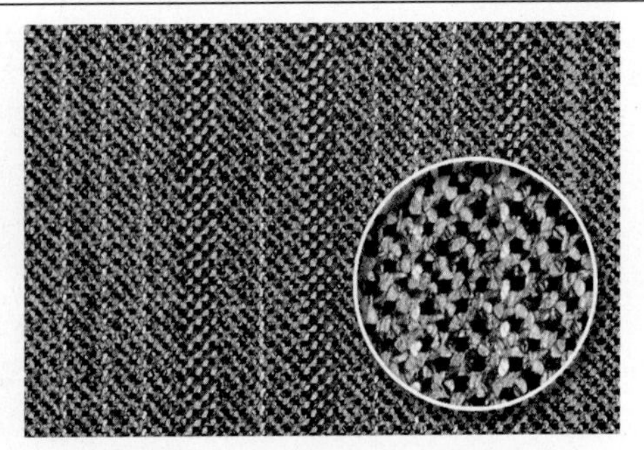

General term for fabrics with a speckled appearance or uniform colour mixture, using mouliné yarns (*see page 70*). See also **Fresco, Twist.** Used for suits and costumes.

Mousseline

General name for a broad range of soft, sheer, light weight plain woven fabrics made from wool, cotton, silk, or man-made fibres, finer than muslin. Used for blouses, dresses, skirts, squares, and furnishings.

Mull

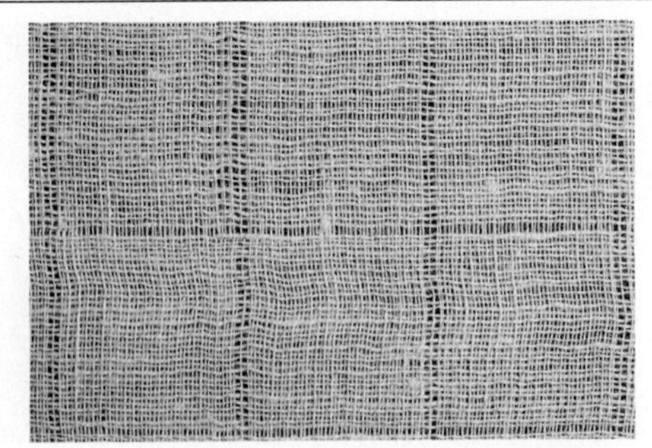

Soft, fine, open, plain weave cotton fabric with a very low thread density in both warp and weft. Used for blouses and squares.

Needle Stripe
Pin Stripe

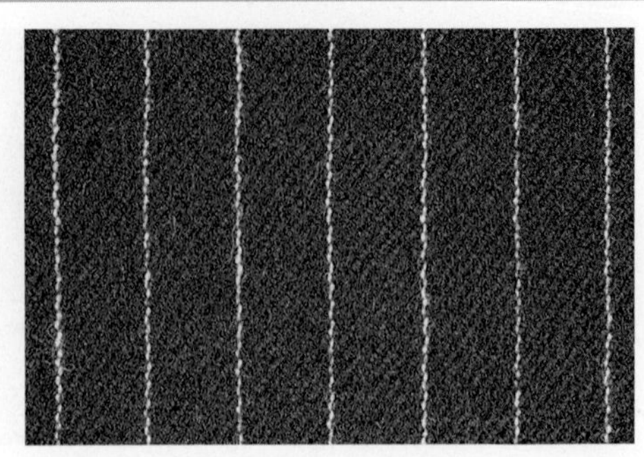

Worsted woven fabric with fine light-coloured lines in the warp direction. Used for suits and costumes.

Natté
Mock leno
Leno

natter (fr) = to plait, braid

Loose, open fabric with the appearance of leno created by the weave and the thread spacing. Picture shows a true leno. Used for shirts, blouses and dresses.

Nicki plush
Knitted plush

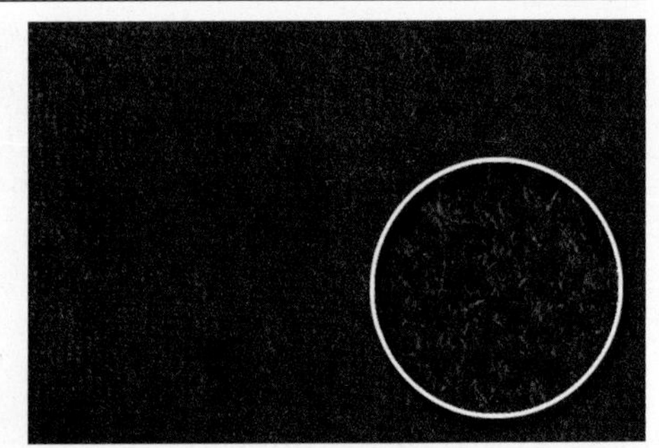

Soft, smooth knitted fabric with a velvety surface, made by shearing a knitted terry. Usually made with a filament polyester ground cloth and cotton pile. Used for home and leisure wear, children's wear, and tops.

Opal
Opaline

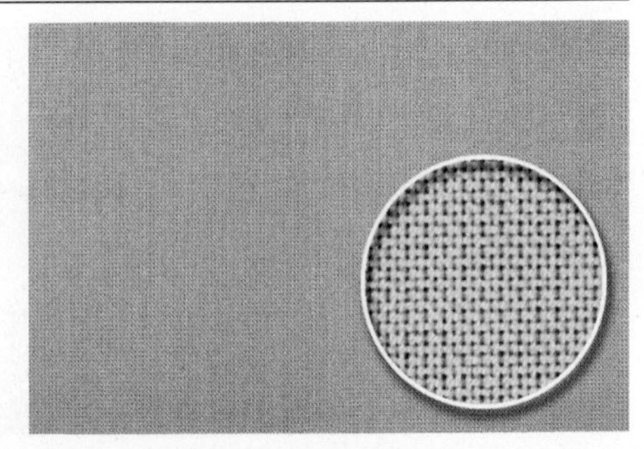

Fine, soft, white, smooth semi-transparent cotton lawn, prepared by shrinking in a mercerizing-type process (*see page 103*) then calendering. Used for dresses, blouses and nightwear.

8.1.2 Top Cloths (14)

Organdie Organdy

Fine semi-transparent lawn or batiste with a permanently stiff finish, plain dyed or printed for dresses, blouses and trimmings.

Basket Weave, Hopsack

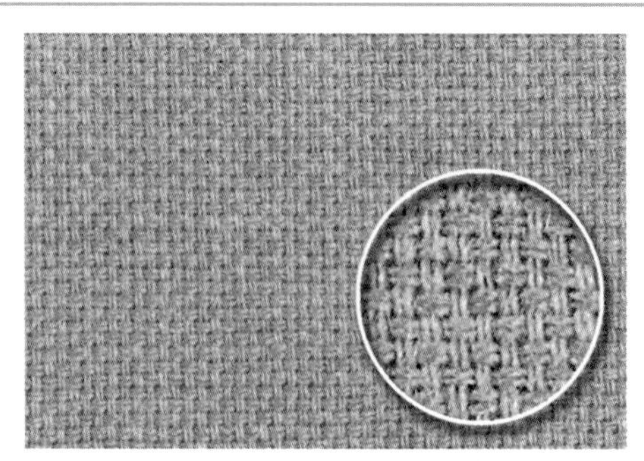

General term for a plain-based weave in which two or more warp and weft yarns interlace as one, giving a granular, chequered appearance. Made from cotton for shirts, tropical suits and leisure wear, or wool for suits and costumes.

Organza

Thin, stiff transparent, plain woven fabric, made from hard-twisted raw silk or synthetic filaments with a stiffening finish. Used for dresses and blouses, accessories, or light-weight interlining.

Panne Velvet

A light weight, highly lustrous velvet fabric made from filament yarns. The pile is flattened and laid in one direction during finishing, by means of heavy rollers. Used for sophisticated women's wear and accessories.

Ottoman

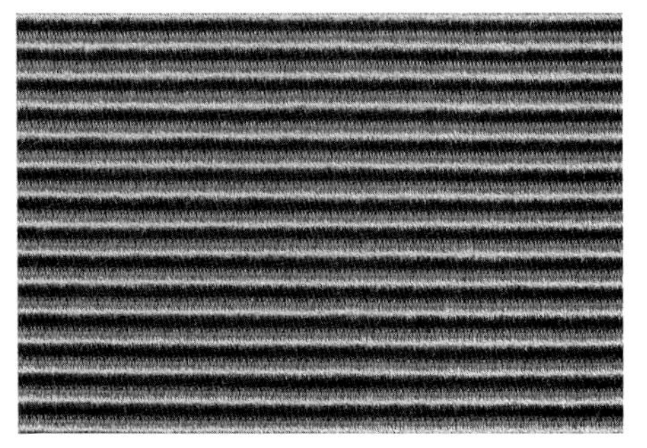

Warp-faced rib fabric with 3 to 10 ribs per cm (*see page 80*). A high gloss is obtained by using filament warp in high thread count. Used for coats, jackets, and furnishings

Shepherd's Check Houndstooth Pepita

Small checks in contrasting colours, usually on a 2/2 twill base with 4:4, 6:6 or 8:8 colouring. Houndstooth has a 4:4 colouring on a 2/2 twill. Known as Pepita in Austria/Germany. Used for suits and costumes.

Oxford

Good quality cotton shirting and blouse fabric made in plain weave, often with two ends weaving as one. Contrasting colours in warp and weft give a miniature diced pattern.

Piqué, knitted

Weft knitted fabric in cotton or blends, with a small relief diamond pattern. Based on single jersey with regular tuck stitches. Used for polo shirts.

8.1.2 Top Cloths (15)

Piqué

piqué (fr) = quilted, padded

Cotton double cloth showing rounded, wavy welts in the weft direction, with pronounced sunken areas between. The face fabric is in plain weave with fine yarns. Used for women's Summer clothing and trimmings.

Ratiné
Ratine

Raised pile fabric in which the pile has been mechanically treated to give various curled and twisted effects (*see page 110*). Used for jackets and coats.

Plush

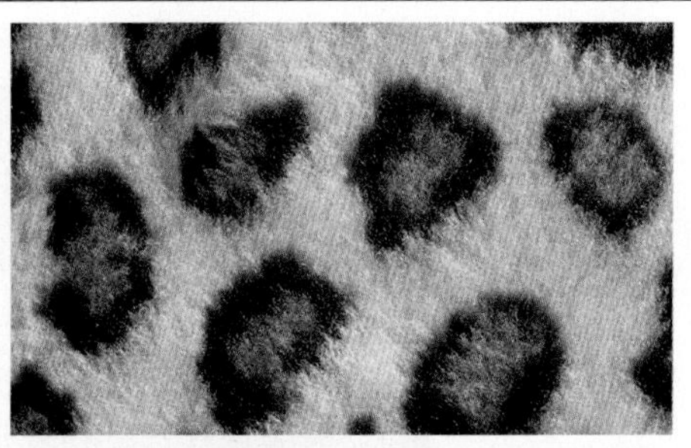

Woven or knitted fabric with a long pile. Can be made by the double plush technique (*see page 87*) or by various knitting routes (*see pages 93 and 98*). The pile is usually acrylic or viscose and may be printed to imitate an animal skin. Used as fleecy linings and imitation furs.

Renforcé

Originally a strong, heavy sailcloth; nowadays also a medium weight plain dyed or printed plain cotton or polyester blend fabric of the percale type for blouses, dresses and bed sheets.

Pongé

Very fine, plain woven fabric in pure, degummed, unweighted silk or synthetic filament yarns. Used for linings, blouses, squares.

Reversible

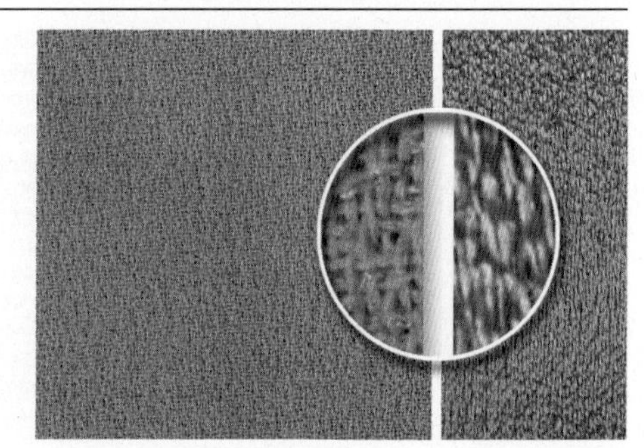

A fabric with different appearance on the two sides, either of which can be used as the face. Usually has either a very dense warp or a very dense weft. Used for dresses and costumes.

Poplin

Plain woven fabric with fine weft-way ribs made by using a fine, dense warp over a coarser weft. Used in different weights for shirts and blouses, jackets and trousers, or coats.

Rib

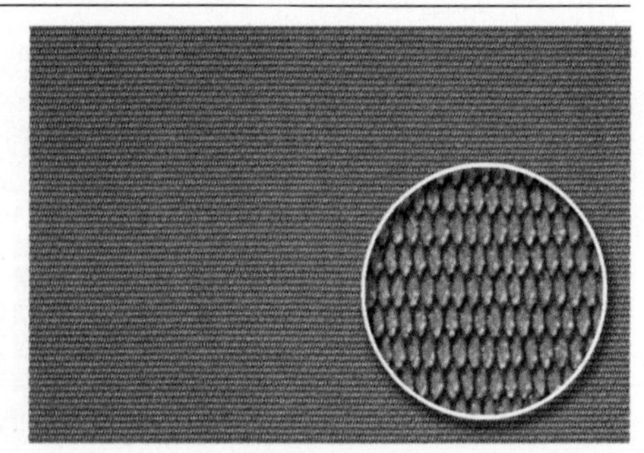

Woven fabric with pronounced ridges in either lengthways (weft rib) or widthways (warp rib). Warp ribs are the more common (see *page 80*). Made in any fibre but often in cotton, wool and silk for dresses, costumes, coats, and furnishings.

8.1.2 Top Cloths (16)

Velvet

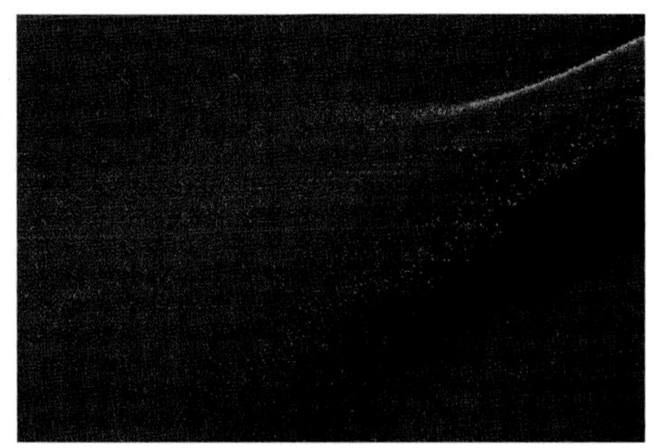

General term for woven cut pile fabrics with a pile height up to 3 mm made from cotton, viscose or silk. The pile is formed from an extra yarn system (*see page 87*). Used for sophisticated clothing and furnishings.

Tartan, Plaid

Cotton or wool colour woven fabrics, usually in 2/2 twill, with block checks in dark colours and large overchecks in light colours. Based on traditional Scottish designs for jackets, skirts, shirts and dresses.

Sand Crêpe

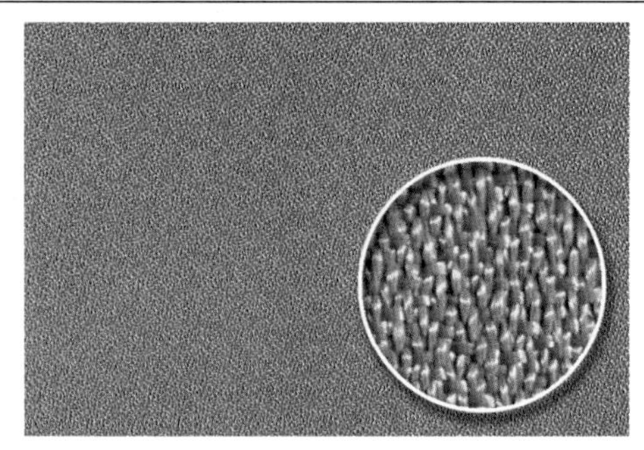

Apparel weight fabrics in crêpe weave made from wool, cotton, polyester, viscose or blends. Short yarn floats in no discernible pattern give an irregular surface texture (*see page 85*). Used for dresses and blouses, suits and costumes.

Seersucker

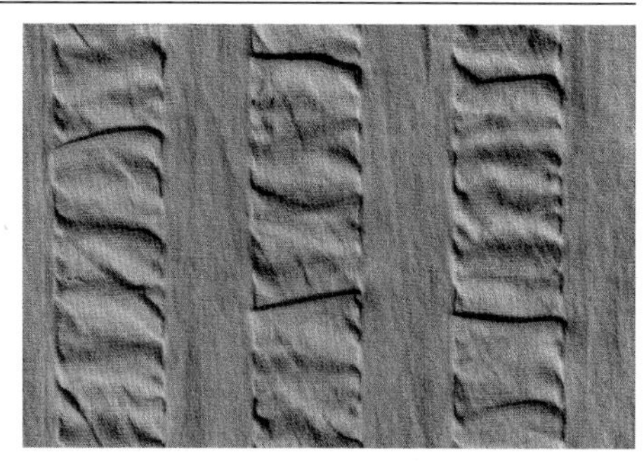

Cotton fabric with crinkled length-way stripes caused by differential shrinkage. True seersucker is generated by differential warp tensions but finishing treatments can produce a similar effect. Used for blouses, shirts, dresses.

Satin

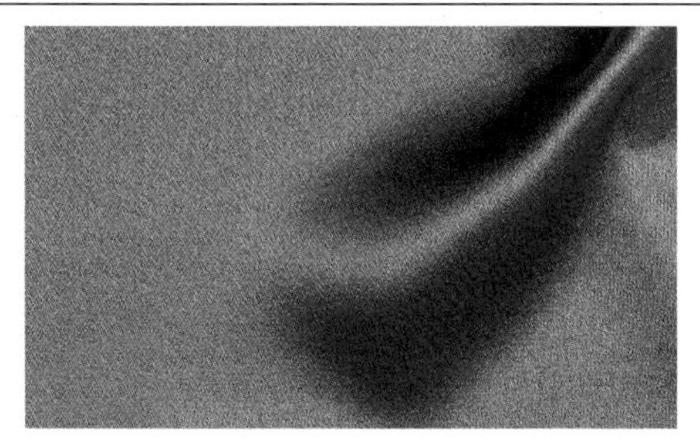

General term for fabrics woven in the satin (or sateen) structure, with a smooth surface and supple drape. Made from silk, wool, cotton, viscose, polyester or blends. Used for dresses and blouses, linings and sheetings, accessories and furnishings.

Serge

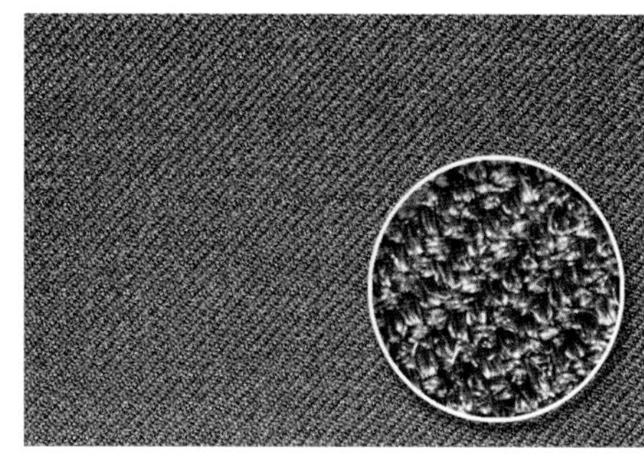

Densely woven twill fabric. Wool serge is lightly milled and raised for suits and costumes. High lustre viscose filament serge is used for linings in lounge suits and coats.

Saxony

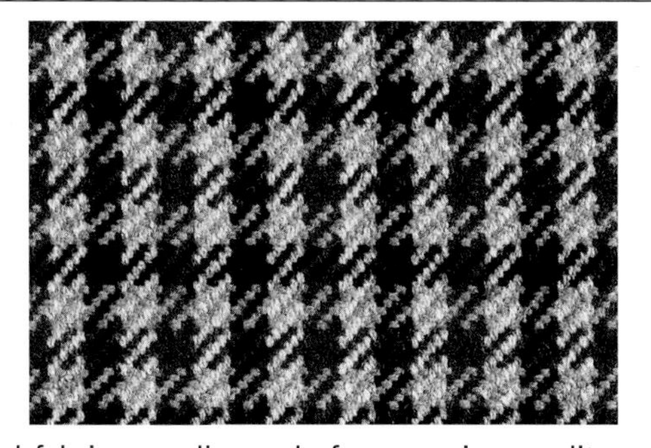

Fine, soft wool fabric, usually made from merino quality. Colour-woven with sporty, classical patterns like houndstooth or checks; softly raised for a flannel effect in sports jackets, blazers and costumes.

Shantung

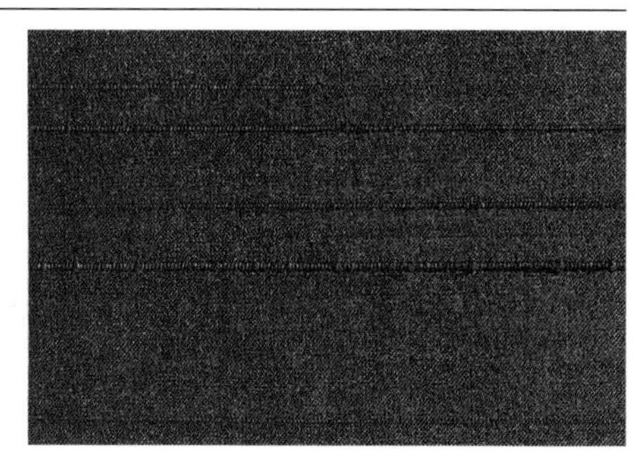

Plain weave fabric originally made with raw tussah (wild) silk. The yarn irregularities and occasional thicker threads in the weft give a rough texture. Used for dresses, blouses and furnishings.

8.1.2 Top Cloths (17)

Shetland

Soft, shaggy, woollen fabrics, usually in regular twill weaves. Often made from mottled yarns containing a proportion of stiffer hairs. Used for suits, costumes and coats.

Single Jersey
Plain Jersey

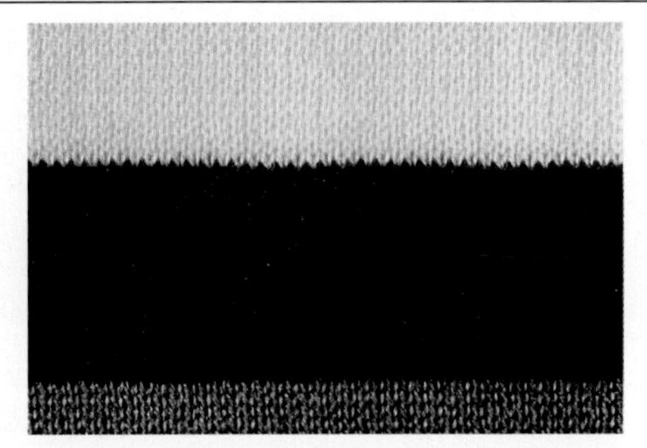

Single-sided weft knitted fabric in plain stitch in a wide range of weights made from practically all fibres (*see page 92*). Usually in cotton for shirts, blouses, nightwear and T-shirts.

Soielaine

soie (fr) = silk
laine (fr) = wool

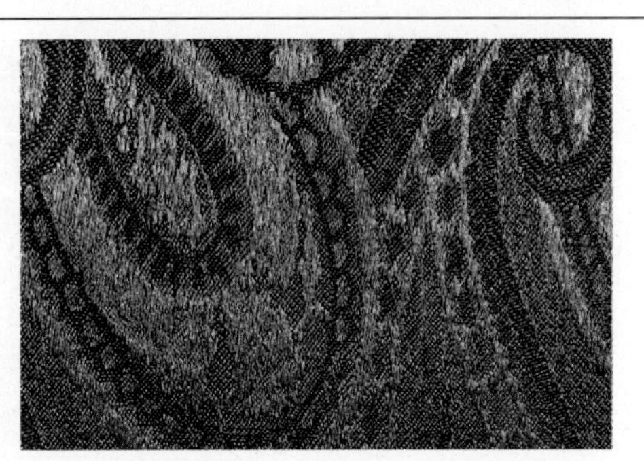

Very soft, fluid fabric with filament warp and fine wool yarns as weft. Illustration shows a Paisley jacquard pattern. Used for blouses, dresses, and skirts.

Surah

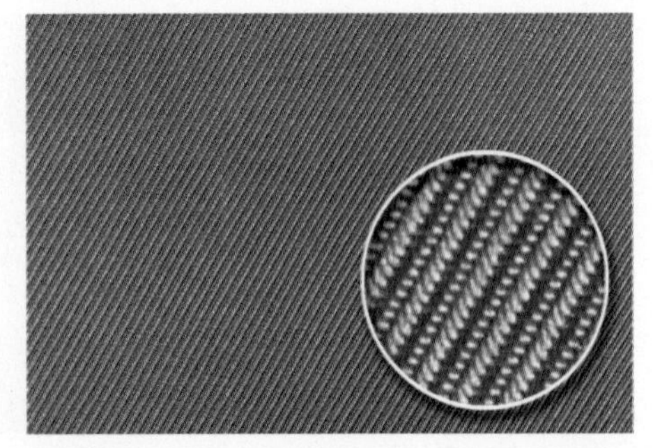

Soft, lustrous, silk fabric with distinct, fine twill lines. High thread density gives a full handle and a flowing drape. Used for blouses, ties, dresses, linings and furnishings.

Taffeta

A general term for smooth, closely woven plain weave made from filament yarns and showing a faint weft-way rib due to a higher density of warp than weft. Handle is firm to stiff. Used for linings and evening wear.

Toile

toile (fr) = fabric

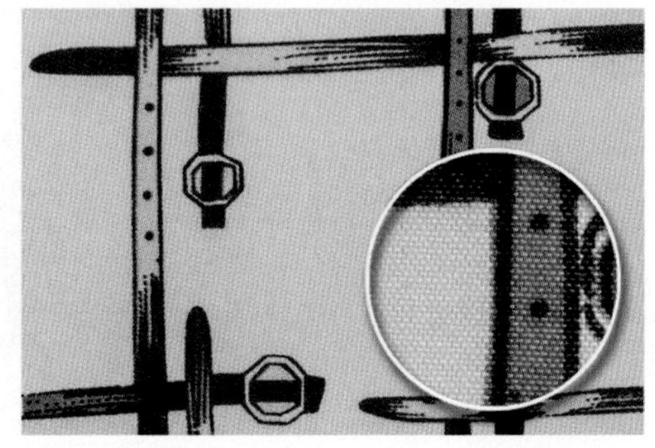

Softly, flowing, fairly open plain weave fabric in soft twist filament or schappe silk yarns for blouses, dresses, fine nightwear, lingerie, and bed clothing.

Tricotine
Cavalry Twill

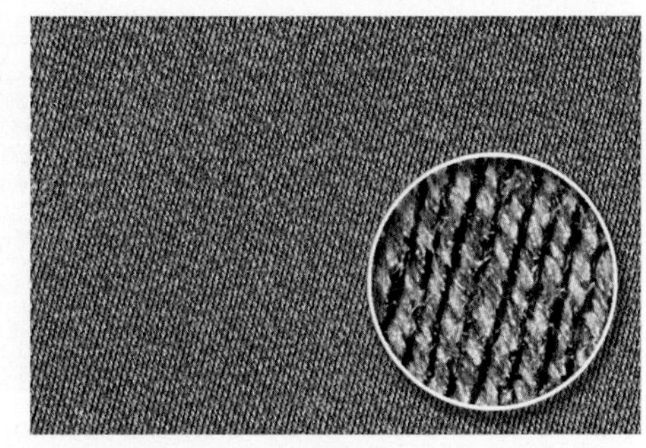

Firm, durable, clean-finished, warp faced fabric with a fine, steep twill line in the family of whipcord and gabardine. Used for trousers, uniforms and coats.

Tropical

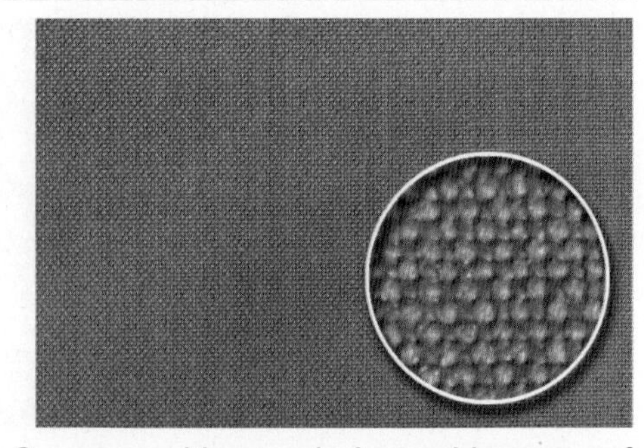

Light weight Summer suiting made in a wide range of weaves and fibres. Fine, hard-twisted worsted fabrics in plain weave are wrinkle-resistant and breathable and have been termed "Cool Wool".

8.1.2 Top Cloths (18)

Woollen

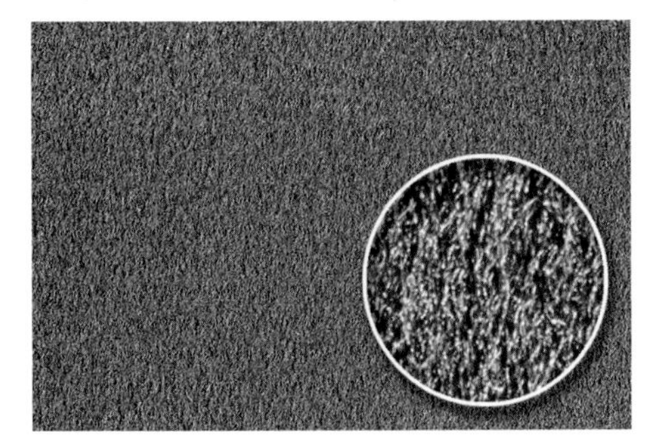

Heavily milled, raised, brushed and cropped woven woollen fabric with a dull lustre for suits, costumes and coats.

Twist

Durable plain or twill worsted fabrics, often made with multicoloured folded yarns for a speckled effect. Used for jackets, trousers and suits.

Tulle

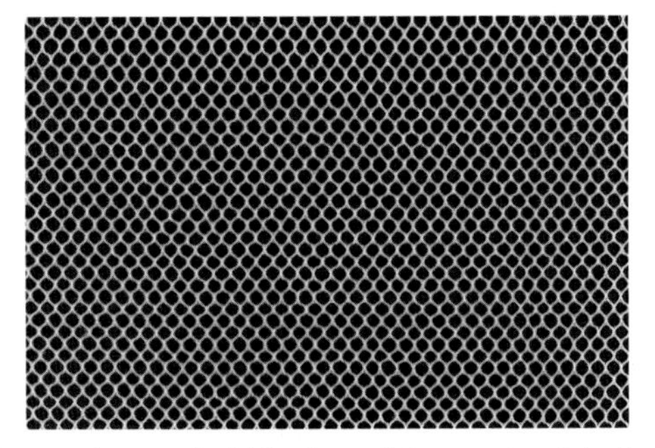

Plain net fabrics made on a bobbinet machine or simulated by warp knitting. The honeycomb-type structure may be used as such or as a base for embroidery, for sophisticated blouses and dresses, trimmings, layering or veils.

Velour, woven

Soft, closely woven fabric with a short thick pile formed by raising, brushing and sometimes cropping, then laid in one direction and pressed. Medium weights made in satin or sateen weave; heavier weights in double cloths. Used for jackets and coats.

Tweed

Homespun-type woven woollen fabrics made from coarse, irregular, mottled yarns, usually in twill weave. Often warp and weft have contrasting colours. Used for jackets, suits, costumes and coats.

Velveteen

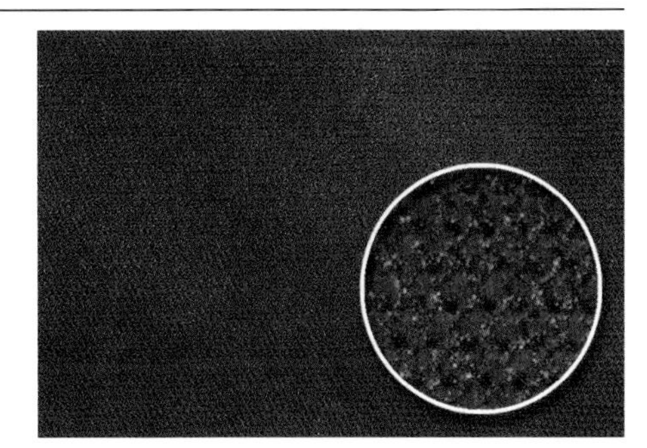

General term for a weft cut pile fabric made on a velvet loom. Usually made from cotton with a short, dense, uniform pile. Used for ladies outerwear, suits, ribbons, accessories, drapes and furnishings.

Twill

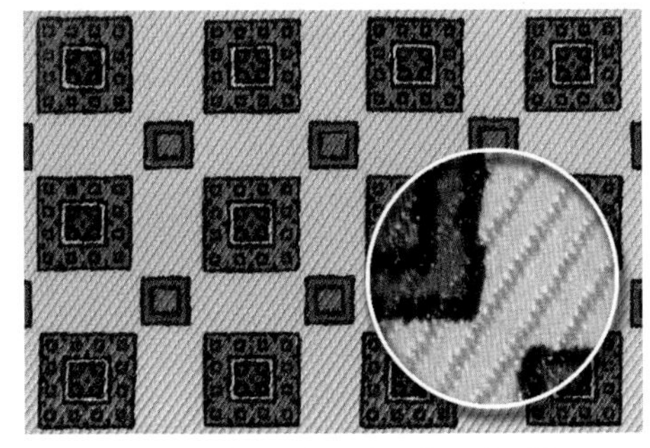

Soft, light twill weaves, usually printed, often in filament yarns for dresses, blouses, ties, scarves.

Velveton

Medium to heavy cotton sateen with an emerized or raised and cropped suede surface, like Duvetine and Moleskin. Firm, durable and washable. Used for trousers, jackets, trimmings and furniture covers.

8.1.2 Top Cloths (19)

Vichy
Gingham

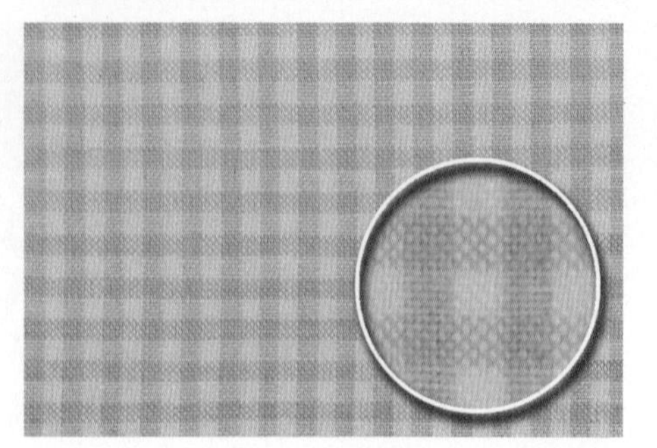

Plain woven cotton fabrics with block checks in contrasting colours for shirts, blouses, aprons and table linen.

Weveknit

Weft knitted double piqué which has a firm construction and can be handled like a woven fabric (*see page 94*). Used for dresses, costumes, trousers, jackets, and coats.

Birdseye

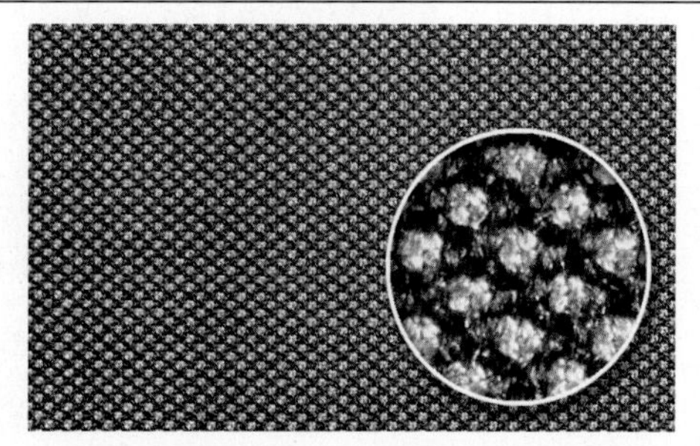

Close-cropped worsted fabric with typical point pattern effect achieved by contrasting colours in both warp and weft, in e.g. 2:2 or 4:4 colouring on plain, 2/2 twill or derivatives of these. See also the spot effect on page 126. Used for suits and costumes.

Whipcord

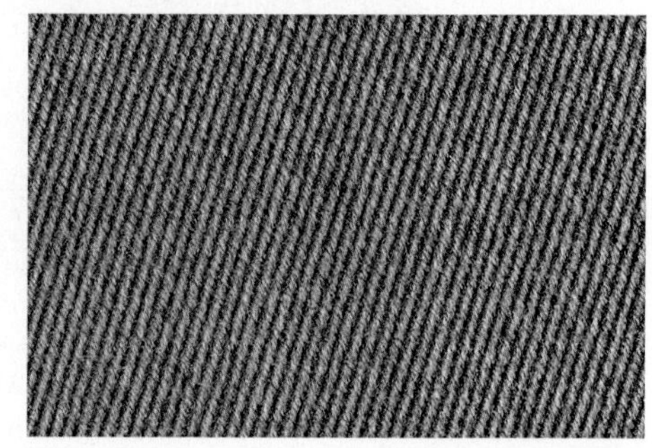

General term for densely woven warp-faced fabrics with a steep twill line. In worsted yarns with a clean finish for trousers, suits and coats.

Voile

Lightweight, sheer, plain woven fabric with a crisp, wiry handle made from hard-twisted yarns, for dresses and blouses.

Wild Silk,
Tussah

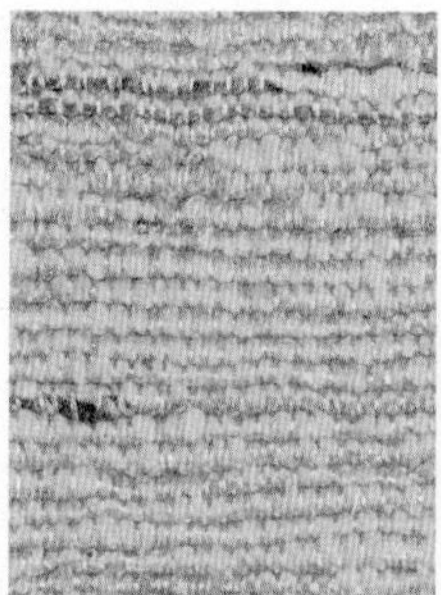

General term for materials made predominantly from wild Asiatic (tussah) silk. These yarns are very irregular, with slubs, neps and knots. Used for dresses, costumes and furnishing fabrics.

Waffle
Honeycomb

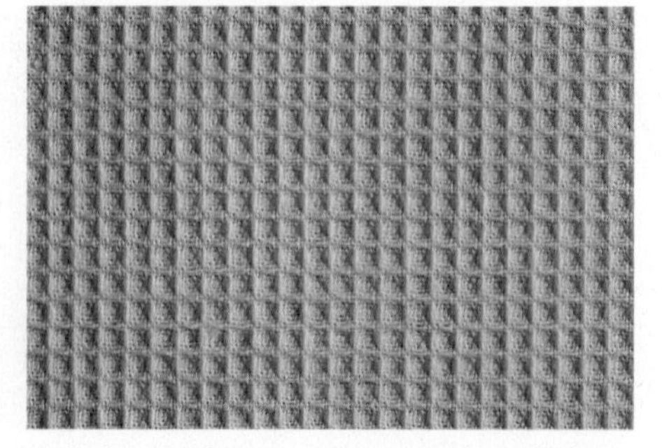

Woven cotton fabric in which warp and weft threads form ridges and hollows, giving a cellular appearance. Fine qualities for blouses and trimmings; heavier types for towels and bathrobes.

Zephyr

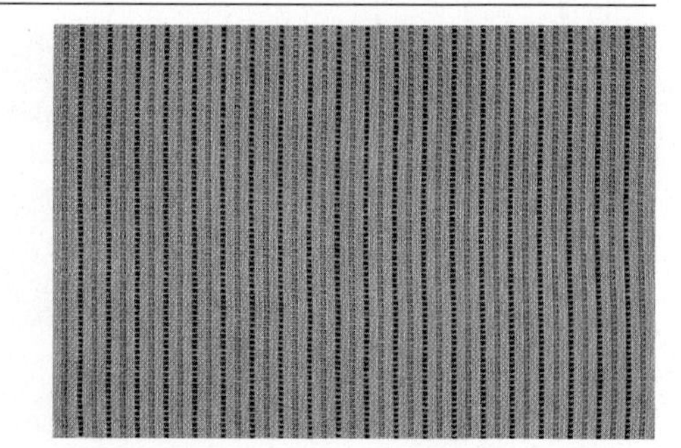

General term for light weight, sheer, soft fabrics used for shirts and blouses. Usually made in plain weave; often colour woven with stripes on a white ground.

8.2.1 Interlinings

Interlinings are attached to the back of the top cloth. Their primary purpose is to ensure that the garment maintains its shape. Stabilisation is achieved by careful attention to **point stitching** (invisible sewing), **layering,** and **fusing.** During garment **finishing,** shape can be imparted by forming and steaming.

A large number of interlining materials is available to satisfy the widest range of **performance requirements,** such as extensibility, padding, stiffening, shape retention, and tolerance to different manufacturing, end use, and aftercare regimes. They may be constructed as woven, knitted or nonwoven materials and they may be supplied either as fusibles or for sewing. Fusible interlinings with a **continuous coating** of adhesive give a stiff finish. A softer finish is obtained with **dot coated** fusibles.

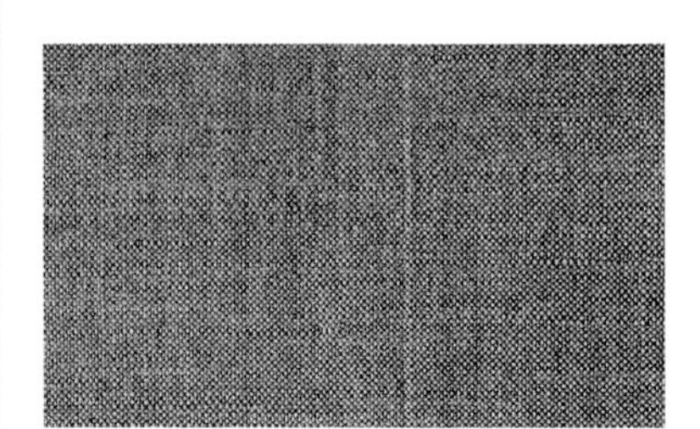
1: Haircloth

2: Wool interlining

3: Cotton interlining

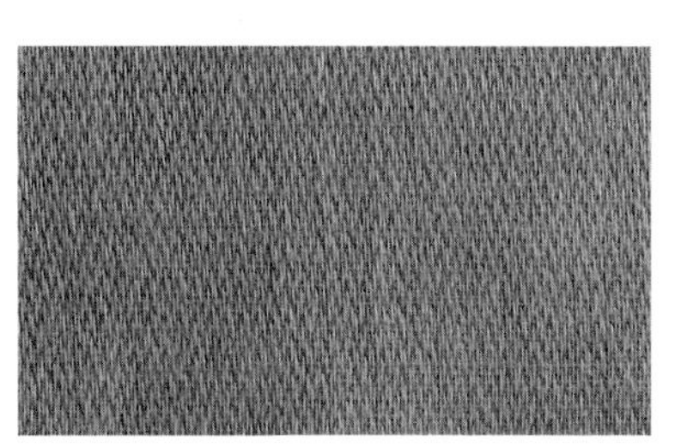
4: Polyquick®

5: Buckram

6: Green Linen

7: Stitch bonded nonwoven

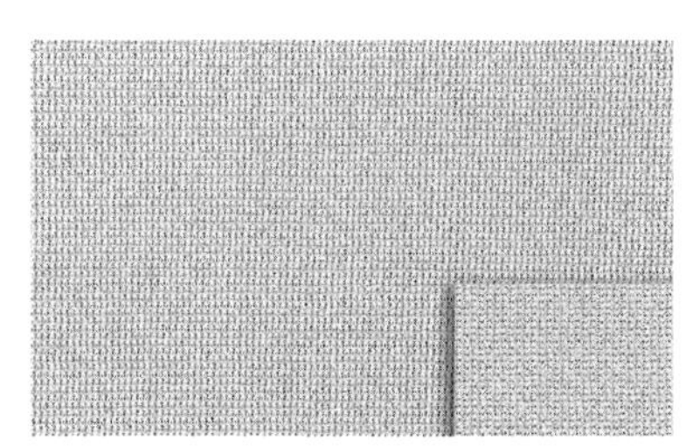
8: Locknit fusible

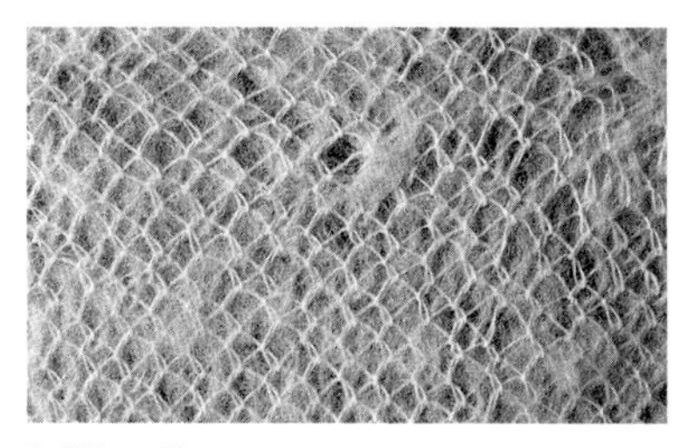
9: Watteline

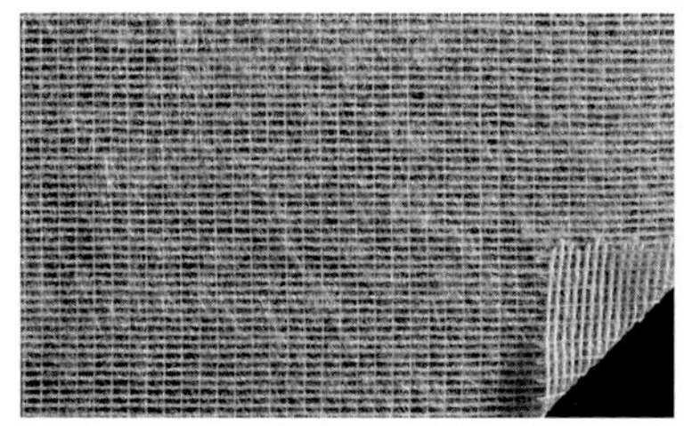
10: Raschel fabric

Woven Interlinings

Haircloth (*Figure 1*) is very resilient in the weft direction and clings to the outer cloth because of its rough surface texture. It has a cotton or wool warp and a horsehair, or sometimes camelhair weft. Together with lighter **wool interlinings** (*Figure 2*), they are used for the front parts of suits, jackets and coats made from medium to heavy weight fabrics.

Cotton interlinings of various weights are used in ladies outerwear. For especially soft applications, they are lightly raised (*Figure 3*).

Woven interlinings are usually made in plain weave, for good stability. **Polyquick®** (*Figure 4*) is a supple fabric made in broken twill.

Stiffening fabrics are often treated with natural or synthetic polymers, such as starch or pva, to provide extra firmness. Cotton stiffeners, such as **buckram** (*Figure 5*) are used mainly for collars and cuffs in shirts. Linen interlinings are used mainly in men's tailoring. **Stiffened linen** or **cutter's linen** is stiffened with size; **green (raw) linen** is unfinished (*Figure 6*). **Organza** is used as a light stiffener in women's outerwear.

Nonwoven Interlinings

A very wide range of nonwoven interlinings is available: from light to heavy, from soft to stiff, from thin to bulky. Stitch bonded materials (*Figure 7*) are very stable.

In general, it is the lightweight nonwovens that are used most often.

Warp Knitted Fabrics

Charmeuse (locknit) (*Figure 8*) is a combination of tricot and 2x1 plain stitches. It is used mainly in combination with extensible top cloths. **Watteline** (*Figure 9*) is a very loose, soft tricot construction, raised on the back. It is used for waddings and padding between top cloth and lining. **Raschel** interlinings made in chain stitch with inlay can be both flexible and stable (*Figure 10*). They are used in jackets and coats.

8.2.2 Linings

The purpose of lining is to upgrade the quality and value of a garment by improving both its appearance and its performance. It helps the outer cloth to hang well and protects it from perspiration, rubbing, and staining. Lined garments keep their shape better, are easier to put on and remove, and are warmer. Seams and stitchings are neatly covered and thin fabrics are made less transparent. Linings also allow the construction of invisible details such as outer pockets and inside pockets, covering of lapels and small parts, finishing of waistbands, and back panels for waistcoats.

The main **performance requirements** for linings are comfortable wearing properties and tolerance to use, dry cleaning and washing conditions. These are secured by appropriate choice of fibre type, fabric structure and density, and finishing.

1: Printed taffeta

2: Pongé Venezia®

3: Serge lining

4: Croisé changeant rayé

5: Satin sleeve lining

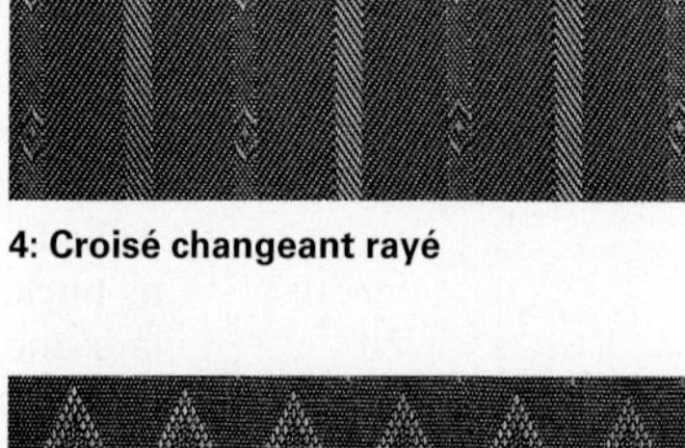

6: Taffeta changeant façonné

7: Moleskin

8: Pocketing

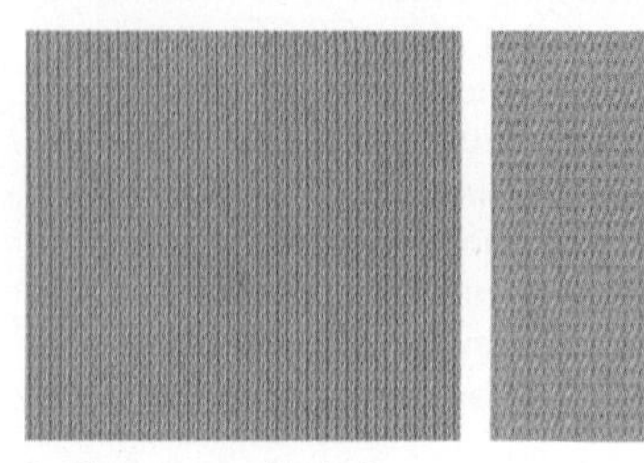

9: Charmeuse, locknit

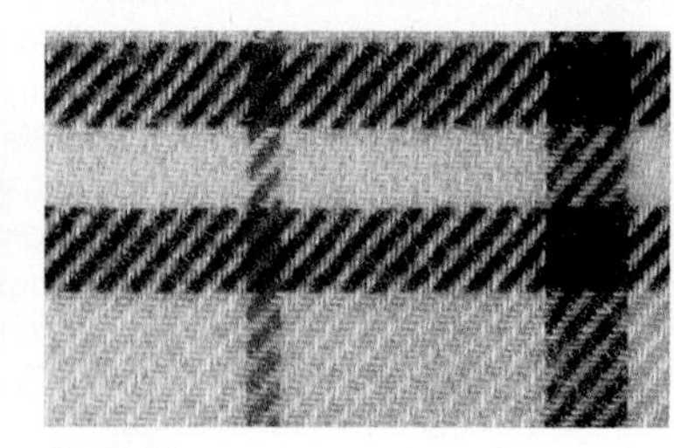

10: Plaid

Body Linings

Body linings are used for outerwear. They are constructed from filament yarns of viscose, polyester, nylon, acetate, cupro, silk, and mixtures (viscose/nylon, triacetate/nylon, acetate/cupro).

Taffeta (*Figure 1*) and **Pongé** (*Figure 2*) are made in plain weave. **Serge** (*Figure 3*) and **Croisé** (*Figure 4*) are twills (Fr: croisé = twill). **Duchesse** is a satin weave.

Sleeve Linings

Popular patterns for sleeve linings are stripes on a light ground. They are mostly made of viscose filament yarns. Examples are **Taffeta, Satin** (*Figure 5*) and **Croisé.**

Waistcoat Linings

Linings for waistcoats are often in colour and weave effects such as **Changeant** (*Figure 4*) and **Façonné** (*Figure 6*). They are made from e.g. viscose or silk/acetate ("half-silk"). These richly patterned fabrics are also used for lining jackets and coats.

Pocket Linings

Cotton sateen fabrics such as **Moleskin** (*Figure 7*) or plain weaves such as **Pocketing** (*Figure 8*) or **Pocketing Twill** may be finished with e.g. starch or pva and calendered. Brushed fabrics like **Pocketing Velveton** are warm synthetic fibre fabrics and are very durable.

Warp Knitted Linings

Linings that are extensible and conformable can be made from nylon or viscose warp knits such as **Charmeuse** (*Figure 9*).

Warm Linings

Outdoor jackets and coats are lined with warm fabrics made from cotton, acrylic, viscose, wool, or blends.

Plaid (*Figure 10*) is a colour woven check design, usually brushed. **Plush** is a pile fabric with a pile height of more than 3 mm, either woven or knitted. **Quilt** is a combination of two or three fabrics sewn together.

8.2.3 Ribbons and Decorations

A garment is made not only from the apparel fabric but also various accessory items. These have to be chosen in such a way that they complement the outer fabric both aesthetically, in terms of decoration, and practically, in terms of ensuring that the garment performs as expected in its intended end use.

The manufacture of ribbons, tapes, and decorations is similar to that of textile fabrics; weaving, knitting, braiding, or nonwoven techniques. In many cases, different patterning elements are combined such as fibre and colour effects, structure and finishing.

The commercial names for ribbons often follow from the application or the structure, for example piping ribbon, velvet ribbon. Decorative ribbons (trimmings) are also used for ornamentation.

Ribbons and Tapes

1: Trimming

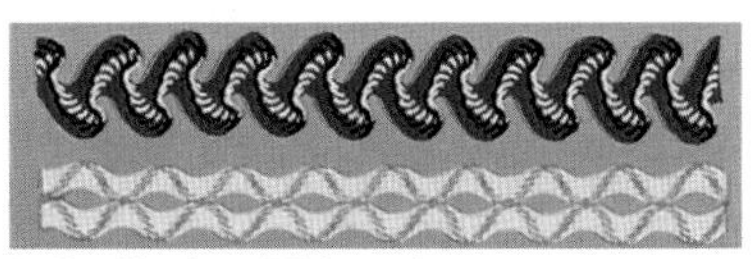

2: Scalloping, Rick-rack

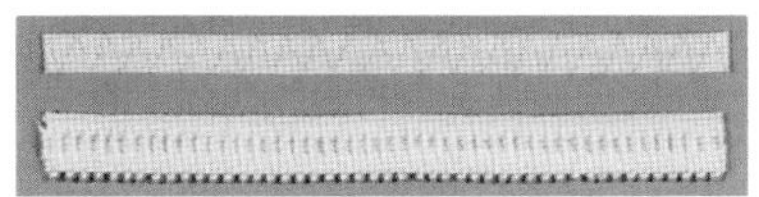

3: Elastic tape

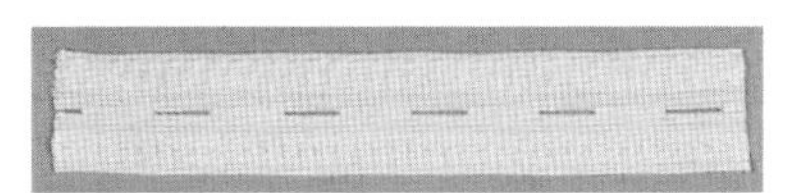

4: Buttonhole tape

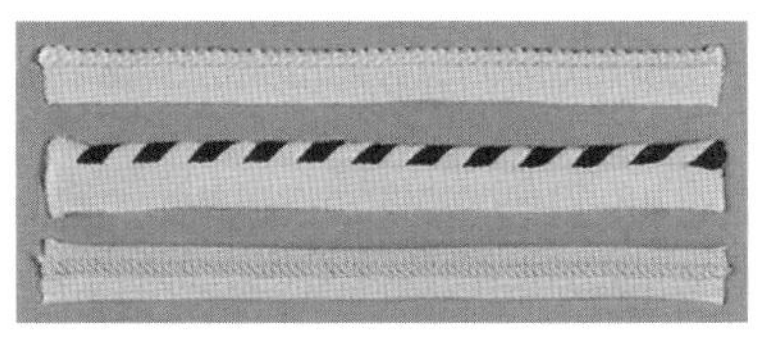

5: Welted tape

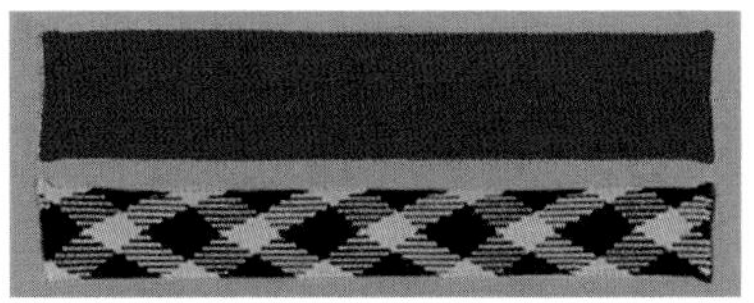

6: Galloon

Name	Features, Properties, Applications
Trimmings	General name for a patterned, woven or knitted ribbon in cotton, silk, wool, or man-made fibre (*Figure 1*).
Scalloping, Rick-rack	Narrow bowed, zigzag, or scalloped ribbon, plain or multi-coloured in cotton or man-made fibres for edge trimming of traditional costumes and children's wear (*Figure 2*).
Elastic tape	Highly elastic, flat, braided band containing rubber or elastomeric fibres (*Figure 3*).
Buttonhole tape	Broad elastic tape with buttonholes located in the centre (*Figure 4*).
Piping	Cotton or linen plain woven ribbon about 1 cm wide, used as a tailoring aid for edges, reveres, and collars.
Moiré ribbon	Cotton, silk or man-made fibre ribbon with a moiré pattern for hat bands and bows.
Seaming tape	Cotton or viscose twill woven tape for stabilising seams.
Welted tape	Cotton or viscose tape with a narrow welt at the edge (*Figure 5*).
Ribbed tape	Cotton, silk, or viscose tape with pronounced ribs for decoration or for waistbands.
Velvet ribbon	Cotton, silk or viscose narrow-woven velvet; sensitive to handling and laundering.
Bias binding	Tape cut on the bias (diagonally) in various widths and materials, plain or patterned, either flat or folded for use as binding.
Stamped tape	Interlining tape with pre-stamped marks to show sewing width and seam allowance. Aids more efficient working.
Taffeta ribbon	Filament yarn ribbon, plain or check patterned, for ribbon bows.
Galloon	A particularly supple, plain or patterned braided ribbon for piping or binding in outerwear (*Figure 6*).

Decorations

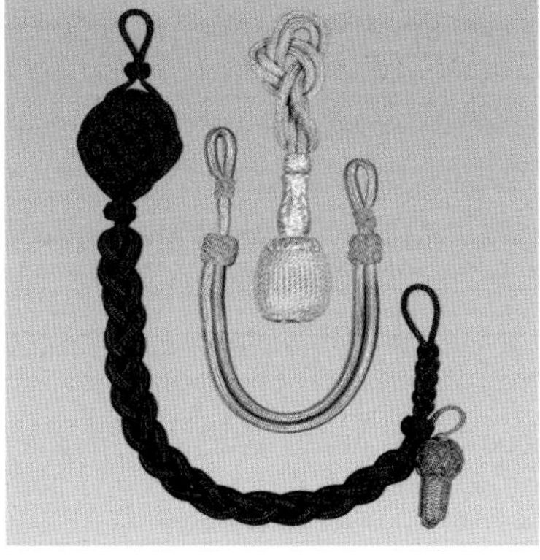

7: Decorations

Fringes	A narrow edging of projecting yarns which are not woven into the fabric, in viscose, wool, or silk.
Cords	Circular braided materials of various thicknesses in viscose, cotton or synthetics. Used as decoration for clothing, in household textiles, and in sporting goods.
Tassels	Expensive, hand-made articles in silk or viscose. A combination of fringes, cords, and braids.
Rosettes	Decorative items used either alone or in combination with ornamental textiles.
Soutache	A mouldable flat braid with two ribs in silk or viscose used for formal clothes.
Pompons	Bunches of wool, silk or synthetics used as trimmings, hanging alone or in groups.

8.2.4 Fastenings

Buttons

Buttons are not only functional **fastening devices,** but also **decorative items,** supporting a distinctive style, genre or quality level. The shape may be round, elongated, oval, crenellated, rhomboid, globular, flat, etc. Buttons are secured to the fabric by means of attached or machined rings, by elongated loops of yarn, or by stitching through a set of two, three, or four bored holes.

1: Synthetic buttons

2: Metal buttons

3: Leather buttons

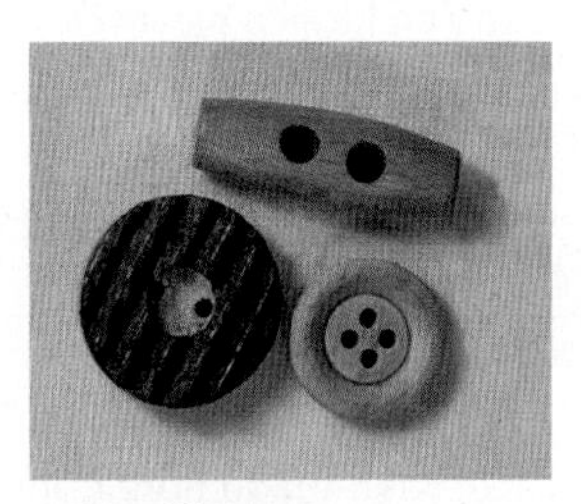

4: Wood buttons

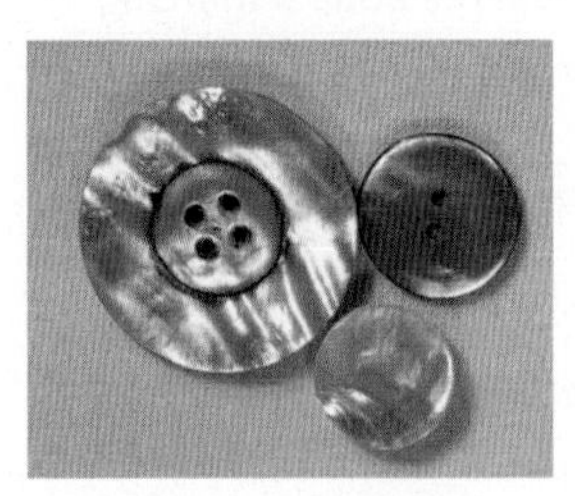

5: Mother of Pearl buttons

6: Horn buttons

Even though sustainable natural materials are coming back into fashion, **synthetic buttons,** made from thermoplastics like **polyester** and **nylon** still have by far the greatest share of the market. They are made in a wide range of colours and shapes and they can imitate all kinds of natural materials. Imitation horn and mother of pearl buttons are resistant to heat and dry cleaning and find wide application in shirts, blouses, trousers and underwear (*Figure 1*).

Metal buttons are made in brass, nickel or aluminium with an engraved or stamped face and used for blazers, jeans, knitted waistcoats, and traditional costume (*Figure 2*).

Leather buttons are sensitive to moisture and not very resistant to abrasion. They are used in leather and sports jackets as well as knitted jackets (*Figure 3*).

Wood buttons, are light and mostly from sustainable sources. They can split and are sensitive to heat and moisture. They are suitable for knitted goods and sporting goods (*Figure 4*).

Mother of pearl buttons are made from the shells of oysters or pearl mussels. With their uneven scintillating surface, they are resistant to heat and maintain their lustre but can be damaged by knocks. They are used for women's outerwear and lingerie (*Figure 5*).

Horn buttons e.g. **buffalo horn** are uniquely patterned and very durable. They are used in high quality men's and women's wear. Horn from the domesticated **deer** is used for traditional costume and children's wear (*Figure 6*).

The **corozo nut** provides hard, uniquely patterned material that can even be dyed. It is used in high quality traditional costume and children's wear.

Decorative buttons are elaborated with braids, cords, etc. and can be used as sparkling paste jewellery items, with glass and metal embellishments, in elegant formal ladies wear.

Much less common are materials such as **bone, jet, coconut, celluloid, glass** and **porcelain.**

Other Fastenings

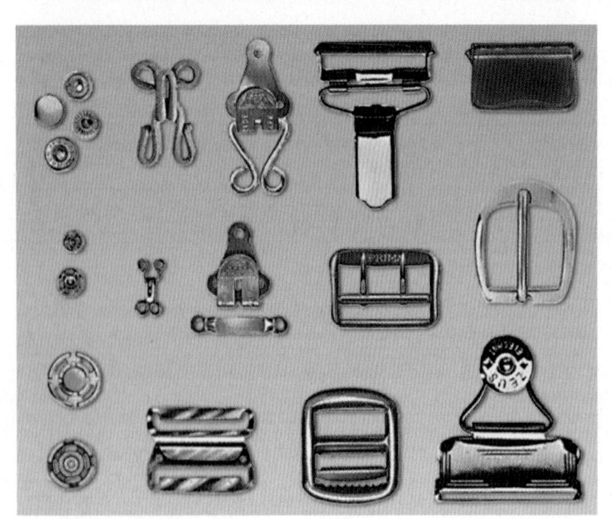

7: Other fastenings

Next to the button, the **zip fastener** is the most important fastening accessory. For lightweight and fine fabrics plastic zippers should be used. For trousers, the tab of the slider has a locking tooth. Metal zippers for sporting goods are broad and firm. Single and double sided zippers are used in leisure and sportswear.

Velcro® fastenings have one surface covered with small nylon hooks and an opposite surface covered with loops.

Hooks and eyes in a wide range of sizes and types are used for trousers, skirts, dresses and foundation garments.

Press studs in various sizes are made from metal or plastic. The type which require no stitching are practical and economic.

Buckles and clasps are made from metal, leather or plastic. They are used to fasten narrow articles such as belts and suspenders.

9.1.1 Leather Manufacture (1)

The **conversion of hides and pelts to leather** is one of the oldest of human activities. Hides and pelts can not be utilised in their raw state because they decompose quickly and become hard and brittle when dried. Therefore, it was necessary to develop tanning materials and processes to preserve the hides. Different regions developed different tanning and preservation techniques, including smoking, mastication (Eskimos), use of fats or various bark extracts (tannins) dissolved in water.

Traditional tanning techniques were not refined and improved until the 19th century with the development of technology for extraction, manipulation, and storage of tanning materials. The first synthetic tannins were introduced at the beginning of the 20th century.

The Raw Hide

Raw hides are produced in and exported from many different parts of the world.

The hides of cattle, lambs, sheep, pigs, deer, and reindeer are all used for leather clothing.
There are two basic types

- **domesticated hides** from farmed animals, and
- **wild hides** from wild animals.

Structure of the Hide

outer skin (epidermis)	keratin layer	ca. 1% of the skin
grain layer	papillary layer reticular layer	
corium	main part of the structure made into leather	
under side (subcutaneous material)	removed before tanning	

The following terms are also used (see page 143):

- **Grain side:** the outer side with respect to the animal; also called the skin side.
- **Flesh side:** to which the subcutaneous connective tissue adheres; also called the suede side.

Skin Quality

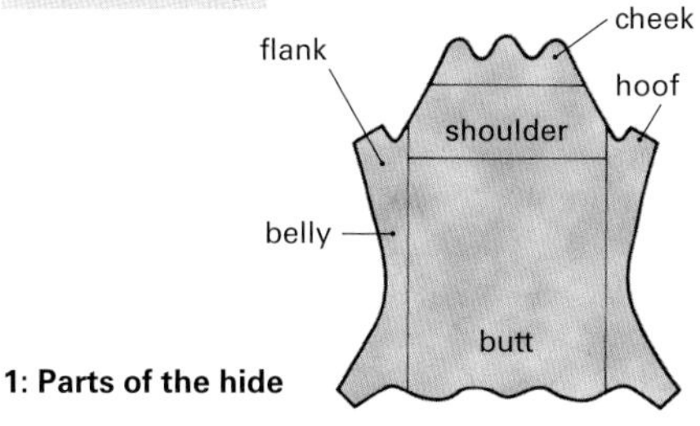

1: Parts of the hide

In leather making, the term Hide is used for the product from large animals (cow, horse, buffalo), whereas Skin refers to smaller animals (sheep, goat, pig). When the skin or hide is laid out, different areas can be recognised which are given specific names (*Figure 1*).

The highest quality is found in the butt area. Large hides are sometimes cut into segments (segmented). The segments will usually correspond to the butt (first grade) shoulder (second grade) and belly and flanks (third grade), and will be processed separately. Smaller skins are almost always processed whole, without segmenting. Most clothing leather comes from skins rather than hides.

The Tannery

There are three stages in leather production:

Preparation	Tanning	Finishing
beamhouse	conversion of the skins to leather	making the tanned leather suitable for clothing

2: Soaking in vats

Preparation (Beamhouse)

The skins have almost always been cured or preserved so they can be stored until needed. Skins which have not been preserved ("green skins") must be put into work immediately. There are three main stages in preparation, which may take up to a week in all.

- **Soaking:** the dried or salted skins are softened in water containing additives such as detergents, salts, enzymes etc. This removes dirt and restores to the skin the moisture, which has been removed by curing or preservation.
- **Liming:** the skin is treated with a chemical (originally lime) to loosen and remove the hairs. Very thick hides intended for shoe leather may be split at this stage (see page 143).
- **Fleshing:** a machine is used to strip away any material which cannot be made into leather, leaving the hide or skin in a clean state, ready to absorb the tanning chemicals.

As a final preparation, the skin may be shaved, smoothed and trimmed.

9.1.1 Leather Manufacture (2)

The Tanning Process

The skin is placed in the tanning drum (*Figure 1*) from which it takes up the tanning liquor. The liquor penetrates into the protein fibres and converts them into leather fibres. Thus a new substance is created with new properties, especially resistance to water and decomposition. Leather is naturally breathable but wind resistant, strong but comfortable to wear, with a characteristic "friendly" handle.

There are several tanning systems:

Vegetable tanning — The tannins are natural extracts of certain barks, woods, fruits, leaves, or vegetables. The tanned hides are light brown to dark reddish brown and can not be dyed to light shades.

Mineral tanning — This is the most popular. About 80% of all apparel leathers are tanned with chromium salts in large drums (*Figure 1*). Other mineral salts, such as aluminium salts, can also be used. Chrome leather is grey-green in colour. It is easy to dye, is strong, light, and with good resistance to sunlight.

Oil tanning (chamois) — Oil tanning is an organic, though not vegetable-based process. The skin is impregnated with the type of fatty acid ester which absorbs oxygen. Typically cod oil is used. The chamois process is used predominantly for hides such as deer and elk, and for sheep skin which is made into cleaning leathers.

Combination tanning — It is possible to tan by a combination of methods, e.g. semi-chrome for clothing: a vegetable tannage followed by a chrome retannage.

Finishing

The tanned skins are finished in the sequence described briefly below to obtain apparel leathers.

Dewatering — Excess water is removed by pressing and by passing the tanned skins through thick felt-covered rollers.

Drying — A warm air drying tunnel machine reduces the moisture content further.

Shaving — The leather is scraped on the flesh side to produce a uniform thickness.

Dyeing — Normally, dyeing is done in large drums (*Figure 2*) with a wide range of dyestuff types, but predominantly acid (aniline) dyes. Aniline dyes are "transparent"; they do not compromise the natural look of the leather. Brush dyeing, in which the colour is applied only on the leather side, is uncommon. Spray dyeing is also used for blotch effects and to colour crust leather (flattened, dried skins).

Oiling (fat liquoring) — Oil is applied, usually as an emulsion, to render the leather supple.

Drying — The leathers are brought into a chamber with a controlled temperature and humidity to dry.

Staking — Repeated stretching and bending to soften the leather.

Sueding — For **nubuk** leather, the grain side is buffed. For suede, the flesh side is buffed using emery paper to abrade the surface.

Finishing — A lustrous and protective coating may be applied, usually to the grain side, to improve the appearance and handle, or water repellence (*Figure 3*).

Glazing — The lustre can be enhanced on a glazing machine.

Waxing (brushing) — The waxing machine imparts a subdued lustre to the grain side (important for blotch dyed materials).

1: Tanning drum

2: Leather dyeing

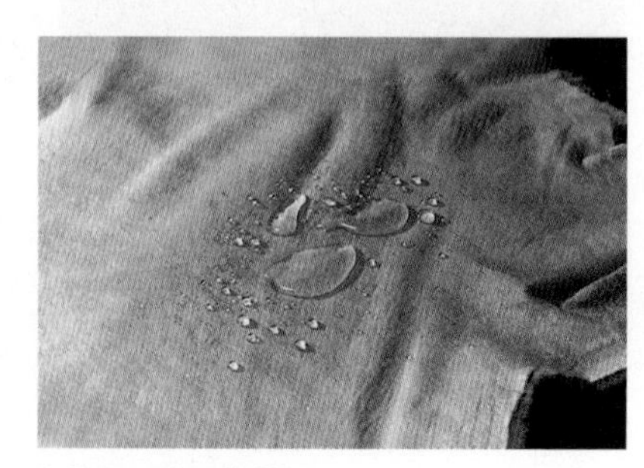

3: Protective finish

9.1.2 Leather Types

Every animal has its own individual skin character. The pore structure depends on the animal's coat – fleece, hair, or bristle – yielding a range of grain patterns from very fine (as in lamb) to deeply-marked (as in pig). The quality of the leather is affected by several factors.

- **Age:** The younger the animal (e.g. lamb, calf) the softer, finer and more expensive will be the leather.
- **Origin:** In humid, tropical regions, the animals have to contend with biting insects, so the leather will be marked by scars and scratches which reduce its value.

Every hide has two distinct surfaces; the outer face is the hair side or the grain side. This side is used to make smooth **nappa** leather. The grain side may be buffed with a very fine emery to make a fine **suede** or **nubuk** leather. The flesh side of the hide is rough. It is buffed to give a short, silky **velour** finish (*Figure 1*).

Thick hides can be split into two or more layers (*Figures 2 and 3*). **Split leathers** are rough on both sides; they are heavy and have a firm handle. Splits are used mainly for upholstery and shoe suedes, but sometimes for garments where very large panels are needed.

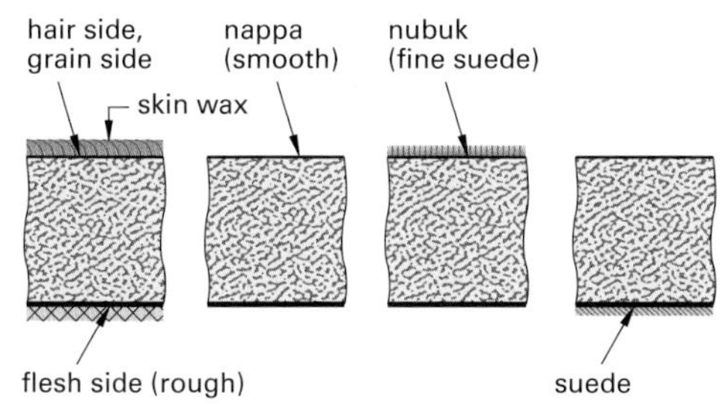

1: Leather cross-section

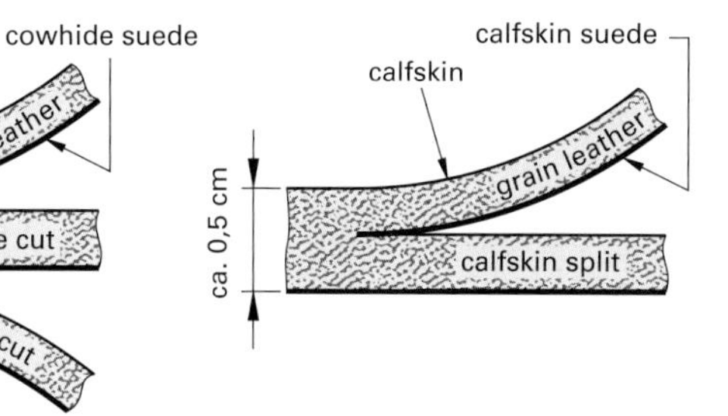

2: Split cowhide

3: Split calfskin

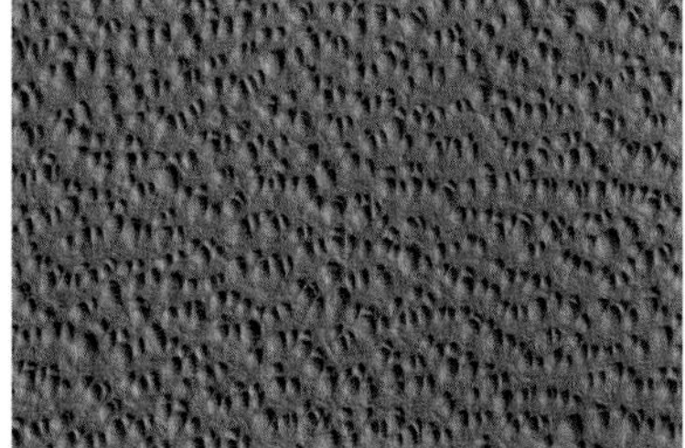

4: Calfskin[1)]

Calfskin is a very expensive leather with a fine and uniform grain.

Calfskin suede is a top quality leather because of its elegant, silky surface.

5: Cowhide[1)]

Cowhide is a strong and durable leather which keeps its shape. It has a fine, regular grain.

Cowhide suede may be used for clothing.

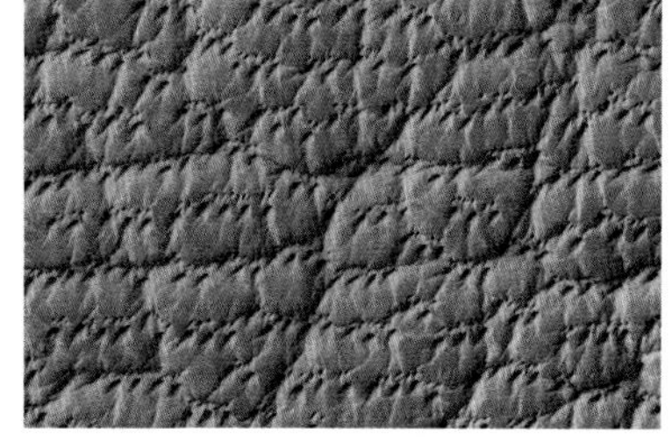

6: Goatskin[1)]

Goatskin has a coarse grain and is used for expensive clothing.

Goatskin suede has a silky surface and a soft handle; it is elegant and keeps its shape.

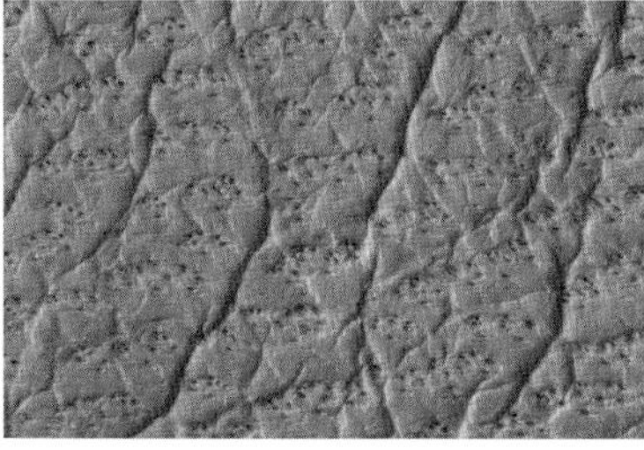

7: Lambskin[1)]

Lambskin has the finest grain, light weight and a soft handle; a fine and sophisticated clothing leather.

Lambskin suede has a short nap. In early wear, some loose fibres may be shed.

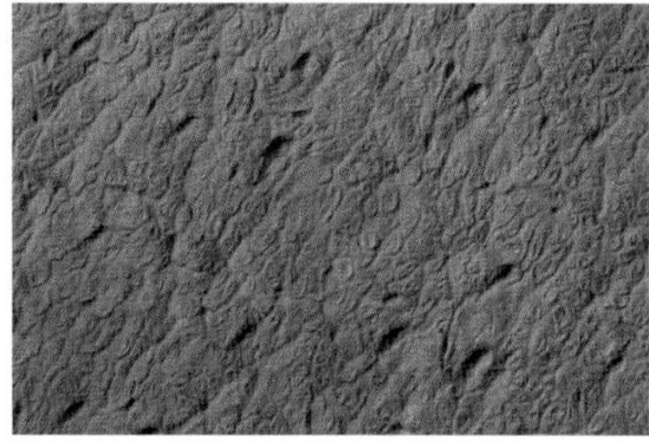

8: Pigskin[1)]

Pigskin is a high value, durable leather. The strong pig's bristle leaves a pronounced pockmarked, sporty appearance on the grain side and typical perforations on the suede side.

[1)] enlarged photograph

9: Deerskin[1)]

Deerskin is a true wild leather with a rustic, heavily grained pore structure.

The term wild leather is often incorrectly used for any leather with a rough or sueded surface.

9.1.3 Leather Garment Manufacture

1: Leather skin

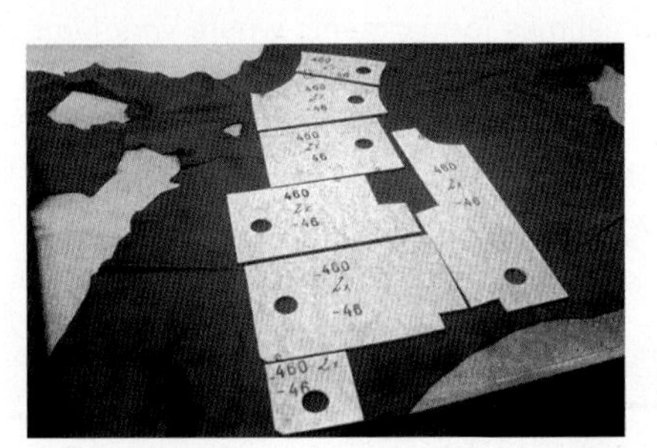
2: Cutting templates in place

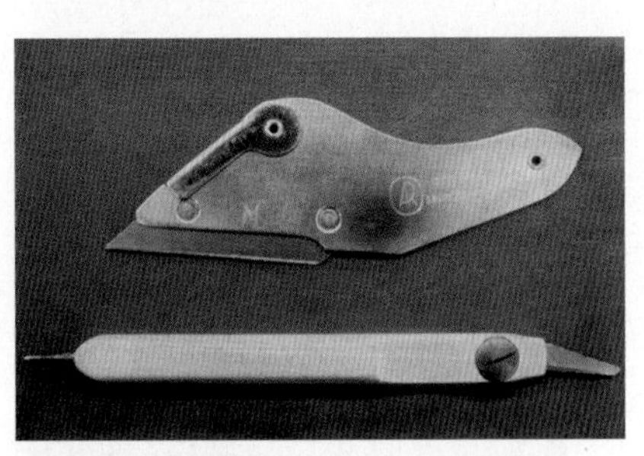
3: Cutting tools

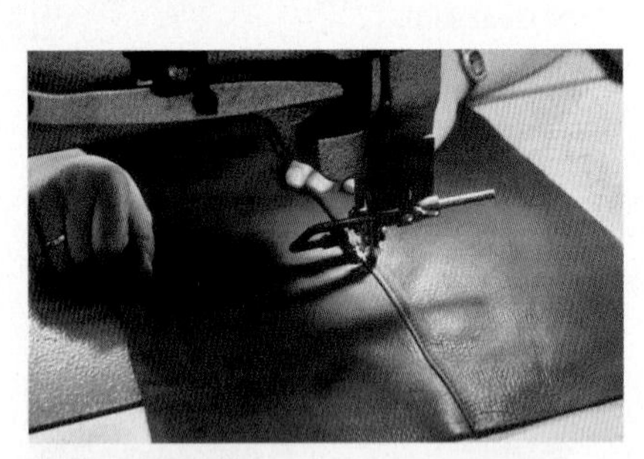
4: Producing a seam

5: Leather clothing

Because of their limited size, it may take from 6 (for a jacket) to 15 (for a coat) skins to make a garment.

The area of each skin is measured with a pinwheel or with a computerised electronic instrument. It is given in square feet. 1 square foot = 30.48 x 30.48 = 929 cm^2.

The construction of a quality garment from several skins, with their natural variations, requires a great deal of know-how. Economic garment manufacture can be achieved only with properly rationalised production technology.

Following are the separate stages of garment manufacture.

Sorting

The skins are sorted according to colour, thickness and structure. In spite of the fact that 3000 to 4000 skins may have been dyed in the same drum, there will be natural variations in the way that the colour is taken up. The different shades have to be identified and grouped. The sorter has to have a very good eye for colour and texture because it is important that different skins in the same garment must look the same.

Cutting

Leather cannot be cut using automated equipment, as is used for textiles. Leather cutting is an expensive, manual process using knives.

Since every skin is different, the following points have to be watched carefully during cutting.

- different sizes
- irregular areas such as scars, bellies
- variations in colour and sueding
- holes, tears

The cutter places his cutting templates on the skin in such a way that he makes the best use of the material whilst avoiding the faults and irregularities. The parts are cut out using a razor-sharp knife.

Interlining

A tape made of woven or nonwoven material, carrying a dot-coated adhesive, is used to strengthen the edges, collars, reveres, etc. Application may be done with an iron or a press.

Sewing

All leather qualities, from fine skins to suede splits can easily be converted into clothing, using high-speed sewing machines, specialised equipment, and automated machines. During all seaming operations, the leather is guided and moved manually through the sewing head by the operator, because this is where the highest demands on quality are felt. A seam which has to be unpicked will leave a trail of holes. Visible seam lines must be right first time. Conditions for a clean and strong leather seam are as follows.

Needle size: Nm 80 to Nm 130
Feed type: alternating top and needle feed
Presser foot: roller or Teflon
Yarn size: Nm 50 to Nm 70

Gluing

After sewing, seams, hems, and linings may be dressed with a special adhesive and pressed. This lays the seams flat and gives the required stability to the garment. In modern clothing production, gluing is increasingly being replaced by the improved design and effective use of interlinings.

9.2.1 Fur Types

Furs are nearly always used as cold weather garments. They are designated as long or short, rough or smooth, according to their length and density.

Furs are produced from the **pelts** of a wide range of animals. Currently about 8 to 10% of furs come from wild animals, via pest control, herding, and hunting, and 90% from specially bred and farmed animals. Trade in wild animals is governed by the Washington Agreement on protected species **(CITES),** to which more than 130 countries are voluntary signatories. It is reviewed every two years by participating states. Appendix 1 of the agreement lists those animals in which trade is completely forbidden. Appendix 2 lists those animals which may be traded only by express permission of the country from which they are to be exported. Appendix 3 lists those animals for which both an export license and an import license is required.

Since January 1997, the Washington Agreement has been incorporated into European law. The EU has established a veterinary inspectorate which oversees conformity to the EU guidelines of June 1999 for keeping farm animals. These guidelines are designed to ensure that farmed animals are kept in healthy conditions.

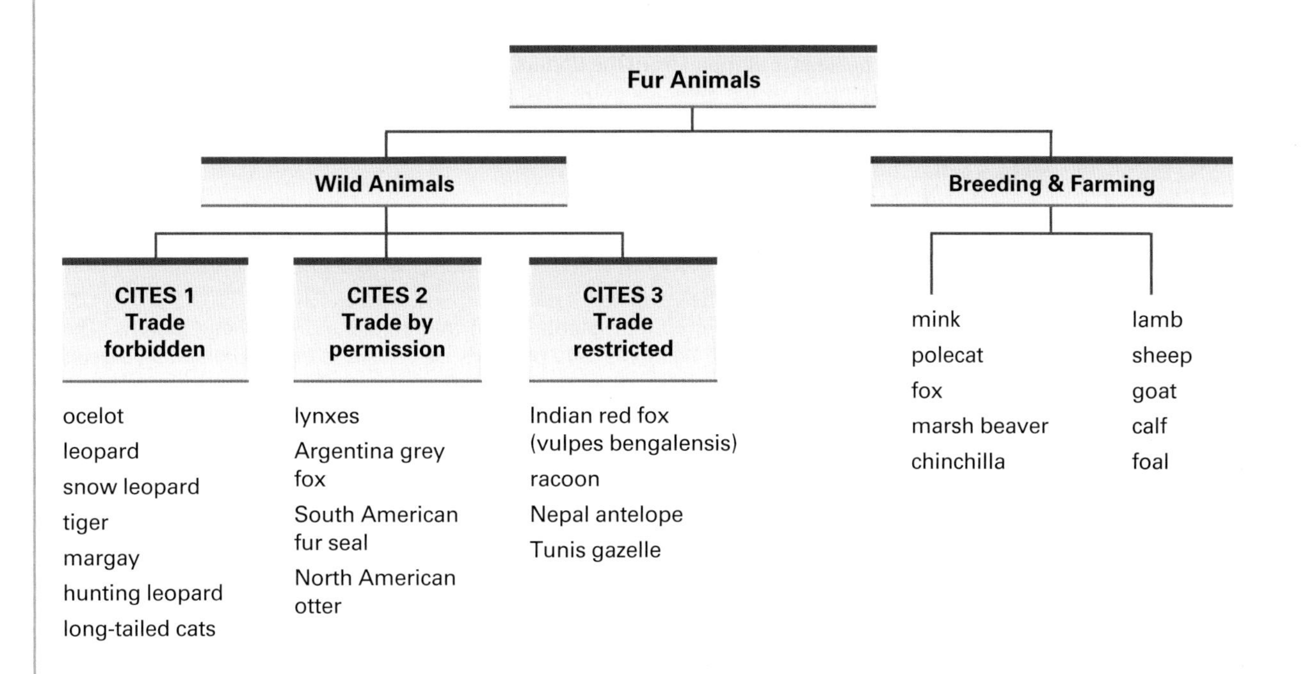

Construction of the Pelt

Pelts comprise the skin, which will be tanned, and the hairs. *Figure 1* shows the different types of hairs. The different layers of hair may be more or less prominent, or absent, according to the type of animal and the climate in which it lives.

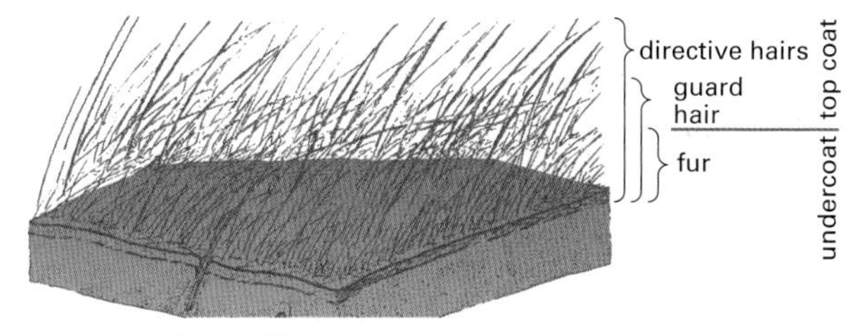

1: Layers of animal hair

2: Protected species: tiger

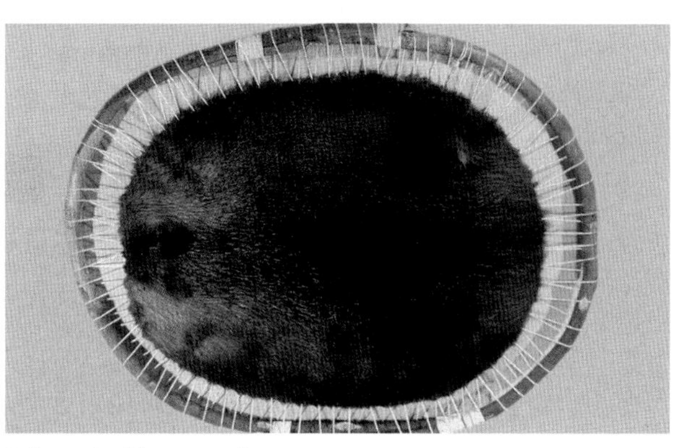

3: Stretched beaver pelt

9.2.2 Pelt Preparation

In leather production, the hair is separated from the skin before tanning. However, in fur production the pelts have to be processed in such a way that the hair remains firmly attached. This is accomplished by up to 140 separate mechanical or chemical processing stages. A few of the important stages are described below.

1: Red fox: Western (left), Eastern (right)

2: Soaking

3: Stripping the flesh

Soaking (*Figure 2*)

The raw pelts are preserved by drying so they are hard and brittle. The pelt is brought back to its original condition by immersion in water, either stationary or agitated. Fine furs cannot withstand mechanical action.

Washing

Heavily stained pelts, such as lamb and sheep, or pelts with high grease content are washed in a neutral liquor.

Fleshing (*Figure 3*)

The flesh is stripped from the underside of the pelt either manually or by machine. Removal of the subcutaneous tissues allows better penetration by chemicals in subsequent processes.

Pickling, Dressing

A solution of acid and salt causes the hair to be firmly locked into the skin, as a preparation for tanning.

Tanning

The skin is converted into leather using mineral salts or synthetic tannins. The degree of tanning has to be very precisely controlled in order to maintain a good bond between skin and hair.

Oiling

The tanned leather is treated on the flesh side with natural or synthetic oils in order to impart a durable softness.

Dewatering and Drying

Loose water is removed by centrifuging and pressing. The remaining liquid water is dried off in special drying rooms or machines.

Sawdust Drumming, Conditioning

Excess oil, dirt, salts etc. are removed, the hairs are polished, the leather is softened, and the correct moisture content is obtained by tumbling in warm air in a drum containing beech wood sawdust with a particle size of about 1 mm. The sawdust particles are later shaken out in a separate cage drum.

Shaving (*Figure 4*)

The leather side is shaved to achieve the required thickness and uniformity of thickness.

Stretching (*Figure 5*)

The pelts are stretched in length and width to recover their original shape.

Mending

A final process in which faults or blemishes are ameliorated.

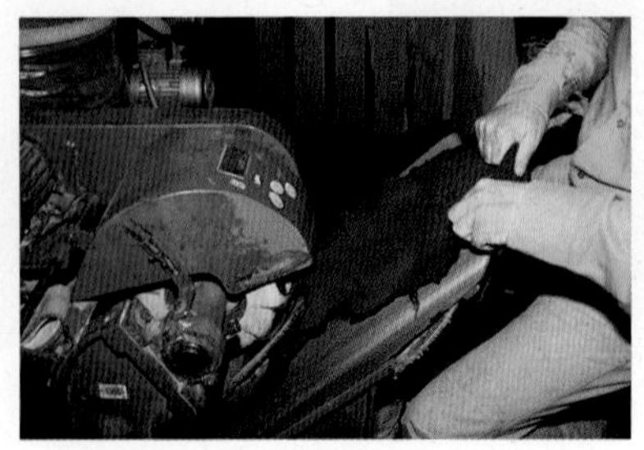

4: Shaving

5: Stretching

9.2.3 Pelt Finishing
9.2.4 From Pelt to Fur Clothing (1)

Pelt Finishing

Pelt finishing is the modification and enhancement of the appearance of the fur.

Coloration

The natural colour of the fur may be enhanced, or made more uniform, or a new colour may be introduced by dyeing. In principle, a wide range of colours is possible but the actual range is restricted by quality considerations. Pale shades require a pre-bleaching which can lead to weakening of the hairs. The sensitivity of the pelt can be reduced by a second, more robust tanning so that hot dyeing recipes can be used. Patterning can also be introduced; for example the fur can be given the appearance of exotic animals, by hand painting or using spray guns or stencils.

Shearing and Deburring

The fur may be shorn, either all over or selectively, or the guard hairs may be removed by plucking.

Sueding, Polishing (*Figure 1*)

In order to have a two-sided pelt, the leather side may be retanned and given a polished or a suede finish.

Ironing

Special rotating ironing machines with combs and heated rollers are used to remove distortions and irregularities, to enhance the gloss of the fur.

1: Finishing Persian lamb

From Pelt to Fur Clothing

Depending on the type of fur, there may be from 25 to more than 45 different stages in creating a garment from a prepared pelt. This can not be done in the same way as with a textile fabric. It is first necessary to create a larger, harmonious assembly from a collection of relatively small pelts.

2: Pelt selection

Pelt Selection and Cutting Pattern (*Figure 2*)

First the material requirements for each cutting pattern must be calculated, according to the type of fur and the manufacturing style. Then the pelts must be selected. If the calculation is not correctly made, there may be too few pelts, so the garment cannot be completed, or too many, so the garment is too expensive.

Stretching and Cutting

If the pelt does not lie flat, it is cut and stretched over the edge of a table. This flattens it and gives it the proper shape. Where appropriate, the pelts are cut into shapes which are specific to particular animals. Portions which are cut away, such as the hoof and tail areas, will be used in patchwork furs.

Mending (*see page 148, Figure 3*)

Upgrading the pelt and making it usable by removing or correcting faults as well as marking on the leather side to indicate nonuniformities in dyeing or hair height, brand marks, or structural peculiarities.

3: Sorting for a mink coat

Sorting (*Figure 3*)

This is one of the furrier's most important tasks. Sorting is the assembly, in correct placement, of all of the pelts that will go to make a garment. This determines the appearance of the finished product. Successful sorting is heavily dependent on skill and experience; there are no fixed rules but the best pieces are placed where they will be most apparent in the garment, such as the back, collar, front edge, and top of the arms. Sorting is according to colour, lustre, hair structure, and pelt size.

After these processes, the pelts have to be assembled into a larger piece. There are several ways to do this, depending on the type of garment, the type of pelt and the required effect. The pelts will first be cut into sections and the sections will be sewn together in particular patterns.

9.2.4 From Pelt to Fur Clothing (2)

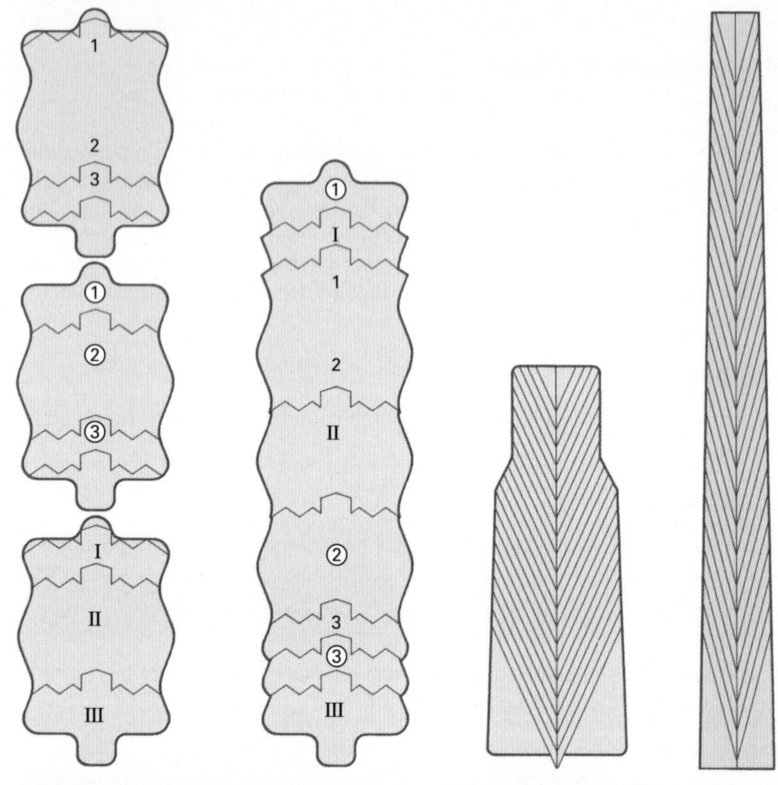

1: Interleaving; e.g. Persian lamb

2: Stranding; e.g. mink

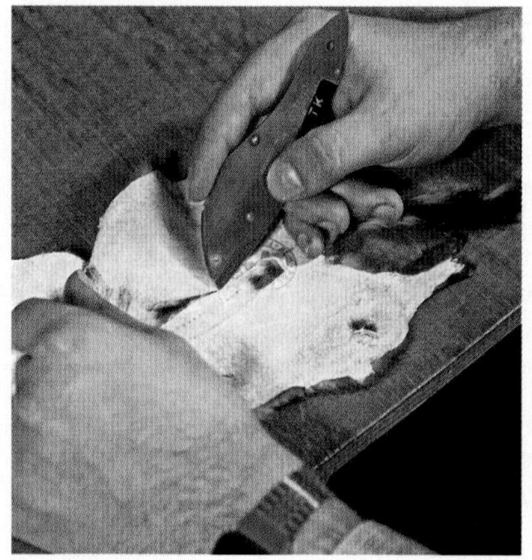

3: Pelt repair

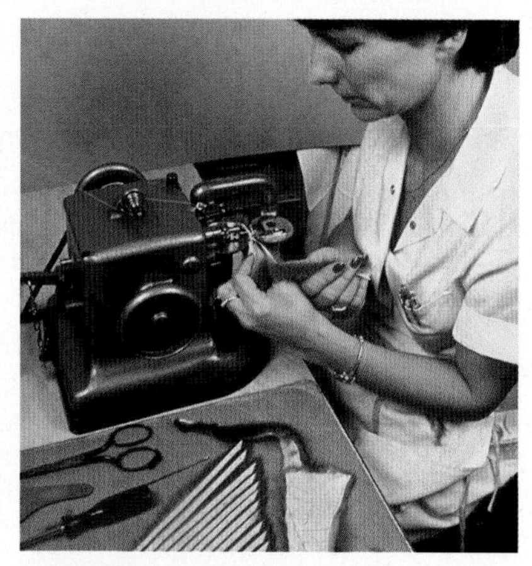

4: Stranding at the fur machine

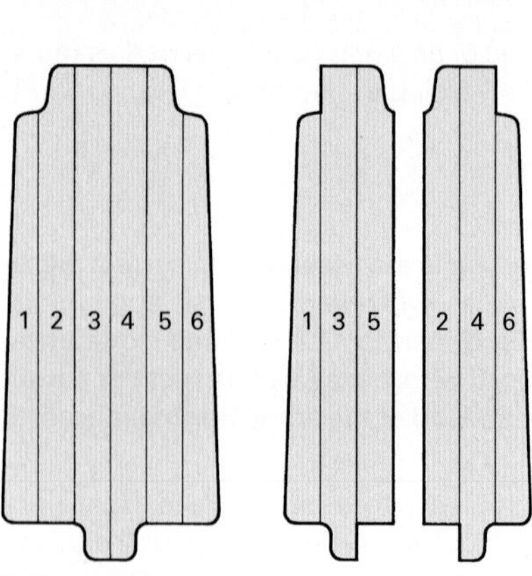

5: Rearranging

6: Cut pelt (front).
Sewn (stranded) pieces (behind)

Cutting Techniques

During cutting, it is important to ensure that only the leather is cut; the hair must not be damaged. Cutting is done either with a furrier's knife or on a cutting machine. There are several cutting techniques.

Assembly: This system is also known as whole-pelt sewing. The pelts are simply sewn together side by side and end to end, without significant alteration of their natural size and shape.

Interleaving: This technique (*Figure 1*) allows pelts to be enlarged or made smaller. Two or more compatible pelts are cut across their widths into shoulder, back, and rump sections to form interlocking shapes which later can be sewn into invisible joins. When the pieces are reassembled with the appropriate sections from several pelts interleaved, the effect is of a single pelt of several times the length. The width is extended by sewing several interleaved panels together, to make an area sufficient for a whole garment.

Stranding: This technique allows short, wide pelts to be converted into much longer, narrower pieces, having a uniform fur structure from top to bottom, without cross sewings. Stranding is a very expensive procedure but it gives an elegant chevron effect e.g. in mink coats (*see page 149, Figure 3*).

In *Figure 2* a pelt about 50 cm long is cut into narrow strips in a V formation. The strips are then assembled into a strand of about 120 cm on the fur sewing machine (*Figures 4 and 6*). Because the colour and structure of the fur has been changed, the strands must then be sorted again to decide exactly how to assemble them into a whole garment. Finally, the strands are sewn together to obtain an area sufficient for the garment piece.

Rearranging: Variations in hair structure and colour can be evened out by cutting the pelt into narrow longitudinal strips which are then systematically rearranged (*Figure 5*). The strips are numbered in order and then assembled into two or three smaller pieces, e.g. using strip numbers 1, 3, 5 and 2, 4, 6; or 1, 4, 7 and 2, 5, 8 and 3, 6, 9.

Trimming: Pelts with a pronounced undercoat can be cut into strips and assembled together with leather strips to reduce the density of the fur and increase the area.

9.2.4 From Pelt to Fur Clothing (3)

1: Shaping

Shaping

The assembled pieces destined for individual garment parts are moistened on the leather side and are stapled to a cutting pattern engraved on a wooden platen (*Figure 1*). Moistening makes the leather more or less plastic so that it can be shaped to the required form. After a twelve hour drying period, and after removal from the platen, the shaping is retained. The seams are smoothed out using wooden shapers with rounded edges or with seam rollers, especially when the stranding technique has been used.

Conditioning

After removal from the wood platens, the pieces are again conditioned in sawdust (*see page 146*) and then cut exactly to the required pattern.

2: Garment assembly

Finishing

Since the fur may have been more or less compressed by the heavy forces it has endured during some of the previous procedures, a range of final finishing processes is carried out to restore the fur to its original condition. These may include ironing, beating, conditioning, glazing and combing.

Garment Assembly (*Figure 2*)

Unless they are destined for further treatment on the leather side (polishing, velour) the individual pieces are strengthened with interlining, then assembled on the fur sewing machine into the finished garment and finally lined.

3: Stranded mink coat

Construction of Furs Compared to Textile Clothing

Different construction techniques have to be used for furs, as compared to textiles, because of the basic differences in properties and behaviour.

- Sewing techniques have to be quite different. Textile seams are made with excess fabric at the seams; furs are joined edge to edge in a butt seam. Therefore the garment pieces in a fur article have to be measured and cut exactly right, since corrections cannot be made by letting out or bringing in the seams.
- Furs cannot be allowed to suffer stretching in use, since they will not recover from extension. Therefore, stretching is prevented by the application of interlinings. Every garment must be assembled from its parts in such a way that possible distortions, caused by stretching when damp, are avoided. The garment designer must always take heed of the shape, the size, and the placing of individual pelts in a garment.
- The supple and uniform draping qualities of textiles cannot be obtained in furs, because of the natural variations in thickness, weight, and roughness which will be found within a given garment. A large size fur garment can be uncomfortably heavy, and also will be very expensive.
- Novel fashionable effects can be obtained through printing, shearing, trimming, and patchwork techniques.

10.1.1 Design and Pattern Construction

Pattern development requires two principle areas of expertise. **Design** is the initial, creative step, followed by **pattern construction,** the technical realisation of the creative design.

Design

1: Design sketch

2: Modelling

3: CAD-System[1]

Design can be done manually (haute couture) or by using a CAD system.

When a CAD system is used, a wide variety of shapes, colours and patterns can be selectively "painted" at will to individual areas of the figurine on the screen. The work can be saved for later recall and re-use.

Together with the fabric type and colouring, these designs are the basis for planning a collection (*see page 235*).

Pattern Construction

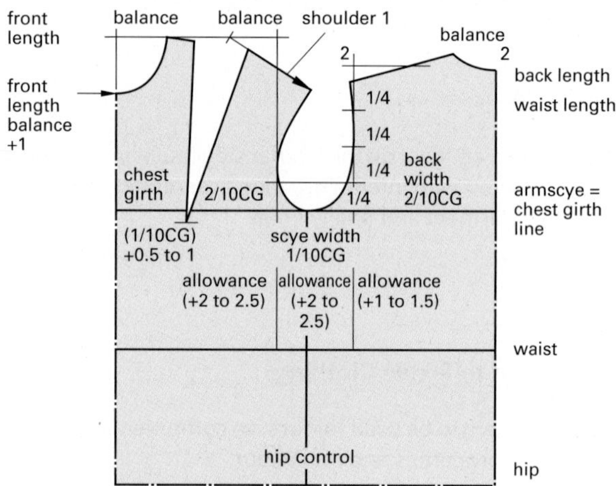

4: Manual pattern construction

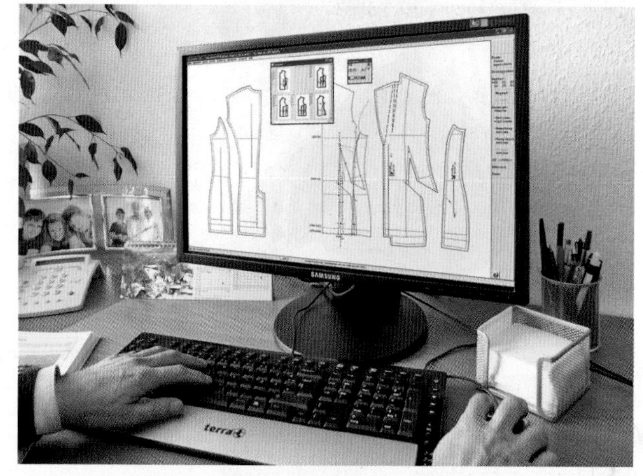

5: Computer aided pattern construction

A pattern is a diagrammatic representation of the way a garment part is constructed. It can be generated either manually or by software.

First, a very basic pattern is developed, in a particular size, and the actual pattern draft will be developed from this, to include seam allowances, guide marks and particular styling details.

The **pattern draft** is developed by calculation, taking account of the following measurements.

- Actual **body size** measurements, developed into **size charts** (*see page 231*).
- **Grading increments** representing the company-specific increments between garment sizes, (*pages 151 and 233*).
- **Ease allowances** to allow space for the body within the garment (*see page 233*).

In practice the development of a new pattern is usually effected by appropriate modification of existing, stock designs **(block patterns).** These are basic patterns constructed from appropriate body measurements but without any styling features.

This time-consuming work is made considerably easier and faster through the use of a **CAD system.** With computer software the basic patterns can be retrieved from the computer, displayed on the screen and modified at any time. Thus the whole shape can be adjusted, lines can be deleted or extended, lines and points can be superimposed. Darts can be altered; parts can be moved and rotated. The result can be saved, in a range of sizes, and is immediately available either for printing or for sending directly as input to grading software (*see page 151*).

[1] CAD: Computer aided design

10.1.2 Pattern Grading (1)

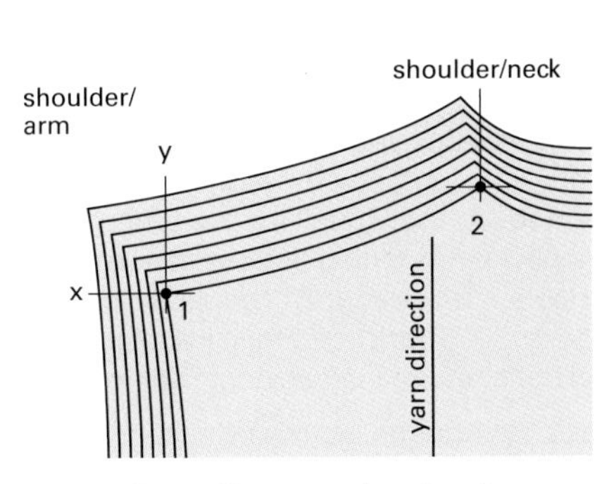

1: Part of a grading operation showing grading points

Grading means the stepwise increase or decrease of a master pattern piece to create larger or smaller sizes. The steps between sizes are the **grading increments.** The starting point for the grading operation is normally size 34 or 36 or 38 for ladies wear, and 48 or 50 for menswear.

Grading does not alter the overall look of the style, only the size.

There are two basic methods:

- Apportioning of **grading increments** to the X and Y coordinates of a series of grading points.
- **Constructive design** using measurements taken from **body size** tables.

Size Table with Grading Increments

Measurement (cm)	Dimensions and Grading Increments						
	Size 34	Incre-ment	Size 36	Incre-ment	Size 38	Incre-ment	Size 40
waist girth	64	2	66	4	70	4	74
hip girth	87	3	90	4	94	4	98
chest girth	16	1	17	1	18	1	19
back width	15.5	0.5	16	0.5	16.5	0.5	17
back height	18	0.5	18.5	0.5	19	0.5	19.5
back length	40.9	0.1	41	0.1	41.1	0.1	41.2
front length	44.1	0.4	44.5	0.4	44.9	0.4	45.3

The table shows an extract from the German size tables for Ladies Outerwear in sizes 34, 36, 38 and 40 with the grading increments to be used for the waist, hip, chest, back, and front measurements[1].

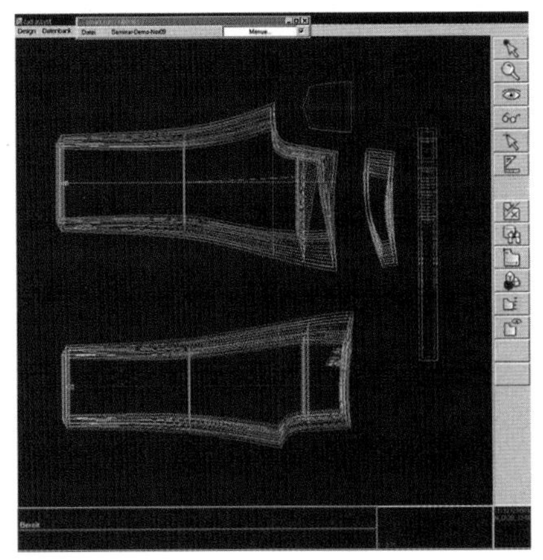

2: Grading of trouser front leg, back leg, seat and waistband

In this case, the starting point for the grading operation is size 34; this is the master pattern. To find the next larger size, the grading increments are added to the master dimensions. These differences are applied to a series of fixed points (grading points) around the outline of the pattern.

Figure 1 shows two of the fixed **grading points**: those at the shoulder/arm and the shoulder/neck corners of a back part. Depending on the location of the grading point, the grading increment is translated into displacements of the point in the X and Y directions to locate the corresponding point in the next size. The grading increments have been established from past experience, from size charts, or from body measurements. The translation, from one size to the next, is called the **grade rule** for that particular grade point. Thus a grade rule of (-40, +40) means "move the grading point 4 mm horizontally to the left and 4 mm vertically upwards".

Most CAD grading systems use tables of grading increments and grade rules. There are two methods of working.

- The grading increments are applied directly to the grading points.
- The grading increments are fed into the computer in tabular form and the different sizes are generated automatically using appropriate numerical algorithms built into the grading software.

The grading operation applied to one garment part can be transferred to all other parts of the same garment (*Figure 2*).

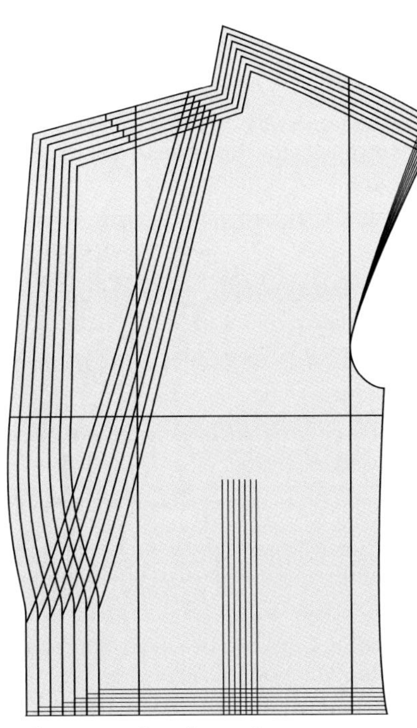

3: Pattern set for a front piece

The **pattern set,** is the set of all parts and sizes, for a given style, generated by the grading operation. The term can also be applied to the nest of patterns for a single garment part (*Figure 3*).

The set of all of the parts for a given size and style, generated by the grading operation, is the **block pattern.** From this will be generated all of the patterns required for production of the garment: top cloth, linings, interlinings and trimmings as well as the markers and lay plans.

[1] Note that the size tables of other countries will refer to different measurements and different size codes: see e.g. ISO 3635, ASTM 6192, EN 13402

10.1.2 Pattern Grading (2)

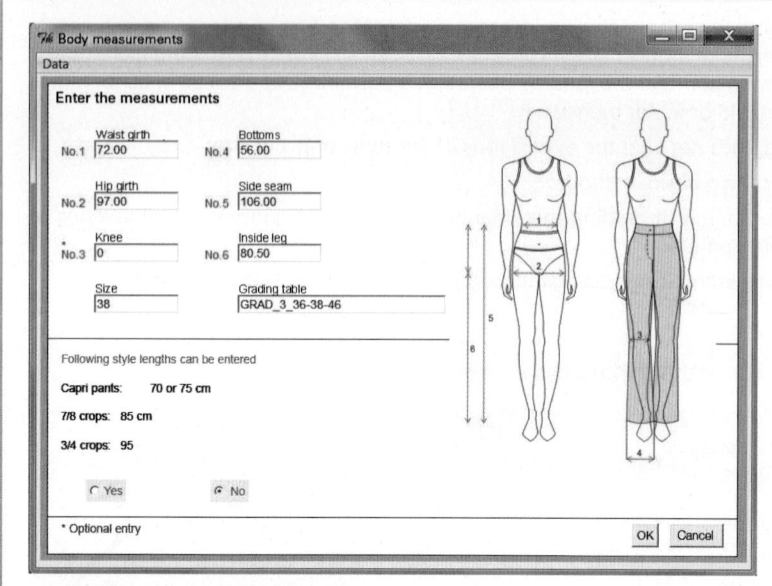

1: Data input for pattern construction

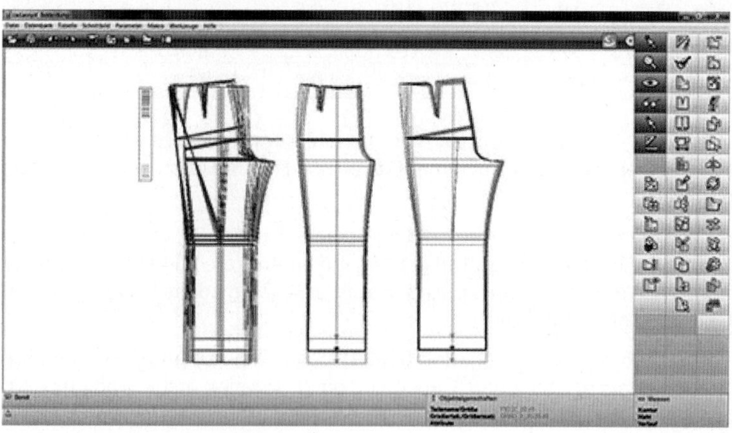

2: Pattern construction with grading

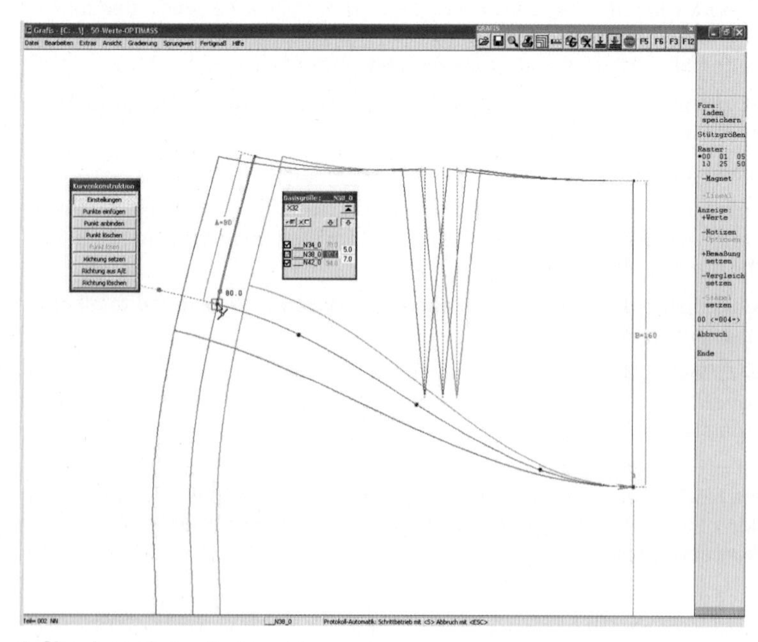

3: Size-dependent adjustment for a yoke

Constructive Grading Using Body Size Tables

Constructive pattern grading uses computer software linked to stored body measurement tables, supplemented by individual measurements, to produce a new or modified cutting pattern. The precise manner of calculation depends on the construction algorithms of the particular software. *Figure 1* shows a typical input screen.

These patterns can be adjusted according to different body measurements and also by changing specific parameters, such as the waist girth, depending on a particular size or a particular customer. Thus an individual pattern size can be constructed, for example as part of a factory-based **made-to-measure** operation.

The basic pattern and the separate steps in building the cutting pattern can later be adjusted for different sizes (*Figure 2*).

The various stages in the construction of a pattern are automatically saved.

The basic pattern and the separate steps in building the cutting pattern can then be modified at will according to the required sizes (*Figures 2 and 3*).

General Features of a Computer Based Grading System

Pattern construction software **(CAD software)** can include many special functions designed to cater for various aspects of clothing manufacture.

Some examples of these useful features are the following.

- Any change in one pattern piece can be automatically applied over all sizes.
- A particular size can be altered without affecting the others.
- Grading rules established for one pattern piece can be applied to another.
- Graded sizes can be displayed and edited individually.
- Sets of grading rules can be laid out in tabular form.
- A set of grading rules can be saved along with the corresponding pattern set.

Further options for processing the patterns are available depending on the level of technology and automation in the factory.

10.2.1 Making a Lay Plan (1)

The pattern pieces representing all of the individual components of a garment have to be laid out together in such a way that they fit within the confines of the fabric width as closely and efficiently as possible, in order to minimise waste. This is the **lay plan** or **marker** (*see page 155*).

The pattern pieces have to be laid in a way that takes account of the **directional properties** of the fabric, such as thread directions, pattern direction, and grain of nap or pile. It may also be necessary to allow for **matching** of stripes, checks, or designs.

Examples for Laying up Orientation

Lay in length and width

Fabrics with no pattern direction; Stripes working in length or width direction on different pieces e.g. sleeves and cuffs.

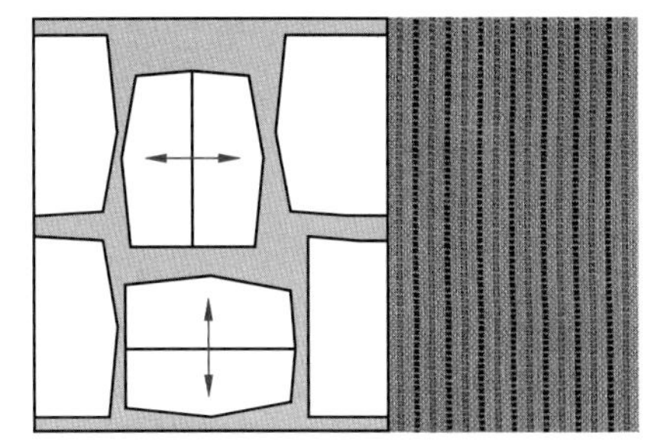

1: Zephyr

Length, either way

Fabrics with left-right symmetry in all aspects e.g. weave, patterning and finish.

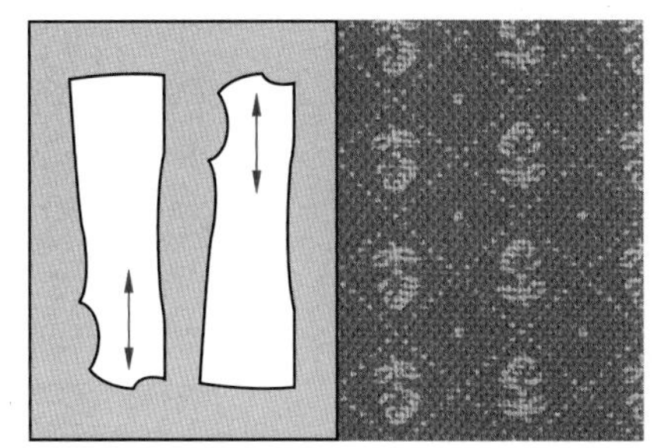

2: Cretonne, printed

Length, one way only

Fabrics with a directional pattern or pile; knitted fabrics.

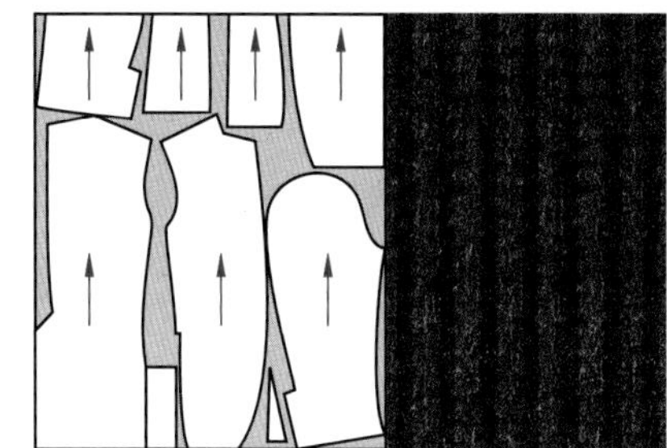

3: Corduroy

4: Pattern matching with stripes

5: Pattern matching with checks

Pattern Matching

The quality of a product is affected significantly by the accuracy of pattern matching. A flawless execution, especially with checks and stripes, demands a high consumption of fabric and takes a great deal of time. The colouring, the repeat size and the prominence of the pattern, as well as the degree of matching required between individual garment pieces are crucial in determining the cost and difficulty in making the lay plan, in spreading the cloth, and in cutting.

Cutting of striped or checked fabrics may have to be carried out in two stages, with a preliminary rough cut being followed by more precise second cutting together with pattern matching.

When producing the first **block pattern,** each pattern piece will be provided with lines in length and width directions **(matching lines)**. During the **laying up** every pattern piece will be oriented according to the matching lines, usually on a **matching grid,** to facilitate the first, **rough cut.**

Before the second, **precision cutting** the individual pattern pieces have to be carefully aligned and may be securely fixed in position on needle beds. For bulk production the fabric is laid on a **needle bed** and, **at the same time,** the pattern is **automatically aligned** before the rough cut.

- **Symmetry**

  The pattern must be symmetrical about the central axis. Examples: left and right front panels.

- **Vertical continuity**

  The pattern must not be interrupted or displaced at horizontal seams. Example: pockets.

- **Horizontal continuity**

  The pattern must not be interrupted or displaced at vertical seams or across adjacent parts. Example: arm and front panel.

- **Overall continuity**

  The form and the repeat of the pattern must be maintained across all seams, facings, trimmings, patches etc. Examples: patch pockets, flaps, darts, facings.

10.2.1 Making a Lay Plan (2)

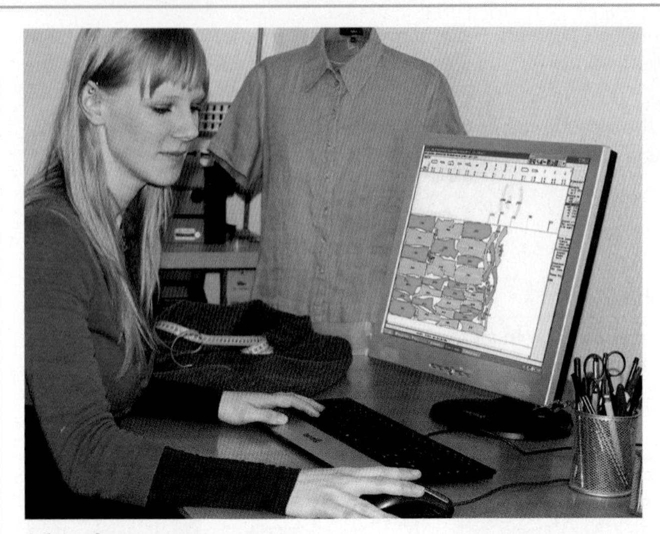

1: Lay plan on a computer screen

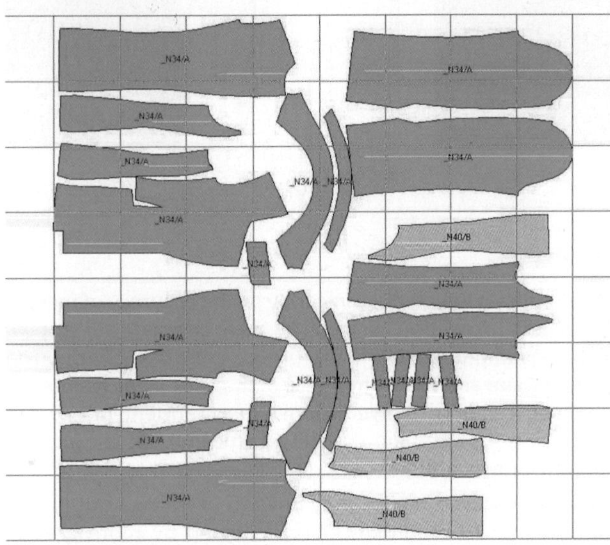

2: Section of a lay plan with matching lines

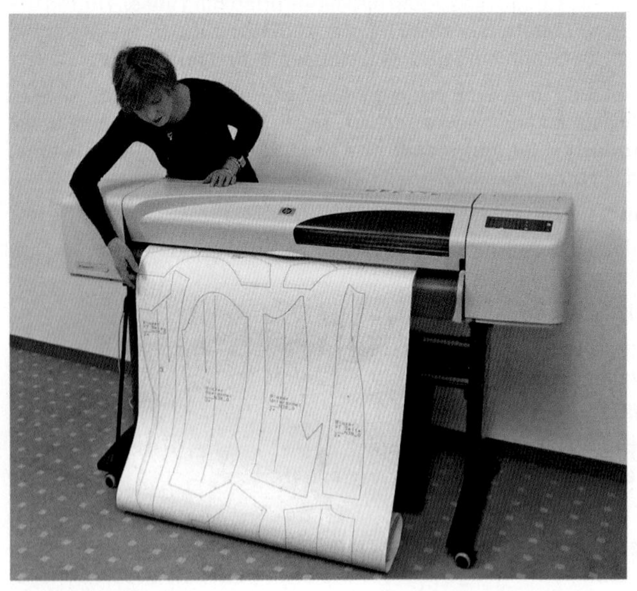

3: Printing a lay plan

Manual Methods

A lay plan is composed by laying up all of the individual cutting templates for a given style side by side. For manual operations, the outlines of the templates are then traced either directly onto the fabric or onto special marker paper. The outlines are traced with tailor's chalk or special pens.

Computerised Systems

CAD systems allow more efficient laying out of the pattern pieces.

Typical functions of such systems include the following.

- Rotating and flipping of pieces.
- Inclusion of safety margins and allowances.
- Attention to cloth faults and shrinkage.
- Setting of pattern matching points for stripes and checks.
- Implementation of whole-garment lays.
- Grouping of parts destined for fusing.

In addition, there are software modules that will lay out the pattern pieces automatically within the usable width of the fabric (*see page 156*). The pieces are laid in such a manner as to minimise cutting waste.

The lay planning software can allow for multi-size lays and will calculate the number of lays according to the planned production quantity of the given style.

Output of cutting pattern and lay plan

Cutting patterns and lay plans for a particular style can be sent to a printer or a cutter at full or reduced scale. These can serve as the basis for manual cutting. The lay plan is ironed onto the top of the fabric lay followed by either manual or computer controlled cutting.

The output can also be sent to a template cutting device (*see page 158*).

In mass production facilities, it is not necessary to make a physical cutting marker. The cutting instructions are sent direct (on-line) to the fully automatic cutting machine (*see page 158*).

Data Interchange

Standardised data formats have been devised to allow data interchange between different CAD systems, e.g. AAMA (Asia America Multitechnology Association) and ASTM (American Society for Testing and Materials.

Data in these formats can be transmitted over the internet to individual production locations anywhere in the world.

At the local production site, the data can be imported into the locally-installed software and used to implement, or modify the transmitted lay plans.

10.2.2 Types of Lay Plan

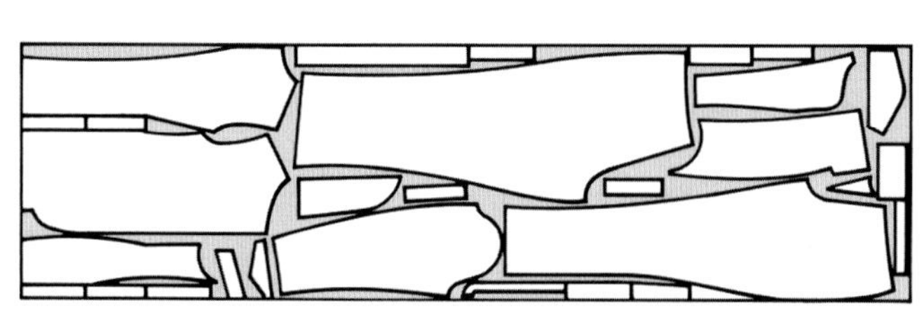

1: Half garment lay

Half Garment Lay

This includes only half of the garment pieces (for example the right side) for a style.

They are used for folded or tubular fabrics and for fabrics which are spread face to face.

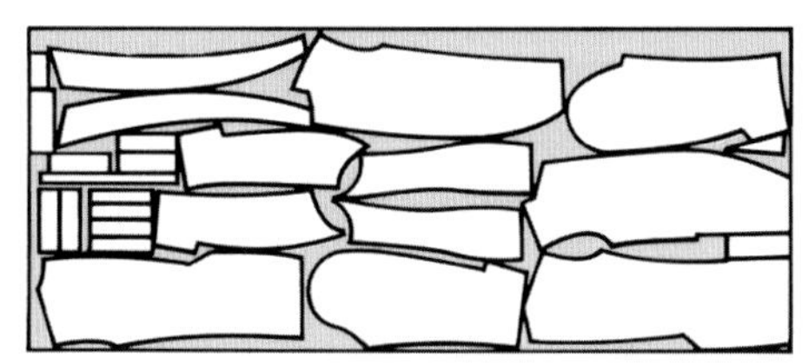

2: Whole garment lay

Whole Garment Lay

All of the garment pieces, left and right sides, are included in the lay.

Used for open width fabrics.

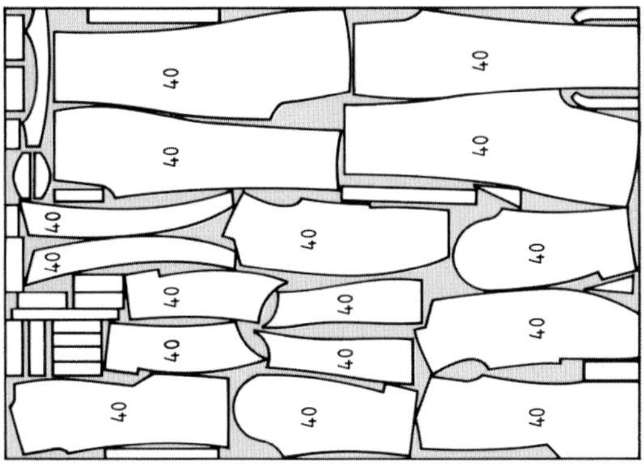

3: Single size lay

Single Size Lay

The lay includes all of the pieces for a single size.

Restricting the lay to a single size makes order planning and laying up the fabric easier, but the disadvantage is a somewhat higher material consumption, compared to multi-size lays.

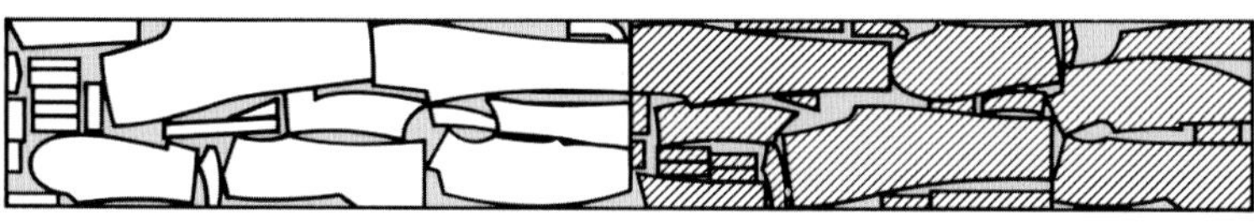

4: Sectional multi-size lay for two sizes

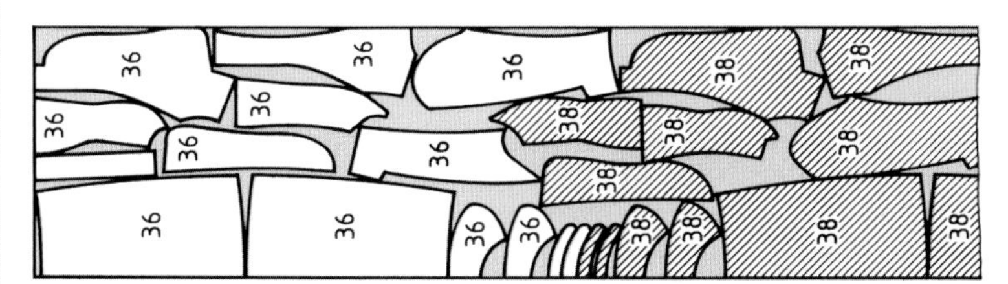

5: Interlocking multi-size lay for two sizes

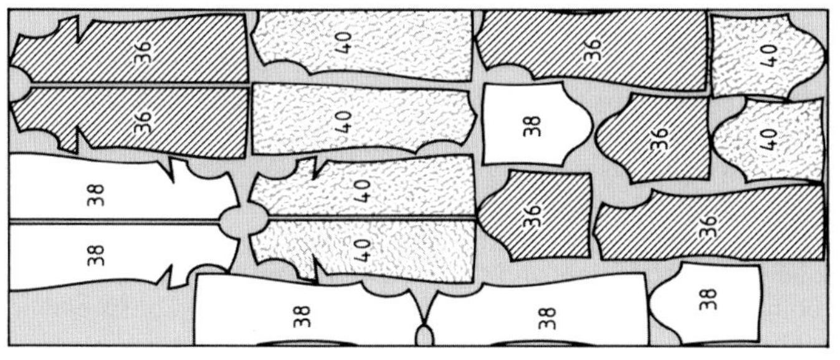

6: Mixed multi-size lay for three sizes

Multi-size Lays

- **Sectional lay:**

The lay is made in at least two distinct rectangular sections. Each section contains all of the parts for a single size. Adjacent sections may be the same or a different size.

- **Interlocking lay:**

Two or more sections, one after the other, usually different sizes, but the sections are not confined to strict rectangular areas; the pieces for the different sections may merge at the borders.

- **Mixed multi-size lay:**

In this case there are no distinct sections; the pieces for the two or more different garment sizes are intermingled. This is the arrangement which normally gives the best material utilisation.

10.2.3 Spreading (1)

Spreading means the smooth laying out of the fabric in superimposed layers (plies) of specified length. The cutting marker is laid on the topmost layer. The maximum width of the cutting marker is constrained by the usable width of the fabric. The **usable width** is the width of the narrowest place minus the width of any unusable selvedges. Fabric **utilisation** is the amount of fabric actually utilised in the marker as a percentage of the total fabric area.

Depending on the quality level of the manufacture, cloth faults may be identified at **fabric inspection** and tagged. This is a costly process so it is used only for high-value goods. Faults can be cut out by **overlapping** during the laying up of the fabric on the cutting table, or they may be left in and dealt with later. Depending on the type of garment, the severity of the fault and its location, the faulty garment piece can be discarded or mended, or it can be made up – with the final garment being assigned to **"second grade"**.

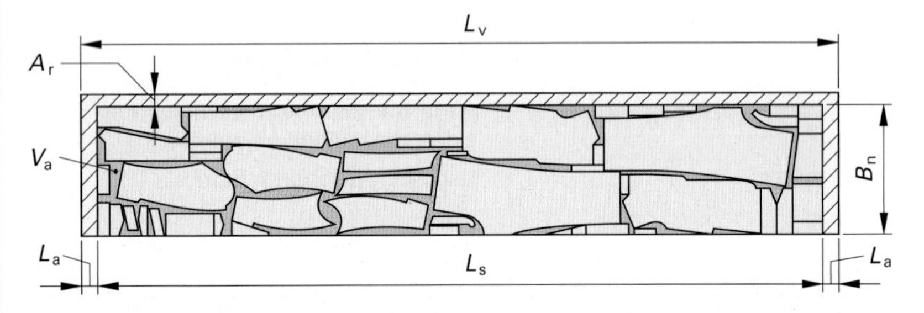

1: Example of a cutting marker

- L_a End allowance = allowance at the beginning and end of a layer
- L_v Lay length = marker length + end allowance
- A_r Edge allowance = allowance at the fabric edges
- V_a Cutting loss = waste from within the lay plan
- B_n Usable width = cloth width – edge allowance
- L_s Marker length

Types of Lay

Single ply
A single layer of fabric, e.g. for cutting a prototype garment.

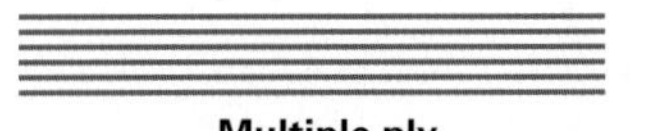

Multiple ply
A number of fabric layers stacked one on the top of the other.

Stepped lay
A multiple ply lay in which groups of layers have different lengths, e.g. for multi-size lays.

Presentation of Fabrics

Presentation of fabrics means the form in which the material has been delivered.

Presentation depends on the type of material (e.g. velvet), the application (sample length, sale in the retail trade) and the internal handling equipment (unrolling stands, platform trolley, fork-lift truck with pallets). Presentation has to be taken into account when making the lay plan and choosing the type of spreading. The following symbols are sometimes used:

open-width: 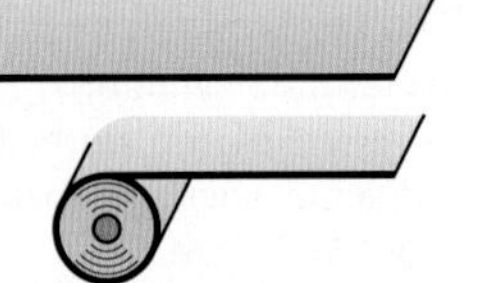

folded: 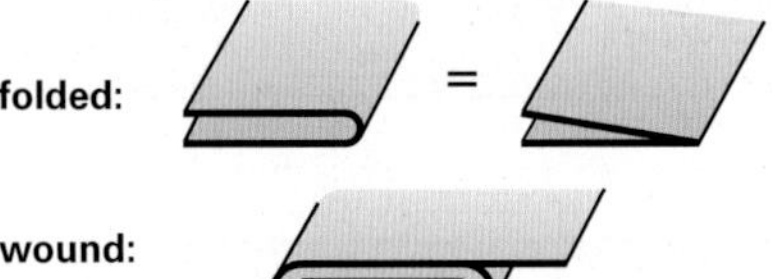

tubular: 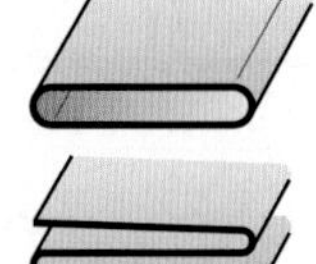

rolled:

wound:

plaited:

Forms of Spreading

One-way	Each layer of fabric is laid the same way up, with the grain, or pattern running in the same direction. The fabric has to be cut at the end of each ply and, in machine spreading, the carriage must return inactive to the beginning of the lay. This method is used for fabrics with a grain or a directional pattern.
Face-to-face	The plies are laid in pairs, face to face. The grain or pattern runs in the same direction. After each ply is cut off, the fabric has to be turned and, with machine spreading, the carriage has to return, inactive, to the starting point. Used for the same types of fabrics as the one-way system.
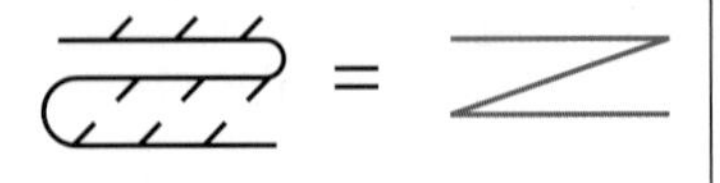 **Two-way**	The plies are laid continuously from left to right and right to left, without cutting and without returning to the starting point for each ply. This is the most efficient method of spreading but it can not be used for fabrics with grain or directional patterns.

10.2.3 Spreading (2)

The fabric is spread out on the laying-up table according to a predetermined plan, as single ply or multiple ply, ready for cutting.

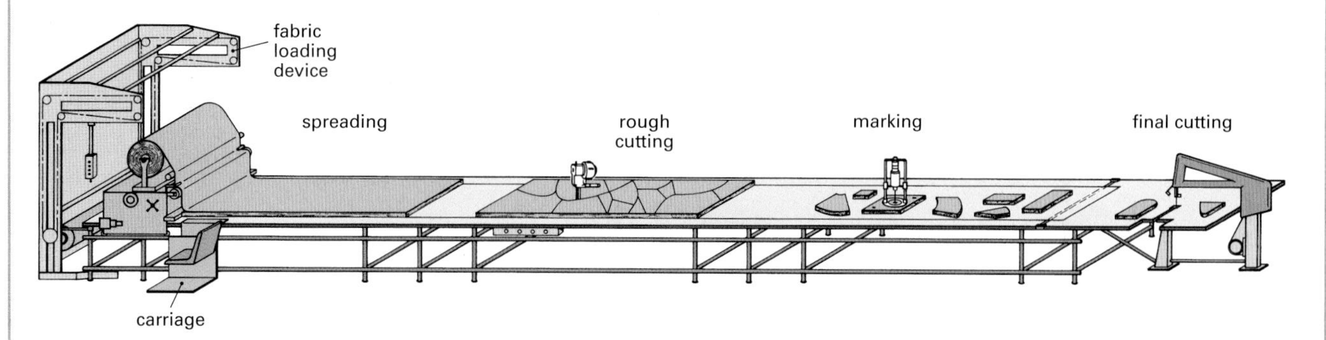

1: Sequence of cutting operations

In the first section the fabric is spread into a lay.

A lay consists of multiple plies. When a cutting marker is applied, this is a **cutting lay**.

In the second section the individual pieces are cut out roughly with an electrically driven knife.

Next, various important reference points, such as pocket folds and notches are **marked.**

The accurate **final cutting** of the pieces may be done with templates and a band knife. This procedure allows a high precision to be achieved.

Spreading Methods

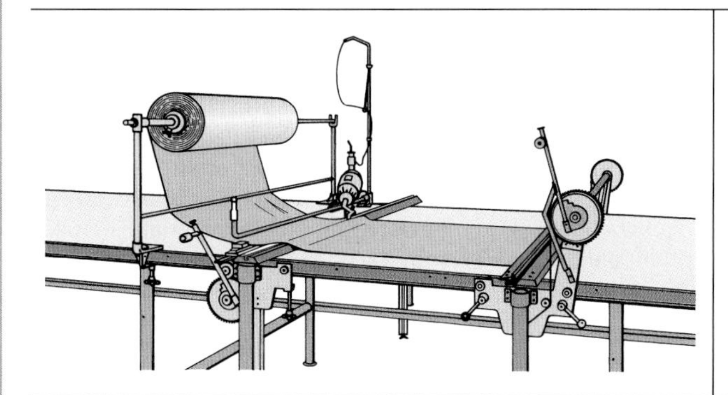

Manual Spreading

The cloth is pulled carefully from the fabric roll by hand and is cut to the appropriate length. Mechanical devices can be provided to facilitate the unrolling and cutting operations but the proper alignment of the fabric edges is the responsibility of the human operator.

This procedure is suitable for short lays and for frequent changes in fabrics and colours. It is often used in small businesses.

Spreading Carriage

The cloth is unwound and spread semi-automatically, using a manually guided carriage.

The carriage is moved back and forth over the laying-up table. Built-in mechanisms take care of aligning the fabric edges and smoothing the plies. This system is favoured when the lays are long and broad and/or if the fabric is presented in large batches for relatively large orders.

The method is very efficient and is suitable for small businesses.

Automatic Spreading Machines

The moving carriage has been more or less fully automated to provide a more efficient production for large-scale enterprises.

Common attachments for such equipment include photo cells for correct alignment of the selvedges, fabric loading and threading devices, cutting devices at the end of the lay, a platform on which the operator can sit or stand while the machine is traversing.

10.2.4 Cutting

In this context, cutting means to cut out the garment pieces from lays of fabric with the help of cutting templates (markers). Generally the marker is applied (drawn, traced, sprayed, stuck, clipped, pinned) to the top ply of a lay.

Cutting often is carried out in two stages; **rough cutting** (separating the individual pieces) and the **final cutting** (accurate cutting of the individual shapes). Different types of cutting tools have different degrees of precision.

Circular Cutters

Circular cutting tools use a rotating circular blade.

The smallest devices (power shears) are used for cutting single ply lays and for cutting fabric plies to length during manual spreading. Depending on the size of the device it is possible to cut to a depth of about 10 mm.

The larger circular cutter is used mainly for dividing a lay into sections. It is suitable only for cutting in straight lines or very gradual curves, in depths of up to about 150 mm.

Straight Knives

A straight knife cutter has a vertical blade which reciprocates up and down. It is capable of both coarse and precise cutting to a depth of about 300 mm. Corners and curves can be cut accurately. Since all of the layers are cut at the same place (unlike a circular cutter), and provided that the knife is held vertical, then all of the pieces cut from a lay are identical.

Circular cutters and straight knives are pushed by hand through the stationary material.

Band Knives

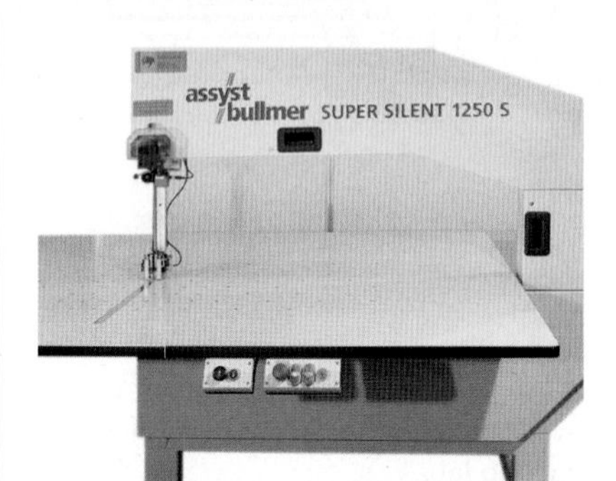

The band knife cutting machine contains a narrow, sharpened, endless steel band moving vertically through the layers of fabric. The fabric layers are guided by hand against the blade. An air cushion will often be provided below the fabric layers to make it easier to guide the material. The plies may be stapled together to prevent slippage. Band knives are used for precision cutting to a depth of up to 300 mm. Corners, tight curves and pointed incisions are cut precisely.

Die Cutting

A die cutting machine is provided with prefabricated cutting tools (cutting dies) having the exact shape of the garment pieces. The fabric pieces are stamped out on a base plate. Die cutters are used mainly for leather, coated and laminated material and in areas where the same patterns are used over a long period, e.g. production of working clothes. The dies are expensive to make.

Automatic Cutter

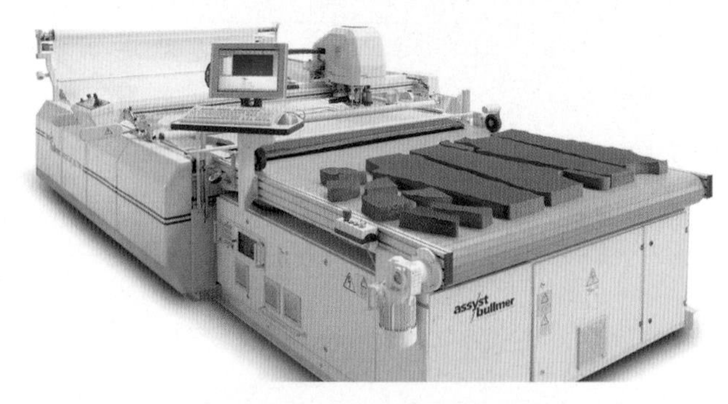

There are also fully automatic, computer-controlled cutting machines. Apart from special vertical knives, it is possible to use laser beams, high-energy plasma (ionized gas) beams, and high pressure water jets as the cutting medium.

10.2.5 Marking, Preparation for Sewing

Position Marking

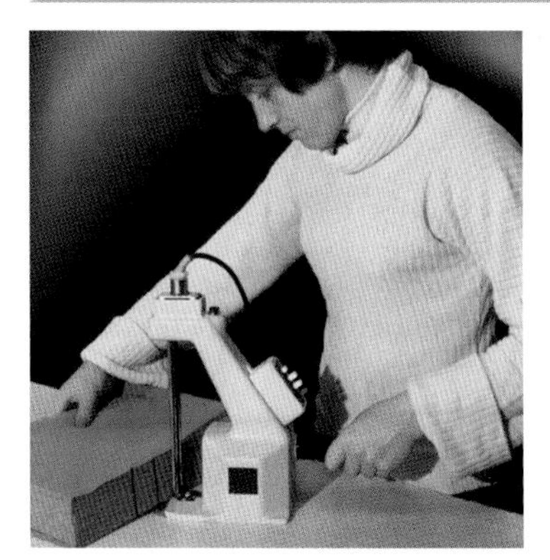
1: Hot notcher

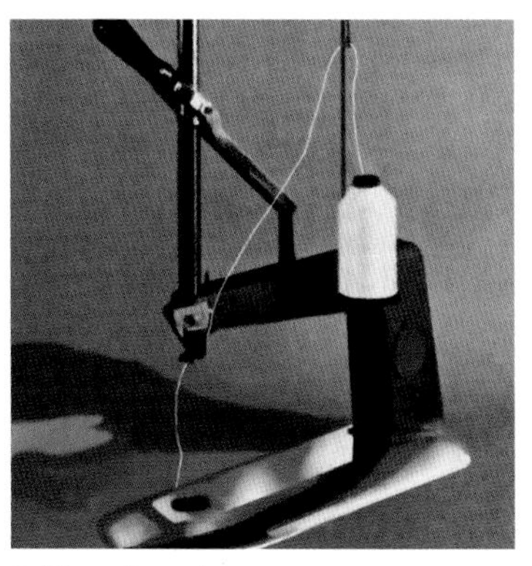
2: Thread marker

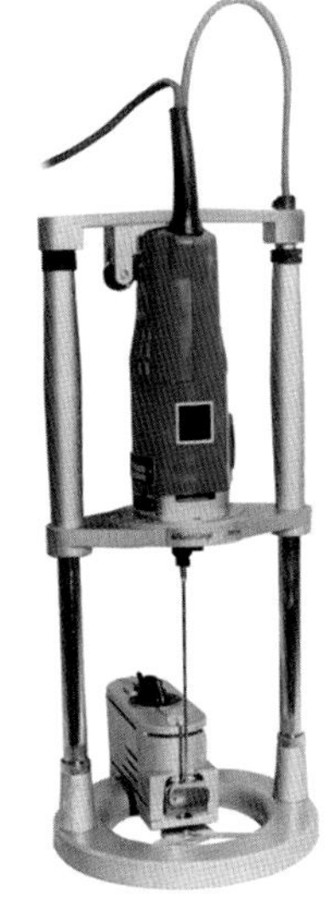
3: Drill marker

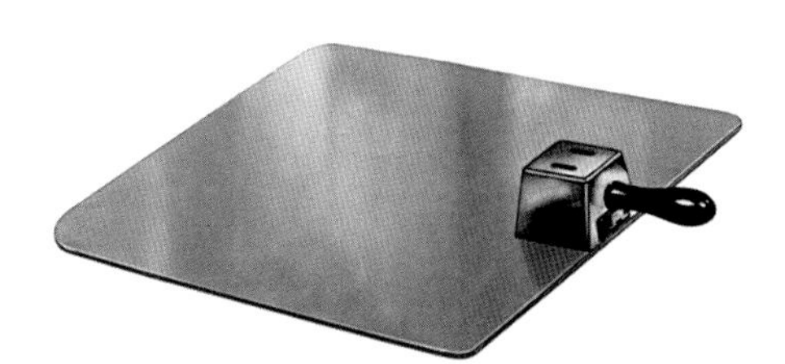
4: Sensor plate

Special **marks** or **notches** have to be made on the garment pieces in order to provide guides for accurate sewing and assembly in the sewing room. These cuts or marks must not be visible in the finished garment.

Hot Notcher

The **hot notcher** is used to make position marks at the edge of a stack of fabric plies. The temperature and the depth of the notch are adjustable (*Figure 1*).

This device is mainly used for knitted fabrics made of natural fibres. The edges of synthetic fabrics can fuse.

Thread Marker

With the **thread marker** a tacking thread is stitched vertically through the layers and is cut off beneath the bottom ply. The thread is then cut between the single layers. If a fluorescent thread is used then the mark will have improved visibility where ultra-violet lamps are installed at the sewing machine or other equipment. The thread marker is used when a drill would damage the cloth (*Figure 2*).

Drill Marker

A small hole, which will remain visible for some time, is drilled through the fabric layers. The drill needle can be heated to make the holes more durable. (*Figure 3*).

Sensor Plate

The drill marker may be provided with a **sensor plate** which delivers a buzzing tone when the drill has penetrated through to the bottom layer. This avoids damage to the table top (*Figure 4*).

Dye Marker

The drilled holes are additionally marked by a colour delivered in a fluid which runs down flutes in the drill. A distinct coloured dot can be made on any kind of fabric. Used for marking e.g. pocket locations, dart lengths.

Preparation

5: Hand-held labelling device

Preparation means all of the work which has to be carried out prior to sewing:

- **numbering and labelling** of pattern pieces
- **marking** pockets
- **sorting** of pattern pieces
- **sorting** of trimmings
- **bundling** of the sorted pieces and trimmings.

Shade marking is to ensure that components cut from different shades of the same colour-way are not mixed within a garment. Every cut bundle is provided with a numbered ticket. Bundles of components will also be provided with a label containing a serial number, the size and other operational data. The labels have to be clearly visible but must not interfere with further processing (sewing, fusing) (*Figure 5*). Modern labelling systems provide data in computer-readable form, which allow some automation in production control and progress chasing to be introduced.

10.2.6 Drawing and Measuring Tools

Tool	Features and Uses
Set-square 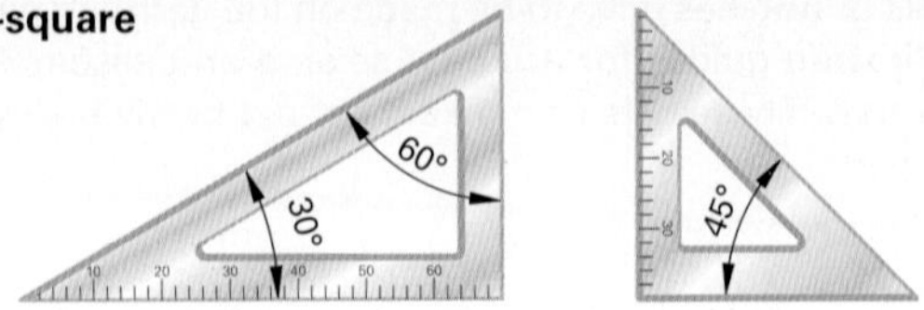	Set-squares are made of crystal-clear, shatter-proof synthetic material, metal or wood. They are used in the design and pattern departments.
Pattern square 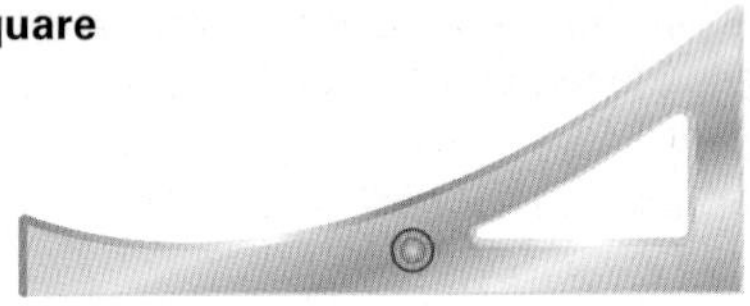	Pattern squares are generally made of light metal or synthetic material. Their special feature is the curved edge. They are used in the design and pattern department for drawing curved lines (hips, collars).
Hand ruler 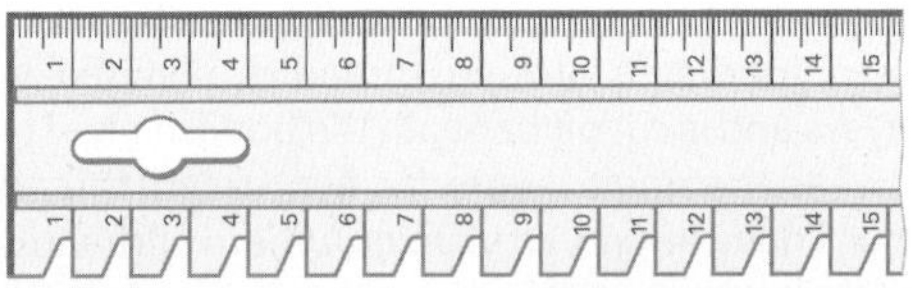	The hand ruler is a measuring edge, 20 to 30 cm long, made from flexible plastic. One edge may be notched. It is especially suitable for measuring short distances and placing marks, e.g. distances between pleats or buttons.
Tape measure 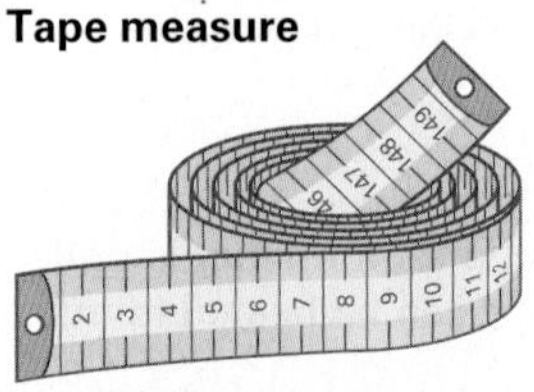 / **Waist measuring tape** 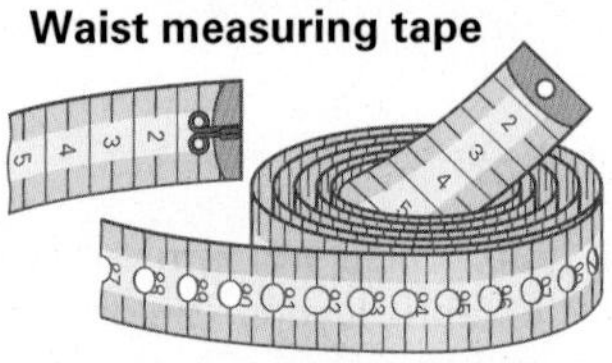	Tape measures are woven bands with a durable synthetic coating. They are generally 1.5 to 2 cm wide and 1.5 to 2 m in length. They are used to take body measurements and measure curved surfaces. The waist measuring tape has a hook at the end and a series of eyes at appropriate distances.
Pattern wheel, Tracing wheel 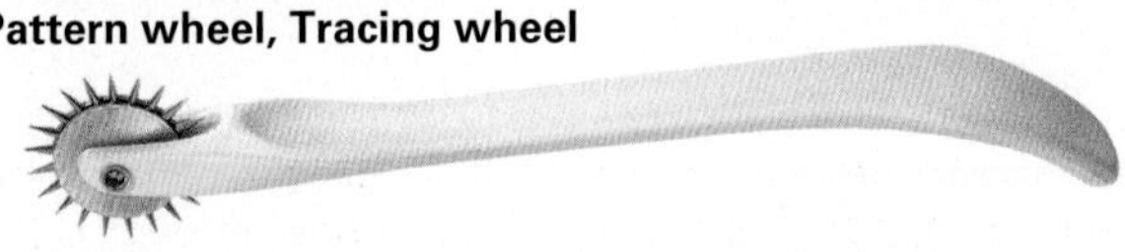	Pattern wheels are small toothed or pinned metal wheels. They are used for transferring pattern and construction lines onto paper.
Marking chalk  (solid,  powder)	Marking chalk is made from various materials. Clay chalk can be brushed out easily. Wax chalk is melted by ironing. Synthetic chalk disperses after some time. Marking chalk is used for drawing cutting lines and positioning marks on the top cloth.
Marking pens 	Marks made by marking pens may be self erasing after 2 to 8 days, or can be removed either by water or by ironing. They are especially useful for marking on the top cloth e.g. pocket positions.
Hem marker 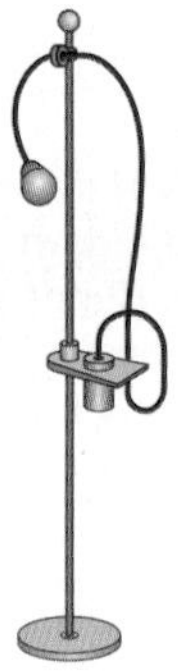 / **Hem tacker** 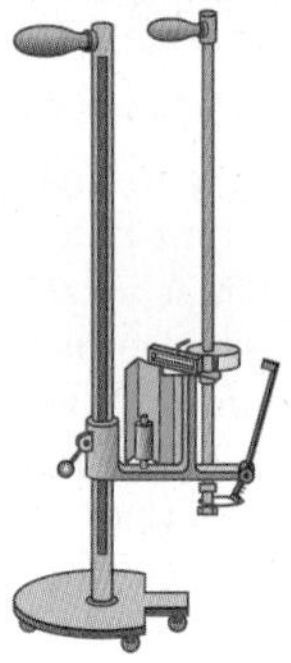	The hem marker applies chalk marks using puffs of air. The hem tacker marks the hemline with a thread. This equipment is used to ensure that hem lines are marked at a uniform height all round.

10.2.7 Hand Sewing Tools

Sewing Needles and Finger Protection

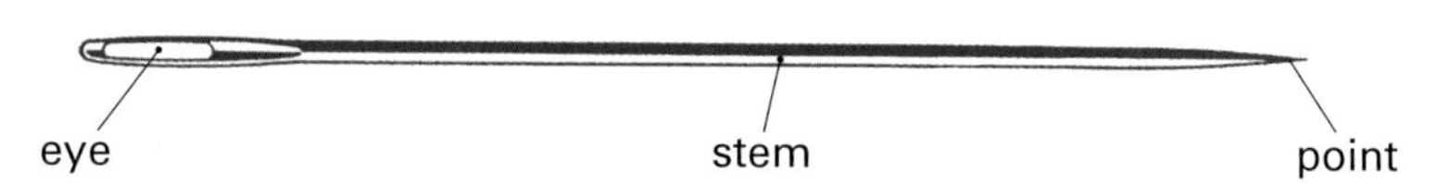

1: The sewing needle

Name	Features and Uses
Sewing Needles standard 3 5 7 9 long 1 3 5 7 9	Sewing needles are classified by their length and thickness. The usual types are "standard" and "long". The numbering system is not directly related to the length or thickness of the needles; it serves only to distinguish one needle from another. The length and thickness of a needle will be chosen according to the fabric to be sewn, the thread to be used and the sewing technique. Sewing needles are made of nickel-plated steel. They have to be flexible, smooth and sharp.
Embroidery Needles pointed 14 16 18 20 22 24 rounded 14 16 18 20 22 24 **Darning Needles** 3/0 1/0 1 3 5 7 9	Embroidery and darning needles are particularly thick sewing needles. Material and yarn thickness determine the length and thickness of the needle to be used. The numbering system is not directly related to the length or thickness of the needles; it serves only to distinguish one needle from another. Rounded needles are used for coarse materials; pointed needles are used for finer materials.

Steel Pins

Length mm	Thickness ∅ mm
30	0.60 extra fine
34	0.60 extra fine
30	0.70 fine
34	0.70 fine
40	0.85 fine

Plastic-head Pins

Length mm	Thickness ∅ mm	Head Colour
30	0.60	white
30	0.60	black
30	0.60	coloured
40	0.70	coloured
48	0.80	white
48	0.80	coloured

Pins are made of steel or brass and may have plastic heads.

The length, thickness and type of pins are chosen depending on the type of fabric and the application (component assembly, decoration and packaging).

Dressmaker's Thimble

Diameter mm approx.
18.0
17.0
16.5
16.0
15.0
14.0

Tailor's Thimble

Diameter mm approx.
20
19
18
17
16
15
14

Thimbles are made of steel or brass. The many small depressions are provided to prevent the needle from slipping off.

Protection of the middle finger allows for easier and quicker sewing.

10.2.8 Cutting Tools (1)

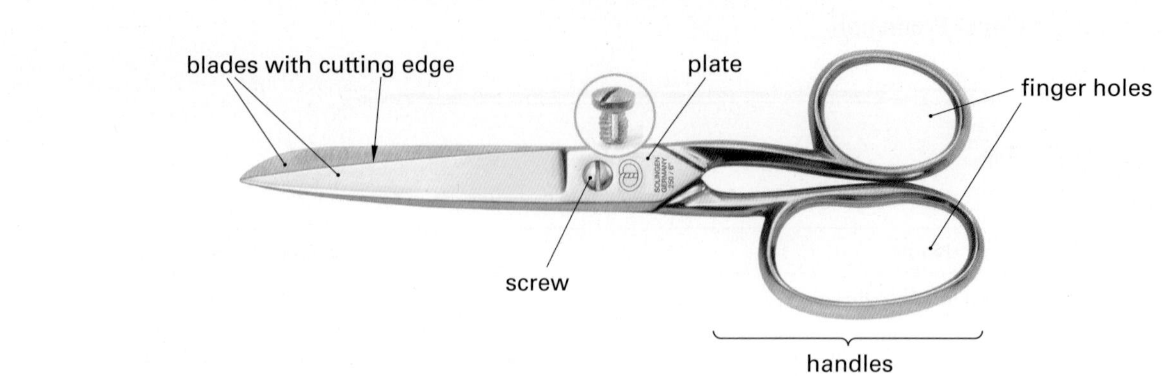

1: Scissors, shears

Types of Scissors	Features and Uses
Paper Shears	Paper shears have long pointed blades. The blades are longer than the handles. They can be used for accurate cutting of thin paper.
Hand Scissors	Hand scissors are designed to be easy to handle, with their differently-shaped blades and finger holes. Hand scissors are used in all general-purpose cutting operations.
Tailor's Shears fine serrations	Tailor's shears are large and stable. The finger holes are specially contoured, shaped and positioned to make it easier to cut thick fabrics. One of the blades is provided with serrations, which helps to prevent smooth fabrics from slipping. Tailor's shears are suitable for cutting garment components from single layers.
Pattern Shears	The handles, which are strongly contoured, are much longer than the short, strong blades. In heavy-duty types the blades are screwed on and can be changed. They are used for cutting out pattern templates from thick cardboard, or plastic.
Pinking Shears	The shape and handling characteristics are somewhat similar to tailor's shears, but the cutting edges have a zigzag profile. The zigzag edge of the cut fabric reduces the tendency for the cut edge to fray and may provide a more attractive trimming.

10.2.8 Cutting Tools (2)

Types of Scissors (continued)	Features and Uses
Buttonhole Scissors 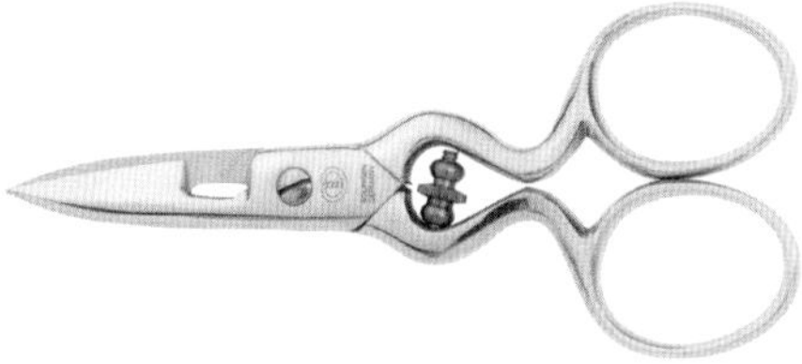	A special gap in the blades allows short cuts to be made inside the edge of the fabric. The length of cut can be adjusted by a screw.
Embroidery Scissors 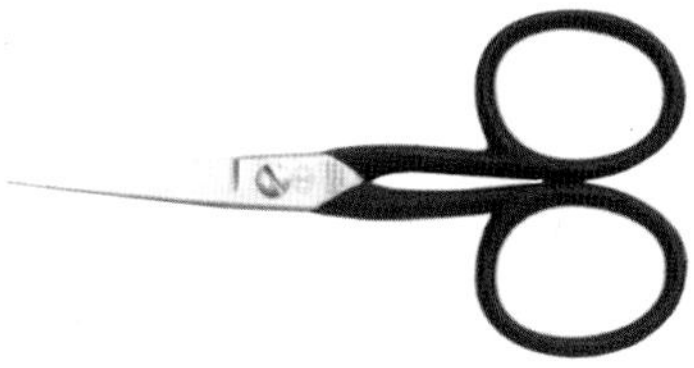	The handles are longer than the narrow and pointed blades. They are suited for catching and cutting fine, short threads.
Snippers 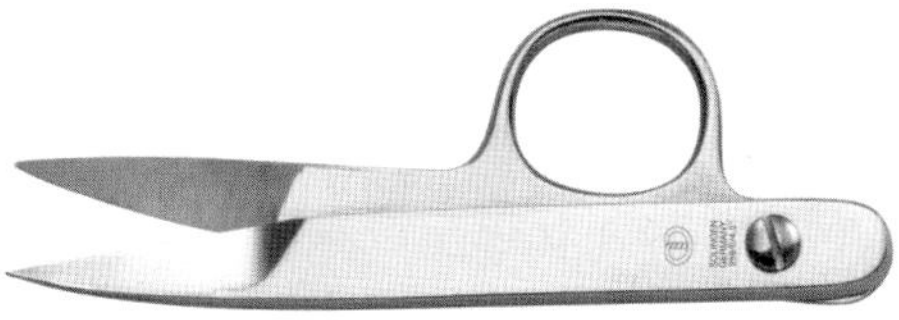	The small, lightly spring-loaded blades open automatically. Allows very rapid and easy snipping and trimming of waste thread, or removal of tacking stitches and opening of seams. Used e.g. in fitting, final inspection, and reworking.
Other Tools	
Stitch Cutter, Ripper 	The stitch cutter has a hooked edge with an arrowhead. It is especially suitable for opening up machine-made button holes.
Awl bone awl steel awl 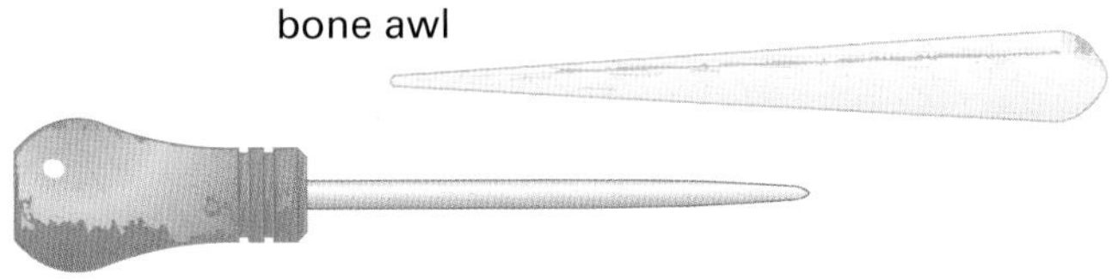	An awl is made of bone, plastic or metal. It tapers to a point and has a smooth surface. It is used for rounding off button eyes or draw-string holes, and for pulling out threads.
Hole Punch 	Punches are available in diameters of 2 mm to 25 mm. The punch is generally used for making holes in card or plastic pattern templates or cutting patterns.
Revolving Hole Punch 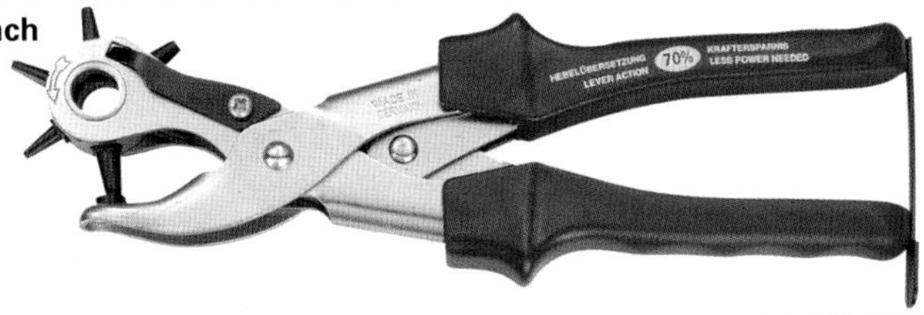	The revolving punch has a magazine of punches of different diameters. It is used to make holes close to the edge of the fabric.
Notcher 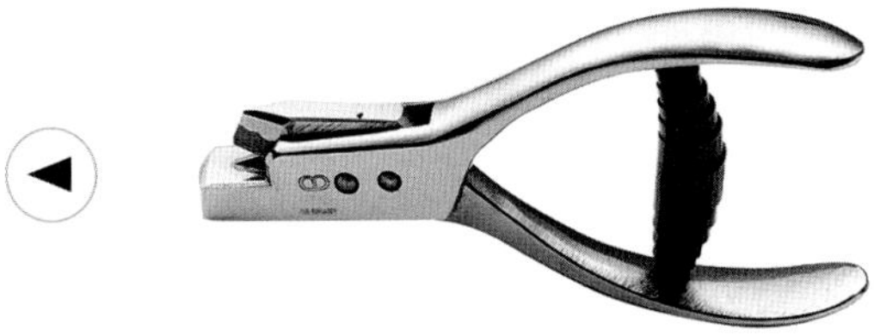	Makes notches of various shapes according to requirements. Used for placing positioning marks on cutting patterns, e.g. balance marks and seam allowances.

10.3.1 Types of Sewing Machine

The simplest form of sewing machine is the flat bed type, with the following basic components:

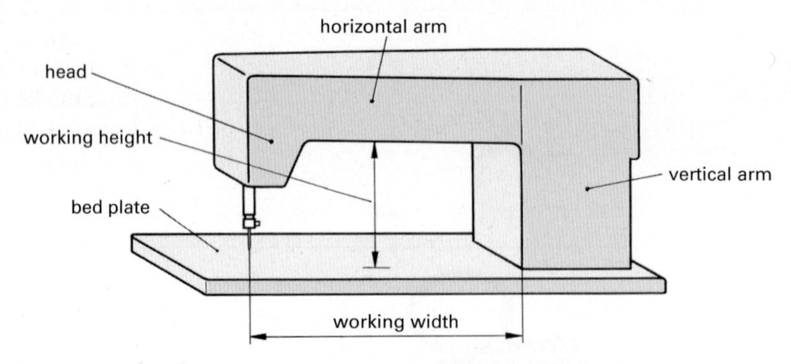

Modifications of the basic flat bed machine have been developed for particular operations.

Types of Sewing Machine	Stitch Type	Features and Uses
Flat bed machine (basic type)	lockstitch chain stitch	The large working area allows a wide range of applications; the material can easily be guided around the needle and the presser foot. This basic type is used for all kinds of flat sewing work.
Raised bed machine	lockstitch chain stitch	The bed plate is in the form of a plinth. It facilitates the assembly of pre-sewn parts and is especially suitable for the fitting of accessories and special attachments. This is the basic form for various specialised machines such as buttonholers.
Post bed machine	lockstitch chain stitch	This type has an increased working height and a vertical hook (*see page 174*) in a post. Special applications are found in the working of three-dimensional products, e.g. shoes and bags. The post makes it easier to work on tight curves and corners, to sew in sleeves and to complete large, half-assembled products.
Cylinder bed machine **Cylinder bed** **Feed-off-arm bed**	lockstitch chain stitch	These machines have an increased working height and a bed in the shape of a horizontal arm. They are especially suitable for working on tubular parts, such as cuffs, sleeves, and trouser legs, and also for button sewing and bar tacking. They are used extensively in the making of clothing from knitted fabrics.
Side bed machine	chain stitch and overedge stitches	Machines which are specialised for sewing at edges need only a small working area.

10.3.2 Sewing Machines: Overview

Machine Types	Applications
1: Lockstitch machine; 2: Chain stitch machine; 3: Multi-thread chain stitch machine	Straight seams, zigzag seams (*see pages 176 to 178*).
4: Blind stitch machine; 5: Linking machine	Blind stitch machines for invisible stitching and hemming Linking machines for attaching collars, cuffs and waistbands on knitted fabrics (*see page 183*).
6: Overedge machine; 7: Safety stitch machine	Edge neatening, combined neatening and seam closing, safety stitching (*see pages 180 and 181*).
8: Flat seam machine; 9: Flat seamer with cylinder bed	Binding cut edges, flat seams on knitted fabrics (*see page 182*).
10: Buttonhole machine; 11: Button sewing machine; 12: Automatic looper	Specialised sewing operations (*see page 191*).
13: Profile sewer; 14: Pocket sewer	Automatic, complex sewing operations (*see page 192*).

10.3.3 Construction of a Sewing Machine

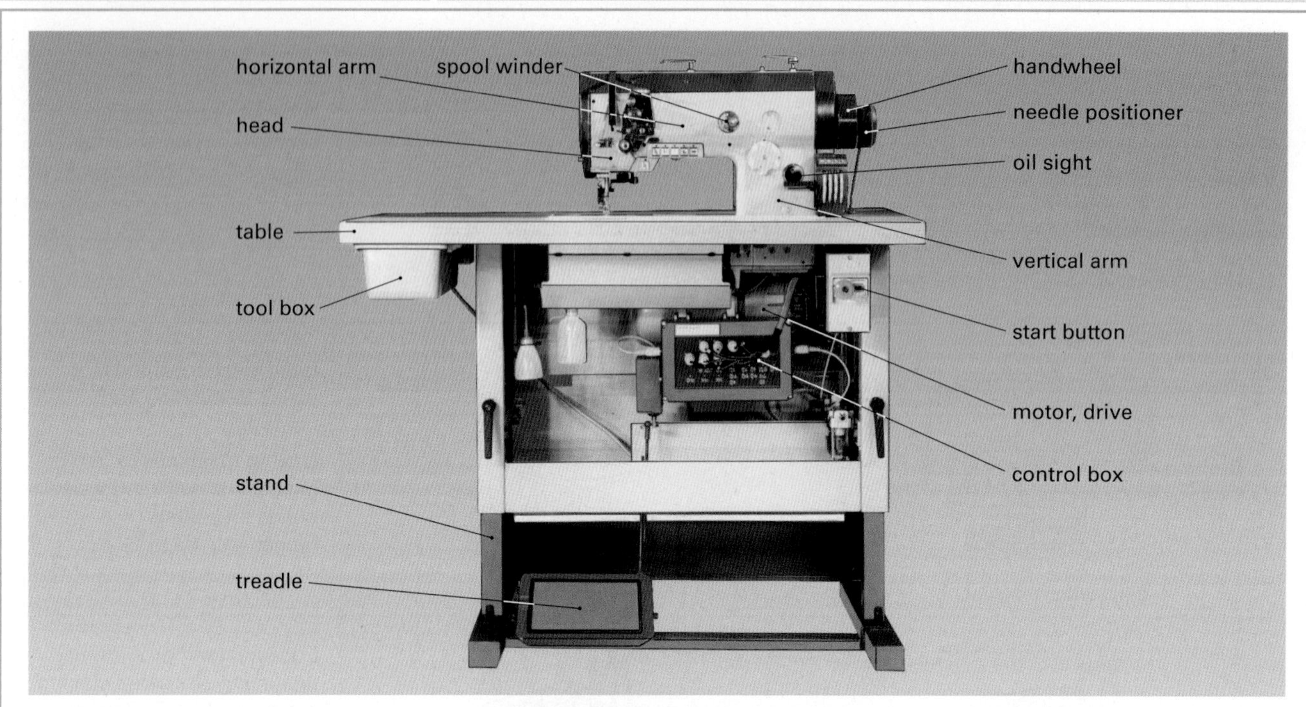

1: Overall view (lockstitch machine)

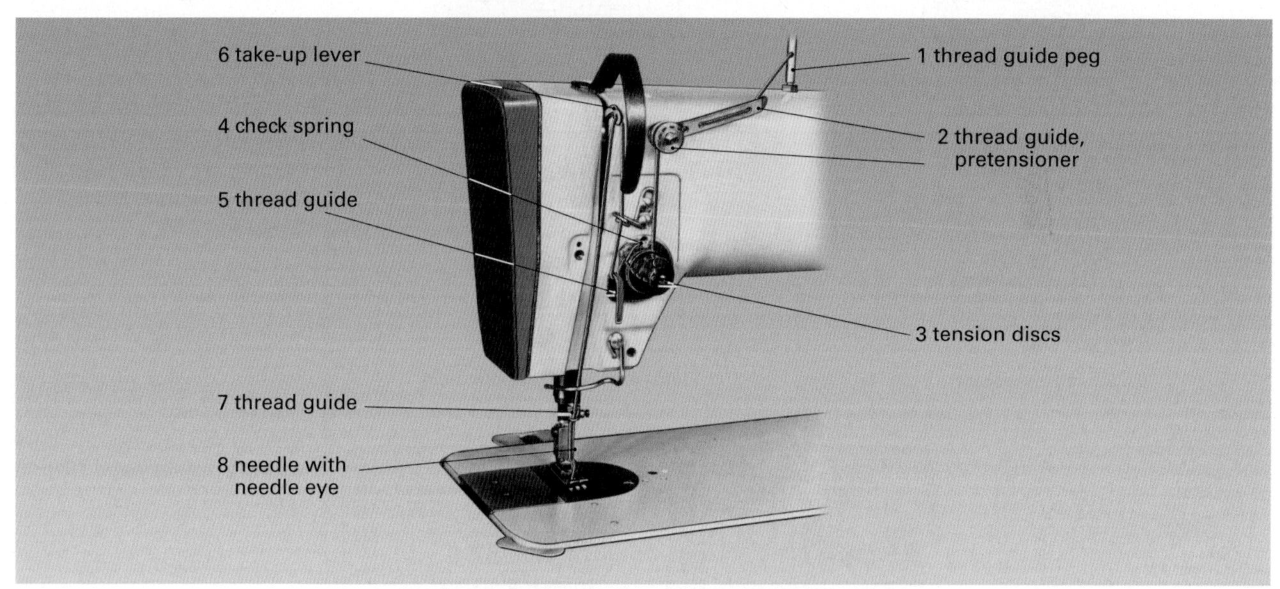

2: Head end with top thread guide (lockstitch machine)

Thread Guiding System – Needle Thread

No	Name	Function	No	Name	Function
1	**thread guide peg**	Ensures uniform draw-off (no snarling).	6	**take-up lever**	Draws the needle thread from the bobbin. Releases the required length of thread for making the stitch. Tightens the stitch.
2	**pretensioner**	Ensures uniform draw-off.			
3	**tension discs**	Ensures correct tension for looping.			
4	**check spring**	Evens out tension fluctuations.	7	**thread guide**	Keeps the thread in its proper course.
5	**thread guide**	Effects a change in direction.	8	**needle with needle eye**	Pushes the thread through the material and forms the loop.

10.3.4 Moving Parts of a Sewing Machine

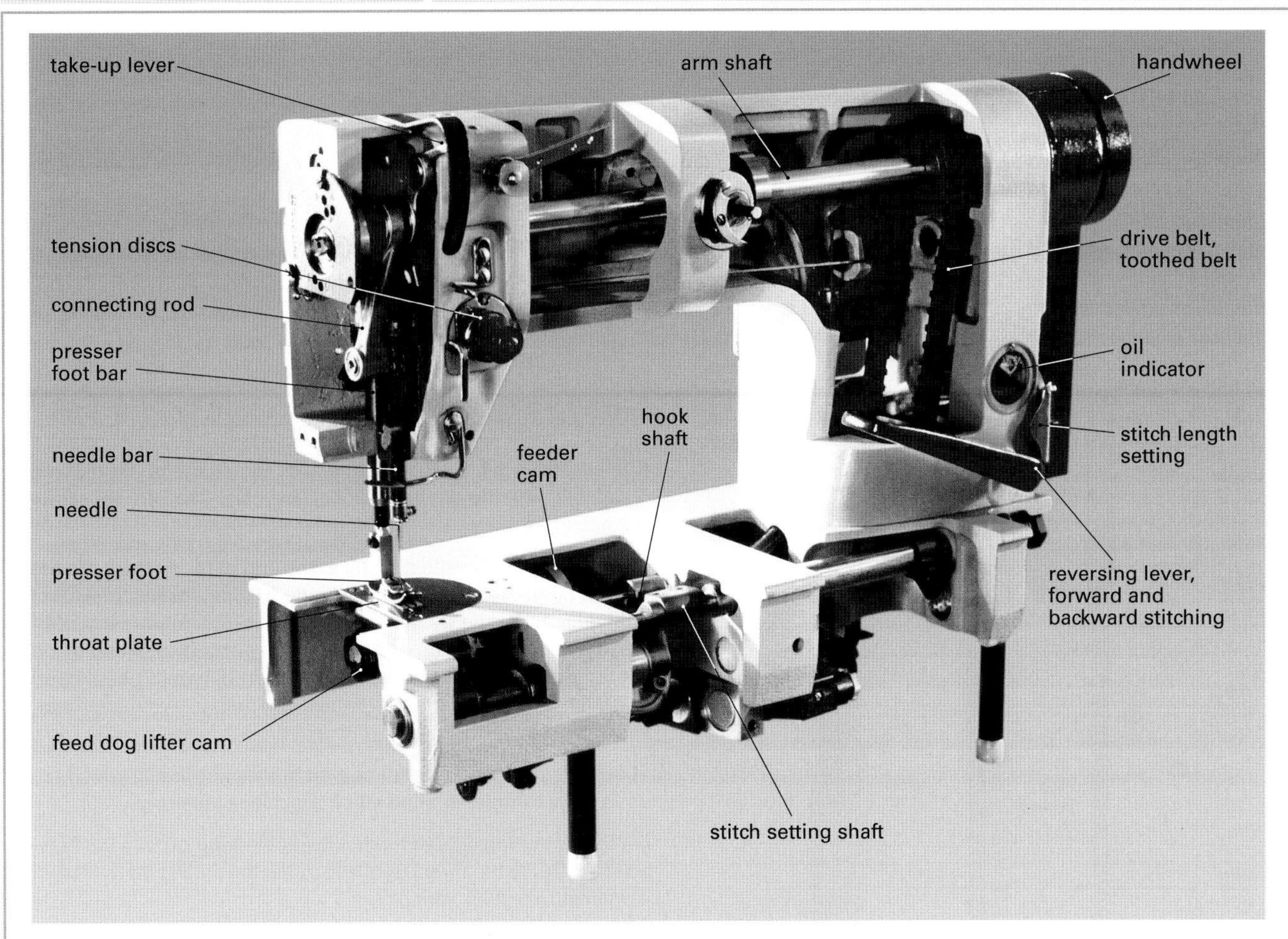

1: Cut-away model (lockstitch machine)

Stitch Formation Parts			
Name	**Function**	**Name**	**Function**
Needle	Guides the needle thread through the material being sewn and forms a loop.	**Tension discs**	Ensures the correct tension for proper stitch formation.
Rotary hook	Catches the thread loop and lays it around the under-thread spool.	**Presser foot**	Presses the material being sewn against the feed dog and the throat plate. Facilitates stitch formation and feeding.
Take-up lever	Draws the needle thread from the bobbin. Releases the required length of thread for stitch formation. Tightens the stitch.	**Throat plate**	Provides openings for the needle and the feed dog.
		Feed dog	Moves the material forward, by one stitch length, after each stitch has been drawn.

Motions in a Sewing Machine

The following applies to the lockstitch machine illustrated above.

The top shaft is driven from the motor via the drive belt. The bottom shaft is driven from the top shaft via the toothed belt and gear wheels.

The rotary hook is driven by the hook shaft.

The feed dog is raised by the feed dog lifter cam and driven forward by the feeder rocker shaft. Co-ordination of feeder bar and needle bar is controlled by the feeder cam.

The incremental feed length is determined by the stitch length setting, the stitch setting shaft and the feeder rocker shaft.

The top shaft is provided with a crank and connecting rod, which convert the shaft's rotation into the vertical movement of the needle bar.

10.3.5 Sewing Machine Needles (1)

Requirements

The needle has to be able to penetrate the material being sewn, without damaging it, by pushing the yarns aside. Solid materials, such as leather or plastic, will be holed. Sewing machine needles of various types are available, according to the application.

Selection of the needle type will depend on the characteristics of the material, the size of the sewing thread, the type of seam and the stitch type.

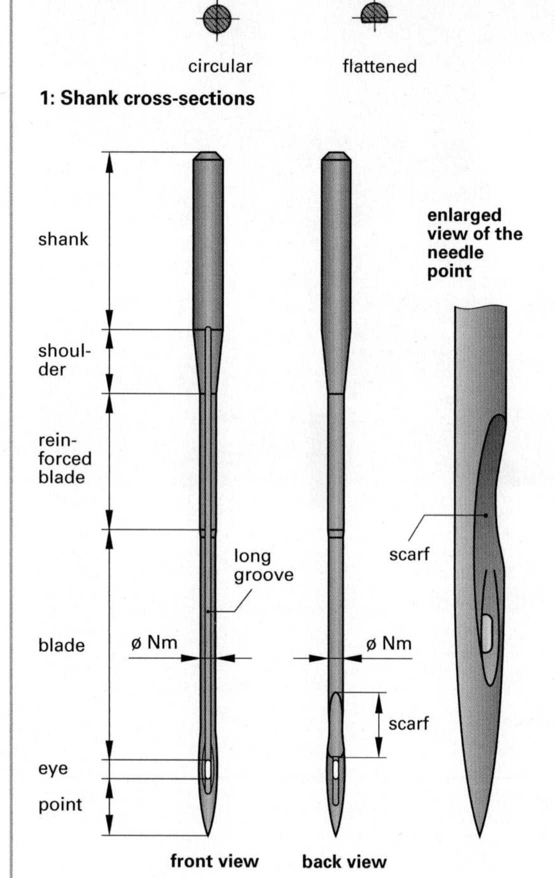

2: Lockstitch needle

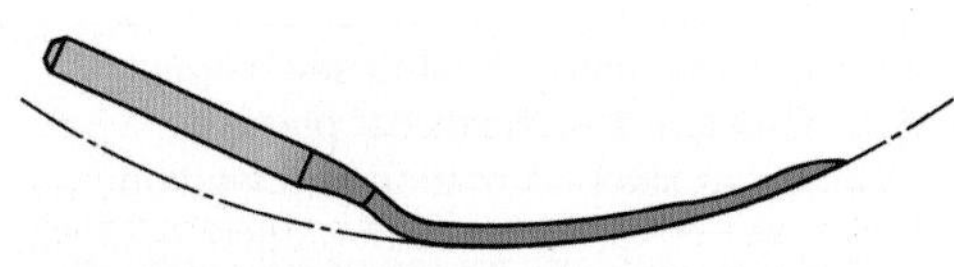

3: Curved needle (blind stitch needle)

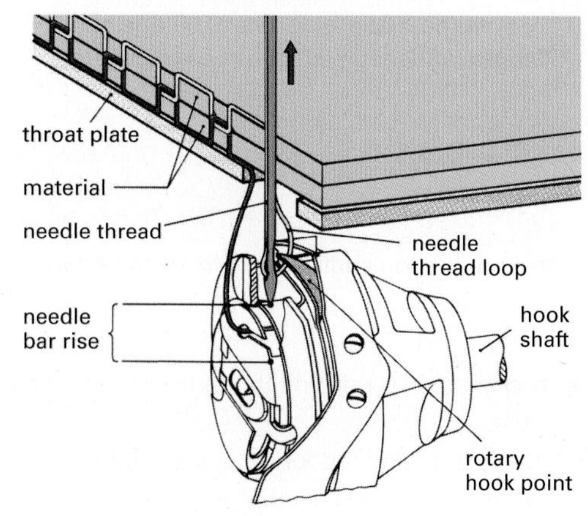

4: Forming a needle thread loop

Characteristics and Terminology

The **shank** locates the needle in the needle bar. The following types are found:

- Shanks with a circular section
- Shanks with a flat side which serves to locate the needle in a specific position in the needle bar
- Needles in which the thickness of the shank is maintained all the way down the blade. They are used in speciality machines.

The **blade** of the needle runs from the end of the shoulder to the beginning of the eye. Often the blade will increase in thickness, in stages, from the eye to the shoulder. This reinforcement of the blade increases its stiffness. Moreover, by widening the stitch hole, it tends to reduce the friction between needle and material during the upstroke, which can help to avoid overheating of the needle.

There are also needles with curved blades (*Figure 3*), which are used, for example, in blind stitch machines (*see page 183*).

On the threading side of the needle is the **long groove.** Its function is to guide the thread while forming the stitch and to protect it against excessive friction.

Above the eye there is usually a recess or **scarf** across the whole face of the needle. This facilitates the passage of the hook into the loop and reduces the danger of missed stitches.

The shape of the **eye** is always extended in its length, because the needle thread has to pass diagonally through the needle in the length direction. The width of the eye is the same as that of the long groove.

Needle Sizes

The metric size "Nm" of a needle gives the diameter of the blade (in 1/100 mm) at a point just above the scarf (*Figure 2*).

Fine needles have a size up to about Nm 70; medium needles are about Nm 80 or Nm 90; thick needles are Nm 100 or more.

Forming the Needle Thread Loop

First, the needle thread is carried all the way through the plies to be sewn and beyond the underside. As the needle begins its upstroke, the thread is retarded by friction between it and the material so a loop is formed in the needle thread. The loop is caught by the point of the rotary hook, enlarged, and passed around the underthread spool. The needle thread is then withdrawn whilst the stitch is tightened by the movement of the take-up lever. These vertical movements are extremely rapid, so the efficient functioning of the long groove, in permitting smooth passage of the thread, is critically important.

10.3.5 Sewing Machine Needles (2)

Needle Points

Needles are manufactured with a wide variety of needle points appropriate for the differing properties of materials that have to be sewn.

There are two basic types of points, namely **Round Points** and **Cutting Points.**

The classification given below is based on the shape of the point and its application

Round Points

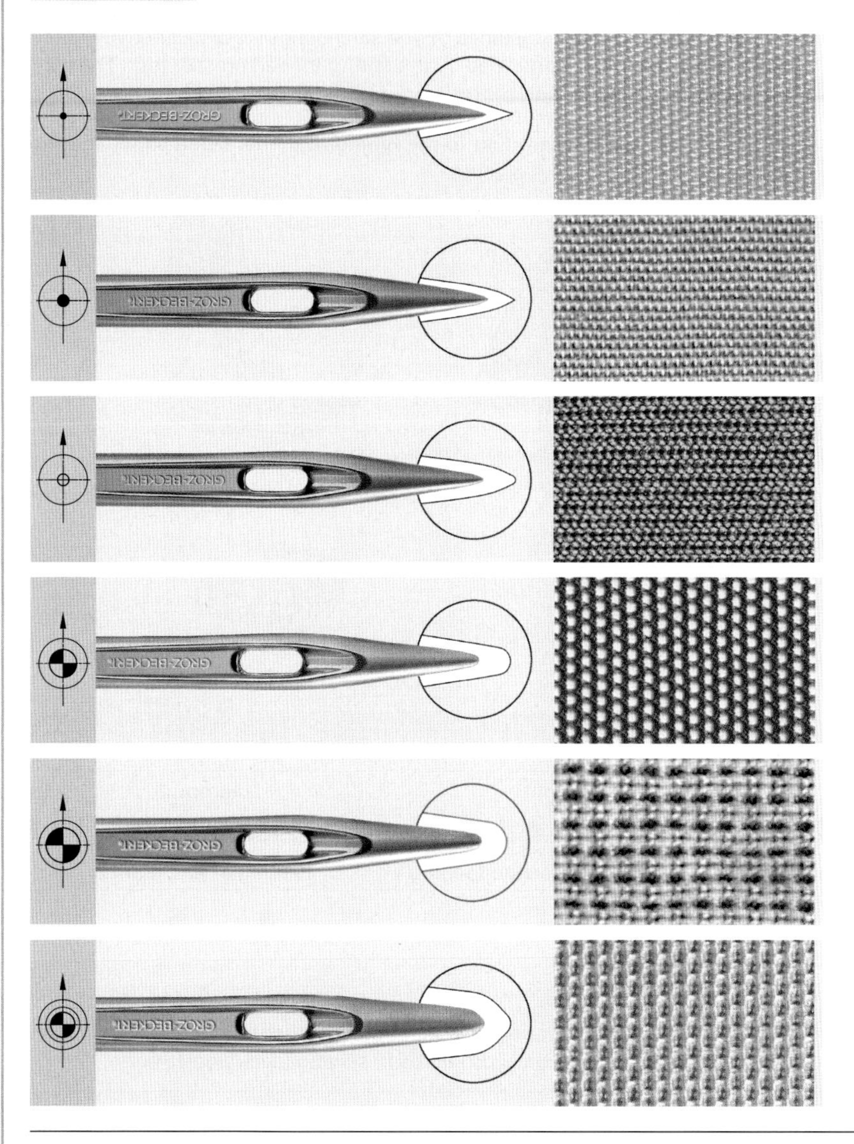

Slim set point needles can penetrate the yarns of the material being sewn. They are used for blind stitches and for fine, densely woven fabrics. They are not suitable for knitted fabrics.

The **set cloth point** is slightly rounded. It displaces the yarns of the material being sewn without damaging them. This is the most versatile point shape and is standard for lockstitch.

The **light ball point** is used for sensitive fabrics such as knits and microfibre fabrics, to prevent damage to the loops. This is the standard point for chainstitch.

The **medium ball point** is used for elastic materials containing rubber or elastomeric threads. The threads are not pierced, but displaced.

The **heavy ball point** is suited for coarse, highly elastic, and open fabrics.

The **heavy set point** is strongly blunted. It is used especially for warp knits with high elastane content, such as medical support fabrics.

Cutting Points

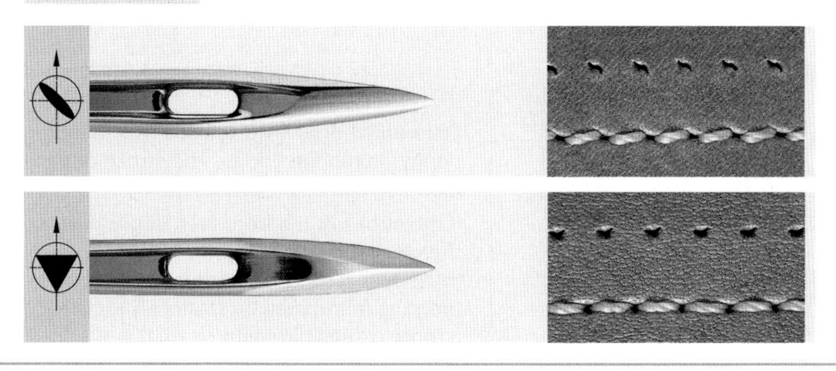

Cutting points are used for sewing leather and films or coated and laminated textiles.

They are classified and named according to:

- the position of the cutting edge e.g. **right cutting point.**
- the shape of the point e.g. **triangular point.**

10.3.6 Feeding Systems (1)

Material feed means the controlled movement of the material being sewn from one stitch position to the next. Moving the material through the sewing point is what converts a series of stitches into a seam. In principle, the material can be moved in any horizontal direction; in most cases, it is only forwards or backwards. Usually the fabric is moved just after the needle point is raised clear of the surface and stops just as it is about to re-enter.

Principle of Material Feed

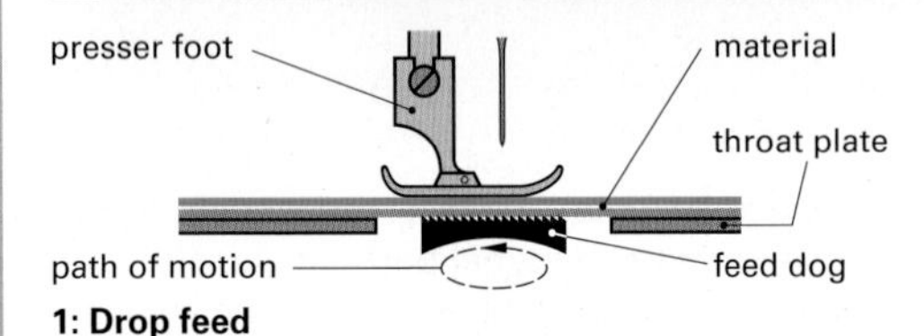

1: Drop feed

Material feed is achieved by the feed dog which contains several rows of serrated teeth. The feed dog is moved upwards and forwards through slots in the throat plate to engage with the under side of the material being sewn and to advance it by a distance of one stitch length. Contact between feed dog and material is controlled by the spring-loaded presser foot. The feed dog is then lowered and moved back to its starting position.

Various designs of feed dog, presser foot and throat plate are utilised according to the type of material being sewn and the particular sewing operation. Feed dogs can have different shapes and types of teeth.

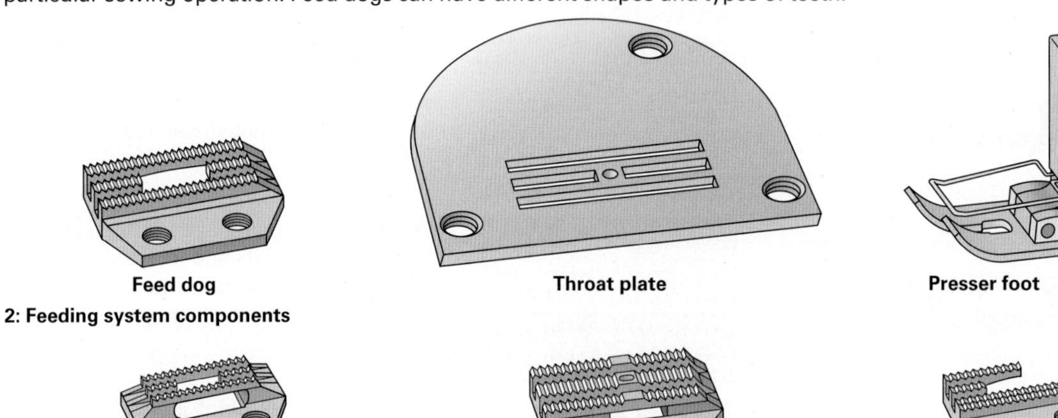
Feed dog | Throat plate | Presser foot

2: Feeding system components

3: Types of feed dog

Feed Dog Teeth

Types of teeth	saw-tooth	upright	diamond
Application	single-direction feeding	uniform two-direction feeding	feeding of fine fabrics

Types of Feed Systems

Feed systems usually work on the underside of the material but can also operate from above or from both sides at the same time, depending on requirements and on the need to avoid particular technical problems in sewing (*see page 194*).

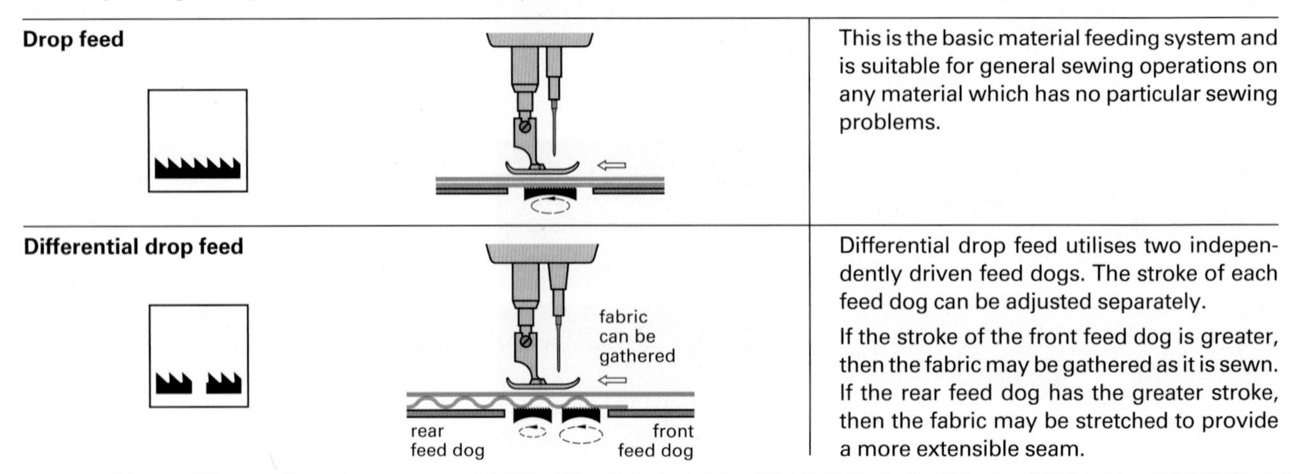

Drop feed	This is the basic material feeding system and is suitable for general sewing operations on any material which has no particular sewing problems.
Differential drop feed	Differential drop feed utilises two independently driven feed dogs. The stroke of each feed dog can be adjusted separately. If the stroke of the front feed dog is greater, then the fabric may be gathered as it is sewn. If the rear feed dog has the greater stroke, then the fabric may be stretched to provide a more extensible seam.

10.3.6 Feeding Systems (2)

Combined Feeding Systems

Compound feed

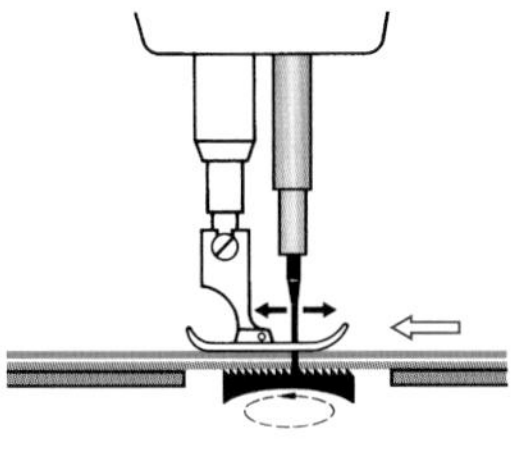

A combination of synchronised drop feed and needle feed. Feeding occurs whilst the needle is still in the material by combined motion of needle bar and feed dog.

The needle holds the fabric plies in registration during feeding to avoid slippage and seam pucker. Used mainly for edge stitching, checks and stripes.

Variable top and bottom feed (before the needle)

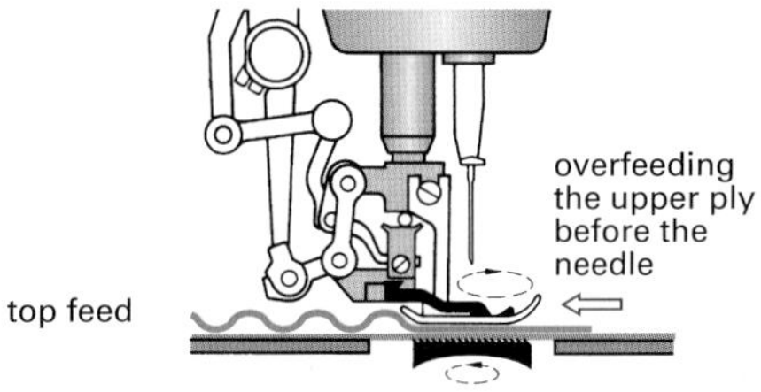

top feed

overfeeding the upper ply before the needle

A feeding foot, similar to the presser foot, is provided with e.g. two rows of teeth and acts alongside the presser foot.

The strokes of the feeding foot and the feed dog can be adjusted independently.

It is used, for example, in gathering the top ply.

Variable top and bottom feed (behind the needle)

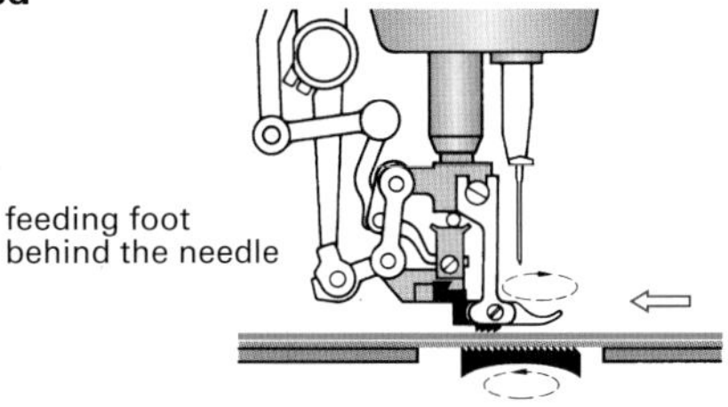

feeding foot behind the needle

In this case, the feeding foot operates behind the needle to deliver especially smooth seams.

This construction makes it easier to install machine attachments.

Alternating compound feed

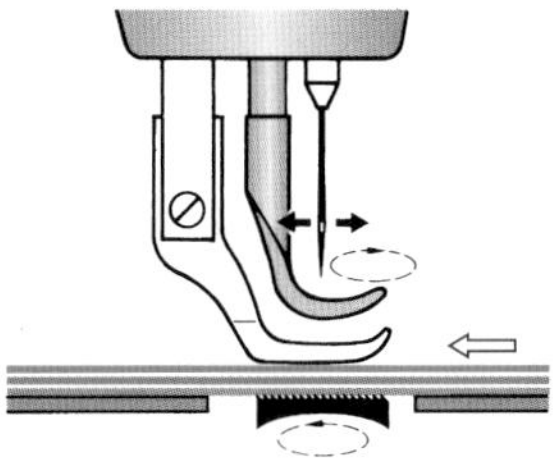

This system involves a combination of three types of feeding; feed dog, needle feed, and feeding foot. The fabric can not be gathered.

Applications:

- Sewing of multiple plies (plies are kept in registration)
- Sewing bulky seams in heavy fabrics

Puller feed, Roller feed

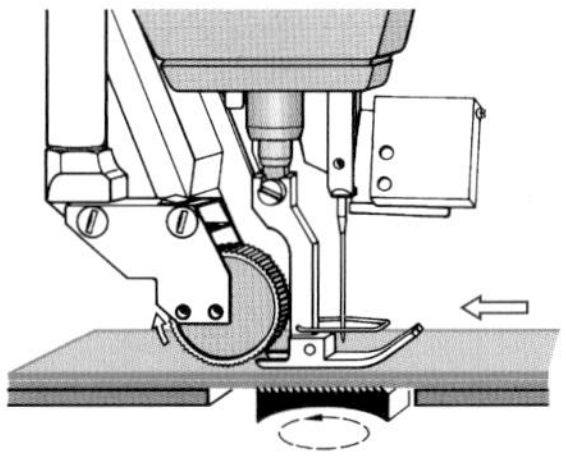

An auxiliary feed, usually a wheel or roller, supplements the normal feeding system. The roller is located behind the needle and operates either continuously or intermittently.

Suitable for long straight seams, such as in bed linen, which can be produced without puckering.

Special Feeding Devices

Clamp feed, Jig

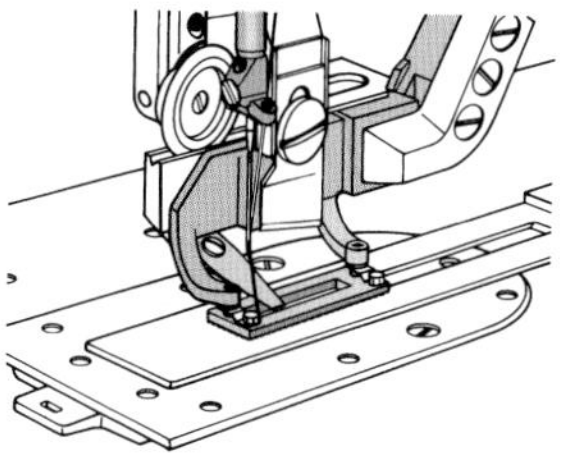

Automatic sewing stations, such as buttonholers, belt loop makers, and small part fabricators are provided with a special jig, which has openings for the stitching line, into which the fabric plies are fixed (*see page 191*). The jig is driven automatically and guides the material under the needle according to the required sewing pattern.

10.3.7 Presser Feet and Fabric Guides (1)

Presser Foot

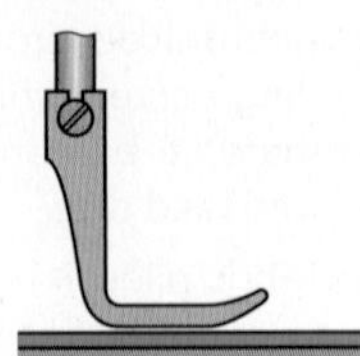

1: Fixed presser foot for seams of constant thickness

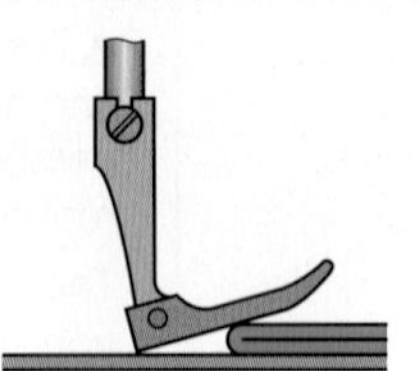

2: Pivoting presser foot for seams of variable thickness

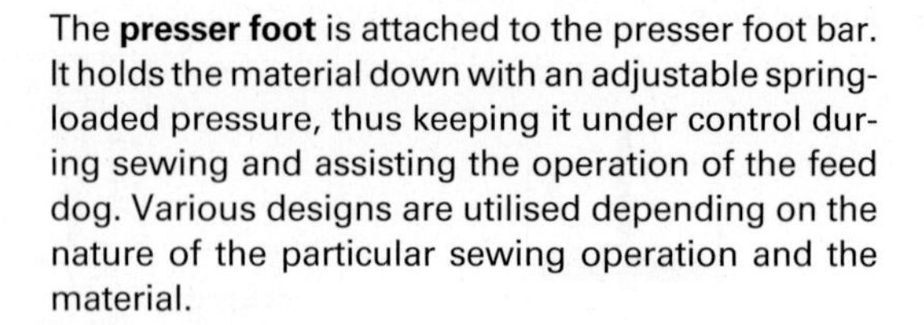

The **presser foot** is attached to the presser foot bar. It holds the material down with an adjustable spring-loaded pressure, thus keeping it under control during sewing and assisting the operation of the feed dog. Various designs are utilised depending on the nature of the particular sewing operation and the material.

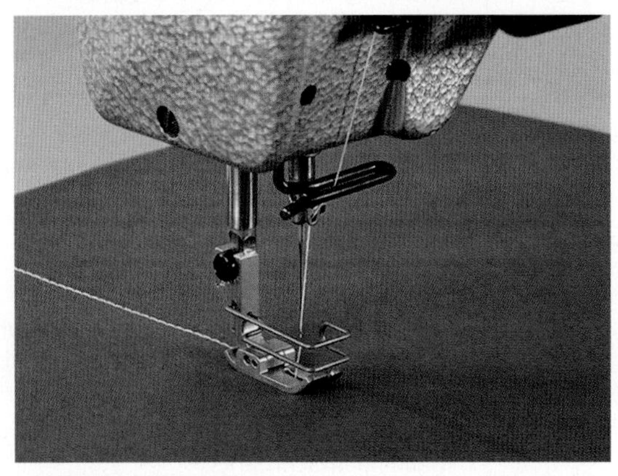

3: Pivoting presser foot

4: Double presser foot with edge guide (5 to 7 mm inset)

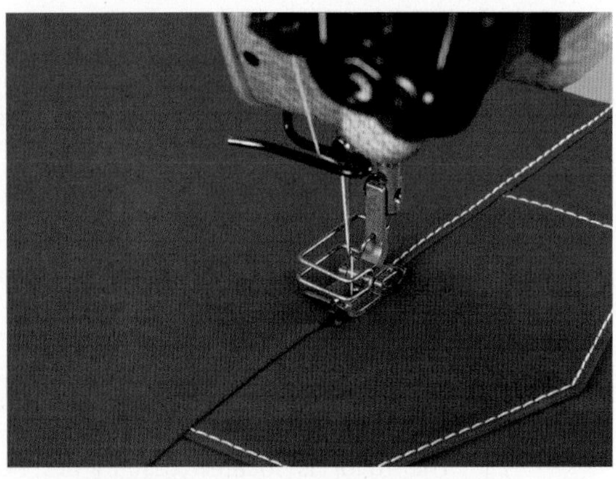

5: Double presser foot with 2 mm edge guide

6: Left hand zipper closing

7: Presser wheel and swivelling edge guide

8: Presser foot with built-in piping guide

10.3.7 Presser Feet and Fabric Guides (2)

Fabric Guides

Fabric guides allow sewing to proceed more rapidly. Hemmers and guiders make it easier to feed the material correctly to the needle and to obtain a regular seam line.

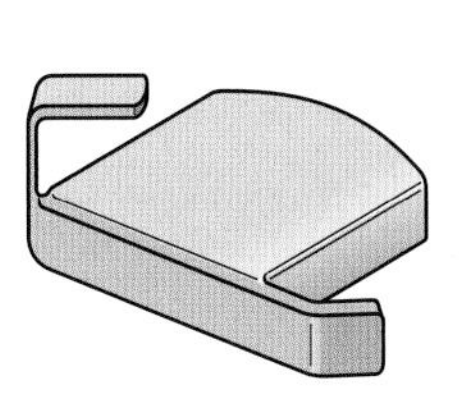

1: Magnetic edge guide

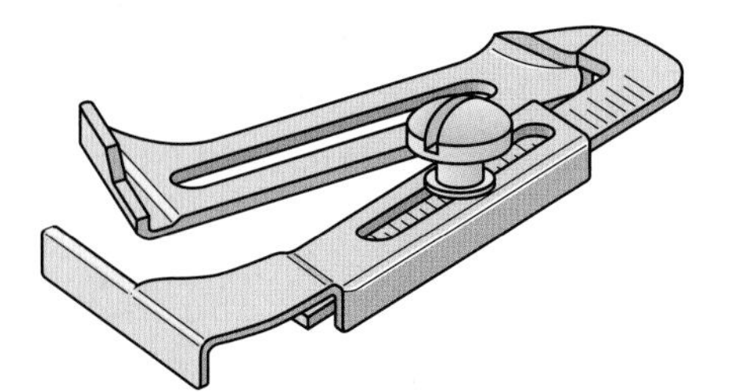

2: Adjustable edge guide

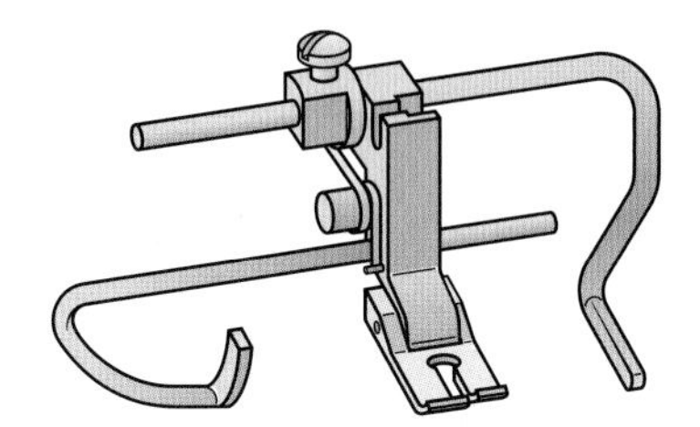

3: Edge guide for following a line

4: Edge binding guide

5: Folded-in seam guide

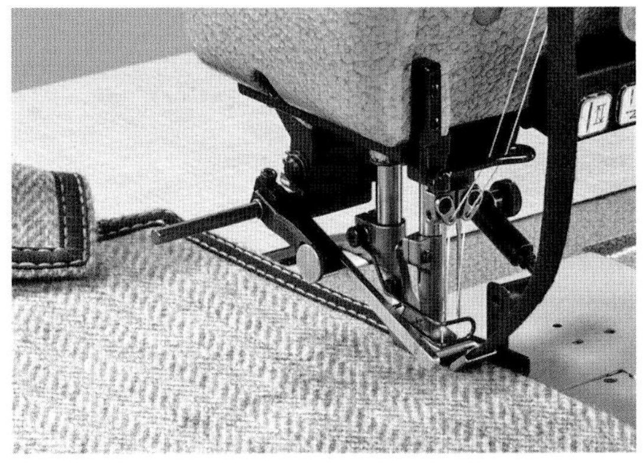

6: Tape guide

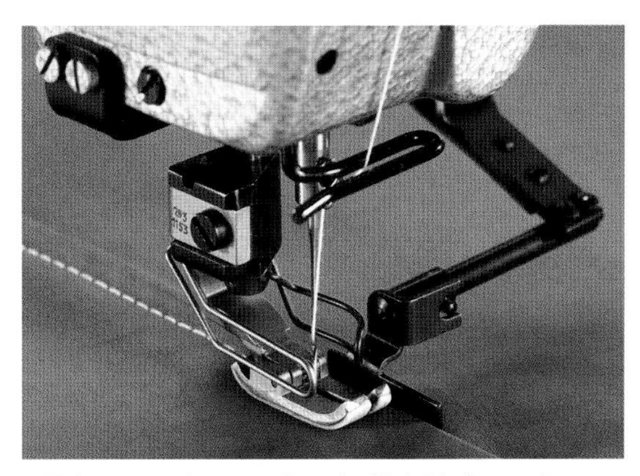

7: Teflon-coated presser foot, for high-friction surfaces

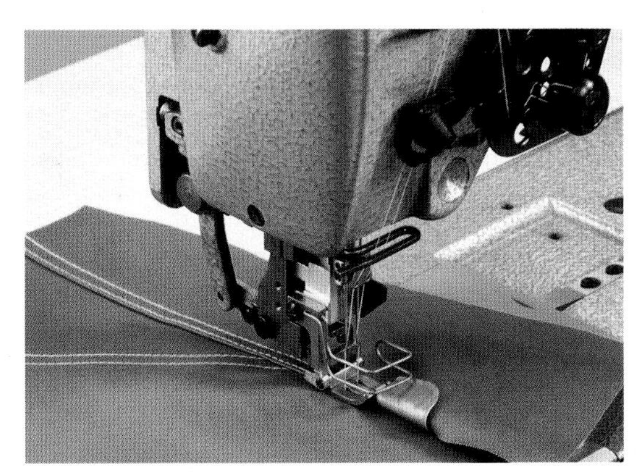

8: Lap seam folder

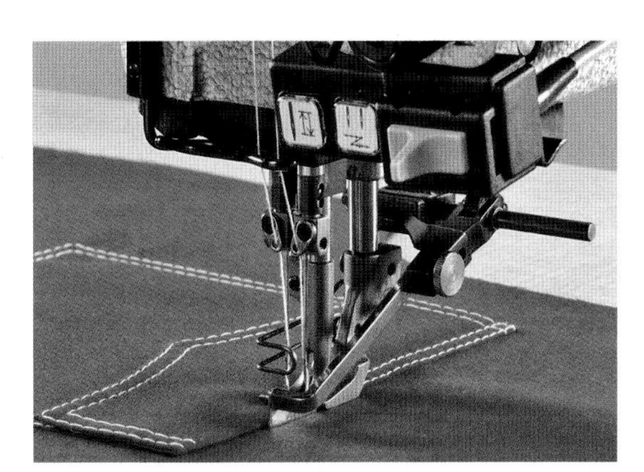

9: Evening lifting foot with edge guide

10.3.8 Shuttles, Hooks and Loopers

Shuttles and hooks are the means by which the underthread is taken through the loop of the needle thread in order to form a lockstitch.

Shuttles for Lockstitch

The shuttle is a carrier for the underthread. It passes completely through the enlarged needle thread loop, or guides the needle thread loop around itself.

Shuttles are used mainly for domestic sewing machines, and for working with stiff materials and thick threads, due to the lower yarn stress compared to rotary hooks. These machines work at up to 2000 stitches per minute. The oscillating shuttle is the most common type.

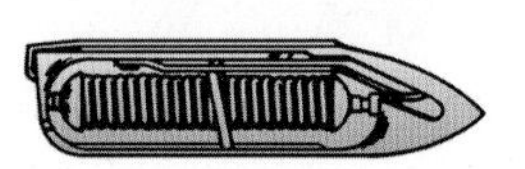

1: Straight shuttle

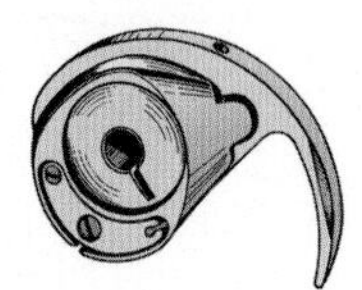

2: Ring shuttle

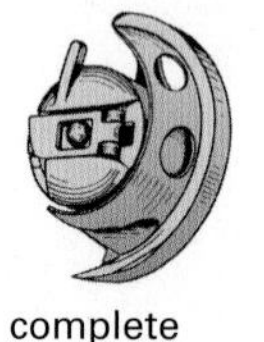

complete shuttle

body

spool case

spool

3: Oscillating shuttle

Rotary Hooks for Lockstitch

The hook guides the needle thread loop around a stationary spool case. The key part for forming a stitch is the underthread spool and its two-part capsule (*see page 176*).

Horizontal Hook

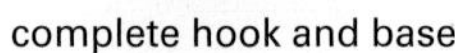

complete hook and base

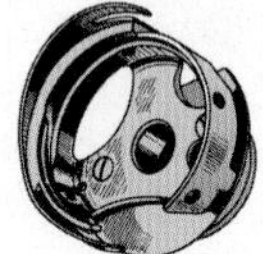

main body

gib

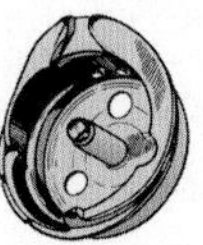

hook base

spool case

spool

4: Rotary hook

The hook is mounted on a horizontal shaft. It has to make two rotations to form a single stitch. Depending on the design of sewing machine and hook, it is capable of working at up to 14000 rpm, making 7000 stitches per minute.

Vertical Hook

This type is mounted on a vertical shaft but works in exactly the same way as the horizontal type. They are mainly used for two-needle lockstitch and post bed sewing machines.

Because of their low susceptibility to contamination, many single-needle speciality sewing machines are equipped with these hooks. The maximum sewing speed of this type of hook is about 5000 stitches per minute.

Loopers for Chain Stitch

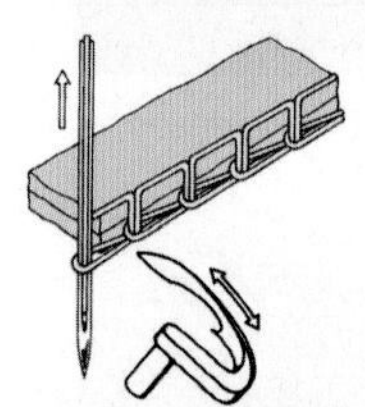

5: Oscillating looper

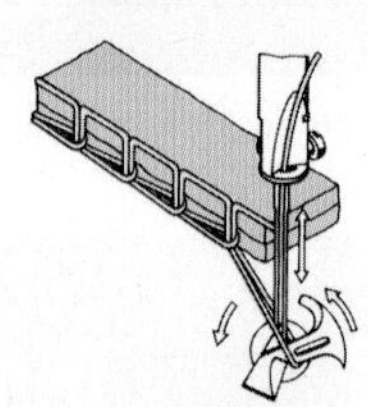

6: Rotating looper

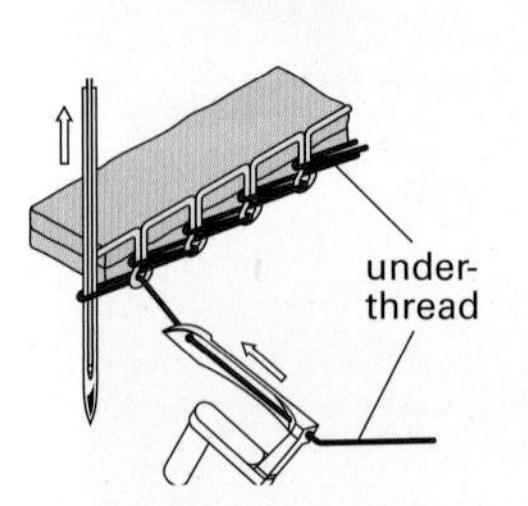

7: Oscillating two-thread chain stitch looper

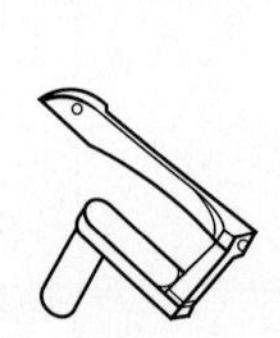

8: Looper without thread

The functions of the chain stitch looper are:

- to catch the needle thread loop
- to hold the needle loop in such a way that the needle is able to stitch through it on the following cycle.

Single chain stitch loopers (*see page 178*) are hooked. There are two types, namely oscillating loopers and rotating loopers.

The oscillating looper has a more complicated drive mechanism. The rotating looper demands less space and is generally used for button sewing machines.

The distinguishing feature of the **two-thread chain stitch looper** (*see page 179*) is the presence of a looper thread. Compared to the single chain stitch looper, it provides the additional function of making an underthread loop and guiding it through the needle thread loop.

10.3.9 Stitch Types[1]: Overview

Stitch types can be classified according to their general disposition in the fabric, the way that they are introduced into the fabric, or the mode and location of interlacing of the separate threads. ISO 4915 (ASTM D 6193) classifies them into six basic types.

In the drawings, stitch formation proceeds from right to left. Needle threads are in yellow, underthreads and looper threads are in red, and cover threads of Class 600 are in blue. With overedge sewing, the fabric is outlined.

Name	Features and Uses
Class 100: Chain stitch 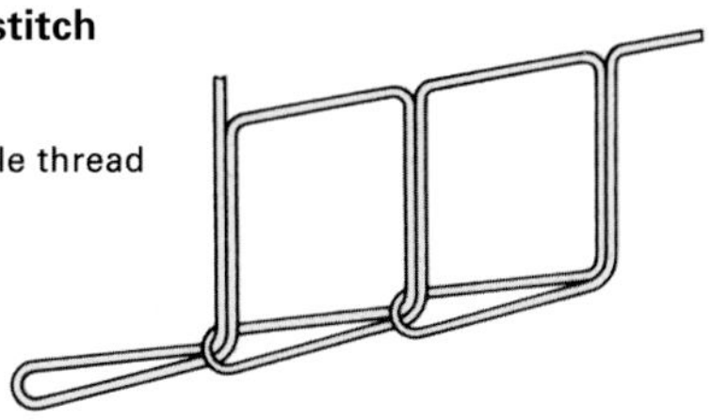 needle thread Type 101	Each loop is interconnected with the following loop of the same thread. Opposite sides of the seam[1] look different. This stitch type can be very easily unpicked by running back from the last stitch to the first. The seam is generally quite extensible. It is often used for temporary stitching e.g. **basting.**
Class 200: Hand stitch 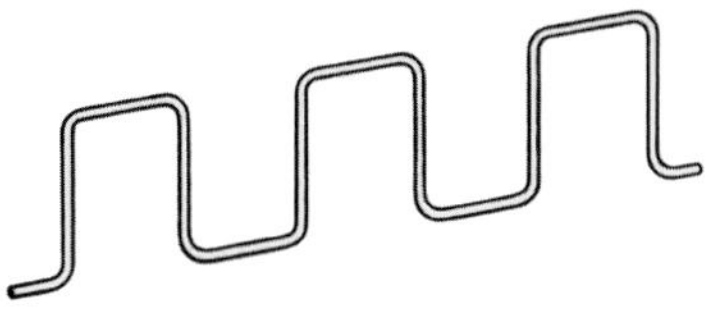 needle thread Type 209	Needle and thread are both passed completely from one side of the material to the other. The thread is held through the material. Originally made only by hand, some of them can now be formed also by a machine. This stitch type is especially suitable for sewing **edges.**
Class 300: Lockstitch 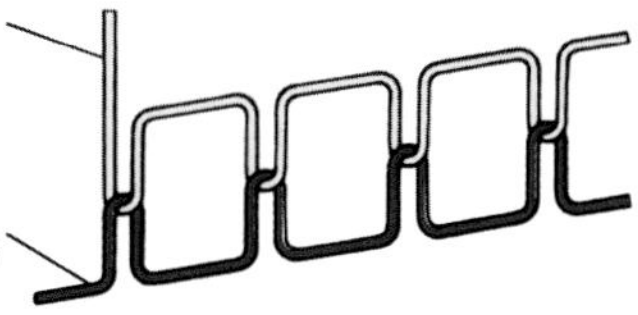 needle thread under thread (spool thread) Type 301	Formed by two different thread systems. A needle thread introduced from one side of the material is interlaced with an underthread supplied from a spool on the other side. This is the most popular type of stitch, e.g. for closing, lapped seams, and decorative stitching. It is difficult to unpick and both sides have the same appearance. Generally less extensible than chain stitch seams and so capable of making a **firm closing of the layers.**
Class 400: Multi-thread chain stitch 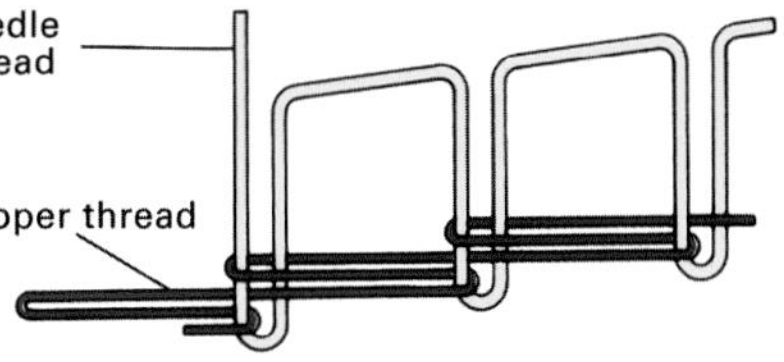 needle thread looper thread Type 401	Also formed from two thread systems. The loops of the needle thread are drawn all the way through the material and are interconnected on the underside by thread supplied from a looper. Top and bottom sides have a different appearance. The seam can easily be unpicked and is quite extensible. The fabric layers are less firmly closed compared to lockstitch. Special applications are **elastic cross-over seams, seat seams,** and **side seams.**
Class 500: Overedge chain stitch 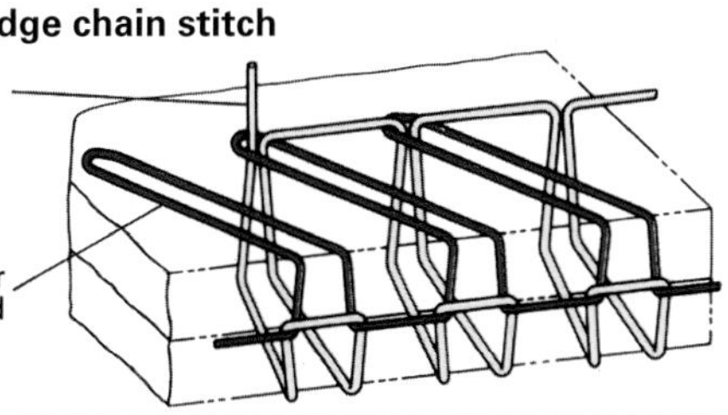 needle thread looper thread Type 503	Formed from one or more needle and looper threads. Needle thread loops are taken all the way through the material and are interconnected with themselves or with another thread. At least one thread system passes around the edge of the material. Overedge stitches of various types are used to **neaten** and to **bind** the **cut edges** of woven and knitted materials.
Class 600: Covering chain stitch 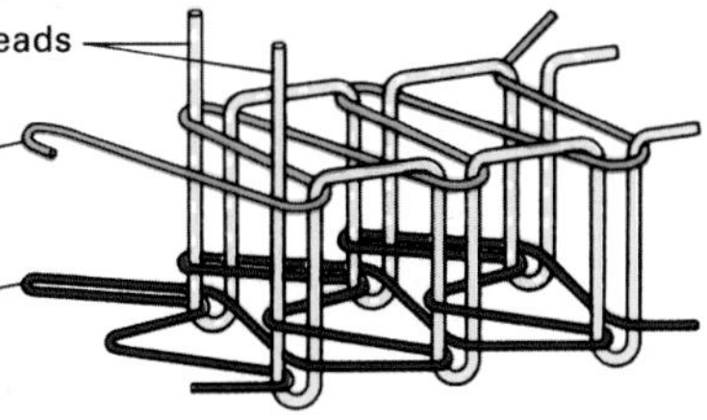 needle threads cover thread looper thread Type 602	This stitch type is generally formed from three thread systems. The covering threads lie on the top surface and are held in place by the needle threads which in turn are interlaced on the back of the seam by the looper threads. They are used especially for making **flat, extensible seams** in knitted fabrics.

[1] One should always distinguish between "stitch types" and "seams", although in practice they are often used interchangeably. Seam types are described on *pages 184 ff.*

10.3.9 Stitch Types: Lockstitch (1)

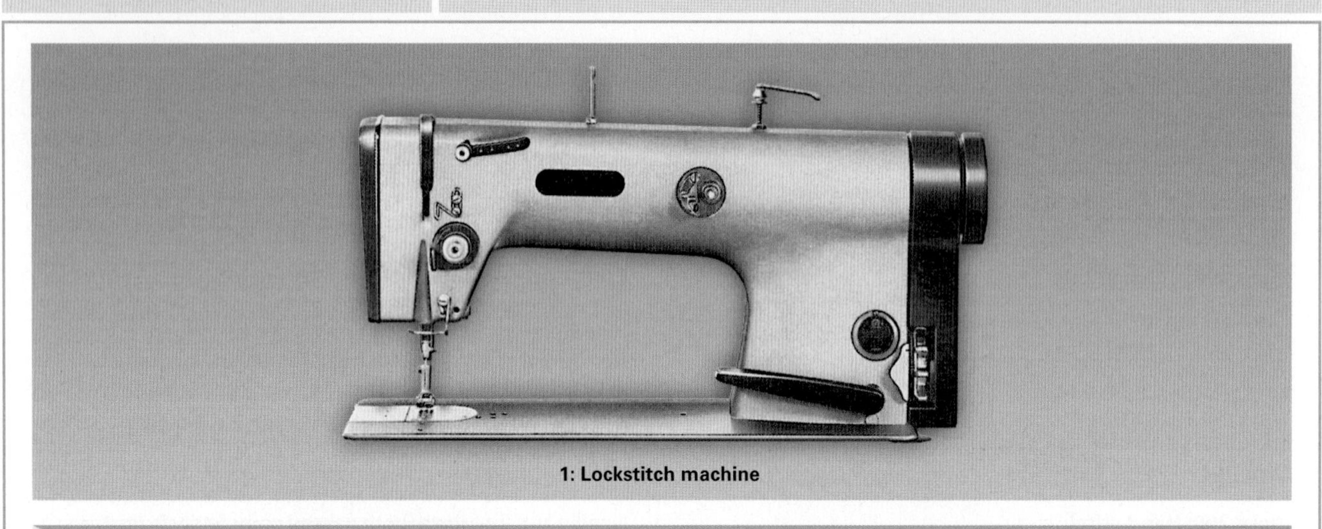
1: Lockstitch machine

Stitch Formation (Horizontal Hook)

The needle thread loop, having been formed on the underside of the material by the needle, is interlaced with a second thread (underthread) by means of a hook.

The lockstitch machine can be distinguished by the winding device provided for the bottom thread.

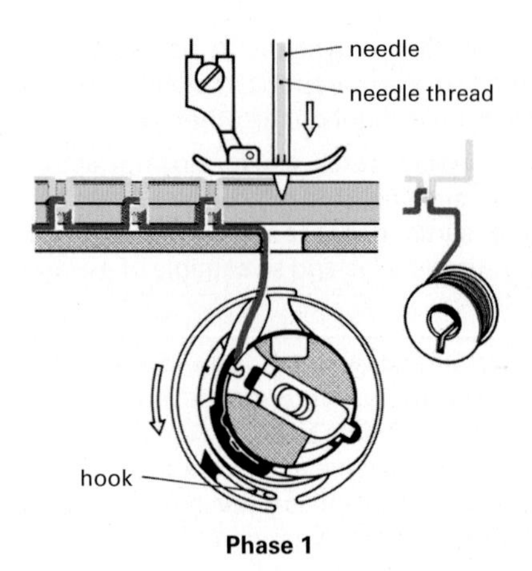

Phase 1

The needle is inserted into the material.

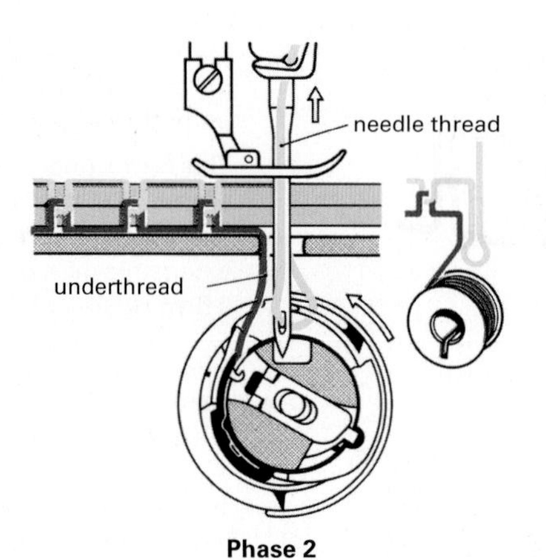

Phase 2

As the needle moves upward from its lowest position, the needle thread forms a loop which is caught by the point of the hook.

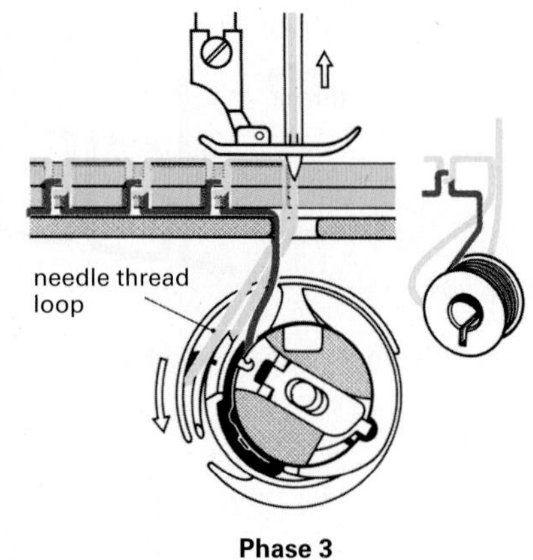

Phase 3

The hook enlarges the needle thread loop.

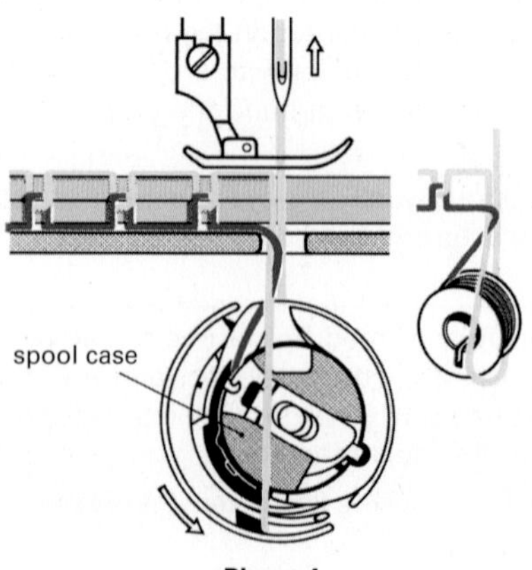

Phase 4

The needle thread loop is guided around the bottom thread spool.

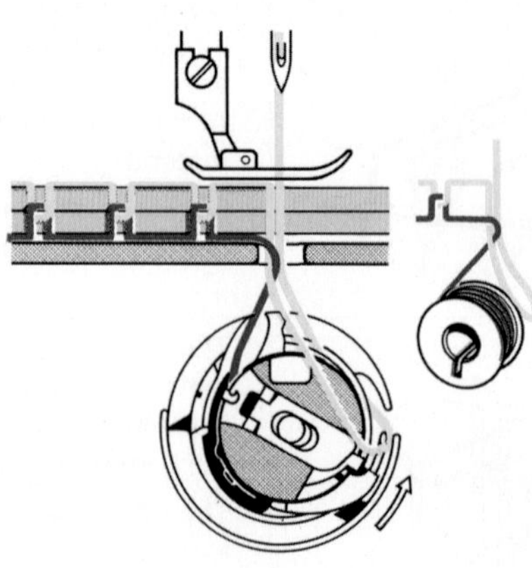
Phase 5

Interlacing begins.

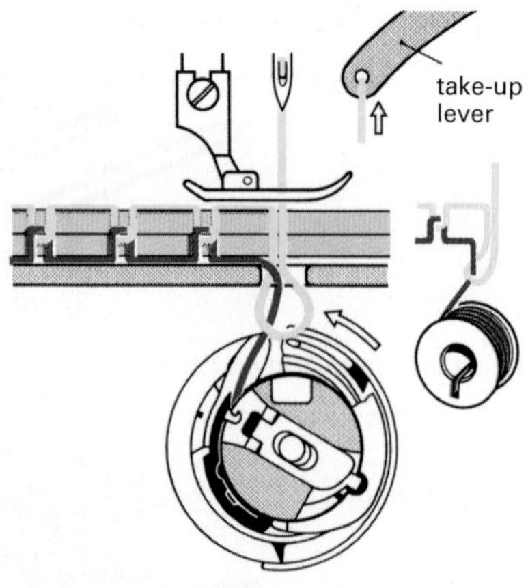

Phase 6

The take-up lever tightens the stitch into the material. The material is fed forward.

10.3.9 Stitch Types: Lockstitch (2)

Features and Applications

Only a limited amount of sewing is possible before the supply of underthread has to be replenished. In contrast to chain stitch, it is not possible to unpick a lockstitch without destroying one of the threads. The interlacing point of the two threads is usually located in the middle of the material being sewn. However, it can be made to lie either on the top or the bottom side. In symbolic notation, the interlacing point is represented by a dot.

Both sides of the seam have the same appearance and the two threads can have different colours, if required. The consumption of thread is about 2.5 times the length of the seam, depending on the thickness of the material. Lockstitch gives a very sound **closing** – the two fabric plies are sewn very closely together.

Important Members of the Lockstitch Family: Class 300 of ISO 4915

Type	Name, Stitch Diagram	Symbol	Seam Appearance
301	**Lockstitch** needle thread underthread (spool thread)	interlacing at: centre top side under side	
304	**Lockstitch (single-step zigzag** needle thread underthread (spool thread)		
308	**Lockstitch (double-step zigzag)** needle thread underthread (spool thread)		
309	**Lockstitch (piping seam)** needle thread needle thread underthread (spool thread) Top and bottom threads are interlaced on the under side of the material. When sewing piping a high tension is applied to the underthread to draw the seam tightly together.		

10.3.9 Stitch Types: Chain Stitch

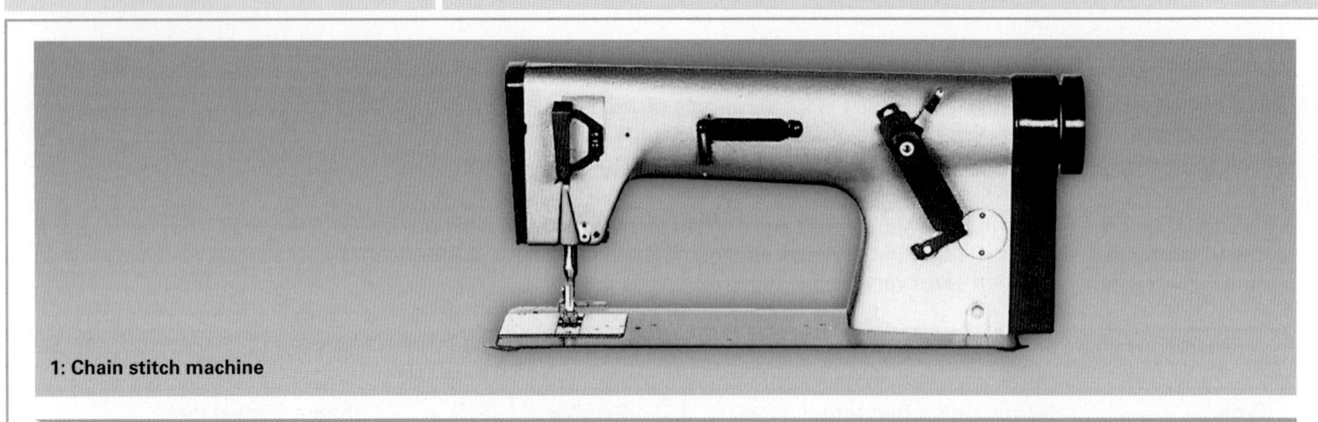
1: Chain stitch machine

Stitch Formation with an Oscillating Looper

Each loop is interlaced with the following loop of the same thread. The single thread machine is distinguished by the thread tension device situated on the arm and the absence of a spool winder

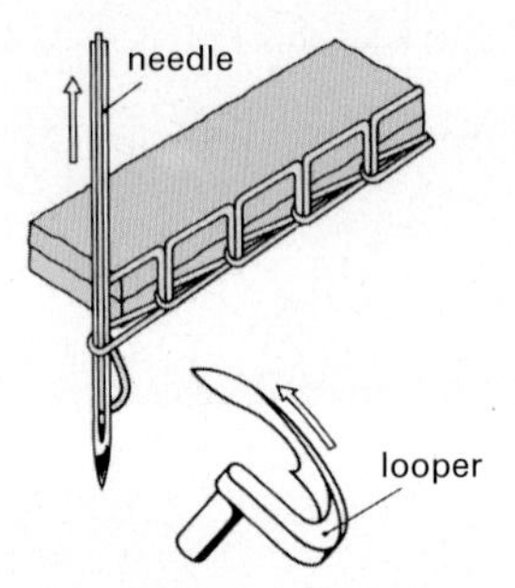

Phase 1

The needle has penetrated the material. It retains the old loop around its blade. As it moves upwards a new loop is formed, projecting sideways, beneath the material.

old loop
new loop

Phase 2

The new loop is caught, by the hook of the looper, above the needle eye but below the old loop. The needle continues upwards.

The old loop is cast off from the needle and slides onto the base of the new loop, which is still held by the looper, thus forming the interlacing on the underside of the material.

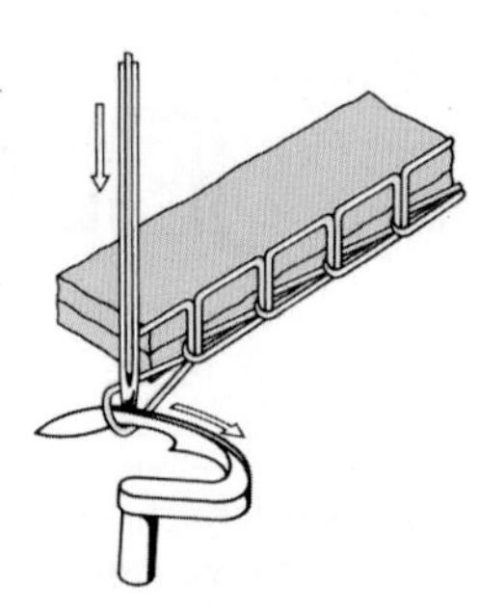

Phase 3

The looper enlarges the new loop so that, when the needle descends again it passes through the loop. The looper retreats, leaving the new loop held on the needle blade. This loop now becomes the old loop for the next cycle.

Features and Applications

This stitch type can be unpicked very easily, but only in one direction from the last stitch to the first. Therefore the simple chain stitch is used especially for tacking and basting. Because of its extensibility chain stitch is suitable for stretchy fabrics, e.g. knitted fabrics. Opposite sides of the seam have a different appearance and the thread consumption is about 3.5 times the seam length, depending on the thickness of the material being sewn.

Important Members of the Chain Stitch Family: Class 100 of ISO 4915

Type	Name, Stitch Diagram	Symbol	Seam Appearance
101	**Single thread chain stitch** needle thread		
103	**Blind single thread chain stitch** needle thread		

10.3.9 Stitch Types: Multi-thread Chain Stitch

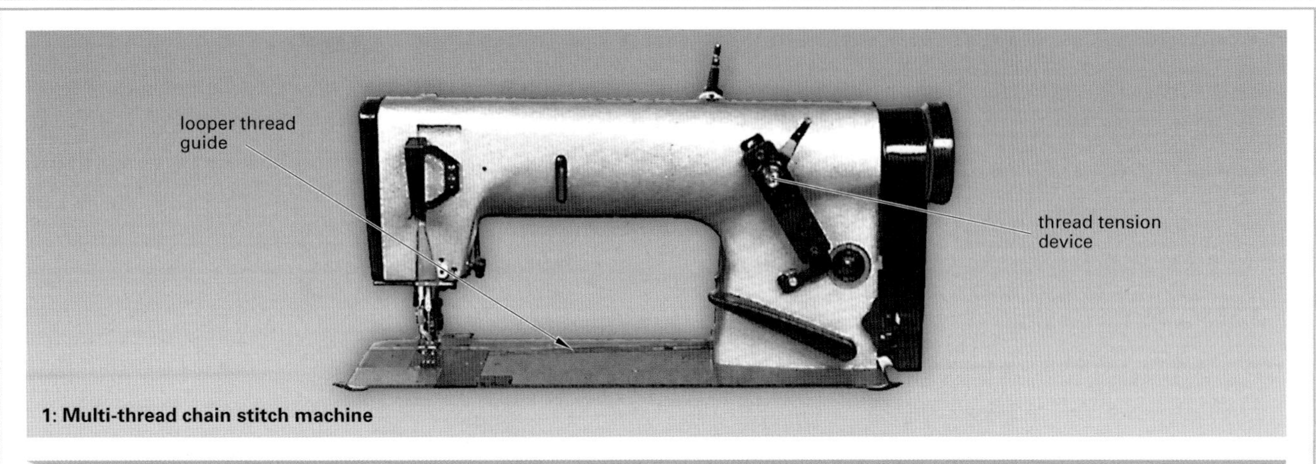

1: Multi-thread chain stitch machine

Stitch Formation

Multi-thread chain stitch seams are made from two or more threads, one of which is an underthread or looper thread. Each needle thread loop is interlaced with the underthread.

The multi-thread chain stitch machine is distinguished by its two or more thread guides, the thread tension devices mounted on the machine arm, and the covering for the looper thread in the base plate.

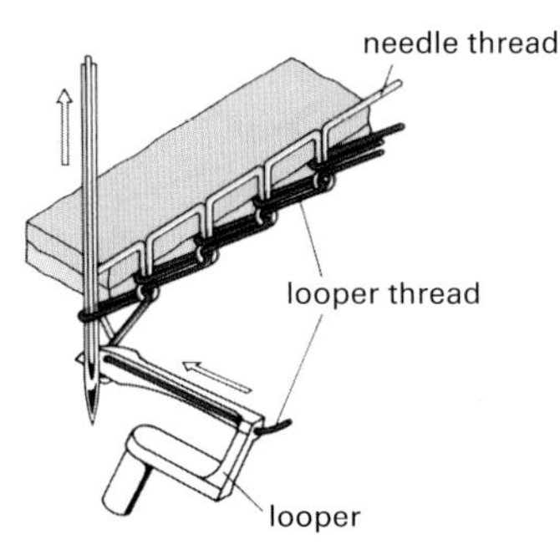

Phase 1

A loop is formed in the needle thread as the needle begins to move upwards from its lowest position. The new loop is caught by the hook of the looper. At this moment the needle is in front of the looper.

Phase 2

The needle rises, casting off the old underthread loop onto the base of the new needle thread loop. Meanwhile the looper penetrates further into the new needle thread loop, taking the underthread with it and clearing a large triangular space for the needle to return to.

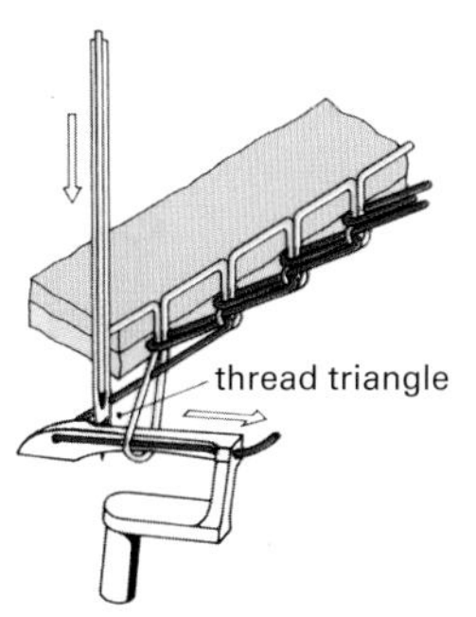

Phase 3

The needle descends into the triangular space formed on two sides by the underthread and on the third side by the new needle thread loop. At this moment the needle is behind the looper.

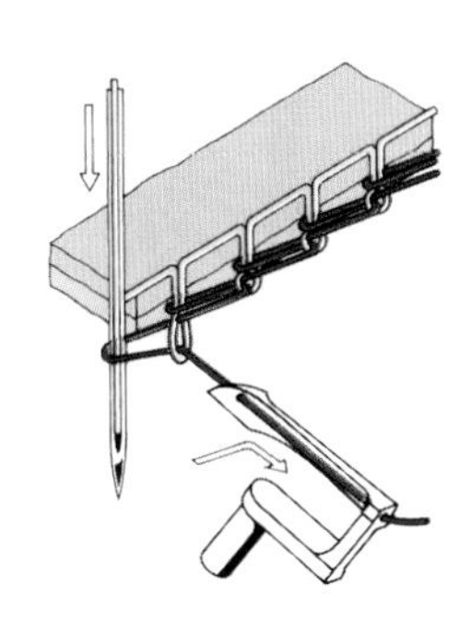

Phase 4

The looper retreats, back through the new needle thread loop, leaving the underthread looped around the needle, ready for the next cycle. Meanwhile, the downward movement of the needle tightens the previous stitch on the underside of the material being sewn.

Features and Applications

The two sides of the seam have a different appearance. The interlacing of needle and looper threads is always on the underside of the material. The multi-thread chain stitch produces extensible seams which usually do not show any puckering. They are especially suitable for load-bearing seams, such as flat-fell seams.

Depending on the seam type, thread consumption can be more than five times the seam length.

Type	Name, Stitch Diagram	Symbol	Seam Appearance
401	**Two-thread chain stitch** needle thread looper thread		

10.3.9 Stitch Types: Overedge Chain Stitch (1)

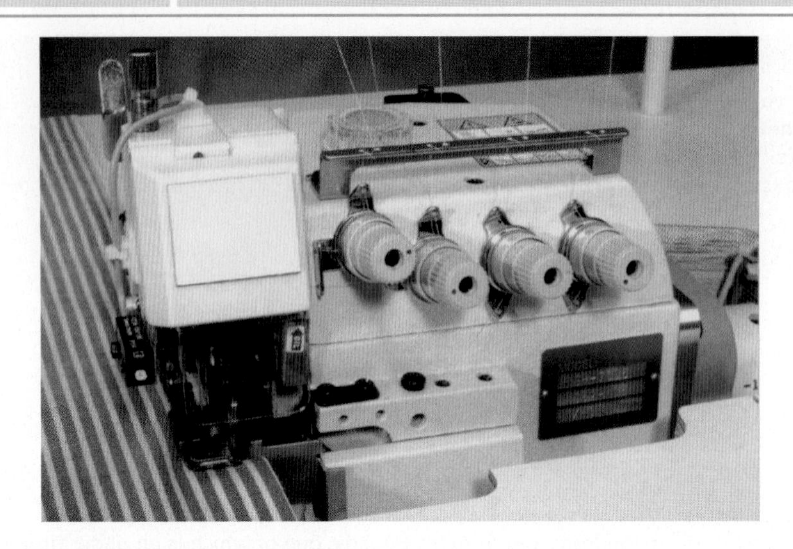

1: Overedge chain stitch machine

Stitch Formation of a Three-Thread Overedge Sewing Machine

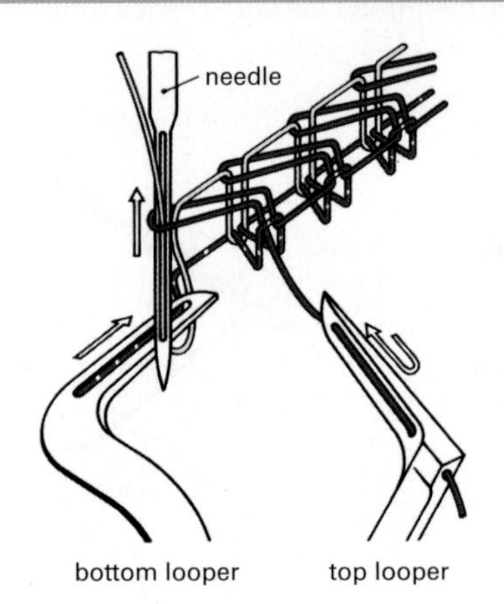

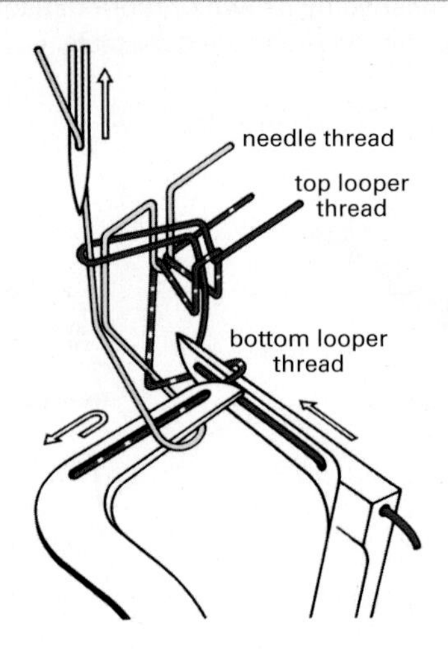

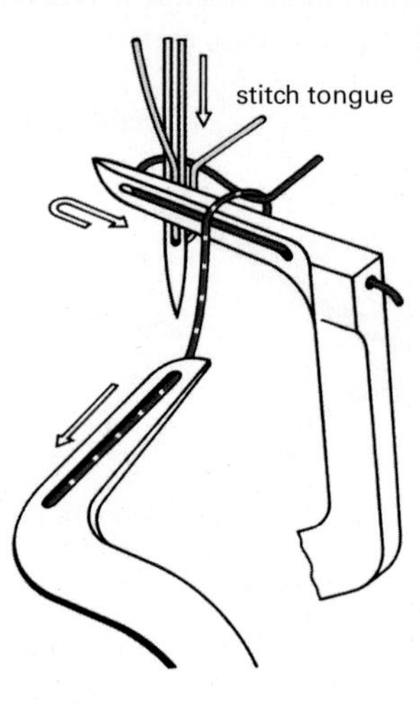

2: Type 504 stitch formation

Phase 1

A new needle thread loop is formed as the needle begins to move upwards from its lowest position.

The bottom looper catches the needle thread loop and lays its underthread into the needle thread loop.

As the needle moves upwards, the old top underthread loop is cast off from the needle and onto the new needle thread loop to form the top interlacing.

Phase 2

The top looper moves forward to catch and hold the bottom underthread loop, and to transfer its own underthread loop over a stitch tongue into the path of the needle. The stitch tongue is a small projection on the presser foot.

As the bottom looper moves backwards the needle thread loop is cast off onto the bottom underthread loop to form the bottom interlacing.

Phase 3

The top looper lays its thread loop over the stitch tongue, preventing the stitch and material from over-tightening. The needle descends into the loop of the top underthread.

As the top looper moves back it casts off the bottom underthread loop to form the overedge interlacing between the two underthreads. Meanwhile, the new top underthread loop is held by the needle, ready for the cycle to begin again.

Features and Applications

Overedge sewing generally uses a variation of the chain stitch. Its distinctive feature is the one or two threads which enclose the edge of the fabric to protect it from fraying.

At the same time it can be used for joining fabric pieces (e.g. knitwear, underwear).

An **overedge seam,** formed of several threads, shows high extensibility. Very clean seams can be made using a built-in edge cutting device. The strength of the seam depends on the stitch type.

Higher strength is achieved by the **safety-stitch** (401.503) in which an additional chain stitch is made a few millimetres inside the overedge seam. The two seams are produced at the same time, but they are independent. This method of seaming is popular in modern operations because it neatens the cut edges at the same time as it joins the components.

10.3.9 Stitch Types: Overedge Chain Stitch (2)

Features and Applications

Overedge stitches have very good extensibility. The strength of the seam and coverage of the cut edges varies between the different stitch types. The stitch type number is determined by the number of threads (1 to 5) and their disposition on the material. A distinction is made between **edge interlooping** (503) and **needle-point interlooping** (504). Safety seams are a combination of two stitch types (401.503). Thread consumption can be up to 16 m thread per 1 m seam.

Important Members of the Overedge Chain Stitch Family: Class 500 of ISO 4915

Type	Name, Stitch Diagram	Symbol	Seam Appearance
501	**Single thread overedge** 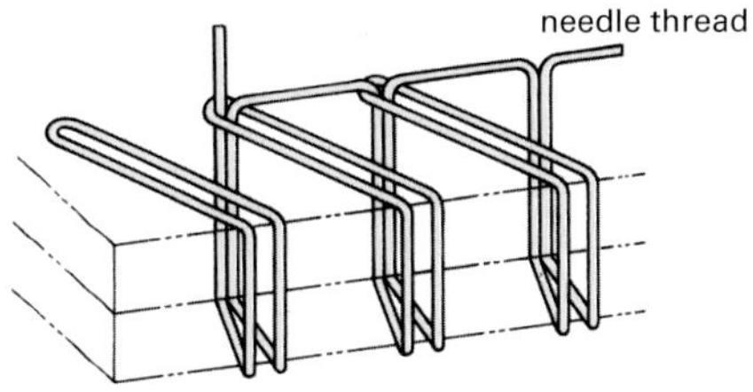 needle thread	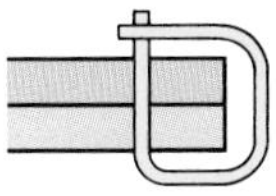	
503	**Two-thread overedge (edge interlooping)** 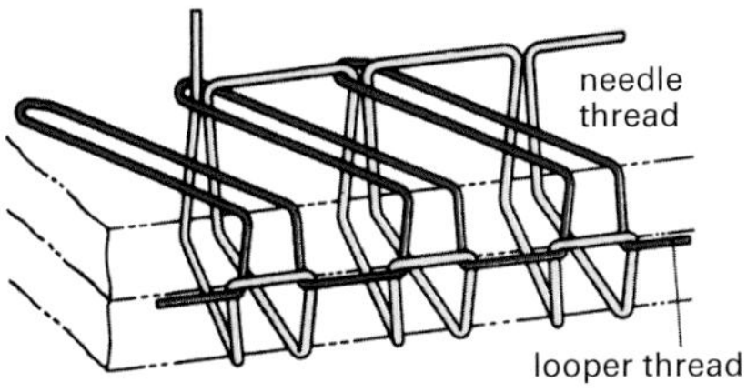 needle thread looper thread	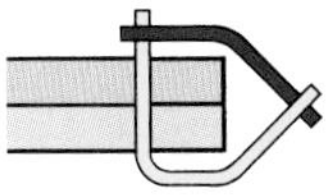	
504	**Three-thread overedge (needle-point interlooping)** 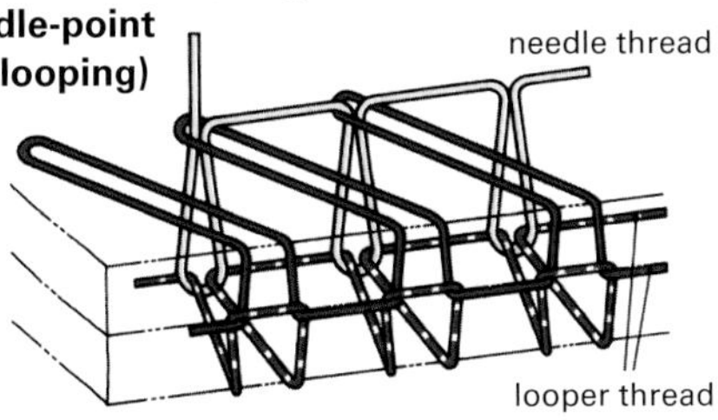 needle thread looper thread	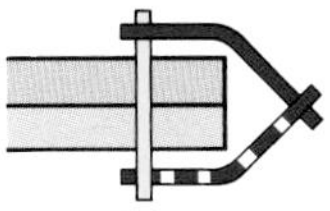	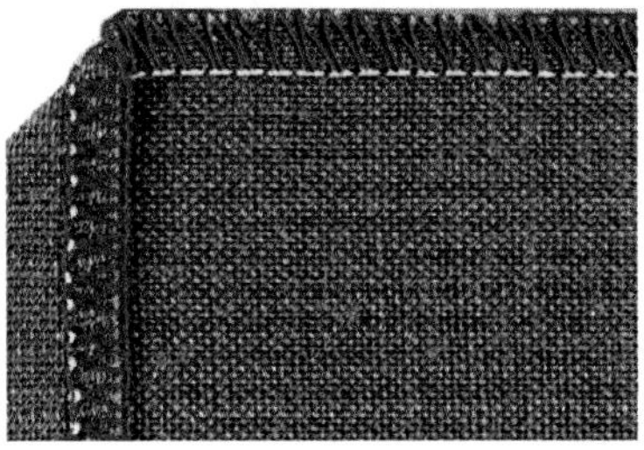
512	**Four-thread overedge (mock safety stitch) Overlock** 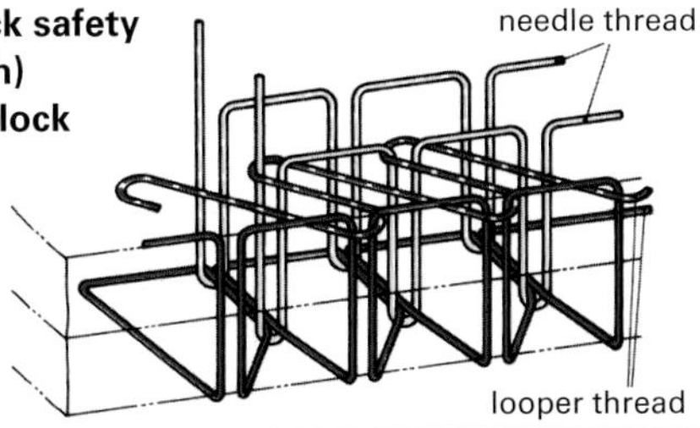 needle thread looper thread	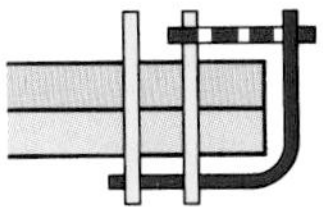	
401.503	**Combination safety stitch Two-thread overedge and double chain stitch** 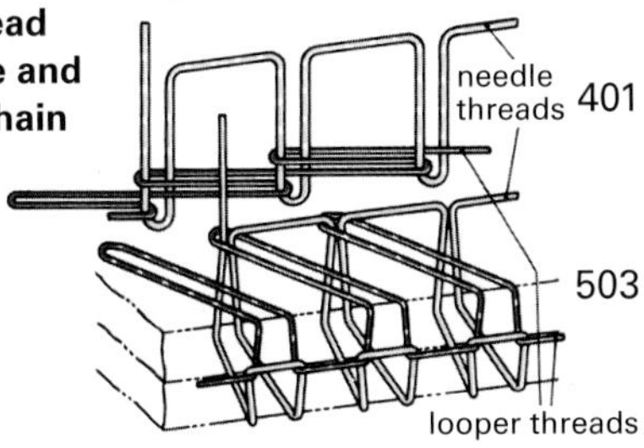 needle threads 401 503 looper threads	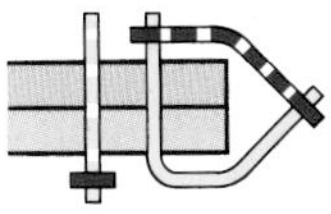	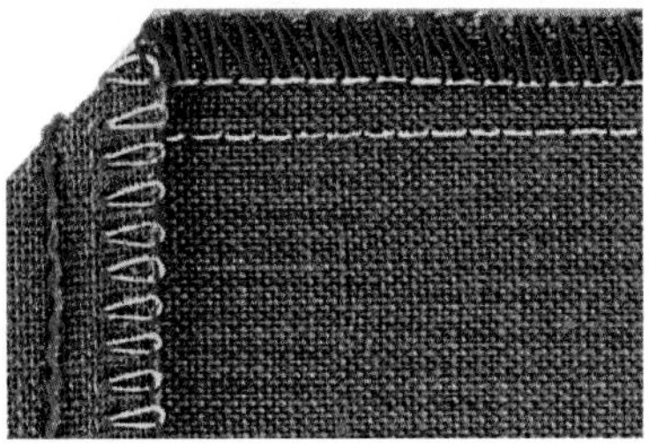

10.3.9 Stitch Types: Flat Seam Stitches, Covering Stitches

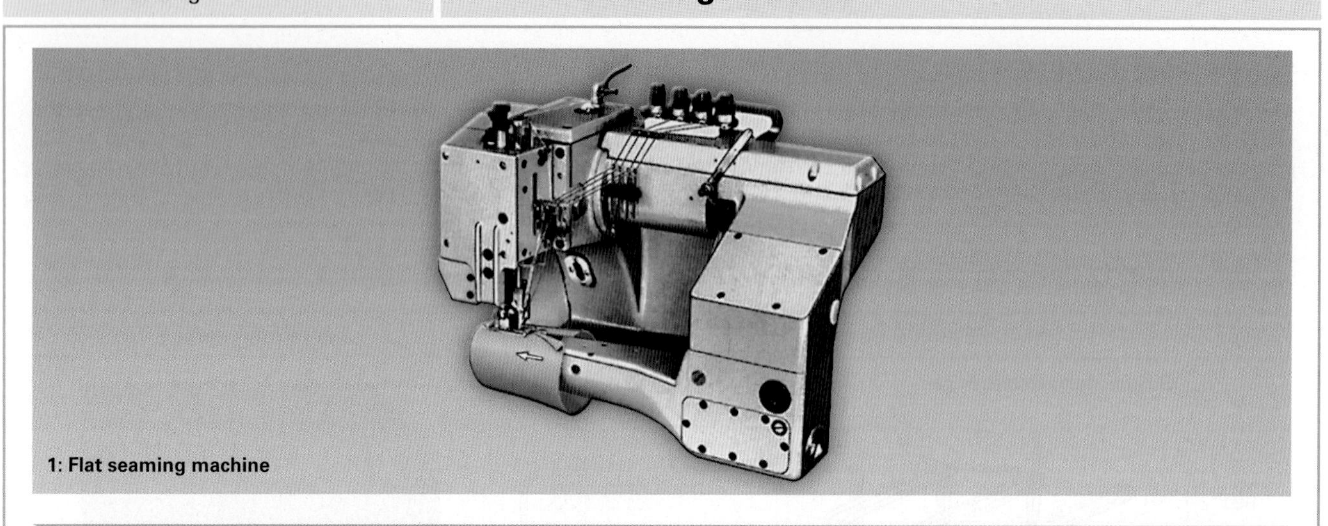

1: Flat seaming machine

Stitch Formation

Flat seams can be made with Class 400 or Class 600 stitches. In the industry both types are known as covering stitches, although only Class 600 is classified as such by ISO 4915.

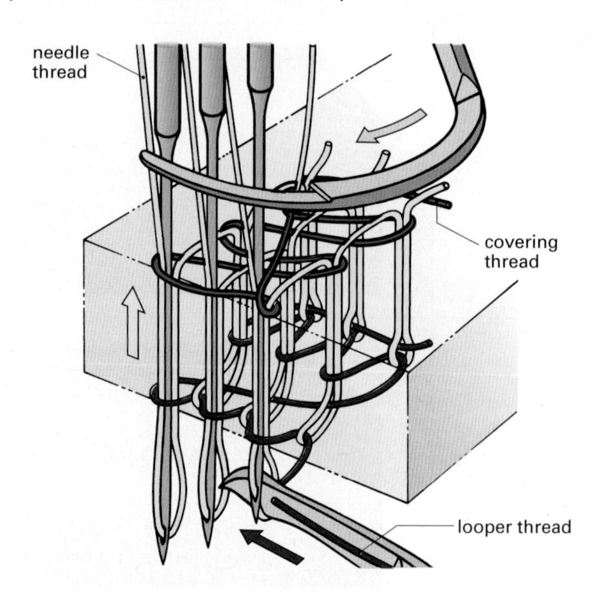

Flat seams made with Class 400 stitches

Two thread systems are used. A looper thread interlaces with two needle threads on the underside, spanning and neatening the cut edge(s) on the underside of the material. This avoids having to fold in and press the cut edge.

Typical applications are hems for knitted fabrics and flat seams on straps or belt loops (402, 406).

Flat seams made with Class 600 stitches

These are made with three systems of threads. Two or more needle threads are interlaced on the underside by a looper thread and on the needle side by a cover thread.

The covering chain stitch types are used when both surfaces have to be covered and a flat seam is required. Typical uses are butt seaming and ornamental seams e.g. knitted fabrics, tights and decorations (602).

Important Flat Seam Stitches

Type	Name, Stitch Diagram	Symbol	Seam Appearance
406	**Two-needle multi-thread chain stitch** needle threads looper thread		
602	**Covering chain stitch** cover thread needle threads looper thread		

10.3.9 Stitch Types: Blind Stitching

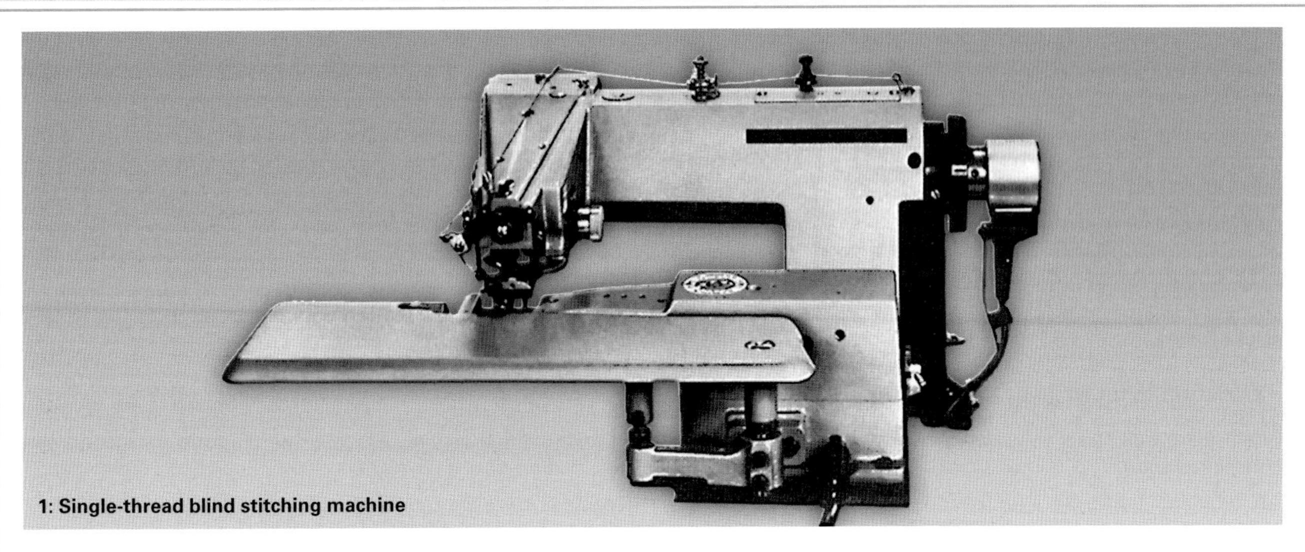
1: Single-thread blind stitching machine

Blind stitching means that the stitches and the needle impressions should not be visible on the outer side of the assembled article. Blind stitch seams are used for **hemming** and for **attaching interlinings.** Blind stitching machines use a curved needle (*see page 168*). A lifter raises the fabric just before it is penetrated by the needle and is withdrawn to allow material feeding. The lifting height is adjustable so that materials of different thickness can be accommodated.

To obtain a loose seam with the minimum of needle marking, the lifter may be raised only every second or third stitch (interval setting).

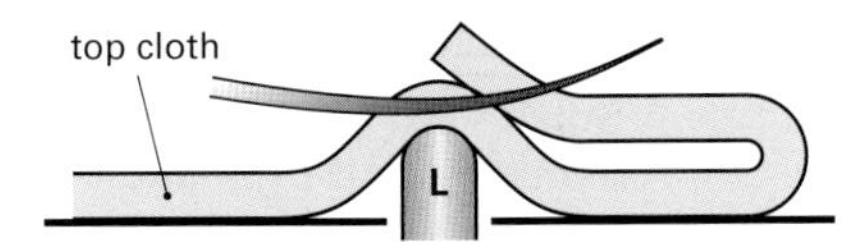

2: Needle insertion with raised lifter

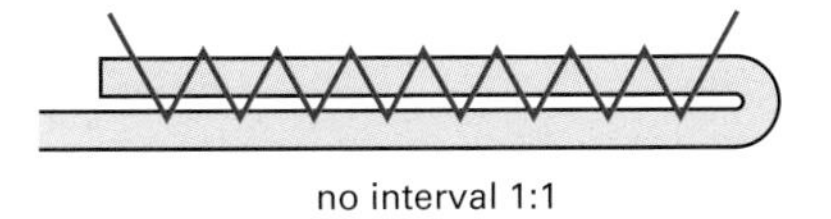

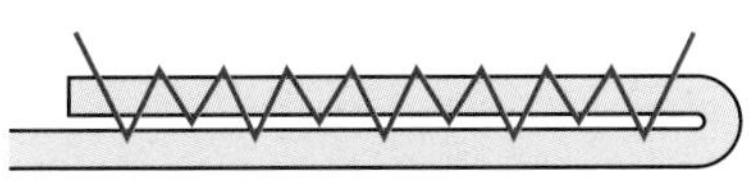

3: Interval setting

Important Blind Stitch Seams

Type	Name, Stitch Diagram	Symbol	Seam Appearance
103	**Blind single chain stitch**		
105	**Blind single chain stitch**		
320	**Blind lockstitch**		

10.3.10 Seam Types: Diagrammatic Representation (1)

A seam comprises a sequence of stitches joining two or more pieces of material.

Seam types for the clothing industry are organised into eight different classes by ISO 4916 (ASTM D 6193). The classification criteria are the way that the fabric plies are laid together, the number of plies and the way that the fabric edges are handled.

The way that the plies are laid together is independent of the type of stitching that will be used. Fabric edges may be laid flat or turned in. Turning in may be with one fold or two. The type of stitching to be used may be specified according to ISO 4915 (*see page 175*).

ASTM D 6193 has an additional descriptive terminology for broader classes of seam types. Thus: **Class SS** refers to superimposed seams; **Class LS** refers to lapped seams; **Class BS** refers to bound seams; **Class FS** refers to flat seams; **Class OS** refers to ornamental seams; **Class EF** refers to edge-finished seams.

Symbolic (diagrammatic) representation of seams is by means of a schematic cross section with the location of the needle strokes marked.

Conventions for Making Seam Diagrams

Seam diagrams show schematically how the seam is constructed for machine sewing. Usually the diagram represents the completed seam.

An individual **fabric ply** is represented by a **thick line**.

Needle strokes are represented by thin **straight vertical lines.**

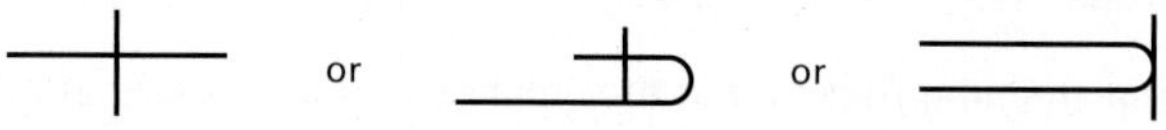

or

or

A **wavy line** indicates that the fabric continues **(not an edge)**.

A **straight line** shows the true **fabric edge** (cut edge).

Class 1 Seams (examples)

They are made from at least two components, with one edge from each mutually aligned. Additional components are laid with one or both edges aligned in the same manner.

ISO Type	**Seam Diagram** (ISO 4916)	**ISO Symbol** (ISO 4916)	**Typical Stitch Types** (ISO 4915)	**Stitch Symbol** simplified	**Seam Designation**
1.01	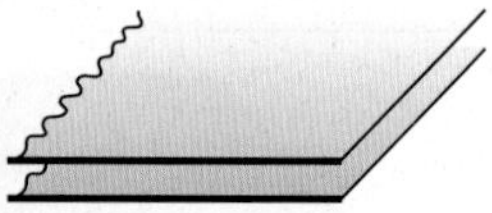	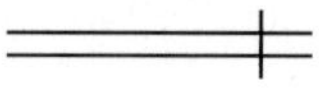	301 Lockstitch (LS)	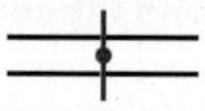	plain seam
			401 Multi-thread chain stitch (MCS)	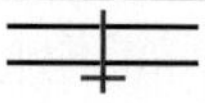	
			504 Overedge chain stitch (OCS)	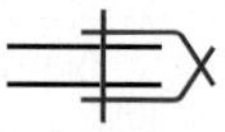	
		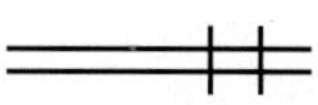	512 Overedge chain stitch (four-thread)	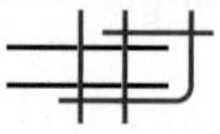	mock safety stitch
			401.503 MCS + OCS		combination safety stitch
			401.504 MCS + OCS	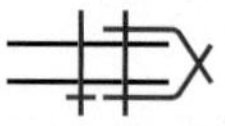	
1.06		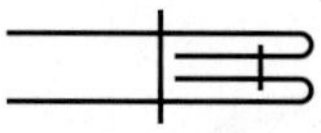	301.301 LS + LS; two sewing stages with intervening re-folding.	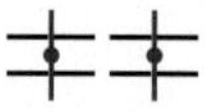	double-turned seam (French seam)
1.12		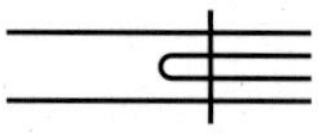	301 Lockstitch		piping seam (piping sewn in)
1.15	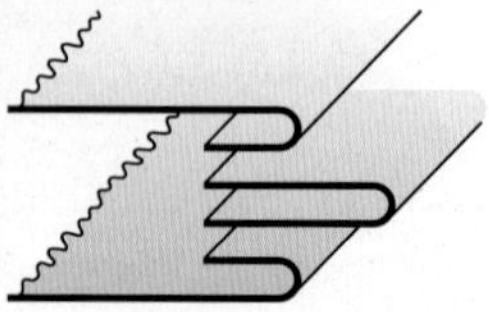	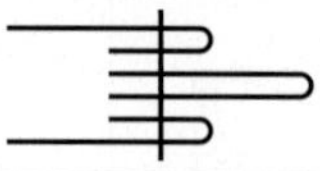	301 Lockstitch		piping seam (piping sewn in)
		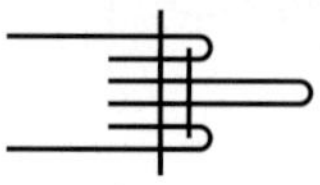	301.301 LS + LS; two sewing stages with intervening re-folding.		

10.3.10 Seam Types: Diagrammatic Representation (2)

Class 2 Seams (examples) They are made from at least two components, with one edge from each overlapping in opposite directions and on different levels

ISO Type	Seam Diagram (ISO 4916)	ISO Symbol (ISO 4916)	Typical Stitch Types (ISO 4915)	Stitch Symbol simplified	Seam Designation
2.01	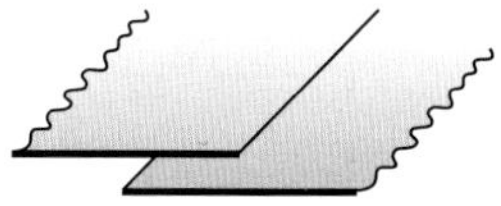	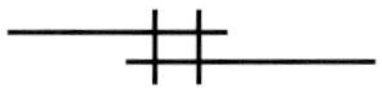	406 Two-needle multi-thread chain stitch (2nMCS)	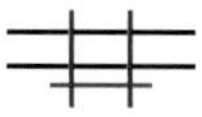	plain overlap
			602 Covering chain stitch	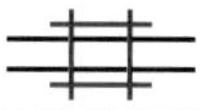	
2.02	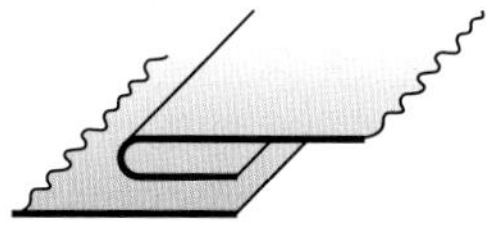	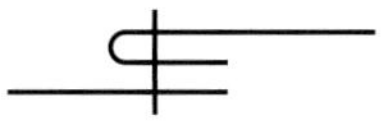	301 Lockstitch		flat fell seam
			401 Multi-thread chain stitch		
		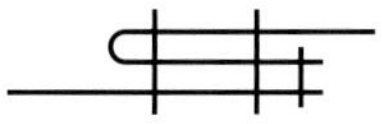	512.(401.401) OCS + 2nMCS; two sewing stages with intervening re-folding	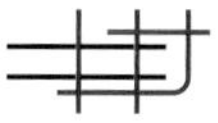 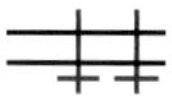	double sewn flat fell seam
			301.301 Lockstitch; two sewing stages with intervening re-folding	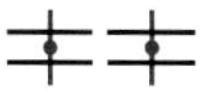	overstitched flat fell seam
2.04	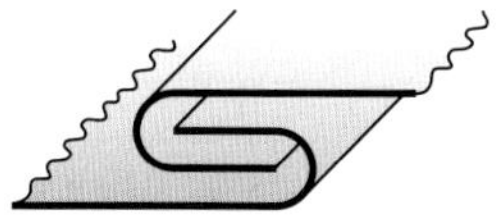	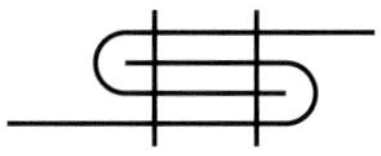	401.401) 2nMCS; one sewing, no re-folding	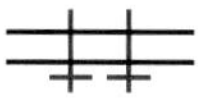	double flat fell seam
		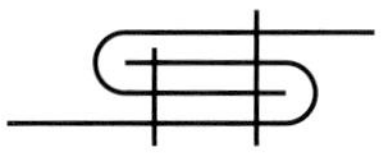	301.301 Lockstitch; two sewing stages with intervening re-folding	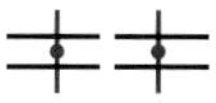	

Class 3 Seams (examples) They are made from at least two components, with one of them wrapped around the edge of the other.

ISO Type	Seam Diagram (ISO 4916)	ISO Symbol (ISO 4916)	Typical Stitch Types (ISO 4915)	Stitch Symbol simplified	Seam Designation
3.01	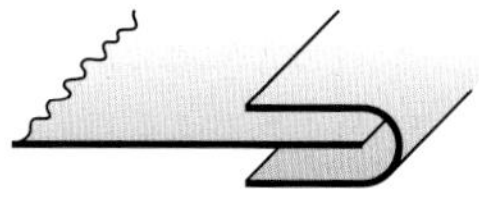	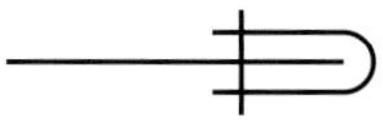	301 Lockstitch		bound seam (open binder edges)
3.03	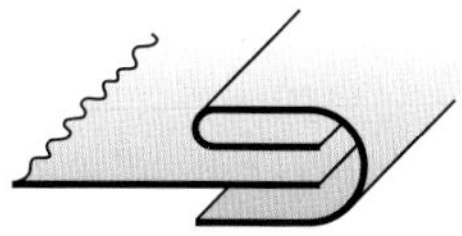	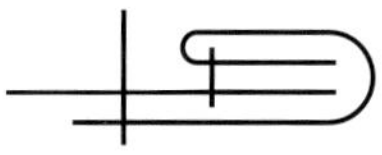	301.301 Lockstitch; two sewing stages with intervening re-folding	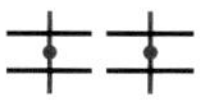	bound seam (one binder edge turned)
3.05	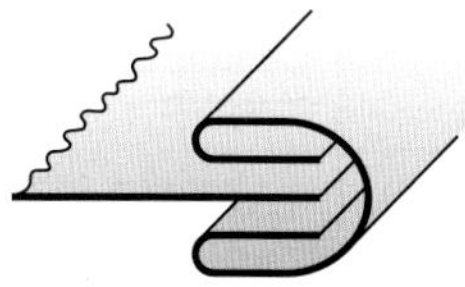	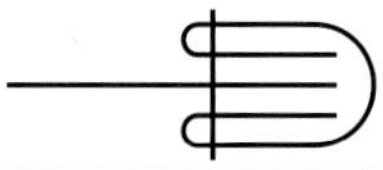	301 Lockstitch		bound seam (both binder edges turned)
		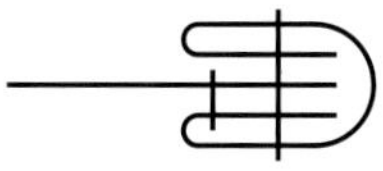	301.301 Lockstitch; two sewing stages with intervening re-folding	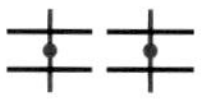	

Class 4 Seams (example) They are made from at least two components, with one edge from each butted up against the other and on the same level.

ISO Type	Seam Diagram (ISO 4916)	ISO Symbol (ISO 4916)	Typical Stitch Types (ISO 4915)	Stitch Symbol simplified	Seam Designation
4.01	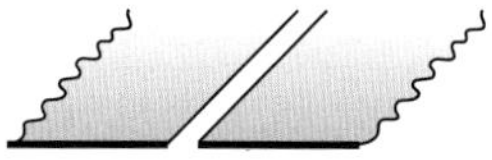	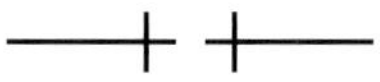	602 Covering chain stitch		flat seam (covered both sides)
			404 Two-needle multi-thread chain stitch		flat seam covered one side)

10.3.10 Seam Types: Diagrammatic Representation (3)

Class 5 Seams (examples) — They are made from at least one component, with no edges included in the seam (only folding).

ISO Type	Seam Diagram (ISO 4916)	ISO Symbol (ISO 4916)	Typical Stitch Types (ISO 4915)	Stitch Symbol simplified	Seam Designation
5.02		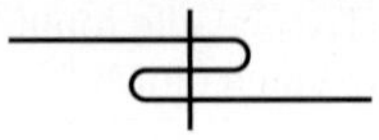	301 Lockstitch		plain single fold
5.03		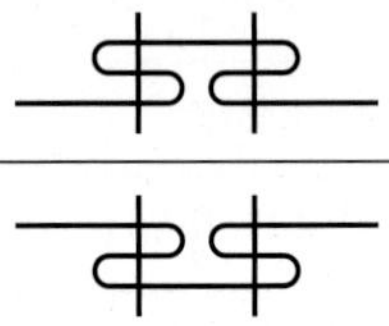	(301.301) Lockstitch; two-needle machine or (401.401) 2nMCS	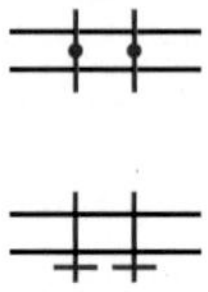	double flat fold inverted double flat fold

Class 6 Seams (examples) — They are made from only one component, with one edge included.

ISO Type	Seam Diagram (ISO 4916)	ISO Symbol (ISO 4916)	Typical Stitch Types (ISO 4915)	Stitch Symbol simplified	Seam Designation
6.01		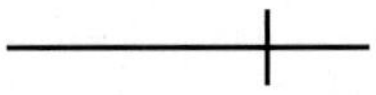	504 Overedge chain stitch	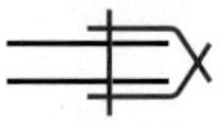	edge binding
6.02	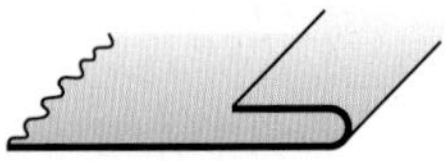	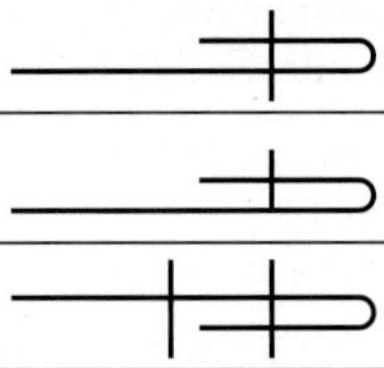	301 Lockstitch 103 Blind chain stitch 406 Two-needle multi-thread chain stitch	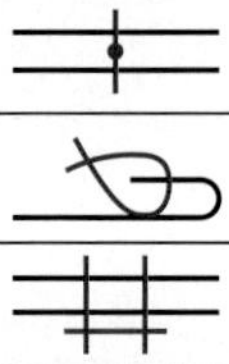	plain hem
6.03		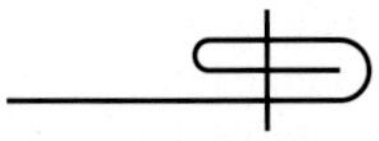	301 Lockstitch		double-turned hem
6.06	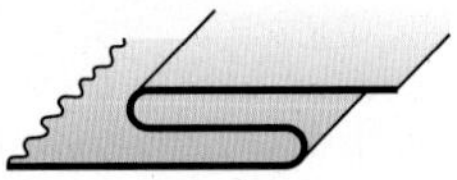	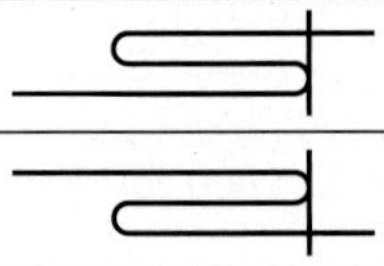	320 Blind lockstitch 503 Blind overedge chain stitch	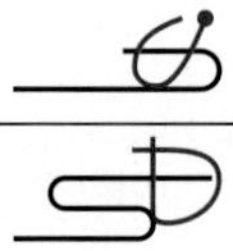	blind edge stitching
6.08			(301.301) Lockstitch; two-needle machine (401.401) 2nMCS	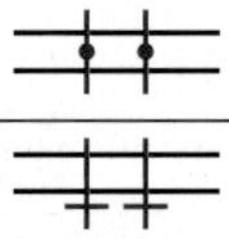	mock selvedge

Class 7 Seams (example) — They are made from at least two components: one of them has one edge included, the other has both edges.

ISO Type	Seam Diagram (ISO 4916)	ISO Symbol (ISO 4916)	Typical Stitch Types (ISO 4915)	Stitch Symbol simplified	Seam Designation
7.15	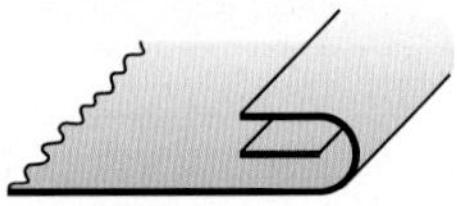	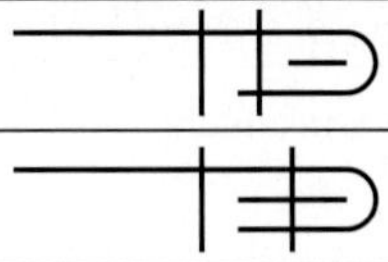	406 Two-needle multi-thread chain stitch 602 Covering chain stitch	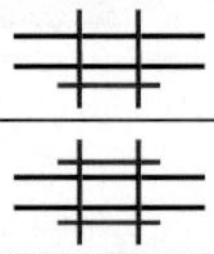	edge binding with single turn and tape insert
7.25		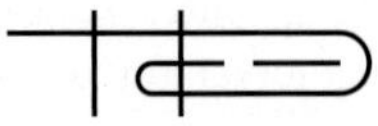	406 Two-needle multi-thread chain stitch 602 Covering chain stitch	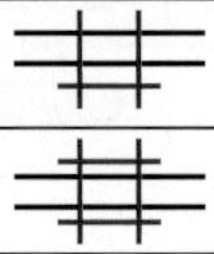	edge binding with double turn and tape insert
7.32	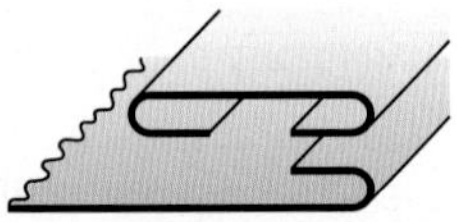	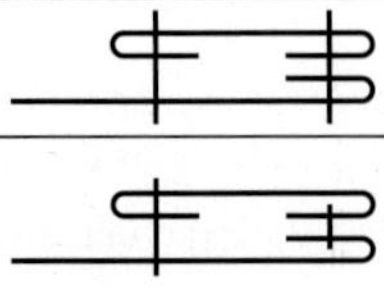	(401.401) 2nMCS; single sewing operation 301.301 Lockstitch; two sewing stages with intervening re-folding		double edge binding double edge binding

Class 8 Seams (example) — They are made from at least one component, with both edges included.

ISO Type	Seam Diagram (ISO 4916)	ISO Symbol (ISO 4916)	Typical Stitch Types (ISO 4915)	Stitch Symbol simplified	Seam Designation
8.02		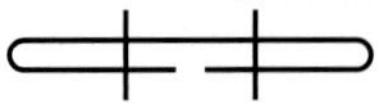	406 Two-needle multi-thread chain stitch	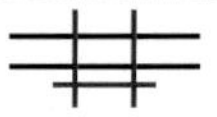	belt loop

10.3.10 Seam Types: Applications (1)

Beside the classifications of ISO 4916 and ASTM D 6193, (disposition of fabric plies, number of plies and treatment of edges) seams can also be distinguished according to their function: joining, strengthening, decoration and filling. A given seam type may serve more than one function.

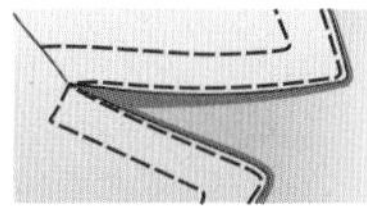
1: Contour stitching

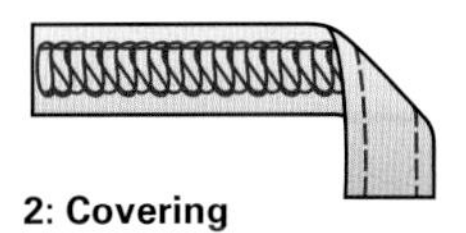
2: Covering

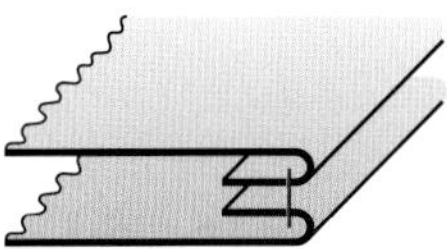
3: French seam

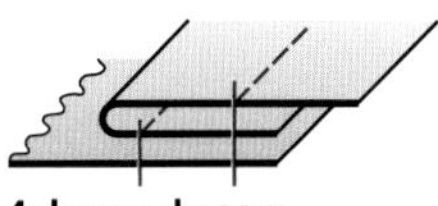
4: Lapped seam

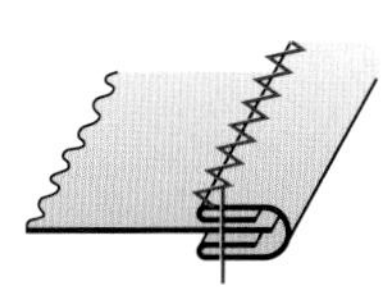
5: Binding

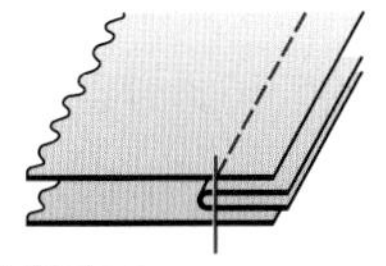
6: Piping

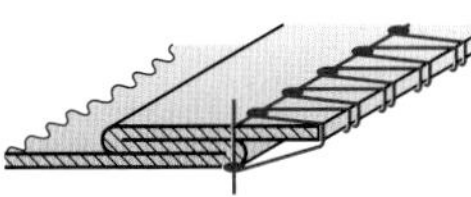
7: Blind hemming

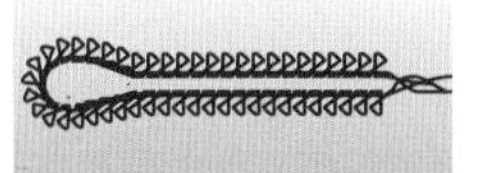
8: Button hole

9: Decoration

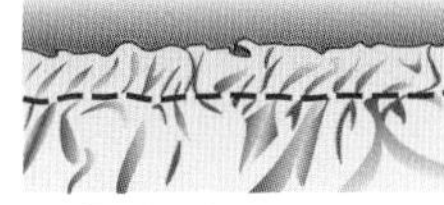
10: Gathering

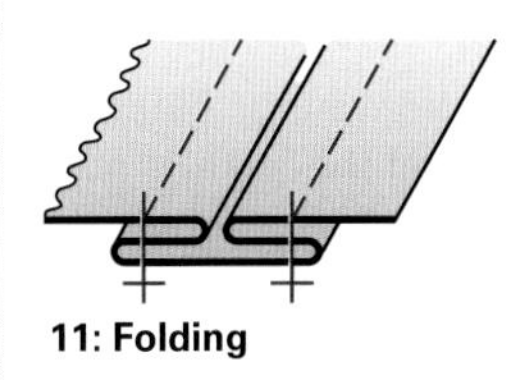
11: Folding

Joining

Function	Characteristics
Joining	Joining of two or more components (top-cloth and attachments) or one component with itself.
Attaching	Sewing on secondary items such as pockets.
Affixing	Adding accessory items such as buttons.
Taking-in	Insertion of darts, tucks and folds.
Backstitching	A joining seam with visible stitching lines having a decorative effect.
Contour stitching	A decorative joining seam, generally along the whole length of a garment edge (*Figure 1*).
Edging	Joining component edges using overedge stitching.
Edge covering	Joining components using covering stitching (*Figure 2*).
Surface covering	All-over attachment of components, such as interlining, using blind or normal chain stitch.
Edge dressing	Blind sewing of an open or closed edge e.g. blind hemming, attaching a lining.
Basting, tacking	Temporary joining of components with long stitches that are easily unpicked.
Blind stitching	Joining of components, or areas of components, with a stitch that is not visible on one side of the finished article (*Figure 7*).
Double-blind stitching	Joining of components, or areas of components, with a stitch that is not visible on either side of the finished article.
Turning	Joining the edges of two components so that the edges are folded inside the seam (*Figure 3*).
Linking	Joining two components of knitted fabric so that the (chain) stitches are in exact register with the knitted loops.
Lapping	A lap seam is when the two components overlap so that at least one edge is covered (*Figure 4*).

Strengthening

Neatening	Reinforcing exposed edges of components to prevent fraying or laddering.
Binding	Reinforcing exposed edges by attaching folded-over tapes or strips (*Figure 5*).
Piping	Insertion of tapes, cords or stripes at an edge (*Figure 6*).
Hemming	Reinforcing an edge by special seams and stitching, or trimmings.
Easing in	Feeding in an additional amount of one of the components to create fullness, shape, or contour.
Bar tacking	Reinforcement of areas of high stress in an assembly by inserting extra stitches, with high stitch density e.g. at the beginning and end of a seam.
Buttonholing	Strengthening the edges of button holes with special stitching or piping (*Figure 8*).

Decoration

Decorative stitching	Enhancing the appearance of an assembly by utilising stitching to provide colour, patterning, and texture (*Figure 9*).
Embroidery	Sewing of patterns, emblems, monograms etc. either in outline or as solid designs.
Gathering	Drawing the material together in a series of small folds (gathers) which are fixed by stitching. Gathers can also be produced by sewing in elastic yarns or by smocking (*Figure 10*).
Appliqué	Superficial addition of decorative items of any kind to add colour and interest.
Striping/piping	Insertion of long, thin decorative strips with or without inclusion of a cord.
Folding	Insertion of various types of folds for shaping and decoration (*Figure 11*).

10.3.10 Seam Types: Applications (2)

The terminology and classification of seam types can also be characterised according to the following criteria: type of stitching (*see pages 175 ff*); general shape of the seam; disposition of components; stitching system (number of stitching lines); location in the garment.

Terminology of sewing

a transport direction, feeding direction
b seam
c component edge
d component
e seam direction
f sewing direction
g stitch spacing
h stitch length
i stitching surface width
j stitch type width
k bight
l stitch type length

stitch type 301

304

1: Hemming **2: Butt seam** **3. Lap seam**

4: Felled seam **5: Selvedge seam** **6. French seam**

7: Lapel seam **8: Yoke seam** **9. Viennese seam**

a lapel seam
b neckline
c shoulder
d armscye
e trimming
f front sectioning seam
g side seam
h back sectioning seam
i centre back seam
j bottom hem

10: Jacket seams

Type of Stitching

stitch construction

- Lockstitch
- Chainstitch

stitch orientation

- Straight e.g. with type 301
- Zigzag e.g. with type 304

stitch disposition

- Blind stitch
- Overedge stitch

stitch interlacing position

- Lockstitch with interlacing in the centre or on the underside
- Two- or three-thread overedge

General Shape of the Seam

e.g. straight, curved, zigzag, dog-leg

Disposition of Components

Flat seam: the component edges are kept flat with a covering stitch.

- **Butt seam:** the component edges are laid up against one another (*Figure 2*)
- **Lap seam:** The component edges are laid overlapping (*Figure 3*)

Selvedge seam (*Figure 5*): a narrow strip is attached e.g. a buttonhole placket; a mock selvedge is constructed.

French seam, piping seam, felled seam

Stitching System

- **Lap seam**
- **Felled seam** (*Figure 4*)
- **French seam** (*Figure 6*)
- **Safety stitch**

Location in the Garment

by body part:

centre-back seam, shoulder seam, side seam, waist seam, leg seam, seat seam, arm seam.

by garment part:

neckline, **lapel** (*Figure 7*), collar trimming, sectioning; **Viennese seam:** front section armscye-to-waist (*Figure 9*); **flank seams:** back section armscye-to-waist; hemming, binding, sleeves, darts and tucks; **yoke, saddle yoke:** the yoke is normally a separate component (*Figure 8*) but may be simulated with a seam; **crotch seam:** joint between seat and fly in trousers.

10.3.11 Sewing Machine Drives

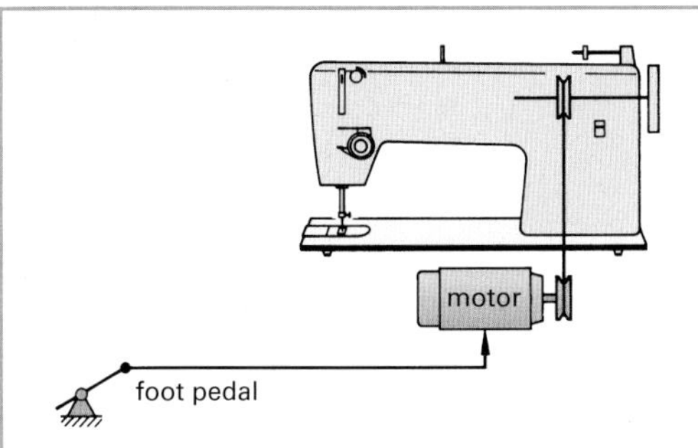

1: Belt drive

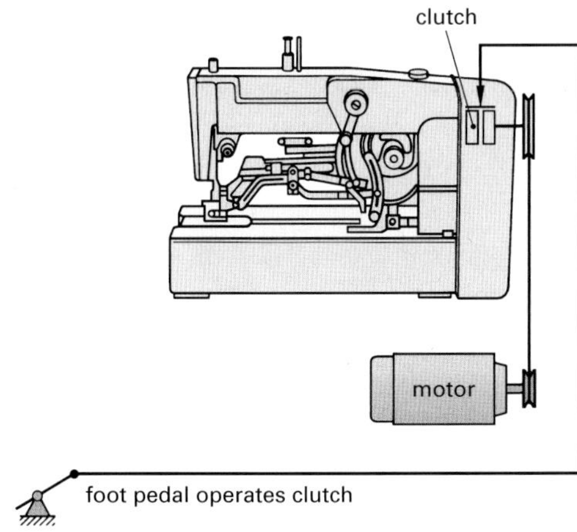

2: Fixed clutch

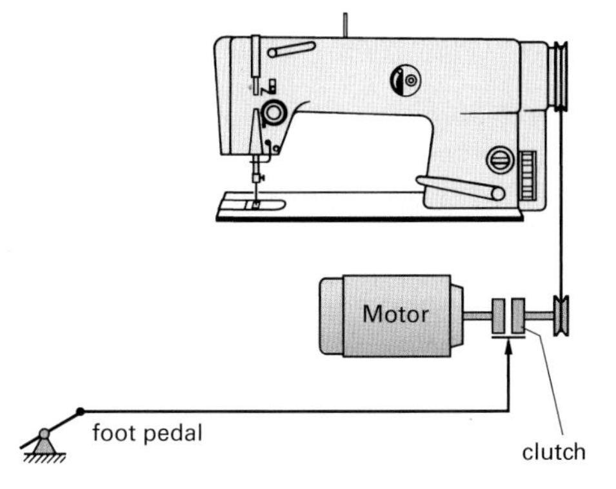

3: Slipping clutch

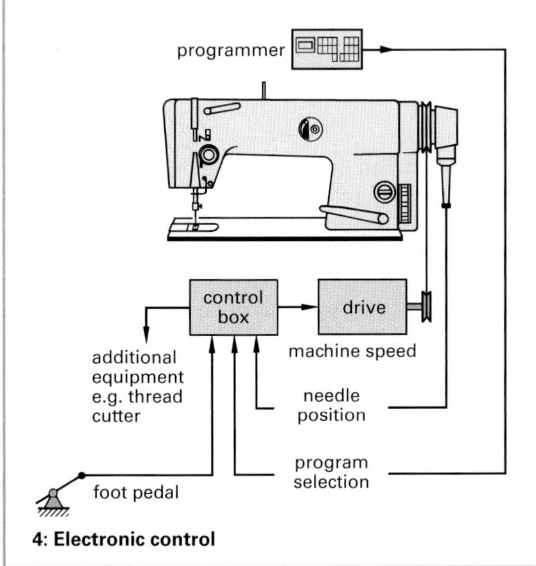

4: Electronic control

Sewing machines are driven by electric motors. Various types of driving arrangements are available, the most important of which are illustrated below.

Belt Drive

This is the simplest way to drive machines which operate at relatively low speeds and low loads. The sewing speed is controlled by a foot pedal which varies the current supplied to the motor according to how far it is depressed. When the pedal is released, the motor is stopped by a brake. This type of drive is used for domestic machines (*Figure 1*).

Fixed Clutch

Once the motor has been started it runs continuously at constant speed. Depressing the foot pedal activates a clutch mechanism contained in the vertical arm and motion is supplied to the top shaft. The sewing program runs automatically to completion, after which the clutch is automatically disengaged. This type of drive is used in cam-controlled machines such as buttonholers (*Figure 2*).

Slipping Clutch

In this case the motor also runs continuously at constant speed. However, the speed of sewing can be regulated by the displacement of the foot pedal which applies increasing pressure to the clutch disk, against the motor disk. When the pedal is fully released, the clutch disk is held by a brake so the machine hand wheel is locked. To adjust the needle position, it is necessary to apply a slight pressure to the foot pedal. This system is used for simple high speed sewing machines (*Figure 3*).

Electronic Control

In the most sophisticated drive systems, a series of sensors is provided which supply information about speed and needle position to a control box. The control logic regulates the speed of the drive motor according to these inputs and a pre-selected sewing program (*Figure 4*). In general, three sets of functions can be distinguished.

Input A sensor on the hand wheel passes an electric pulse to the control box with every revolution. This allows the machine speed and the position of the needle to be deduced. Another sensor reports the position of the foot pedal so that the required machine speed can be deduced. Sewing programs can be selected from a programmer which may be placed at the top of the machine, or on the control box. Additional mechanisms such as thread cutting, presser foot operation, needle raising etc. can be operated by pedals, knee buttons, or hand buttons.

Processing The data from the sensors are analysed in the control box to decide the control actions required.

Output Signals from the control box determine the speed of the motor, the positioning of the needle and the starting or stopping of the various sewing or additional operations. The most modern sewing machines are equipped with infinitely variable motors, which operate only when the pedal is pressed.

10.3.12 Ancillary Mechanisms for High Speed Sewing Machines

Industrial sewing machines are robustly built for continuous operation at high sewing speeds (over 2000 stitches per minute). Therefore they are called **high speed machines** and they are generally provided with several ancillary mechanisms whose function is to reduce the time needed by the operator for non-sewing activities. A prerequisite is an electronically controlled drive system (*see page 189*).

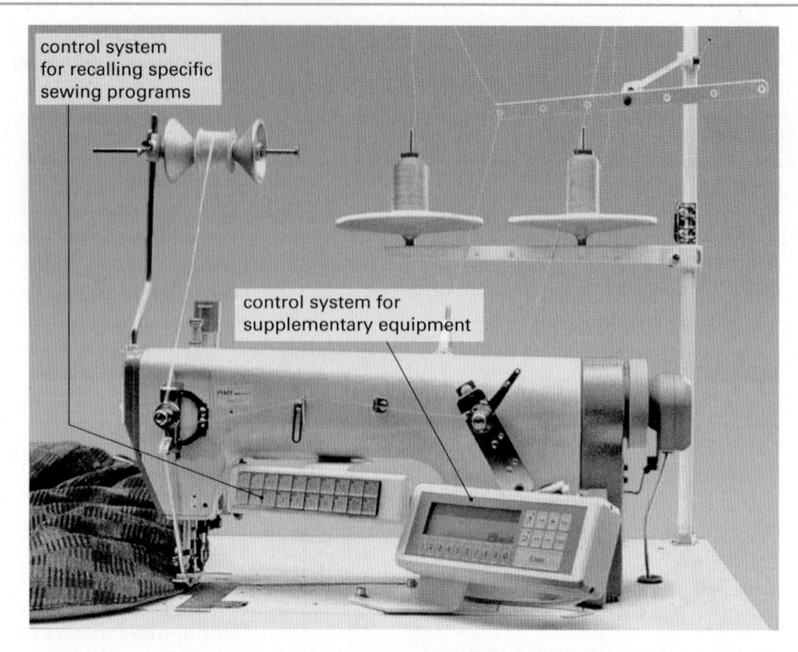

1: High speed sewing machine with ancillary controls

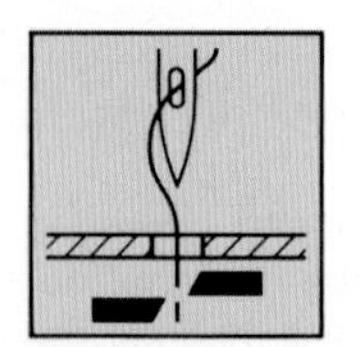

2: Thread cutter

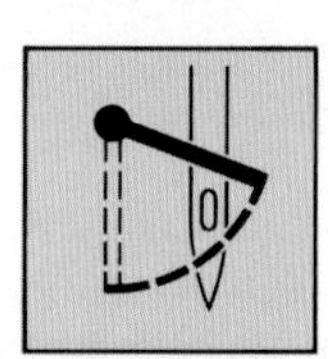

3: Thread wiper

4: Automated presser foot

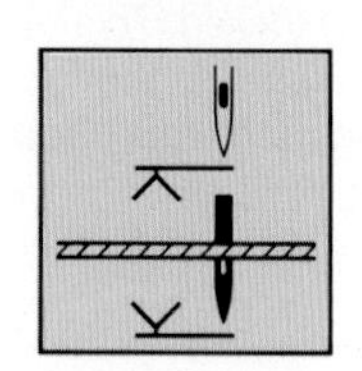

5: Needle positioning

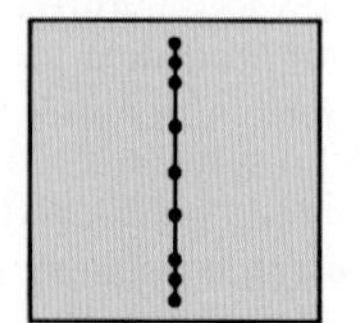

6: Stitch compression

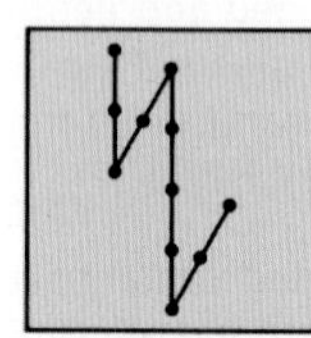

7: Bar tacking

8: Automatic start using an optical sensor

9: Automatic stop using an optical sensor

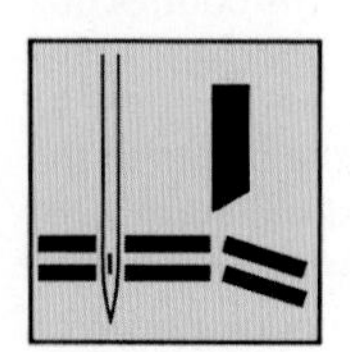

10: Edge trimmer

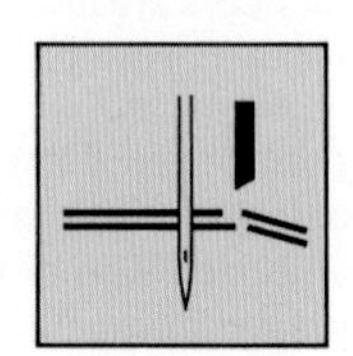

11: Edge trimmer (stepped)

Ancillary Equipment for Industrial High Speed Sewing Machines

The automatic **thread cutting** device (*Figure 2*) trims both needle thread and underthread at the material surface.

The **thread wiper** (*Figure 3*) lays the needle thread on top of the presser foot after the thread has been cut and the presser foot had been lifted. This avoids the needle thread becoming trapped when sewing begins again.

The **automatic presser foot** device (*Figure 4*) causes the presser foot to be lifted automatically when the sewing process is interrupted. At this time the needle is either in its lowest position (e.g. for rotating the work) or in the highest position (e.g. after cutting the thread).

The **needle positioning** device (*Figure 5*) allows the needle to stop in the low position whenever sewing is interrupted. This allows the work to be turned e.g. when sewing corners. It is also possible to raise both presser foot and needle to the higher position e.g. to adjust the fabric plies.

Stitch compression (*Figure 6*) ensures sufficient safety on lockstitch and chain stitch seams when it is not possible to sew backwards.

Bar tacking (*Figure 7*) provides back and forth stitching at the beginning and end of seams. The number of stitches to be given at the beginning and end of sewing can be predetermined.

Edge detection devices can control the start and finish of the sewing operation. Optical sensors detect the beginning (*Figure 8*) or the end (*Figure 9*) of the material and send the corresponding signals to the control box. These signals will be used by the control logic to initiate or terminate the appropriate operations such as bar tacking or needle positioning, depending on the programming. Sensors can also work inside the material being sewn.

Edge trimming (*Figure 10*) allows the seam allowance to be trimmed away, for example when binding seam edges. It is also possible to cut in steps (*Figure 11*) or to scallop the edges.

Automatic fabric feeding and guiding devices are also used to improve the efficiency of sewing operations.

10.3.13 Automatic Sewing Machines

A higher level of automation than high speed machines with auxiliary mechanisms is provided by the fully automatic machine and the dedicated, automated workstation.

- An operator simply places the material to be sewn at the sewing station, monitors the process, and removes the completed work.
- The process is completely self-contained.
- Monitoring systems will stop the machine if a fault occurs, e.g. via a thread breakage detector.
- They are very easy to use; inexperienced operatives can use them effectively after only a short training period.

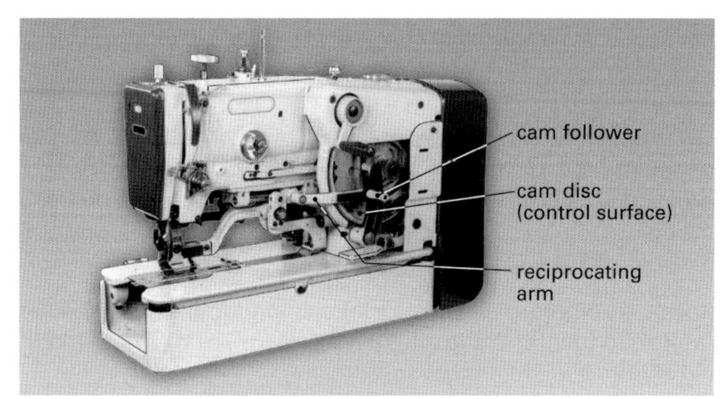

1: Cam-controlled automatic machine

With **cam-controlled automatic** machines, the required pattern of movement of the material to be sewn is replicated in the shape of the cam. The motion is delivered to a reciprocating arm via two cam followers running in the cam track, and linked to the material guide system by levers (*Figure 1*).

Alternatively, movement of the components can also be realised through **CNC**[1] technology via a stored computer program.

Zigzag stitching patterns are automatically provided in lockstitch, chain stitch or multi-thread chain stitch.

Typical applications include making button holes, sewing on buttons, and sewing short seams such as on belt loops.

2: Finishing a buttonhole

Buttonhole Sewing Machine

They stitch the shape of the buttonhole. The material is cut automatically either before or after the sewing process. With **cam-controlled machines,** the stitch density and buttonhole length can be varied by adjustments to the control cam and the gear drive. The distance between buttonholes is fixed manually, or automatically, via transport rails.

CNC-controlled buttonholers enable the production of buttonholes of different lengths and shapes by recalling stored programs.

Straight buttonholes are used mainly for shirts and blouses; **eyed** buttonholes are for outerwear such as jackets, coats and trousers.

3: Sewing on a button over a spacer bar

Button Sewing Machine (*Figure 3*)

The buttons may be introduced either manually or by a special button magazine. The needle bar is made to oscillate between the two holes being sewn. If there are four holes, then the button clamp is also moved, at the appropriate moment, to bring the second pair of holes into work.

Buttons sewn with chain stitch can be unstitched easily if the final stitches are not fastened properly.

4: Bar tacking a belt loop

Bar Tackers

Bar tacking machines are used for special, short seams such as in strengthening the ends of pocket and fly openings, or attaching belt loops (*Figure 4*) and labels.

With **cam-controlled machines,** the sewing program is given by the shape of the cam. Usually, every different seam type demands its own design of cam and material clamp.

With **CNC-controlled bar tackers,** the various movements are mediated by stored computer programs. Additional programs can be produced, stored, and recalled as required.

[1] CNC = computerized numerical control

10.3.14 Automated Sewing Equipment

CNC machines are controlled by a computer. The required sequence of movements of the material is converted into X, Y co-ordinates (digitised) in the workspace. These co-ordinates are used by a computer program. During the sewing operation, the program continuously delivers the X, Y co-ordinates to servo motors acting on the material or on the sewing head.

Two different methods of programming are available:

- **Learning mode:**
  The machine is taken manually through each step in the sewing cycle, whilst the computer monitors the operation and stores the positional and operational information as a program.
- **Off-line programming:**
  The required co-ordinates and operations are derived directly from the CAD files.

Seam contour points, stitch density and number of stitches can be entered manually. Programs are saved to a data storage device.

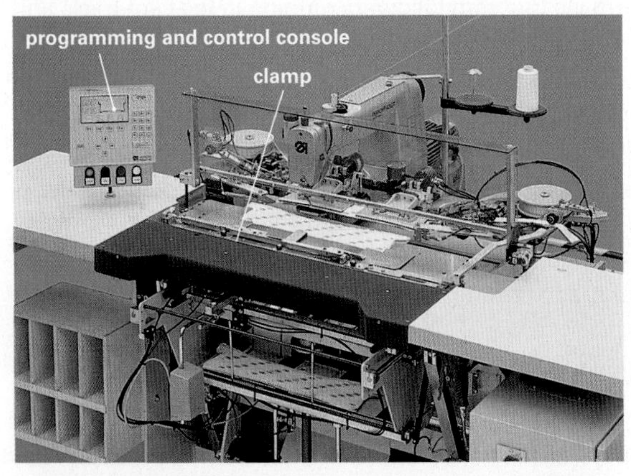

1: Collar assembly

Figure 1 shows a CNC workstation for assembling collars. The components are positioned and clamped on a feeding device. Automatic feeding means that while one collar is being sewn the next is being prepared manually. The required collar style, and size can be selected at a control console.

Electronic monitoring devices for needle and looper threads are programmed to stop the machine if a fault arises or if the under-thread spool needs replenishing.

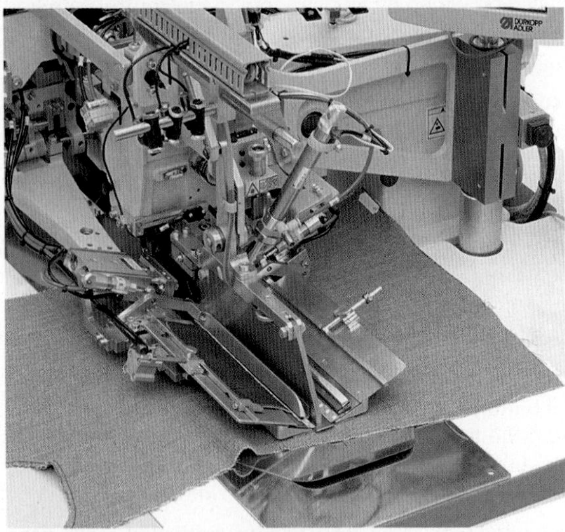

2: Pocket maker

Figure 2 shows a CNC station for pre-sewing of straight or slanted jetted, flapped, or inset pockets.

This workstation can be customised for the requirements of any particular design.

Examples of pocket styles:

Double jetted

Flapped

The level of automation can be raised by additional features, such as:

- automatic flap or pocket bag attachment
- zip fastener insertion
- tape insertion and slit cutting

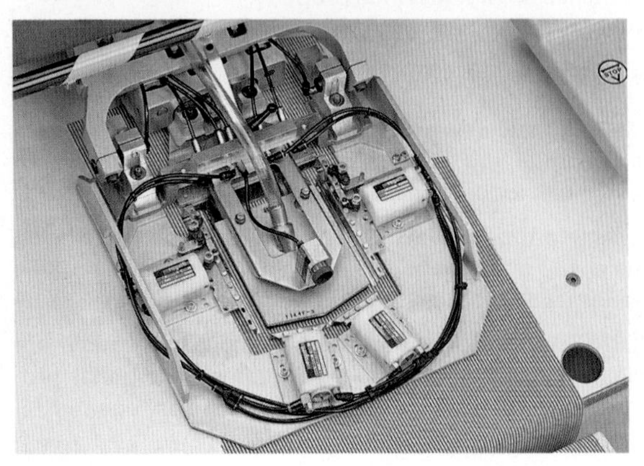

3: Patch pocket maker

CNC Profile Sewing Systems

Profile sewing systems are controlled by a template and jig which assume the functions of presser foot and feed plate. The material is fixed on the jig and, after every stitch, the template is moved by an independent drive system responding to the commands of a computer program. This allows perfect stitching to be obtained.

By changing the design of the template, a wide range of different shapes can be produced.

Examples:

Attachment of patch pockets (*Figure 3*), making pocket flaps, embellishment of sewn pockets.

10.3.15 Welded Seams, Seam Sealing

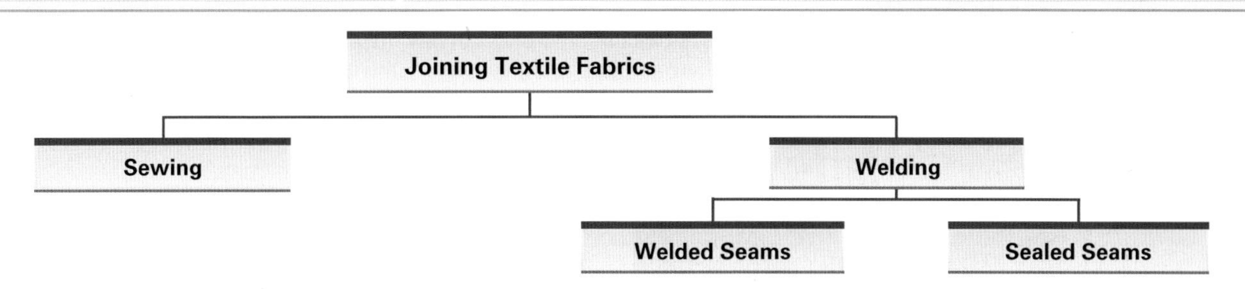

There are two important methods for joining textile fabrics together.

Sewing:
Two or more pieces of fabric are joined using sewing machines, sewing threads and various types of stitching (*see pages 175 ff*).

Welding:
Flexible, thermoplastic films as well as polyester needle felts and nonwovens can be joined by welding.

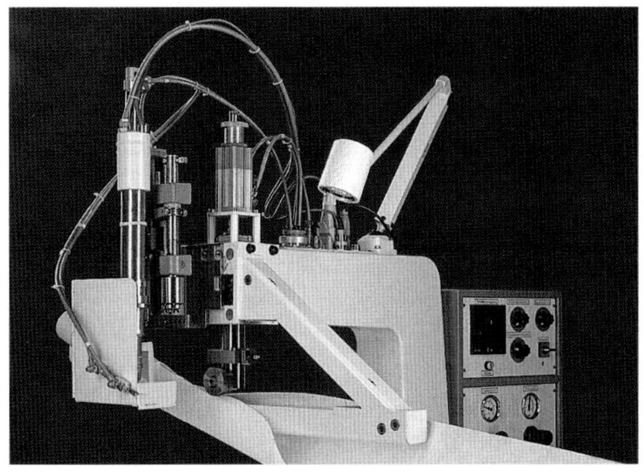
1: Cylinder bed welding machine

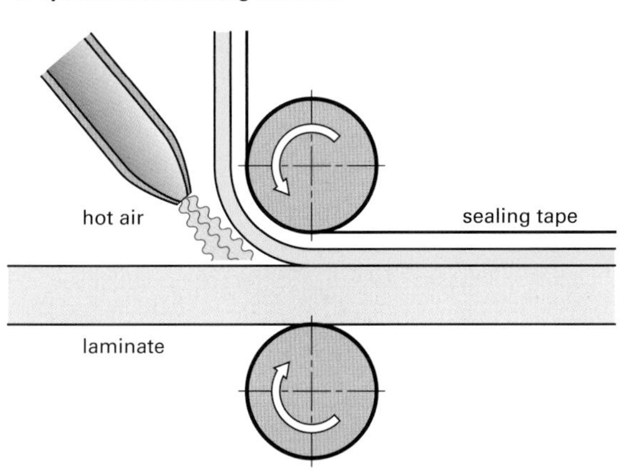

2: Seam sealing for all-weather clothing

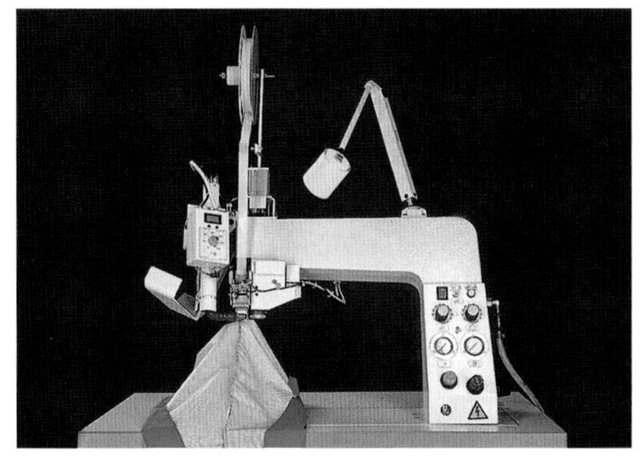
3: Sealing a seam with sealing tape

Welded Seams

There are two main **thermal welding** techniques, namely the **hot edge** and **hot air** methods. In either case heat is supplied to the inside of the seam, to soften the thermoplastic component(s), after which the assembly is forwarded between two transport rollers where it is pressed and securely bonded. Starting, stopping and sharp corners are problematical.

With **radio frequency (RF) welding,** high frequency electromagnetic vibrations soften and weld the thermoplastic materials at a series of discrete points as the assembly passes between two contoured wheel electrodes.

The seam strength can be checked with a tensile testing device.

Welding devices are used mainly for joining flexible thermoplastic materials. Flexibility has to be retained after the welding process.

There are continuous welding systems and also devices that work like a form press.

Mobile welding devices of the thermal welding type are constructed in various forms. They are used mainly for producing straight lapped seams in thin to heavy films, for seam sealing lines, and for coated fabrics. They all use the hot edge principle.

Because of the many different seam types that have to be accommodated, the machines are usually of the post or cylinder bed type (*Figure 1*). These machines can be built for hot edge, hot air or RF welding.

Sealed Seams

Welding machines for seam sealing are usually built as post or cylinder bed types.

In the manufacture of all-weather clothing with Gore-Tex® or Sympatex® water-resistant films (*see page 50*) the seams have to be sealed in a special additional operation (*Figures 2 and 3*).

After the production of a normal seam, the edges and the sewings are durably sealed using a special sealing tape. The heat sealable tape is led by rollers and is fused onto the seam by hot air. The welding temperature is controlled electronically, to ensure consistent and reliable bonding. The result is that the seam is wind and waterproof.

The manufacture of all-weather clothing demands very careful planning in the design, construction and assembly of the various components such as collars, pockets and arm pieces. Usually the seams of all of these parts are sealed by welding techniques.

10.4.1 Seam Puckering

Puckering is a result of the particular sewing conditions, as well as differences in raw materials, constructions, and finishing of the materials being sewn. Distinctions can be drawn between puckering caused by the separate effects of material feeding, fabric structure, and thread tensions.

1: Feeding pucker

Feeding Effects

Feeding pucker is caused by a displacement between the top and the bottom fabric plies. The bottom ply is pushed forward by the feed dog while the upper ply is restrained by the presser foot (*Figure 1*).

The problem is addressed by the use of special feeder mechanisms, by adjustments to the feed dog or presser foot, by using a special presser foot, e.g. Teflon-covered or wheel types, or by reducing the sewing speed.

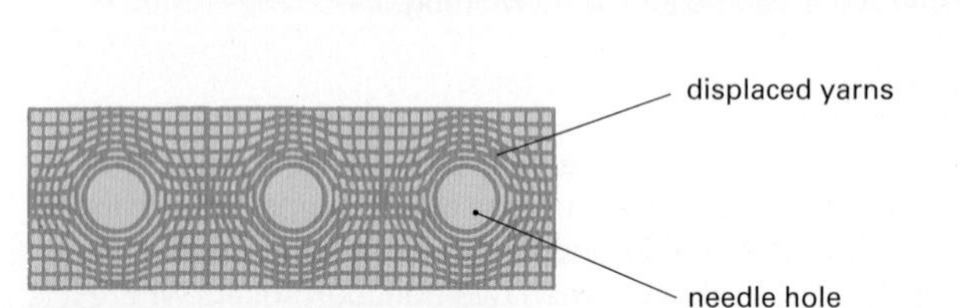

2: Distortion of the yarns in a fabric

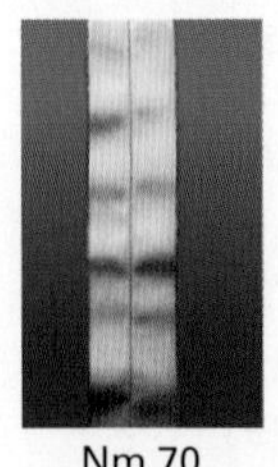
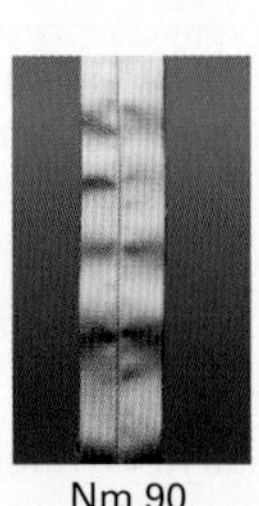
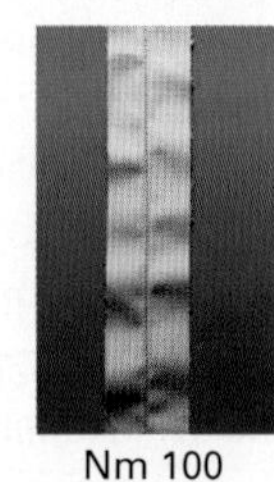

Nm 70 Nm 80 Nm 90 Nm 100

3: Influence of needle size on structural puckering

Seam along the warp **Seam inclined to the warp**

4: Influence of seam orientation on puckering

Structural Effects

Structural puckering is the result of the fabric structure becoming jammed, due to the introduction of sewing needle and thread.

Penetration of the fabric by the needle, and the insertion of the sewing thread, causes adjacent warp and weft yarns in the fabric to be displaced; the fabric structure may become jammed. This can produce small bulges in the fabric, close to the seam (*Figure 2*).

Structural pucker tends to be more obvious with lockstitch than with chain stitch.

It can be reduced by using finer needles, finer threads, lower sewing thread tension and a lower stitch density (*Figure 3*).

Usually, the density and the extensibility of the fabric being sewn is different in the warp and weft directions. Seams which run parallel to the warp will often show more puckering than those sewn along the weft, or on the bias.

This type of problem can often be helped by making the seam at an angle of about 15° to the warp (*Figure 4*).

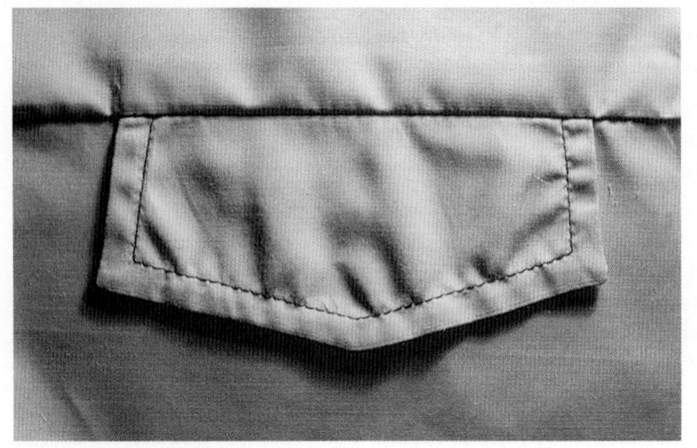

5: Tension puckering

Thread Tension Effects

Puckering can be caused by excessive sewing thread tensions (*Figure 5*).

Threads which are sewn under high tension will be stretched. This extension will later be recovered to some extent; the yarn will tend to return to its original length, forcing a reduction in the length of the seam, which may then pucker. Synthetic threads have higher extensibility and elastic recovery and will tend to show this problem more than cotton.

The recovery does not occur immediately; there can be considerable delay so that the problem may not become apparent until after the garments have been delivered.

To prevent tension puckering:

- the underthread should be wound at low tension
- tension settings for both needle and underthread should be set as low as possible
- high quality, covered threads should be used

10.4.2 Fabric Damage, Sewing Faults

Fabric Damage

A material which is difficult to feed, or which is subjected to high pressure during feeding, can be damaged during sewing. The yarns in the material may be weakened or broken. Damage also can be caused by needles of inappropriate size or type and needles with worn or damaged points. This can cause holes to appear in the fabric (*Figure 1*). Needle points can be tested on the fingernail. A flawless needle point, without a burr, does not produce scratch marks.

Needle damage in a woven fabric may detract from its appearance but generally does not have further serious consequences (*Figure 2*). In a knitted fabric, needle damage may lead to the generation of ladders when the seam is stressed. In high speed sewing, the heat generated by friction at the needle can be enough to melt a synthetic yarn (*Figure 3*).

Fabric damage can be prevented by:

- improved fabric finishing
- using the finest possible needles
- selecting special needle points
- moistening the fabric
- using special needles
- cooling the needle with compressed air

1: Damaged loops caused by a worn needle point

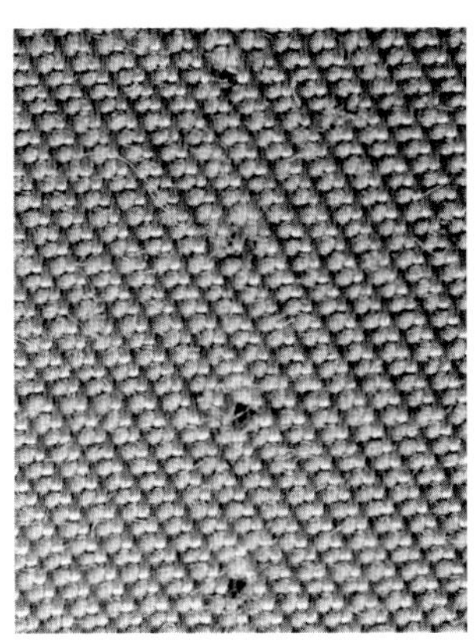

2: Woven fabric: damage depending on the needle thickness

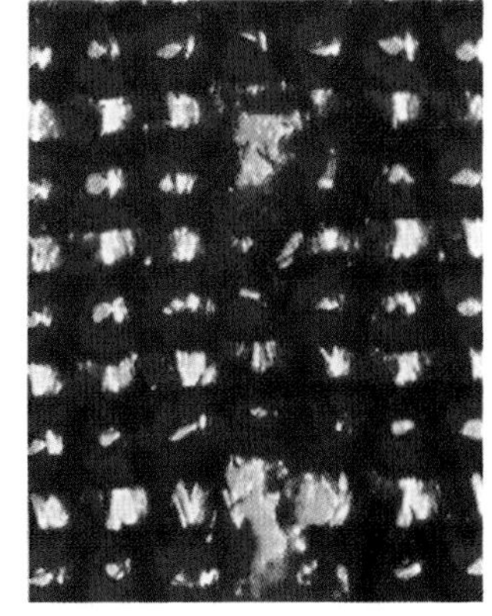

3: Holes caused by melting in a knitted fabric made from synthetic yarn

Sewing Faults and their Causes

4: Thread break

Fault	Cause
Thread break	• Incorrect thread path. • Thread waste fouling the looper. • Worn or damaged hole in the throat plate. • Thread contains knots or has low strength. • Worn or damaged needle eye or groove.
Needle break	• Thread too thick and strong for the needle. • Needle deflected onto the throat plate by the operative pulling on the fabric. • Spool case incorrectly fixed. • Needle is bent and is caught by the looper. • Inadequate needle quality.
Irregular seam	• Needle incorrectly installed. • Underthread badly wound. • Bent needle. • Incorrect looper settings. • Inappropriate needle system. • Poor fabric feed.
Poor fabric feed	• Presser foot pressure too low. • Worn, damaged, or contaminated feed dog. • Feed dog set too low – inadequate penetration through the throat plate. • Inappropriate feeder mechanism.
Missed stitches	• The looper does not catch the needle thread loop because of e.g. a bent needle, an inappropriate needle or thread, or faulty looper settings, threading up, or needle installation.

10.5.1 Pressing (1)

Pressing implies shaping and smoothing a textile material. There are three general types of pressing operations in a garment-making operation:

- **Under pressing:** operations performed on component parts during making up.
- **Moulding:** imparting a three dimensional shape without using darts.
- **Top pressing:** final finishing operations on the fully assembled garment.

Pressing is effected by the application of heat and pressure during a certain time. Moisture, compressed air and suction can assist the process. Steam is an efficient medium for heating and also delivers the moisture which is required for setting natural materials such as cotton, linen and wool, as well as the man-made cellulosic fibres. The setting effect is fixed by drying and cooling, which can be accelerated by **suction** or **blowing.**

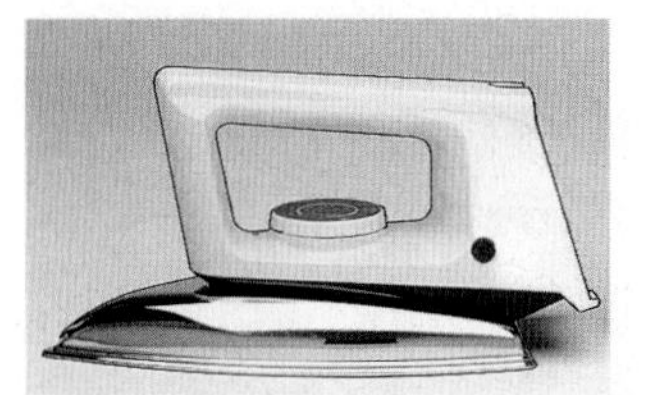

1: Electric iron

2: Self-contained steam iron

Dry Pressing

In a dry iron (*Figure 1*) the heat is produced by an electric heating element. The temperature can be adjusted from 60 to 220 °C to accommodate the characteristics of the material being pressed. If moisture is required, it has to be sprayed onto the material. Mostly used for pressing or fusing of interlinings (*see pages 201 and 202*)

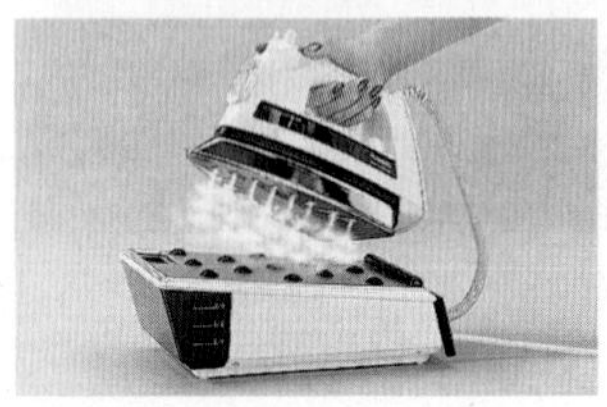

3: Steam iron with separate reservoir

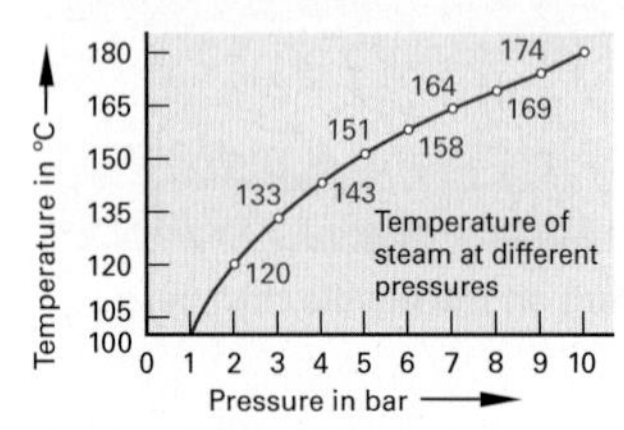

4: Steam generation

Steam Pressing

Steam is generated and utilised in one of two ways:

- **Atmospheric steam generation.**

At **normal air pressure** water boils at 100 °C. In a self-contained electric steam iron (*Figure 2*) (e.g. domestic iron) water is dripped onto the hot ironing plate and vaporises. The escaping steam has a temperature of not more than 100 °C and will condense onto the cooler fabric providing both heat and moisture.

Thus the steam is produced directly inside the iron. The larger the water reservoir (*Figure 3*), the longer are the time intervals between fillings.

- **High pressure steam generation.**

A higher steam temperature can be achieved if the water is heated in a pressure vessel. The graph (*Figure 4*) shows the relationship between steam temperature and pressure. In the garment industry steam pressures of 5 to 10 bar and temperatures from 150 to 170 °C are utilised. The higher temperature accelerates the pressing process.

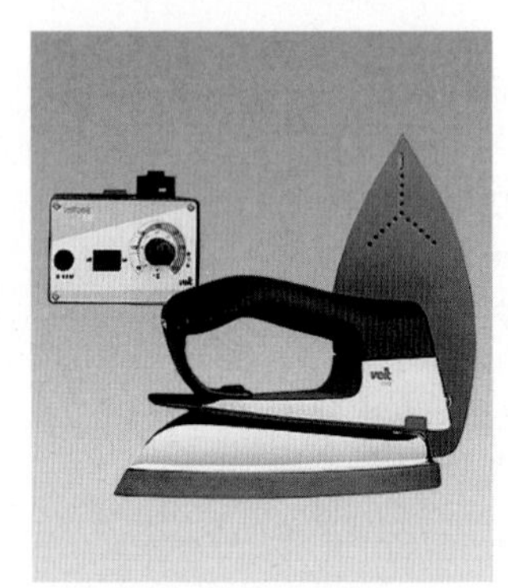

5: High-pressure steam iron

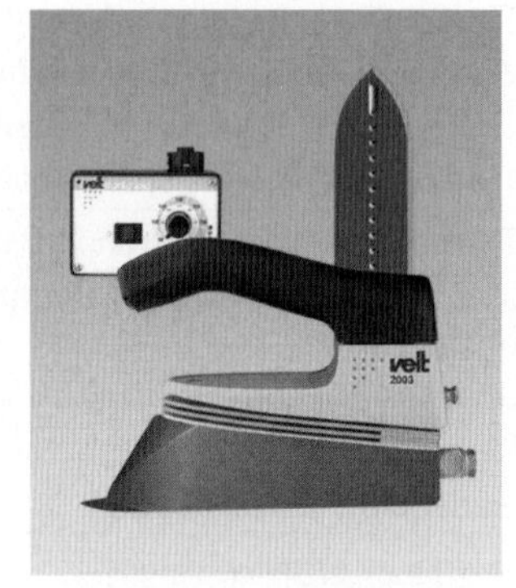

6: High-pressure seam presser

In **high pressure steam irons** (*Figures 5, 6, and 7*) the steam is supplied continuously to the iron through an armoured, insulated tube and is regulated by a valve. The steam issues through holes in the sole. The temperature of the sole is adjustable from 100 to 235 °C. High efficiency heating elements and integrated steam chambers provide steam without condensate.

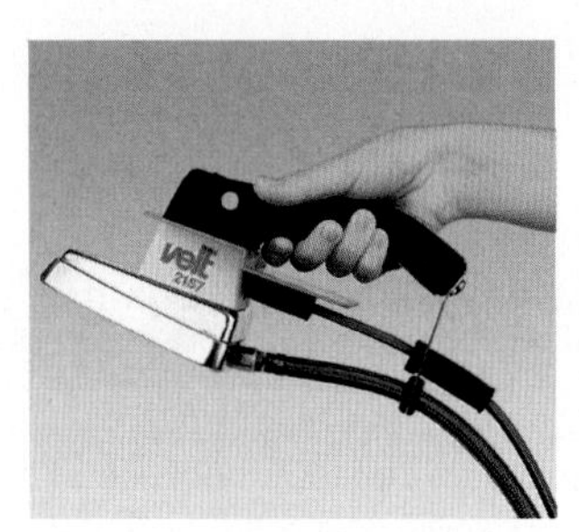

7: High-pressure hand finisher

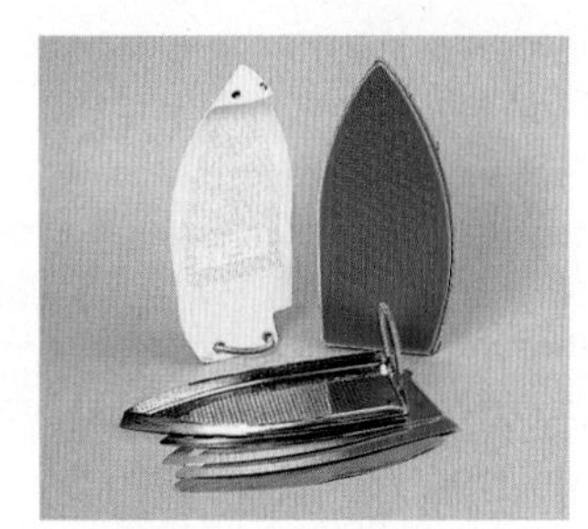

8: Teflon shoe, stainless steel shoe

For operations such as **seam pressing** and **top finishing,** pressing devices may be used with specially designed steam outlets (*Figures 6 and 7*).

The **Teflon ironing shoe** (*Figure 8*) prevents singing and shiny marks when pressing the face side of sensitive fabrics.

10.5.1 Pressing (2)

Accessories

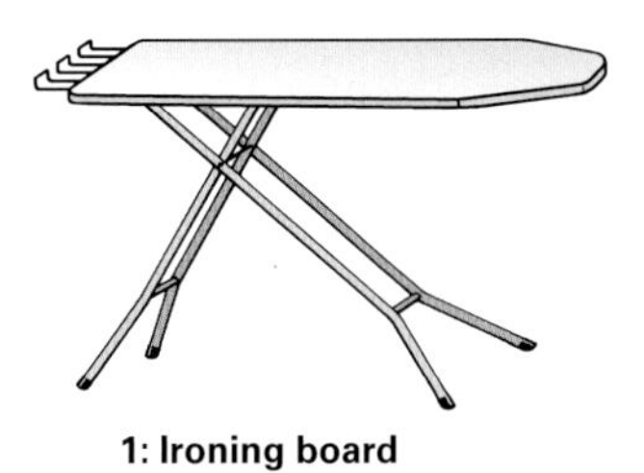

1: Ironing board

The ironing board is used for pressing larger surfaces. Openings in the board allow the steam to escape.

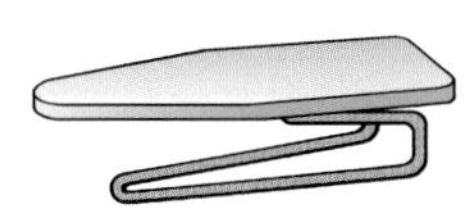

2: Sleeve board

The sleeve board is for pressing small, tubular items.

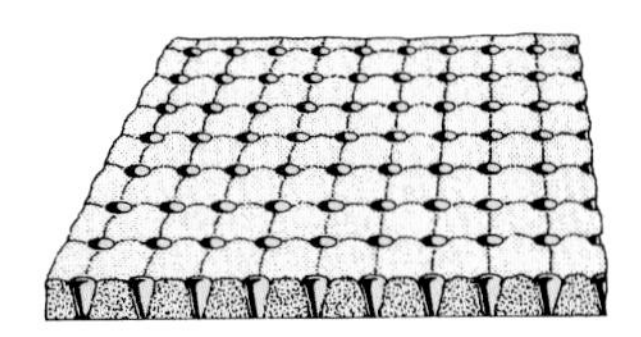

3: Underlay

Special heat reflecting pads, or simple felt materials can be used as underlays for pressing. They spread the pressure and absorb the steam.

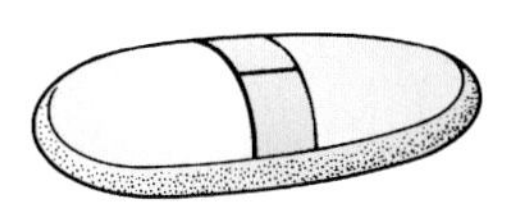

4: Hand buck

Hand-held pads are a useful aid in top pressing garments which are difficult to lay flat.

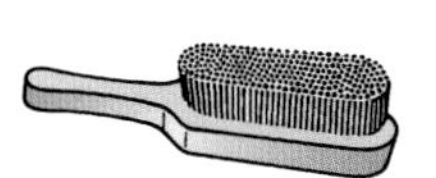

5: Brush

Brushes are used in top pressing surfaces with nap or pile.

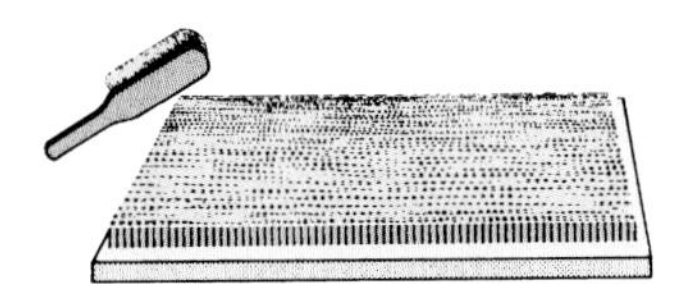

6: Needle bed

Needle beds are helpful when dealing with sensitive pile fabrics (velvet).

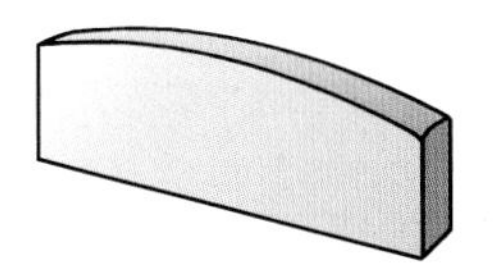

7: Collar anvil

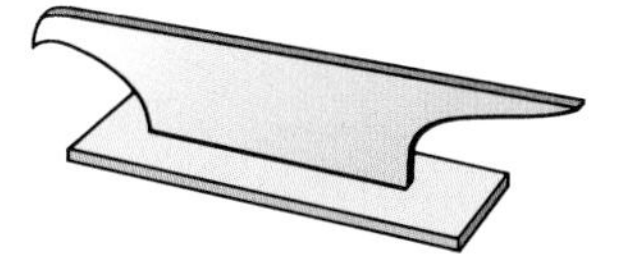

8: Edge anvil

Anvils allow a firmer pressing of particular garment parts.

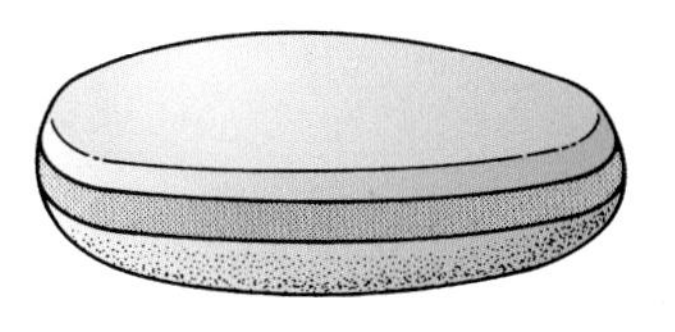

9: Ironing cushion

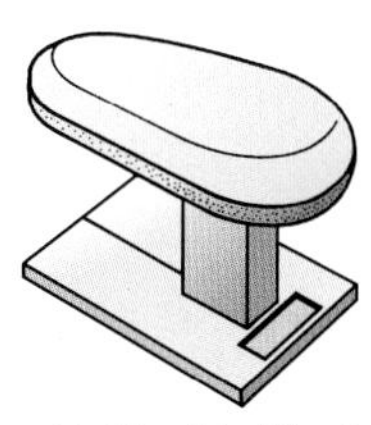

10: Moulded buck

Various shaped cushions and bucks facilitate the pressing and moulding of three-dimensional garment areas.

Pressing at Different Stages in Manufacture

Under pressing	During garment assembly, various parts may need to be pressed before proceeding to the next stage, to improve the ease or accuracy of sewing e.g. flattening of seams or edges before hemming. Under pressing is also required in cases where it would not be possible to achieve the required effect during top pressing, e.g. collars and cuffs before contour-stitching.
Top pressing	This refers to all of the final finishing operations performed on the completed garment. The product is made ready for sale. Also known as finishing.

Pressing Techniques

Flat pressing	Removal of wrinkles before cutting, before sewing, or on the finished product.
Steaming	May be carried out to relax the fabric, to avoid shrinkage during subsequent pressing.
Moulding	Moulding is the creation and fixing of three-dimensional shape in a garment. The location and the extent of the shaping are determined by the cutting pattern. Moulding is most effective with wool fabrics. It involves: Stretching: Rounded forms are imposed by introducing and fixing localised extensions in the fabric e.g. at the shoulder, bust and collar. Pressing in: Superfluous width is eased in and fixed, e.g. centre back, centre waist, and sleeves.

10.5.2 Pressing Workstations (1)

Pressing Workstations

The pressing department usually contains workstations of various types such as flat pressing, trouser pressing, etc. (*see page 199*). The workstations are each provided with a pressing table, an iron and a steam generator. The most important functions of a pressing workstation are illustrated here by a ladies outerwear station.

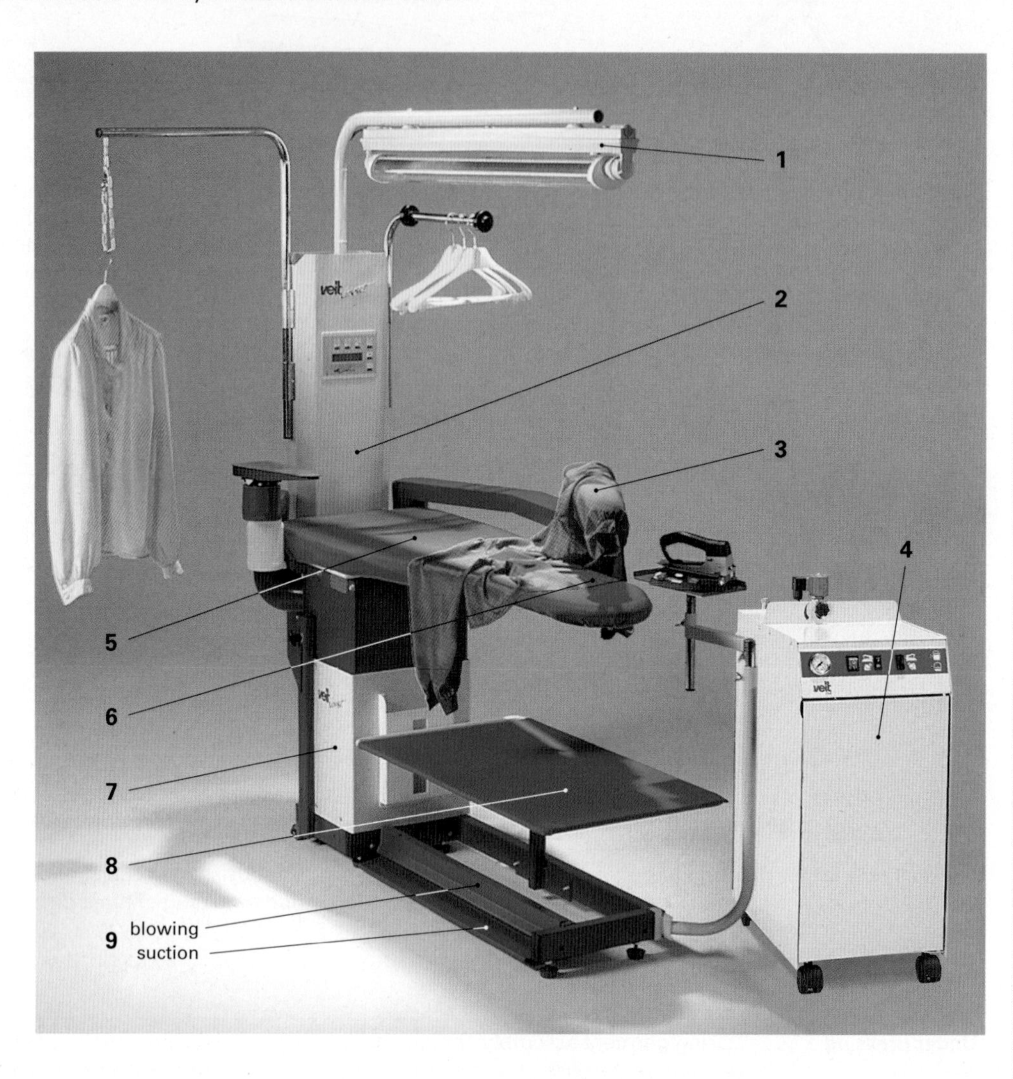

1: Pressing station for women's outerwear

Primary Functions of a Pressing Workstation

1: Overhead rail

Supports the lighting fitment and usually has a track for a mobile counterweight for the pressing iron (spring-loaded suspender).

2: Exhaust duct

Controlled removal of exhaust air and noise reduction.

3: Movable arm

Various forms of movable arm can be installed for specific pressing operations such as turn-ups, sleeves, seams.

4: Steam generator

High-pressure steam is generated in a boiler and piped to the iron.

5: Pressing surface

Constructed according to the main purpose of the particular workstation. Special coverings allow optimal passage of steam.

6: Suction and blowing

Suction accelerates cooling of the material and holds it firmly on the pressing table, without creases. Blowing prevents pressure marks at e.g. seams and hems.

7: Height adjustment

The height of the pressing table can be adjusted so as to allow comfortable working for a standing operative.

8: Catching frame with catch-cloth

Supports dangling parts of the work-piece and protects it from soiling.

9: Foot controls for suction and blowing

- horizontal bar for suction
- vertical bar for blowing

10.5.2 Pressing Workstations (2)

Ironing Boards

Workstation ironing boards are removable and interchangeable. Their shape depends on the specific application.

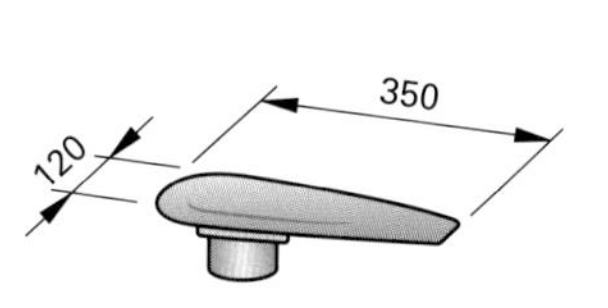

1: Shoulder board for under- and top pressing

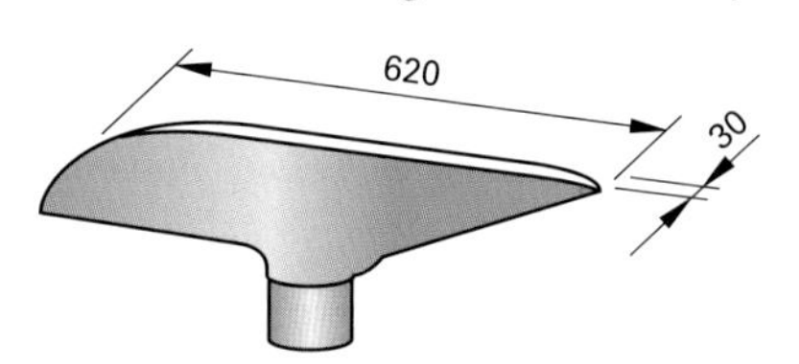

2: Edge board for pressing seams

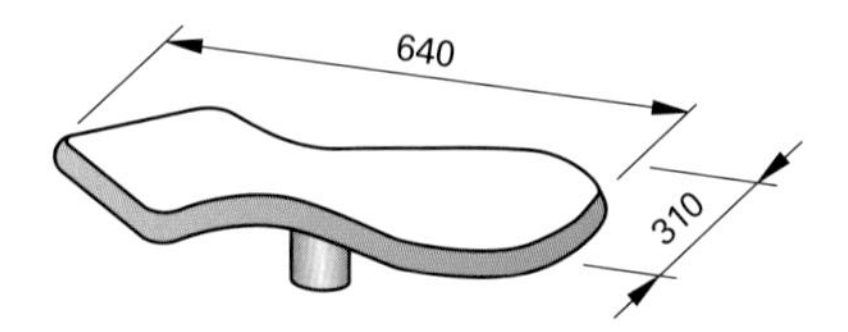

3: Large jacket board for top pressing

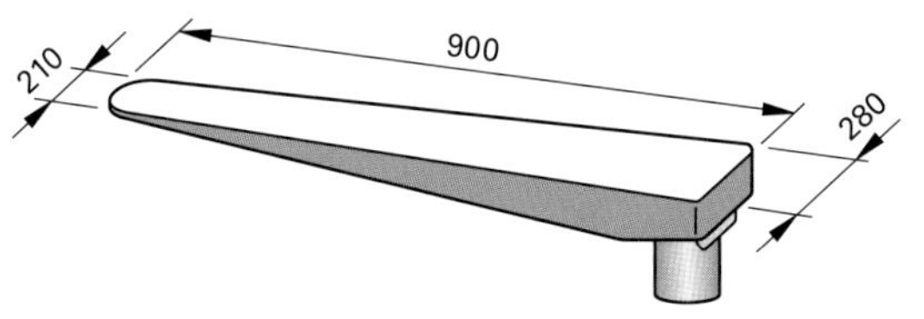

4: Large skirt board for under- and top pressing

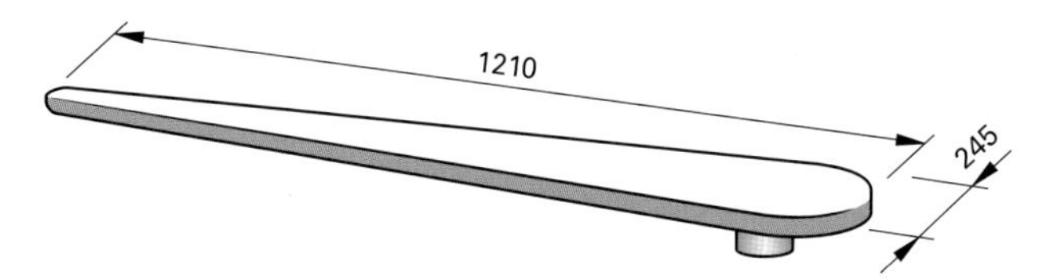

5: Universal board for e.g. trouser legs and sleeves

Pressing Stations

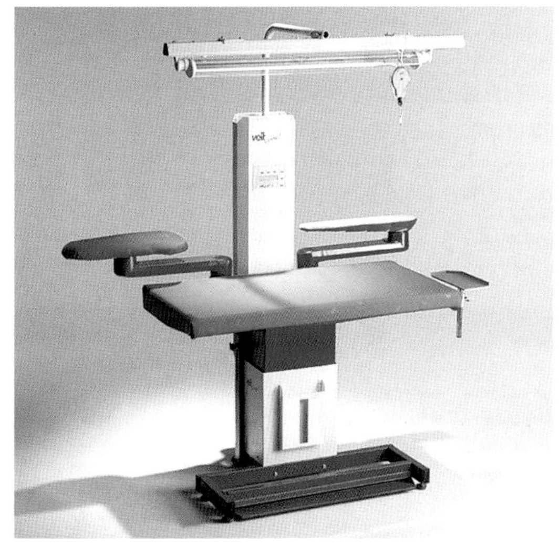

6: Flat pressing

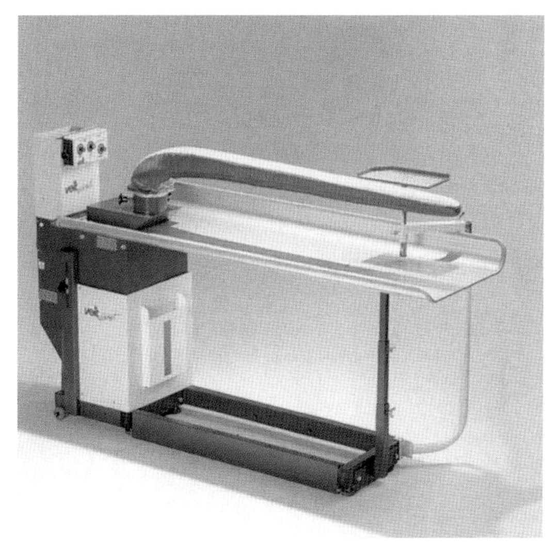

7: Trouser pressing

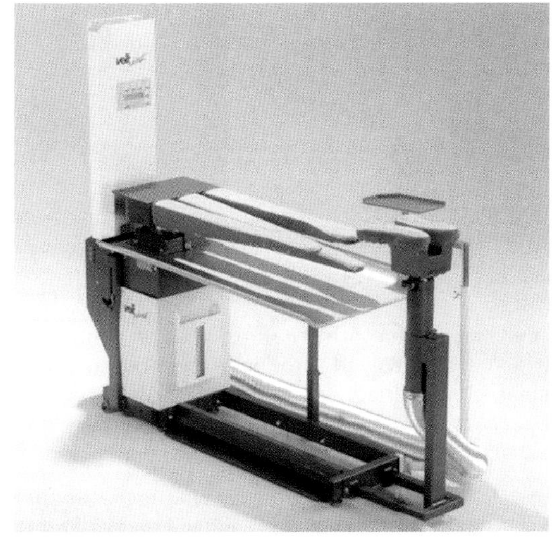

8: Jacket seam pressing

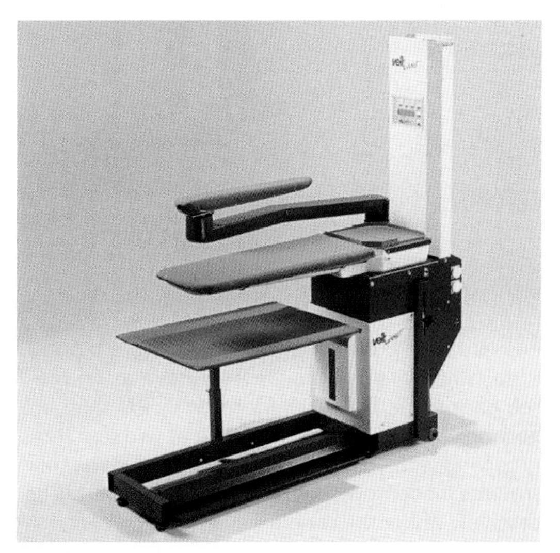

9: Universal ladies outerwear pressing

10.5.3 Mechanical Pressing and Finishing

Mechanical Presses

Specialised pressing units are produced in many different forms for pressing and durable shaping of particular items, such as collars, shoulders and trousers.

Pressing is effected between a stationary buck and a movable head, both of which are provided with special covering materials. After the head has been lowered steam is supplied from above or below. Pressure, temperature and pressing time are adjustable. Suction may be available from the buck.

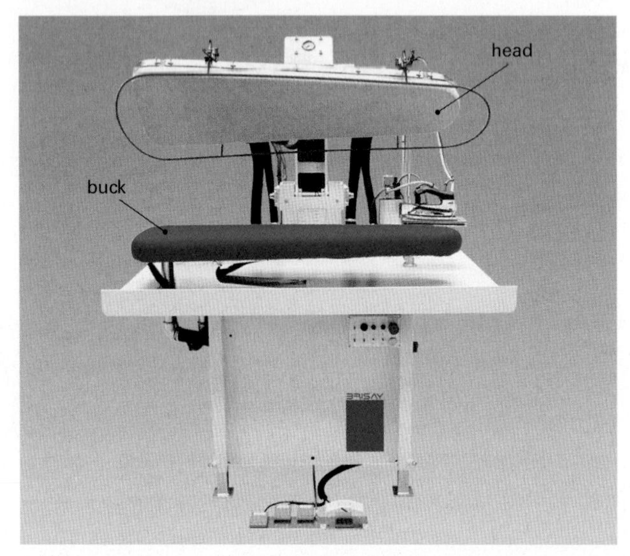

1: Flat press

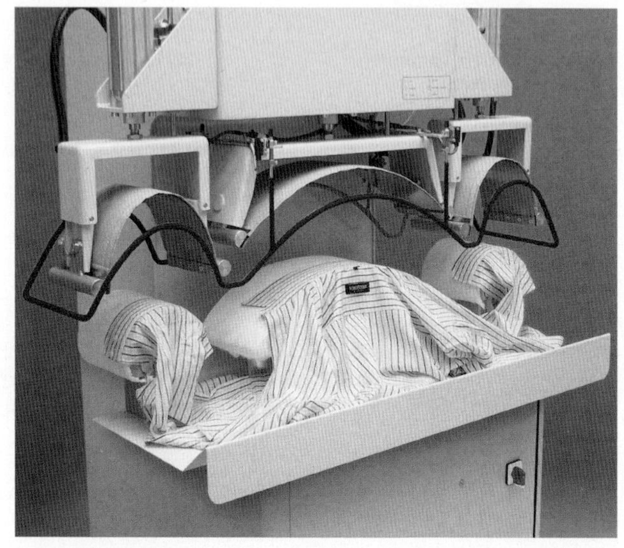

2: Moulding press

Steam Dolly and Tunnel Finisher

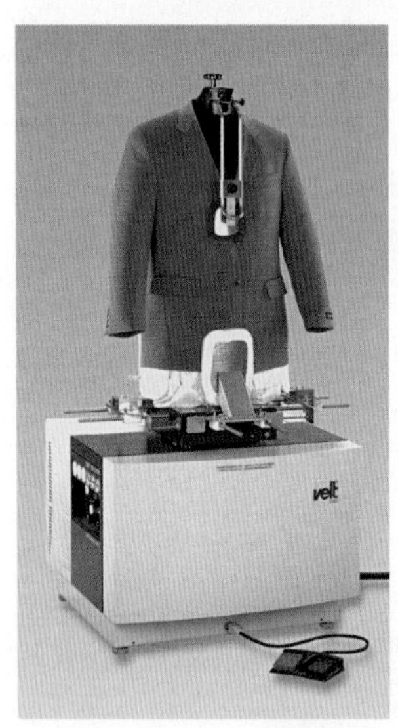

3: Steam dolly

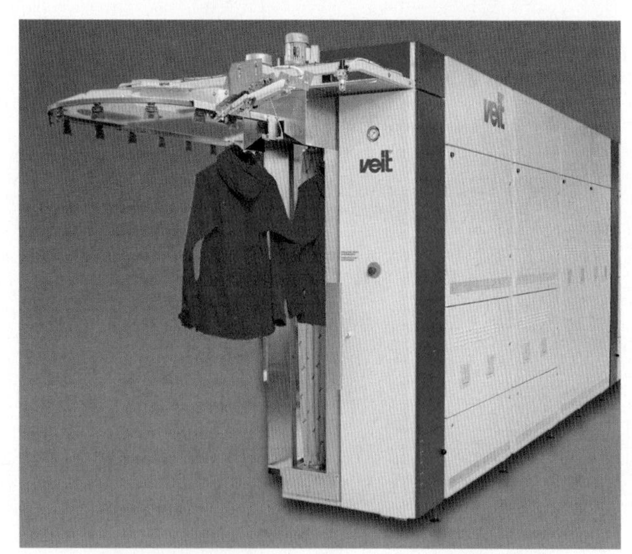

4: Tunnel finisher

Whole garments can be finished with **steam dollies,** although small parts such as collars and cuffs may have to be pre-pressed. The garment is put on the form which is then inflated by blowing with steam and air for one or two minutes, followed by cooling with air. This kind of treatment is suitable only for garments made from fabrics which will not shrink or stretch excessively under the conditions used.

With a **tunnel finisher** the garments are placed on hangers or frames, which are conveyed through a chamber in which they are steamed and dried.

For the highest quality finish, small parts may need to be pre-pressed.

The total dwell time and temperature, as well as the amount of steam and the drying time can be adjusted according to the particular materials being processed.

10.5.4 Fusing (1)

Fusing literally means melting. In clothing manufacture, it refers to the bonding of an interlining material to a top cloth by means of an adhesive, previously applied to the interlining, which melts under certain pressing conditions. Interlining fabrics of this type are called **fusibles,** or **fusible interlinings,** and fusing technology is concerned with the materials, equipment, and methods by means of which a lining may be durably bonded to a top cloth.

An **interlining** has to support the top cloth and possibly to shape it, but must not detract seriously from the look, the structure, the comfort and the utility of a garment. Top cloths can range from sensitive, transparent silks to fashionable high-tech materials, structured or fleecy woollens, and heat-sensitive leathers. In some cases, the interlining must be able to withstand intensive wearing and laundering conditions.

Depending on the end use and the desired effect, interlinings can be made from woven, knitted, or non-woven fabrics (*see pages 74 and 137*). Interlinings for large areas (*Figure 1*) underpin the shape of a garment or provide additional volume and weight. Fusibles in small components (*Figure 2*) give stability in one or all directions. Interlining and top cloth should be oriented in the same direction i.e. the warp of the interlining is aligned with the warp of the top cloth.

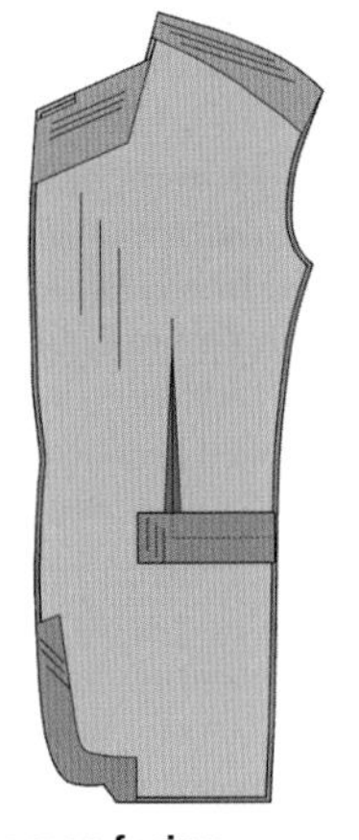

1: Large area fusing

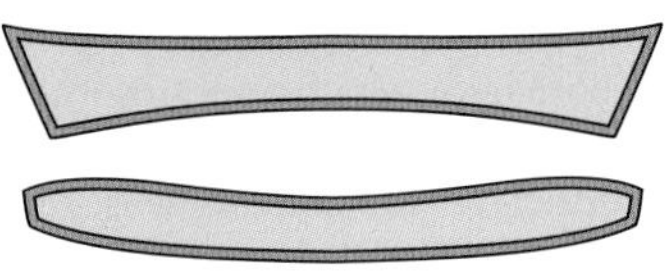

2: Small-part fusing

Fusible interlinings comprise a substrate and an **adhesive** (resin). The resin is almost always a synthetic polymer material which melts and flows within a defined temperature range. The adhesive may be applied to the substrate in a variety of ways, e.g. powder scattering (*Figure 3*), dot printing (*Figure 4*), paste printing, laminating, melt coating.

The quality of the bond, in terms of fastness to washing, ironing, and dry cleaning, as well as the handle and appearance of the fused components, depends on the substrate, the adhesive type, the amount and distribution of adhesive, and the fusing conditions. These have to be matched to the specific requirements of the garment. A thicker, heavier top cloth requires a larger quantity of adhesive. For a given quantity of adhesive, a distribution with fewer but larger dots will result in a softer handle of the fused parts (*Figures 5 and 6*).

Fusing Conditions

Fusing quality is determined by the temperature, the time, and the pressure obtained in the pressing operation.

- **Temperature:** The fusible has to be heated to the fusing temperature of the adhesive. The proper bond strength is only developed after the assembly has been fully cooled. The required temperature may be affected by the moisture content (steam).
- **Pressure:** Application of pressure ensures good contact between substrate, adhesive, and top cloth, whilst the adhesive is molten.
- **Time:** Enough time has to be allowed for proper melting of the adhesive and for any necessary penetration into the top cloth.

3: Powder coated

4: Dot printed

Set Temperature and Applied Temperature

Each type of resin has its characteristic fusing temperature range, within which good results will be obtained. The **set temperature** of the fusing device, i.e. the temperature of the heated plate, is controlled accurately by a thermostat but the **applied temperature** (inside the fabric layers) depends on the particular conditions such as the thickness and the density of the components, the moisture content – including the possible introduction of steam, and the area of contact with the heated plate. The actual fusing temperature can be established by measuring between the layers, using temperature-sensitive strips (*Figures 7 and 8*) or a thermocouple.

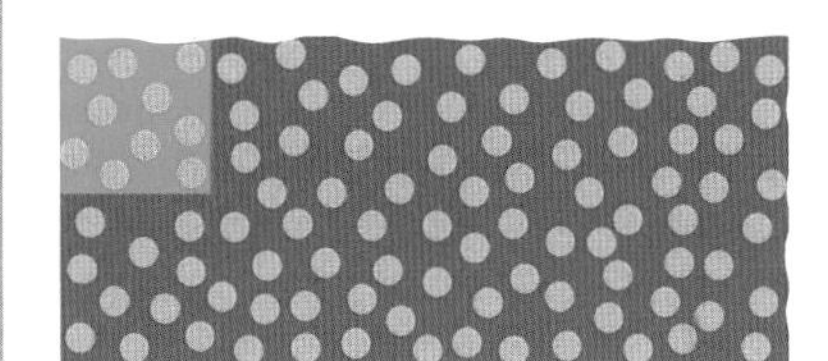

5: Dot printed 10 dots/cm²

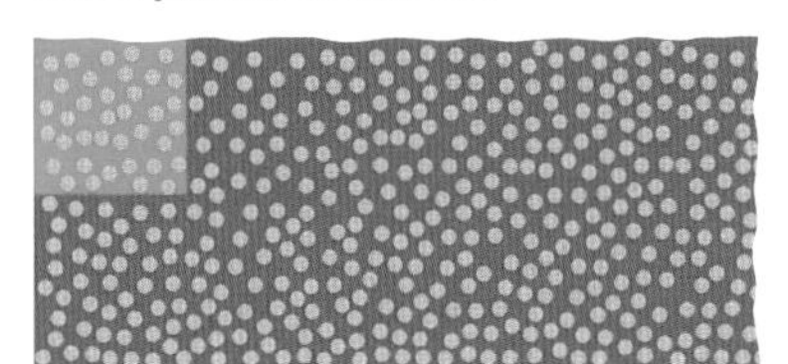

6: Dot printed 37 dots/cm²

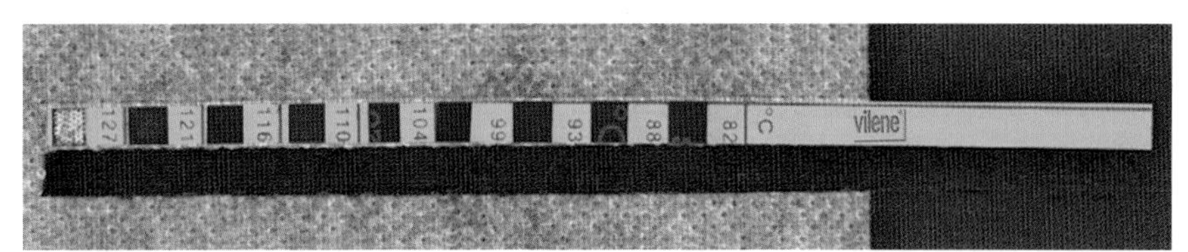

7: Temperature-sensitive strip: colour change at 121 °C

8: Temperature-sensitive strip: colour change at 143 °C

10.5.4 Fusing (2)

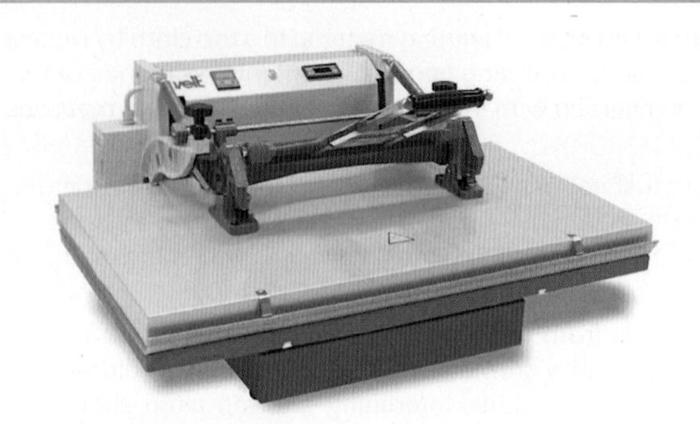

1: Table-top flat bed press

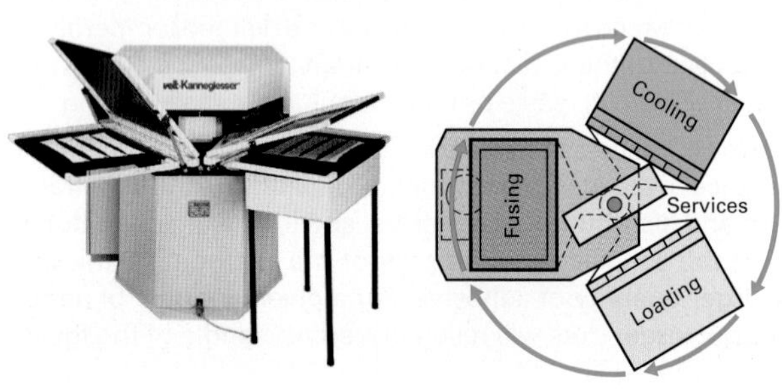

2: Carousel flatbed press station

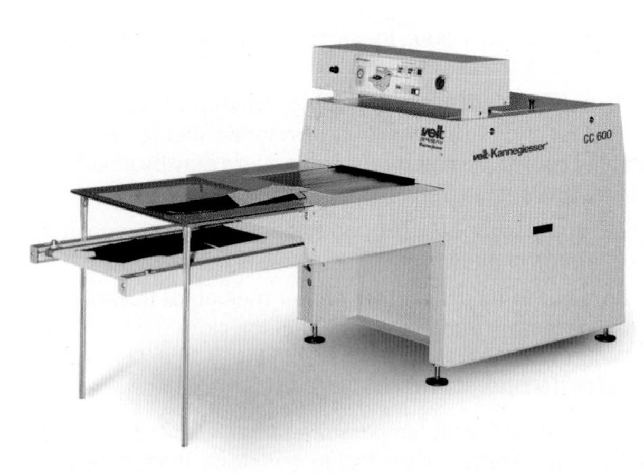

3: Compact return-feed conveyor press

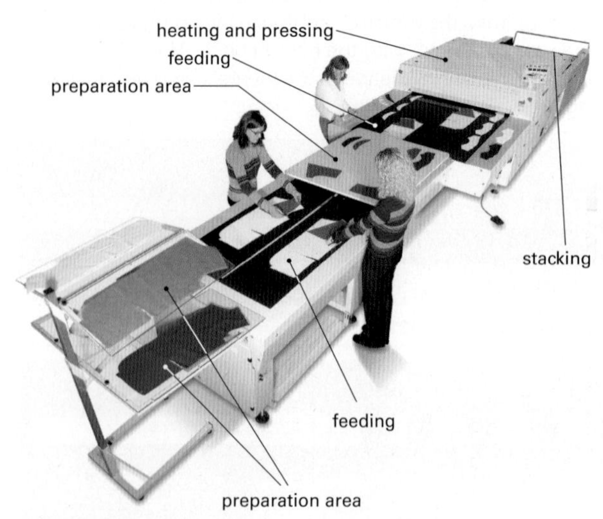

4: End-to-end conveyor press with assembly and stacking facilities

Fusing Equipment and Methods

Fusing equipment includes hand irons, flat bed presses and conveyor machines, depending on the type of fusible assembly, and the size of the enterprise.

In any case the principle of operation is the same: the components are assembled and laid in place; they are heated and pressed; they are allowed to cool; and they are removed.

With a **hand iron,** the control of temperature and pressure is not precise, so the results can be variable. The hand iron is used mainly for fixing tapes and edgings to hems and armscyes. They may also be useful with fabrics that have surfaces that are sensitive to heat and pressing. With polyamide resins, bond formation is assisted by providing steam. Too much steam, however, may cause the resin to be thinned and this can reduce the bond strength.

With a modern **flatbed press,** the pressure, temperature and time can be closely controlled. There are small, manual models (*Figure 1*) as well as large, semi-automated ones (*Figure 2*). The advanced models are equipped with movable beds, or feeding trays which allow for the next work piece to be loaded whilst one is being fused. The operator works in a seated position.

A conveyor fusing press transports the assembly through all stages on a powered conveyor belt. They can be compact, with return feed (*Figure 3*) or large with end-to-end feed (*Figure 4*) according to requirements. Temperature, pressure, and time are closely controlled and infinitely variable within the working ranges. The enclosed construction allows for any vapours given off by the fusible to be exhausted safely. Usually, there will be a specially designed preparation station where the components are assembled and fed to the conveyor. The preparation station is provided with its own feeding conveyor which operates intermittently to allow the operatives to position the parts correctly. An automatic stacker can be introduced at the delivery end, with size recognition capability, to sort the fused assemblies into size-consistent stacks.

Quality Control of Fused Assemblies

The fused assembly should have the correct **handle,** a perfect **surface,** the proper **dimensions,** and a good **bond strength.**

The **handle** is compared to a standard: either an internal standard or one agreed with the customer.

The **surface** should not be wrinkled or show any moiré effect.

The fusing operation should not change the **dimensions** of the assembly. To test this, benchmarks, at least 20 cm apart, are made on the outer components before fusing. The distance is remeasured after fusing and any change is noted.

Bond strength is measured by the peel-strength or delamination test (e.g. ASTM D 2724). The force required to pull apart the top cloth and the interlining is measured on a cut strip of the assembly with a tensile strength test instrument or, more simply, with a good spring balance. The result can be expressed as force per unit width of strip, or as force per unit area of bonded fabric.

Normally, investigations will be made which quantify the effects of the major variables – time, temperature, pressure and steam – upon the bond strength and dimensions of all of the standard assemblies. A new investigation will be launched whenever a new combination is introduced. All of the results are collated, analysed, and maintained in the quality control department who will be able to specify optimum fusing conditions for any given assembly.

10.6.1 Safety at Work: Signs and Symbols[1]

Every manager and supervisor has a legal obligation to protect the health and safety of the operatives at work. Every source of danger has to be removed or at least recognised and marked as one. Safety procedures have to be written down in a safety manual, and included in the training of operatives. In most countries, **health and safety at work** legislation has been enacted and the rules are compulsory for managers, supervisors and all employees. Observance of the regulations is often controlled by local and regional inspectorates who can recommend or require the implementation of improvements to machinery, processes, or working practices. They also may have the power to impose fines, or close the factory in the event of non-compliance. Each enterprise must appoint a **Health & Safety Officer** who is the communication interface between the workforce and senior management.

Personal Protection Requirements

Symbol: Circle

	White on a blue ground	 Safety glasses required	 Safety helmet required	 Ear protection required	 Safety mask required	 Safety shoes required	 Safety gloves required

Prohibitions

Symbol: Circle and bar

	Black on a white ground with a red border and cross bar	  No smoking	 No naked lights	 No entry for pedestrians	 Do not use water on a fire
		 Not drinking water	 No entry for vehicles	 Do not obstruct	 No entry for unauthorised persons

Hazard Warnings

Symbol: Triangle

	Black on a yellow ground with a black border	 Inflammable materials	 Poison	 Explosive materials	 Corrosive materials	 Radioactive materials
		 Vehicles operating	 Suspended loads	 High voltage	 Danger	 Laser radiation

Escape/First Aid

Symbol: Square or rectangle

	White on a green ground	 Escape route to the left	 Escape direction[2]	 First aid	 Emergency exit[3]
		 Emergency shower	 Emergency eye wash	 Stretcher	 Doctor

[1] embodied in local European standards such as DIN 4844 and BS 5378
[2] must be part of a complete sequence leading to an exit
[3] to be mounted over the exit

10.6.2 First Aid
10.6.3 The Working Environment

First Aid

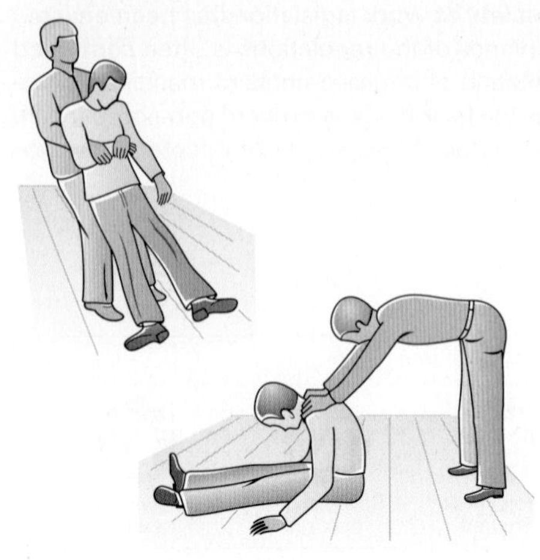
1: Remove casualty from danger zone

2: General recovery position

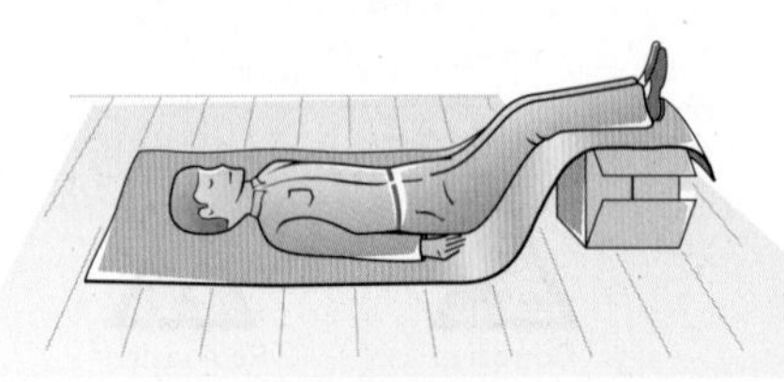
3: Shock recovery position

First Aid Measures

- **Get help (emergency call)**
- **Remove casualty from danger zone** (*Figure 1*)
- **Reassure and comfort**
- **Place a blanket under and/or over**
- **Check critical life functions**

In case of an accident, notify the health and safety office immediately. All employees must be trained to recognise work hazards and to know what to do in an emergency (alarm procedure). They have to know whom to inform in case of an accident. Any accident has to be attended immediately. The first aid person must be clearly identified in each working area and must be readily available. First aid materials must be openly available and regularly checked and replenished. Responsibilities have to be clearly defined.

Common Emergencies and What To Do

- **Loss of consciousness**

Establish whether the casualty is conscious by asking questions e.g. ask for his/her name.

Check **breathing** by supporting the neck and opening the mouth slightly: check for the position of the tongue, teeth (dentures), and any food residues. Breathing will be indicated by **seeing** the rise and fall of the chest, by **hearing** and by **feeling** the breath on one's cheek. If the casualty is unconscious but breathing well, he/she should be placed in the **general recovery position** (*Figure 2*). In this position, the mouth is at the lowest level and the airways are kept free.

- **Bleeding**

Heavy bleeding can be staunched using a tourniquet made from muslin or a handkerchief. Heavy bleeding can lead to shock, so appropriate countermeasures should be taken.

- **Shock**

Shock is the result of a lowering of oxygen levels as a result of a deficiency in blood supply.

Indicators: Pallor, cold and trembling; perspiration on the brow; fretfulness; partial loss of feeling.

Countermeasures: Lay flat, on a blanket with legs raised (*Figure 3*); cover with a blanket; offer comfort and physical contact; keep talking.

The Working Environment

Clothing and Personal Protection

Personal protection equipment such as hair protectors, ear protectors, safety glasses, gloves and shoes must be worn wherever they are prescribed. Close fitting clothing should be worn near machinery with moving parts. Loose overalls, scarves, ribbons and bows are dangerous. Sleeves should be fastened. Long hair should be gathered and pinned up or covered with a cap. Jewellery, watches or rings should not be worn. Breathing apparatus must be available for areas where unhealthy gasses, vapours or dusts are generated and are not exhausted directly to safety.

When transporting hot water the bucket must not be full and appropriate safety clothing should be worn (apron, boots). Damaged insulation of steam pipes should be repaired.

Noise Protection, Cleanliness, Tidiness, Compliance

Technical measures should be taken to reduce noise generation and noisy areas should be designated for the wearing of ear protectors.

Waste should be placed in the bins provided. Traffic lanes, emergency exits and fire appliances must not be obstructed. Stools, chairs, tables, boxes, or shelves are not a substitute for stepladders. Ladders should always be secured against tilting or slipping. Damaged ladders should be replaced.

10.6.4 Working With Hazardous Materials

Hazardous substances must be clearly labelled and the corresponding precautions must be observed. Without such labelling, employees can not tell whether a substance or its vapours is explosive, toxic, corrosive, or harmless. Substances should be stored in unbreakable, sealable and properly labelled containers. Containers intended for foodstuffs (e.g. water bottles) must not be used for chemicals. The **Globally Harmonized System of Classification and Labeling of Chemicals** or **GHS** is an internationally agreed-upon system, for identifying and labeling hazardous materials. For this new system, the earlier (CHIP) symbols have been redesigned: the formerly orange square background has been replaced by a red diamond with a white background. The table shows the **former** and the **new pictograms,** together with the corresponding descriptions of hazards and safety measures.

	Hazard	Description	Alpha-numeric symbol	Former symbol	GHS symbol
Health/Toxicity	**acute toxicity, health hazard**	Contact with the skin or inhalation may cause illness, breathing difficulties, or death according to the toxicity and the dose. Toxic substances are assigned to one of five categories according to their LD_{50} (oral, dermal) and LC_{50} (inhalation). LD_{50}, LC_{50} = median lethal dose or concentration.	**T+**		
			T		
			Xn		
	irritant	Substances that cause reversible skin damage or eye irritation after short term, long term, or repeated contact with skin or mucous membranes.	**Xi**		
	corrosive	Substances that can cause lesions in living tissue.	**C**		
	serious health hazard	Carcinogens, mutagens, reproductive toxins, target organ toxins (chronic toxins).			
Hazardous Materials	**explosive**	Substances that will explode under certain conditions.	**E**		
	oxidant	Substances that can promote combustion by provision of oxygen.	**O**		
	highly inflammable	Gases that form a flammable mixture with air at normal temperatures. Liquids that have a relatively low flash point, classified into four groups according to the temperature of the flash point	**F+**		
	flammable		**F**		
Ecology	**environmental hazard**	Substances that can have acute or chronic adverse effects on aquatic and other organisms.	**N**		

10.6.5 Safety in Clothing Manufacture (1)

1: Mechanical cutters

2: Fusing presses

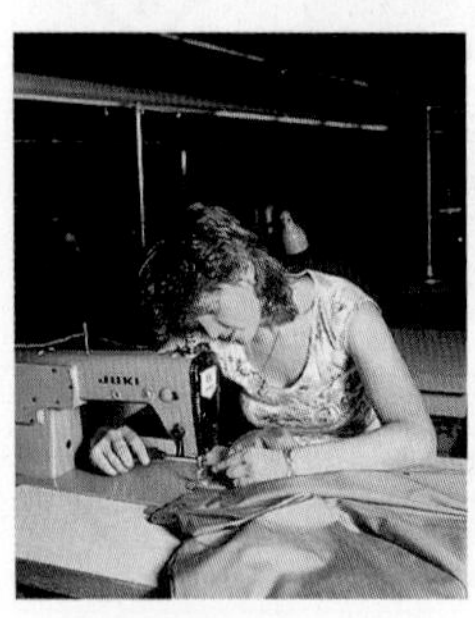
3: Sewing machines

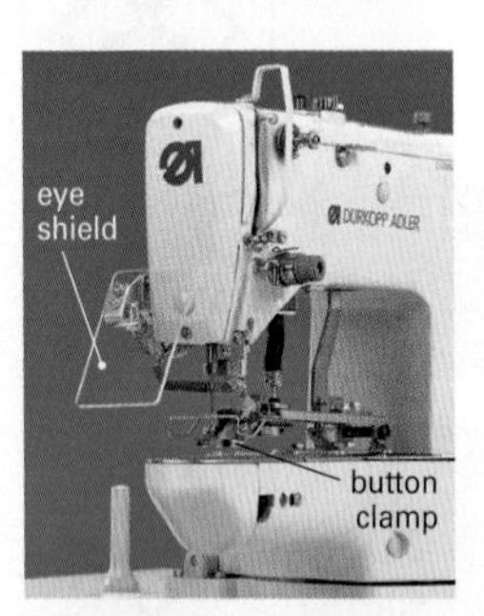

4: Special sewing machines

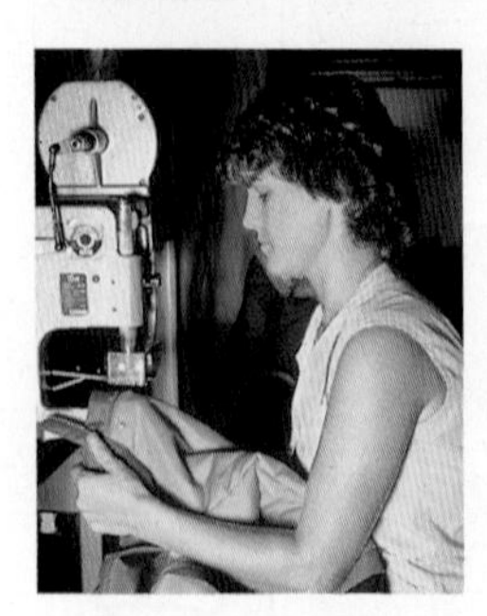
5: Hook, eyelet or rivet machines

Hazards	Safety Measures
Spreading and Cutting	
Finger and hand injuries from spreading machines.	Disengage the spreader carriage when making adjustments on the lay.
Finger and hand injury from moving or idle cutting devices.	Ensure that the finger guard is adjusted to the correct height of the fabric layers before starting to cut. Learn and use the correct handling techniques for the tool.
Finger and hand injury at swinging-arm or flat punch machines.	Ensure that the two-handed control system is functioning properly. A light sensor should stop the machine when the working area is transgressed.
Fusing	
Finger and hand injury in the press.	Safety guards should be checked daily for correct operation.
Burns from hot beds.	Never attempt to retrieve, or adjust the position of components whilst they are being fed, or are on the bed.
Finger and hand injury in feeding and unloading.	A press which has to be controlled using both hands must be operated by only one person. Operators must be well trained and practised in laying the parts on the feeding belt conveyor.
Inhalation of unhealthy vapours.	The manufacturer's handling recommendations should be followed. Vapours should be exhausted safely.
Sewing	
Finger and hand injury during cleaning and repair work.	The machine must be switched off, with the plug removed, and must be stationary before any cleaning or repair work is started.
Finger injury from the needle.	Correct setting of the finger guard should be checked before work starts.
Pulled hair and face injury from the yarn feeder.	Long hair should be gathered and pinned up or a hairnet should be worn. A safety guard should be provided for the yarn feeder.
Hand and finger injury from fastening devices on hook, eyelet and rivet machines.	Correct setting of the safety guards should be checked. Training must be given in the correct handling techniques for holding and feeding materials.
Eye injury from breaking needles or buttons at the button sewer, or breaking needles at the loop sewer.	Proper adjustment of the eye shield should be checked before work starts. Cracked or obscured shields should be replaced, or safety glasses should be issued.
Contact with Scissors and Needles	
Cuts and pricks from sharp points.	Sharp-pointed scissors should not be left unprotected. They should be kept in special holders (leather holsters, cases) carried e.g. on a belt and stowed away properly after use.
Internal injury from swallowed items.	Never store items temporarily in the mouth. There is a danger of swallowing them as a result of coughing, sneezing, or being startled. Place needles in the proper container or in a needle cushion.

10.6.5 Safety in Clothing Manufacture (2)

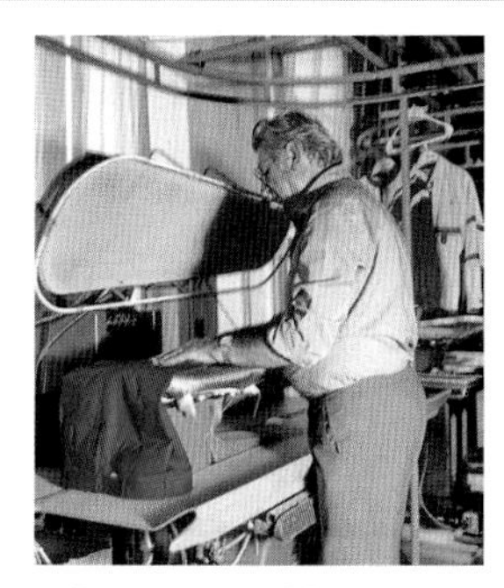

1: Pressing machines

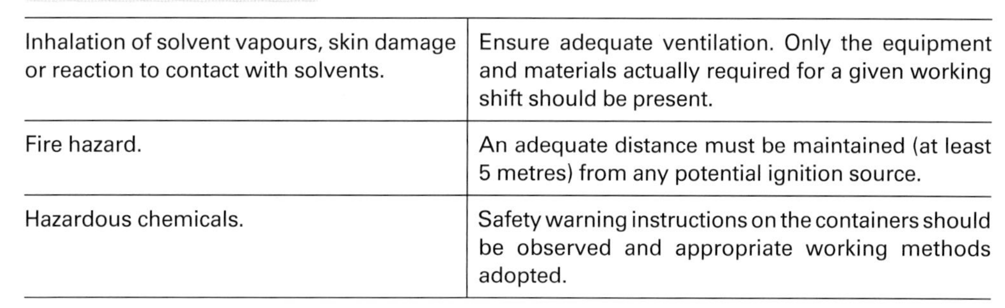

2: Cleaning area

health hazard

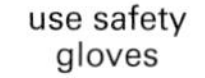

use safety gloves

use safety glasses

3: Warning signs

4: Trolley rails

5: Moveable hanger stands

Hazards	Safety Measures
Pressing	
Burns from hand irons.	Hand irons must be protected from overheating by a thermostat. Non flammable materials must be used for the working area, and a safe parking place provided.
Scalding from steam.	Steam must not be supplied until after the press is closed.
Finger and hand injury from the press.	A machine which requires two hands to operate it must never be operated by two people. Never attempt to retrieve or adjust the position of parts after the closing process has started. A safety bar must be fitted which stops and raises the head when it is touched.
Cleaning, Stain Removal	
Inhalation of solvent vapours, skin damage or reaction to contact with solvents.	Ensure adequate ventilation. Only the equipment and materials actually required for a given working shift should be present.
Fire hazard.	An adequate distance must be maintained (at least 5 metres) from any potential ignition source.
Hazardous chemicals.	Safety warning instructions on the containers should be observed and appropriate working methods adopted.
Materials Handling	
Head injury from overhead transport systems with suspended carriers.	Head protection (padded hard hats) should be provided wherever the transporter rails pass over a walkway. The floor should be marked with black and yellow warning stripes.
Trapped fingers when manoeuvring carriers over points.	Safety guards should be fitted and proper training in handling methods should be given.
Falling from raised service platforms and access points.	Safety guards have to be in place. Specialised equipment should be used for servicing trolleys and proper handling procedures observed.
Hand and finger injury from conveyors.	Equipment must be guarded and the safety guards must never be removed.
Accidental injuries from tripping over the feet of moveable hanger stands.	Moveable hanger stands should be parked only in designated areas. They should not encroach onto marked walkways.
Packaging Machinery	
Hand and finger injury at packaging, welding, cutting and folding stations.	Safety devices (two-handed operation) should be checked every day. Whenever a machine has to be adjusted whilst it is running, e.g. for setting up, servicing, or clearing of faults, only the inching control should be used.

11.1.1 Industry Sectors and Product Groups

The clothing industry ranges from small, hand-made (bespoke) operations up to large industrial garment making enterprises.

Bespoke Clothing Production

In the bespoke ladies' and men's tailoring segment individual garments are made in relatively small operations, according to **personal measurements** or **unique fashion designs** or for **special purposes** such as traditional costume, film and stage sets, historical costume, etc.

1: Intermediate fitting for a bespoke suit

- The clothing is made for individual clients, according to individual size and requirements.
- The cut and the style are agreed by discussion with the tailor, before cutting begins.
- The client selects the material and the design, from sample swatches and fabric collections.
- The cutting can allow for particular characteristics of the client such as body shape.
- During garment assembly, intermediate fittings and adjustments can be made.
- Bespoke tailoring involves a much higher investment of time for each garment, and is correspondingly more expensive than industrial manufacture. However, the client is usually rewarded by a more individual design and a higher quality of material and workmanship.

Industrial Clothing Manufacture

Industrial production is mostly concerned with **series (batch) production,** less often with **mass production** (*see page 209*). Thus the terms **clothing manufacture, garment making** or **making-up** normally refer to medium to large scale series production of a range of individual garments.

- Production is geared to an anonymous, statistically and/or demographically and culturally defined target consumer group (*see pages 235 ff*).
- Garments are produced in a limited range of sizes. Standardised cutting and making procedures mean that all garments have the same shape; allowances for uncommon body shapes cannot be made.
- The consumer has the choice from a wide range of different garment styles but has no direct influence over their design and cut.
- Large-scale manufacturing techniques allow a wide range of garments to be produced in a fraction of the time required for bespoke tailoring of individual items.

Clothing manufacturers can be classified according to, for example:

Target groups: Women's outerwear, men's and boy's wear, children's wear.

Products: Workwear and sportswear, protective clothing, underwear, nightwear, shirts, support garments, lingerie, hosiery, accessories.

Materials: Flat knits, circular knits, denim, leather.

Industrial Made-to-Measure (*see page 231*)

This is a system that combines individual measurements and requirements with cost-effective production techniques. It is offered at a range of price and quality levels.

The manufacturer operates a workshop with a very high division of labour. He offers a defined selection of fabrics, styles and finishing for the customer to select from. An intermediary makes the measurements and sends them, along with the customer's selections for making up.

Some communication between customer and manufacturer (e.g. fittings) can be arranged at intermediate stages.

Designer Fashion

This encompasses a range of operations. The **haute couture** is very expensive, exclusive clothing from top fashion houses with highly promoted **brand logos.** Some of the same brands are licensed to small-scale manufacturers for production of a limited number of each garment for sale in boutiques at high prices. **Designer brands** in general are franchise operations where the designs of prominent designers are produced by selected manufacturers in medium scale at medium to high prices.

11.1.2 Garment Production Systems

Types of Production System

There are different ways to organise the production of garments, according to the type, the quantity and the diversity of products to be made. The number of items to be made and the rate of delivery of these items distinguish individual production, batch production and mass production.

Individual Production	Batch Production	Mass Production
With individual production (making through) each product is made only once. The system requires highly skilled, experienced operators and versatile machinery. Example: made-to-measure costume	Batch, or series production is used for larger, though fixed quantities of identical articles either for stock or to order. Examples: blouses, skirts	Mass production means that large quantities of identical products are made continuously for an extended period. High machinery and labour utilisation allows a high level of automation and specialisation. Examples: T-shirts, work trousers

Sharing a job of work between several people is called division of labour. **Quantitative division** is where the required number of whole items is shared (with each person doing the same work). **Qualitative division** is where the work required for each item is divided into smaller operations (each person performs a different operation).

1: Straight line system with hanger transport

Production Organisation Systems

The **synchronised,** or **straight-line** system is suitable for large volume production (mass production or large batches). As the name suggests, the work flows in a straight line through a series of workstations, each of which is synchronised to the next by ensuring that the time spent at each station is exactly the same. This represents an extreme form of the division of labour.

The system requires that each individual step in the assembly of the product has to be analysed carefully and the steps distributed in a balanced way over the available work stations. Each operator then performs exactly the same operation(s) over and over again on the identical parts of successive garments. Detailed work plans have to be drawn up to facilitate this balancing of the line. Advantages of the synchronised line system include short distances between stations, low volume of work in process, precise planning of production times, highly visible production progress and predictable production quantity. Disadvantages include the need for intensive detailed pre-planning, high cost of style changes, sensitivity to disruption by production difficulties or absenteeism, and the dependence of productivity on maintaining a strict rhythm of work.

2: Bundle assembly with wagons

The **progressive bundle system** is a way of avoiding the rigidity and some of the disadvantages of the synchronised line system. Machines and operatives are organised into sections, each of which specialises either in the production of a major sub-component (collars, cuffs), or the assembly of two or more sub-components.

Within and between sections the work is balanced according to the time required for each sub-function. The combination of small bundles and a line system provides the best solution to the problems of frequent style changes, small lot sizes, and short delivery deadlines.

Material **transport systems** (*Figures 1 and 2*) distribute the work in progress among the different workstations.

11.2.1 Company Structure

Company Organisation

At the highest level of organisation, the major divisions are **Finance, Human Resources, Production,** and **Marketing.** The heads of these departments usually sit on the main Board of Directors. Many companies also place the Quality department at this level. There are two main sets of activities:

- **Direction**
- **Management**

Direction means to determine the general structure of the company and guide its medium to long-term future. **Management** is to ensure the efficiency of current operations with regard to costs, quality, productivity, safety, and environmental impact. This requires the timely provision of finance, information, training, equipment and other resources plus well designed production processes and procedures together with an appropriately selected, well trained workforce. There will be a continual effort to improve the **efficiency and profitability of operations,** the **worker-friendliness of processes,** and the **environmental friendliness** of the enterprise.

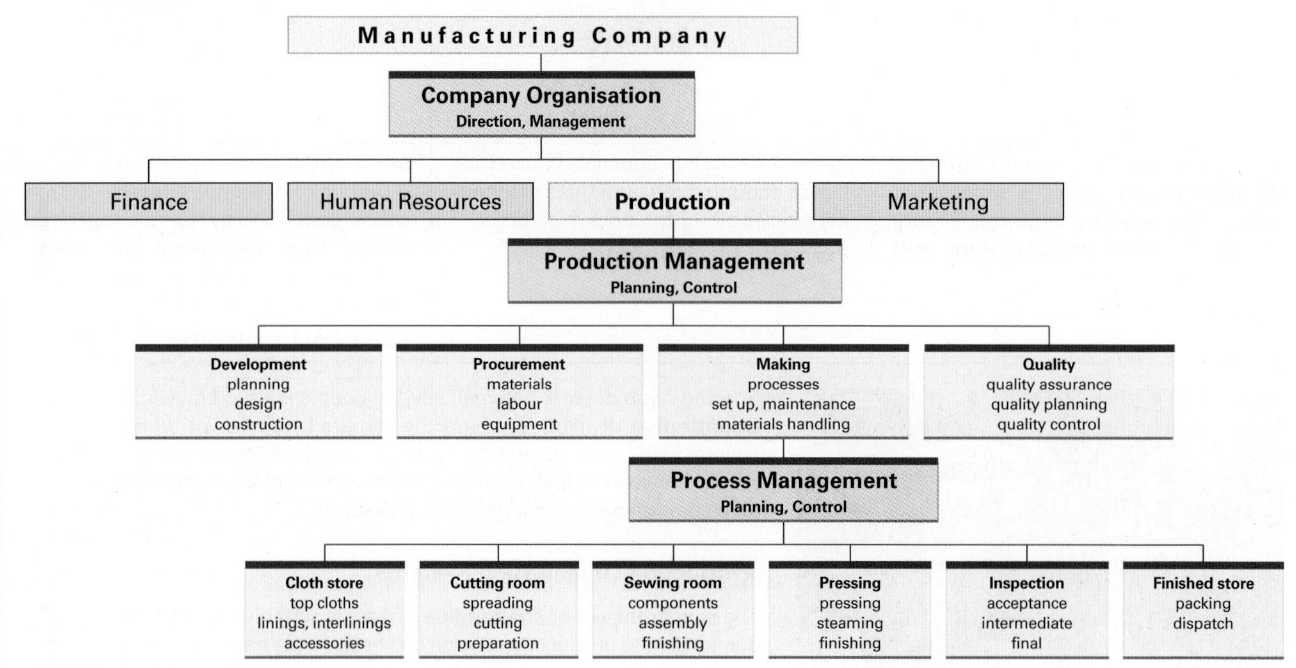

1: Structural outline of a manufacturing company

Production Management

Production usually comprises **Development, Procurement, Making** and **Quality.** Here, the chain (or network) of responsibilities is established and the smooth running of the manufacturing effort is organised. Often, the effort is divided into two main parts:

- **Production planning**
- **Production control**

A production plan is developed for each time period. It details what will be produced and the people, resources and equipment that will be required. The plan may require new research in **Method Study** and **Process Analysis.** The progress of the plan will be closely monitored and controlled.

Process Management

Processes are the technical means by which a job of work is accomplished. The major processes include **warehousing, cutting, sewing, pressing, inspection** and **packaging.** Process organisation involves:

- **Process planning**
- **Process control**
- **Process design**

Process planning involves the scheduling of people and equipment, availability of materials (top cloth, lining, accessories) preparation of information (work plans, parts lists) and a calculation of the time required. The basis for this plan is Method Study, which will have provided detailed information on the requirements for each process and product type, in terms of people, materials, equipment, and time.

Process control means instigation, supervision and checking of processes and their outputs. Appropriate control measures will be written into the production plan and the actual progress of the work will be monitored.

Method study will also have provided the information for the **design of processes and procedures,** the flow of material and information, information carriers (forms, computer screens), and the construction of workstations.

11.2.2 Functional Organisation and Communication

Tasks are defined, grouped and allocated in the overall context of the **company structure** (*see page 210*). The total activity of the company is divided into departments, sections and functions. Individual tasks are allocated as jobs for individual persons.

Organisational structures can vary widely, even between similar companies, e.g. clothing manufacturers. Differences can arise out of differences in product type (suits, pullovers, blouses) or the traditions of the company, but also due to different emphasis on different aspects of manufacturing e.g. the relative importance of quality, expediency or cost.

Tools for organisational planning include organisational charts, functional charts, tables, chains of command and job descriptions.

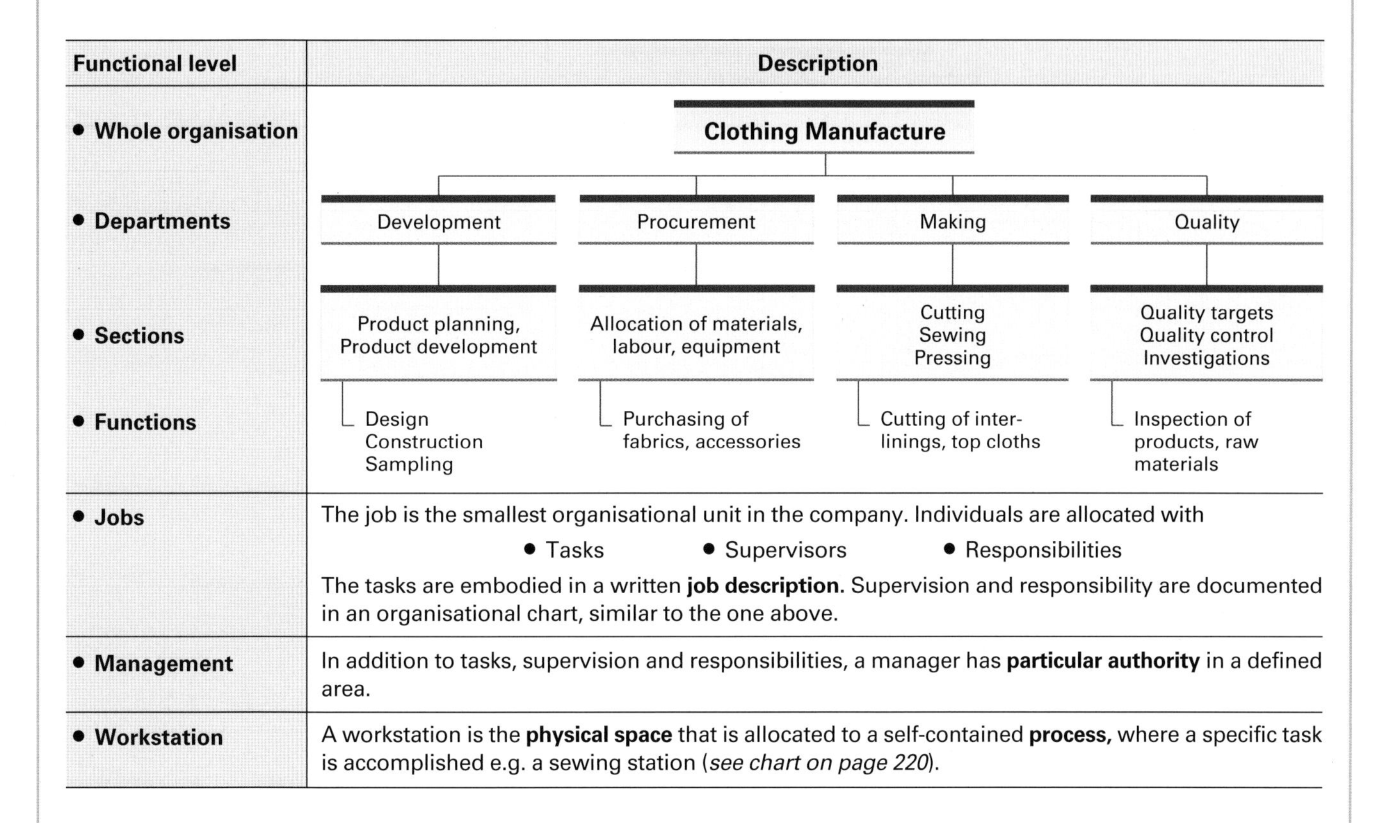

Functional level	Description			
• Whole organisation	Clothing Manufacture			
• Departments	Development	Procurement	Making	Quality
• Sections	Product planning, Product development	Allocation of materials, labour, equipment	Cutting Sewing Pressing	Quality targets Quality control Investigations
• Functions	Design Construction Sampling	Purchasing of fabrics, accessories	Cutting of inter-linings, top cloths	Inspection of products, raw materials
• Jobs	The job is the smallest organisational unit in the company. Individuals are allocated with • Tasks • Supervisors • Responsibilities The tasks are embodied in a written **job description.** Supervision and responsibility are documented in an organisational chart, similar to the one above.			
• Management	In addition to tasks, supervision and responsibilities, a manager has **particular authority** in a defined area.			
• Workstation	A workstation is the **physical space** that is allocated to a self-contained **process,** where a specific task is accomplished e.g. a sewing station (*see chart on page 220*).			

Lines of Authority and Communication

Co-ordination of the various tasks is achieved through a chain of command. This formalises and determines the lines of communication and responsibility.

System	Direct Line	Augmented Line	Functional (multiple line)	Teamwork
Schema	Director, Managers, Super-visors, Operatives	support, support		
Charac-teristics	Direct line systems have a clear, hierarchical chain of command and responsibility which is rigidly respected. They are not very flexible and can be rather undemocratic.	The augmented line system provides for support services to be supplied to directors and line managers by specialist assistants or advisors who have no part in the chain of command.	Specialists in particular areas may have partial authority over staff in other sections. Problems can arise because the lines of authority and communication are crossed. Therefore the distinct responsibilities have to be very clearly defined.	Within any type of system, a team can be formed (shown in black) for a particular, self-contained task that involves more than one section. Examples could be the rapid production of a sample order or the preparation of an exhibition.

11.2.3 Organisation of a Garment Making Factory

Organisation is a resource for company management. Its purpose is to achieve the fulfilment of certain defined objectives by creating a structure of tasks and responsibilities. Specific tasks are allocated to individual persons at identified production stages, and/or groups of individuals are allocated to specific production stages.

The following organisation chart (organigram) serves as a connecting thread throughout this chapter and also provides an overview of the relationship between the individual stages of production.

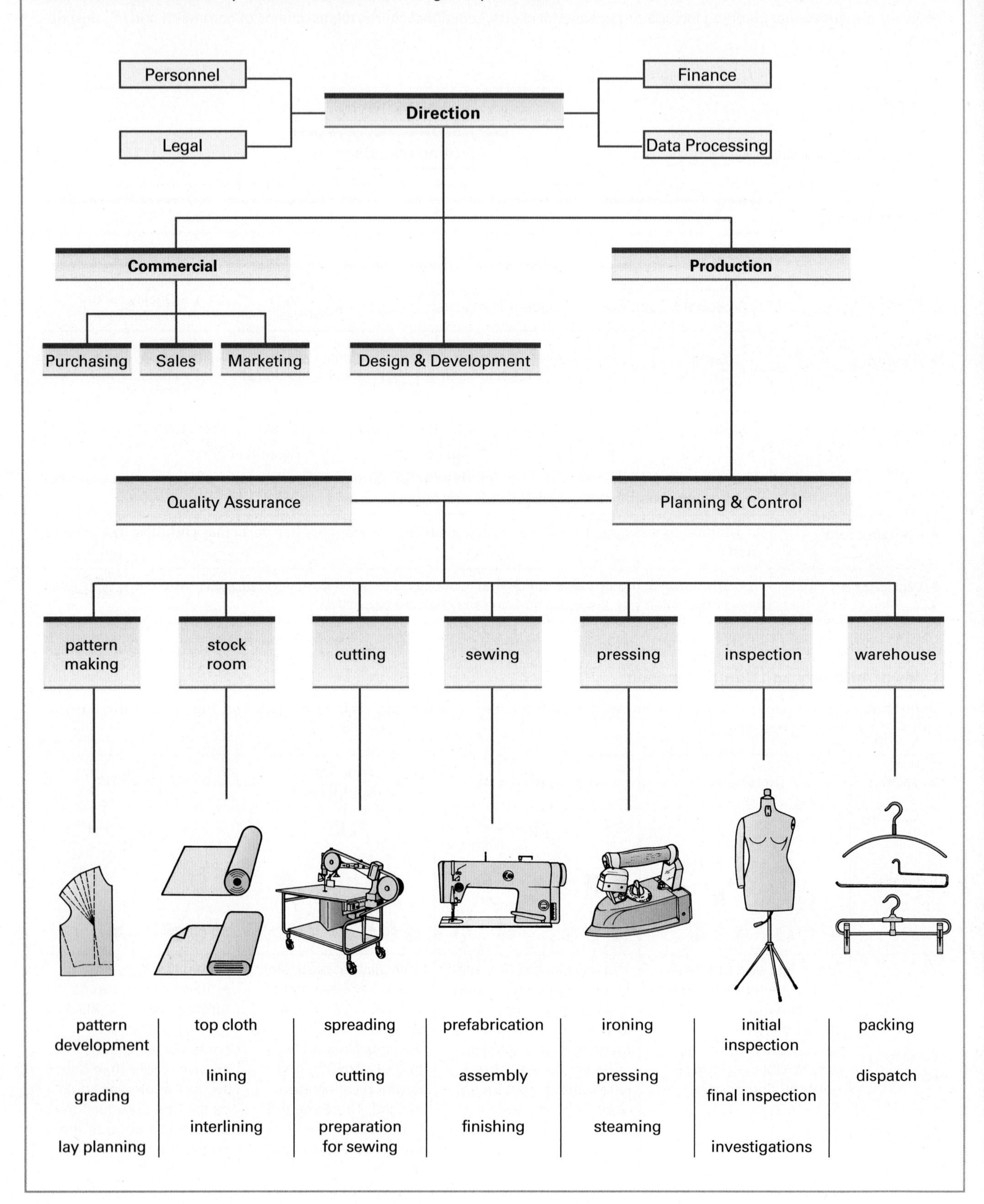

11.2.4 Production Management (1)

Production management provides all of the tools that are required for the smooth and economic operation of manufacturing processes. It regulates the interaction in space and time between people, equipment, information and resources to achieve the objectives of the manufacturing system (*see page 220*). A principle concern is the flow of work in progress and information.

The following tasks are of particular significance.

- Determining the time sequence of the required processes
- Timely provision of materials and equipment
- Timely provision of information

Every **manufacturing company** has a **production program** to follow. For a garment maker, the production program is embodied in the **collection plan.** The collection is the range of products that will be manufactured for marketing in a particular season (*see page 235*).

The **Production** department co-ordinates the development of new products, the procurement of materials and their processing, and the control of quality throughout manufacture.

The **Processing (Making-up)** department is responsible for the processes that complete the work to be done. It is responsible for **production planning and control.**

Data Exchange and Data Formulation

Co-ordination between departments, sections and processes is mediated by the exchange of data (information). Data are supplied in the form of detailed work instructions and process-dependent technical information. Data have to be documented. This can be done via a company computer network and also by the use of standard company forms. The way that data are transmitted in a particular company will depend on its structure, its level of technology, the type and range of its collections and other factors. A wide variation is possible.

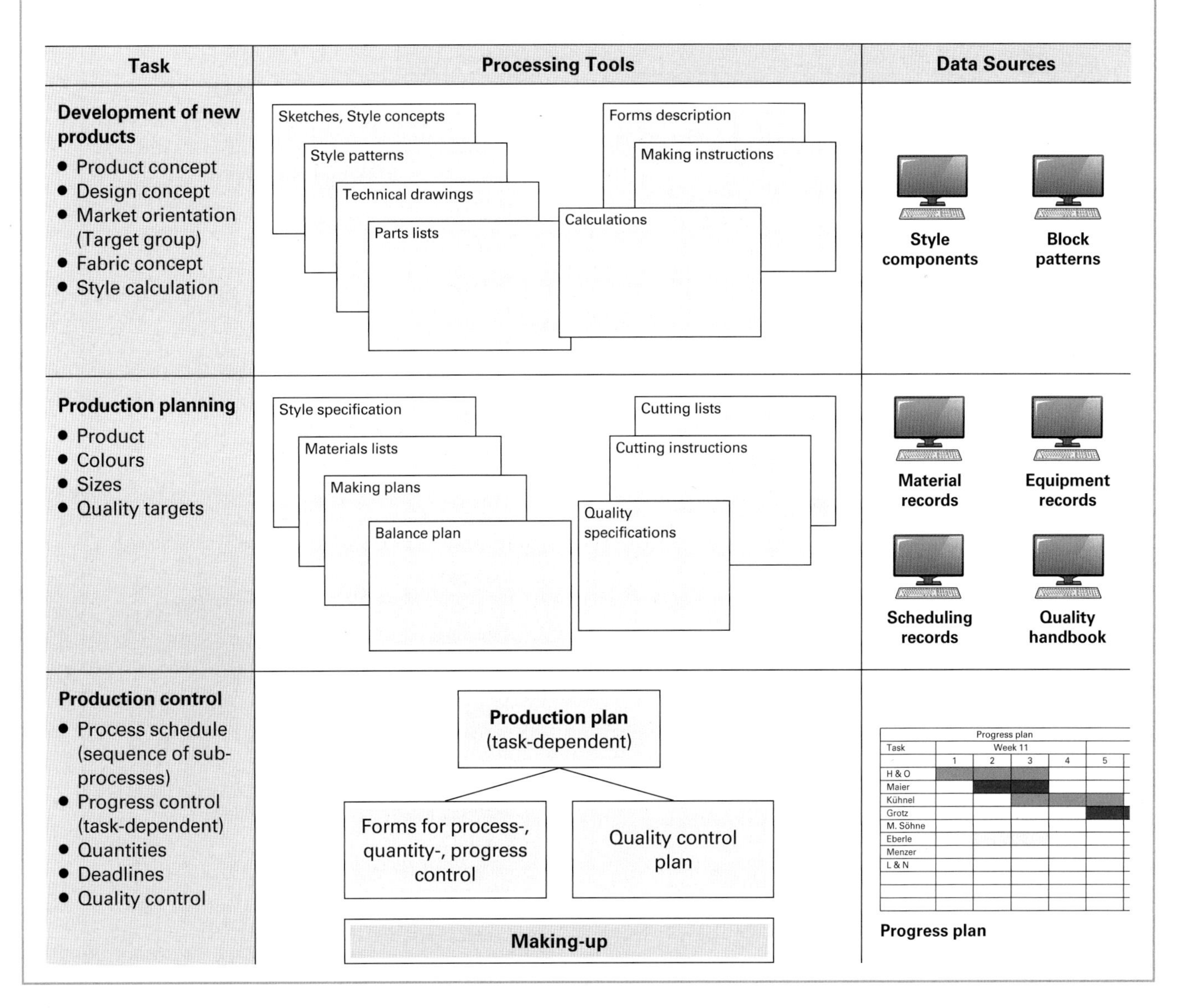

Task	Processing Tools	Data Sources
Development of new products • Product concept • Design concept • Market orientation (Target group) • Fabric concept • Style calculation	Sketches, Style concepts Style patterns Technical drawings Parts lists Forms description Making instructions Calculations	**Style components** **Block patterns**
Production planning • Product • Colours • Sizes • Quality targets	Style specification Materials lists Making plans Balance plan Cutting lists Cutting instructions Quality specifications	**Material records** **Equipment records** **Scheduling records** **Quality handbook**
Production control • Process schedule (sequence of sub-processes) • Progress control (task-dependent) • Quantities • Deadlines • Quality control	**Production plan** (task-dependent) Forms for process-, quantity-, progress control Quality control plan **Making-up**	**Progress plan**

11.2.4 Production Management (2)

The result of the development and planning operation is documentation of the required processes and procedures, style sketches, parts lists, and quality guidelines. These formulations ensure co-ordination of the making up operation. Their main objectives are to:

- Facilitate the **collection of data** and information.
- Facilitate the **communication of data** and information.
- Help to **prevent misunderstandings.**

The objective of production process planning is to ensure smooth and timely processing by efficient data communication – mostly by means of forms.

Product Specification

This document collects together the basic descriptive information about a particular style e.g. product type, collection, quality number, season, size range, materials, originator etc. It will usually include a sketch, a brief description, and specific making instructions. Measurements are given for particular sizes, e.g. size 38. The sketch is not to scale but gives a visual impression of front and back details. A fabric sample supplements the sketch. Hand written remarks may be added to emphasise particular aspects. This form may also be called a **product description.**

Shirtmaker GmbH · 76543 Dingsdorf

Product Specification

Product	Men's shirt
Collection	America
Style	New York
Quality No	123
Saison	S/S 2014
Originator	Renner
Date	12.04.2013

Size	**37/38**	**39/40**	**41/42**	**43/44**	**45/46**
Chest girth (cm)	118	124	132	140	148
Waist girth (cm)	108	116	124	134	142

Oxford

Top cloth quality
Bremen
110 g/m²

Colours 443 444 445

Description

Long-sleeve sport shirt with
button-up front, sport cuffs, shoulder yoke, button placket
single breast pocket, centre-back pressed pleats

Making Instructions

Collar:
Two piece collar with stiffeners
Closing seam 5 mm

Cuffs:
Assembly seam 10 mm, Closing seam 5 mm

Sleeves:
Classic vent edge 2.5 cm
Vent length 13 cm

Pockets:
Rounded with chevron finish, finished to 13 x 12 cm

Front pieces:
Top placket finished to 4 cm,
two-sided closing seam 5 mm
Back placket 2.5 cm + 1 cm turned in, stitched through

Back pieces:
Pleat spacing 4 cm, pleat insert not backstitched

Assembly:
Double shoulder yoke, 1 mm closing seam
Sleeves and side closings double seamed

Thread, seams:
Cotton No 120, 6 stitches /cm

Buttons:
Front placket 8 buttons. Top spacing 6.5 cm,
lower spacings 9 cm. Two sleeve buttons

Labels:
Shirtmaker label No 312, back centre 4 cm from collar seam.
Size label 2 cm up left side seam.
Care label in bottom hem, 10 mm in

11.2.4 Production Management (3)

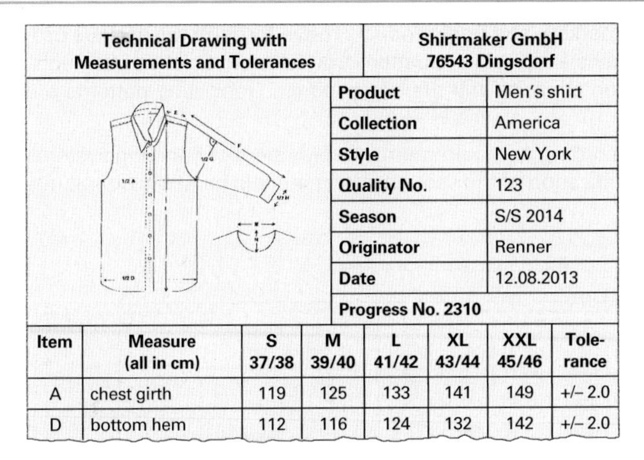

Technical Drawing with Measurements and Tolerances	Shirtmaker GmbH 76543 Dingsdorf
Product	Men's shirt
Collection	America
Style	New York
Quality No.	123
Season	S/S 2014
Originator	Renner
Date	12.08.2013
Progress No. 2310	

Item	Measure (all in cm)	S 37/38	M 39/40	L 41/42	XL 43/44	XXL 45/46	Tolerance
A	chest girth	119	125	133	141	149	+/– 2.0
D	bottom hem	112	116	124	132	142	+/– 2.0

1: Technical drawing, measurements, tolerances

Materials List	Shirtmaker GmbH 76543 Dingsdorf
Product	Men's shirt
Collection	America
Style	New York
Quality No.	123
Season	S/S 2014
Originator	Renner
Date	12.08.2013
Progress No. 2310	

Item	Quantity/piece	Description	Part No.
01	1.4 m	Top cloth: body, sleeves, cuffs	9290 L
02	0.2 m	Fusible: collar, cuffs, placket	1245
03	2	Collar stiffeners	KS 12

2: Materials list

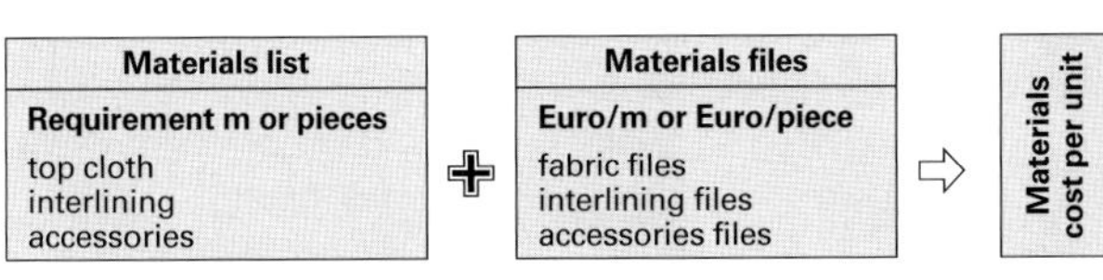

3: Calculating materials costs

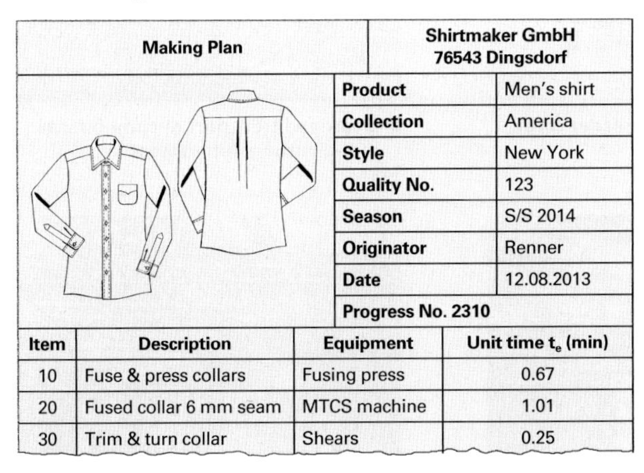

Making Plan	Shirtmaker GmbH 76543 Dingsdorf
Product	Men's shirt
Collection	America
Style	New York
Quality No.	123
Season	S/S 2014
Originator	Renner
Date	12.08.2013
Progress No. 2310	

Item	Description	Equipment	Unit time t_e (min)
10	Fuse & press collars	Fusing press	0.67
20	Fused collar 6 mm seam	MTCS machine	1.01
30	Trim & turn collar	Shears	0.25

4: Making plan

Making plan
time in min
cutting
sewing
pressing

+

Labour files
Euro/min
cutter
machinist
presser

⇨ Making cost per unit

5: Calculating labour costs

Beside the basic product specification, the following forms are the most important.

Quality Specifications

The quality department will develop detailed targets for cutting and making, and will monitor their observance by intermediate and final inspection.

The quality targets and the quality control procedures have to be documented (*Figure 1*).

All of the necessary paperwork is made available in the appropriate locations.

- Quality specifications for sizing and making in the development department
- Construction specifications in the cutting department
- Templates in the production planning and processing departments
- Material requirements in purchasing and production planning departments

Parts Lists

Parts lists comprise everything that is necessary for the manufacture of the product.

The **materials list** shows all of the required materials, based on the quantities required for one item (*Figure 2*). The **materials cost per item** is calculated from the materials requirement and the unit cost of the materials. This amount is included in the predicted manufacturing cost (*Figure 3*).

The data from the materials list are used to calculate the total requirements of the various materials, which are then used to compose the **materials requirement list.** As soon as the product is approved for production, this list is supplied to the **procurement (purchasing)** department.

The **components list** results from the development of the cutting and making requirements. It shows all of the separate components of the product with detailed specifications and quantities to be cut. The components are grouped according to top cloth, interlining, lining, etc. This list is used to prepare the necessary bundles of matching components in the cutting department.

Making Plan

The **making plan** shows what is to be made, how it shall be done, with what equipment, in what time, and by whom. Each of the necessary **procedures** is detailed in the proper order, with the required equipment and the expected time requirement (job time). The actual operatives or work group may also be listed. This is the instruction (formula) for how each **individual product piece** shall be assembled (*Figure 4*). It forms the basis for calculating the labour costs per item (*Figure 5*).

Balance Plan

The balance plan is the means for controlling the rate of production. It is an allocation of all of the operations to specific work stations and operators, in a way which equalises, or balances the time spent at each station so that the work can flow at a uniform pace. The capabilities and productivities of individuals have to be taken into account.

Production Control Plan

Production control plans are **task-oriented progress plans.** They involve **progress charts, delivery charts** (beginning, duration, end of a batch) **work tickets, material requisition notes** etc.

11.2.5 Material Flow

Material flow means the way that raw materials, accessories, intermediate and final products move through the various processing stations in the factory. The schematic diagram (*Figure 1*) shows a typical flow pattern from cloth to finished garments. The pattern will depend on the size of the enterprise, the production capacity and the end product. Good flow patterns are important for smooth, economic manufacturing.

In a garment-making factory, various **handling systems** are used, according to requirements. Deployment of handling systems has a large influence on the production rate. *Figures 2 to 7* give an indication of the sequence of materials handling operations in the factory.

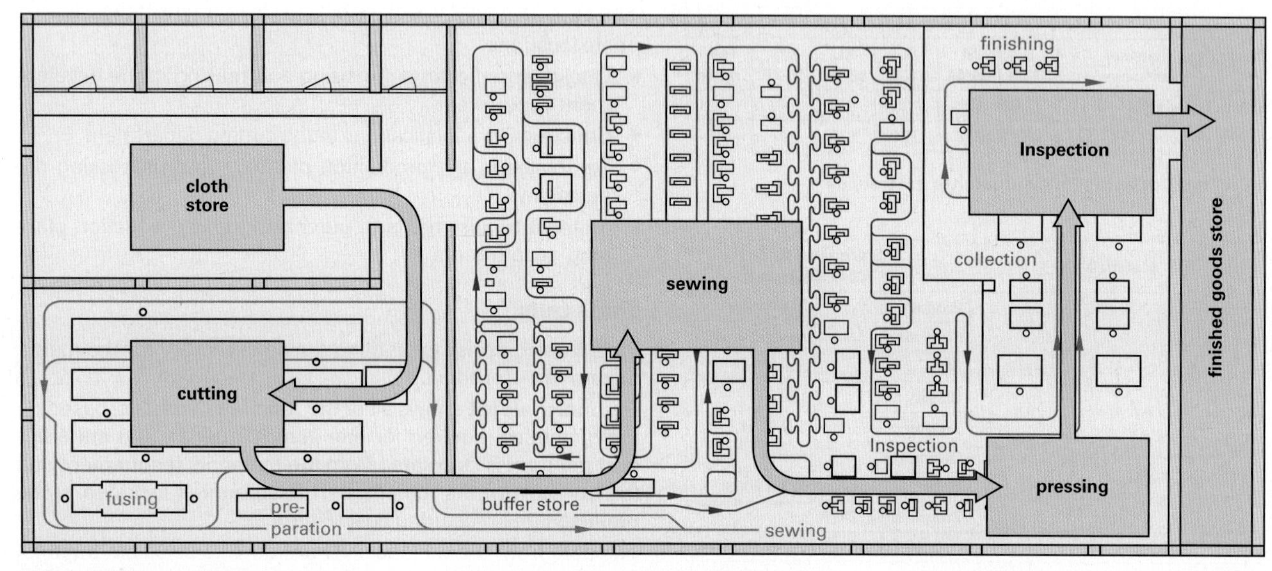

1: Material flow in a factory

2: Fabric trolleys in the warehouse

3: Roll handling at the spreader creel

4: Overhead transport of components in the cutting department

5: Automatic hanger distribution system in the sewing room

6: Hanger transport in the pressing area

7: Computer controlled warehouse for hanging garments

11.3.1 Time Analysis by the REFA System (1)

Work measurement is a part of Work Study. Its objective is to improve profitability through better organisation and higher efficiency. This involves a close study of the needs and the performance of the workers. Various systematic methods have been devised to analyse the time content of work. An example is the methodology developed by the **REFA Work Study Association,** in Germany. In addition to time measurements, Work Study provides the basis for: cost calculations, method studies, demand calculations, incentive schemes and training schemes.

Work Measurement after REFA

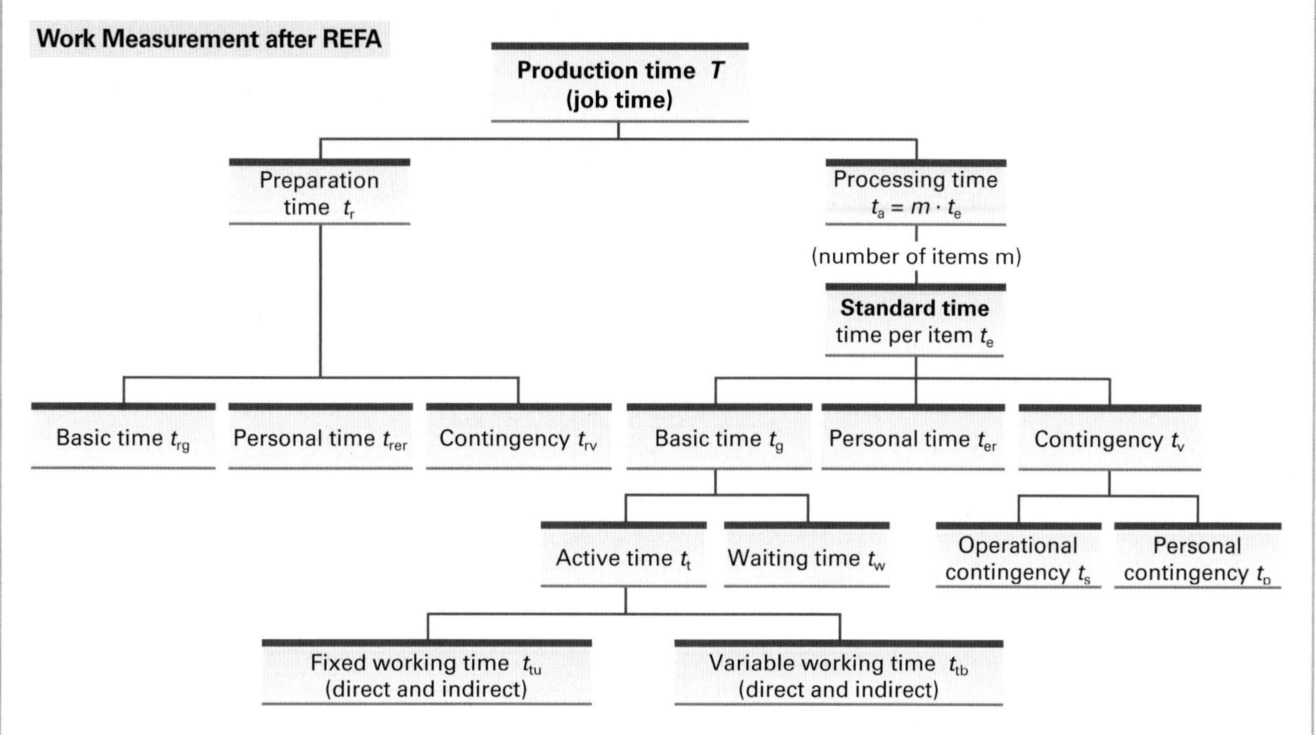

Time Classification		Definition	Example
T	**Production time** (job time)	The total time allowed for the complete operation. It comprises preparation time and working time.	Sew 5 button holes in each of 100 components, after first setting up the machine for the new button hole length.
t_r	**Preparation time**	Time required for operations that have to be carried out only once, to make ready, before starting the main task.	Set up machine, lay out parts
t_a	**Processing time**	Time required to carry out the operation on all m components. In general, ta = m . te.	Sew 500 button holes
t_e	**Standard time** (time per item)	Time allowed for each individual operation.	Sew 5 buttonholes in one component.
t_g	**Basic time**	Time required for the actual operation.	Pick component, offer to needle, sew seam, place sewn component.
t_{er}	**Personal time**	Interruption of work to relieve fatigue.	Rest after heavy work, relaxation after close concentration.
t_v	**Contingency time**	Interruptions at irregular intervals which are necessary from time to time. They are usually allowed for as a percentage of the basic time.	**Operational contingencies:** include bobbin changes and thread changes. **Personal contingencies:** include visits to the toilets.
t_{rg}	**Basic preparation time**	Time allowed for necessary preparation work.	Read order form, set up sewing machine, enter data on work ticket.
t_{rer}	**Personal preparation time**	Interruptions to preparation work to relieve fatigue.	Rest, relaxation.
t_{rv}	**Preparation contingency**	Interruptions at irregular intervals which are necessary from time to time.	Consulting mechanic.
t_t	**Active time**	Direct work is when the product itself is being worked on. Indirect work is when some auxiliary function is performed. Active time may contain periods whose duration can not be influenced by the operator.	Time used to close a seam. Picking and placing components. Fixed: automatic operations. Variable: positioning the work.
t_w	**Waiting time**	Waiting for work to be delivered from the preceding station.	Waiting for the next component in a straight-line system, or for the completion of an automatic, unmanned process.

11.3.1 Time Analysis by the REFA System (2)

Time Measurement after REFA

To evaluate the **total time** required for an operation, actual timings may be made.

All of the relevant data about the operation are entered onto the front of a standard form, including the operator, the equipment and the task. The operation is analysed and broken down into logical sub-units, each of which is timed repeatedly and the results are entered onto the back of the form. Analysis of all of the data allows the **Observed Time** to be calculated. Meanwhile, the operator will have been assigned a **performance rating** which is used together with the Observed Time to calculate the Target Time for the operation.

Example: **Observed time t_i** = 3.5 min, Performance Rating L = 120 % | **Target Time t** $= \frac{L \cdot t_i}{100} = \frac{120\% \cdot 3.5 \text{ min}}{100} = 4.2 \text{ min}$

The sum of the times for the sub-units, Σ_t, is entered on the front of the form as the **Basic Time, t_g**. Allowances for Personal time and Contingency are estimated as a percentage and are added. The result is the **Standard Time, t_e** for the operation. The Standard time is used to make predictions, for production planning, manufacturing time, production capacity, and for determining labour costs.

Z2 new	REFA Time Measurement Form for repetitive operations			File No: / Page of Pages
Operation: Set loop to trouser side seam				
Job No	Number m of operations 60	Department Standard – underwear	Cost centre	
Date of study	Start time quantity 31	End time quantity 45	Duration	
		Breakdown of time per unit	Time in min/100	Source
		Basic time t_g	12.31	
		Personal time t_{er} with z_{er} = 10 %	1.23	
		Contingency t_v with z_v = 8 %	0.98	
		Other allowances		
		Time per unit t_e	14.52	
		t_e in min	0.15	
		Preparation time t_r in min/h		

Operations: Grasp the trousers by the waistband at the right side seam and place under the clamp, set the loop, take the trousers from the machine and place on the table at the left side.

Materials (inputs)	Designation	Material	Input state	Drawing No	Material code	Size, shape, weight
	Mens trouser					all sizes
	Style Young					

Personnel	Name	Works No	M	F	Age	Experience similar operations	Experience this operation
	Maria			X	37		2 years

Equipment	Designation, Type	Quantity	ID No	year	Technical data, condition
	Automatic looper				
	Dürkopp Adler				

Environmental influences | Wage rate: Standard

1: Extracts from the front of a Time Measurement Form

No.	Sub-unit and measuring point	Quantity	Weighting	Value, Class	Zy / m_z	1	2	3	4	5	6	7	8	9	10	11	12	13	14	15	ΣL/n / Σt_i/n	$\bar{L}$ / $\bar{t}_i$	$t = \frac{\bar{L}}{100} \cdot \bar{t}_i$	Time-class
1	Grasp by waistband place under clamp	1			L															130	130 / 1	130	7.89	
					t_i	7	5	5	6	6	7	6	7	6	6	6	7	4	7	6	91 / 15	6.07		
	lower clamp				F	7	15	23	32	41	52	61	72	82	92	101	112	119	129	139				
2	Set loop on the waistband place trousers on stack	1			L															130	130 / 1	130	4.42	
					t_i	3	3	3	3	4	3	4	4	4	3	4	3	3	4	3	51 / 15	3.40		
	let go trousers				F	10	18	26	35	45	55	65	76	86	95	105	115	122	133	142				

n =	k =	Sum of times per cycle t_z			Σt_z	Σt	12.31
		Range per cycle R_z	cycle	cycle	ΣR_z		
		z – (R_z/t_z) 100% = (/) 100% = %	ε =	ε' =	n' =		

No	from	to	time	Additional sub-units

2: Extracts from the back of a Work Measurement Form (landscape format)

11.3.2 Time Analysis by the MTM System

Time Measurement by MTM (Method Time Measurement)

Other methods of work measurement include PMTS (Pre-determined Motion Time Systems). The most popular of these is MTM (Method Time Measurement). MTM provides a description of any procedure by analysing it into a series of basic movements, each of which has been allocated a time requirement.

Within any procedure, about 80 to 85% of the operator-dependent actions can be ascribed to the **MTM basic movements – reaching, grasping, bringing, putting, letting go.**

For each basic movement, a time value is allocated depending on the extent of the movement and the required mental and physical effort, and degree of control. It is not necessary to make detailed time measurements. The unit of time is the **TMU (Time Measurement Unit)** = 1/100,000 hour, which is 0.036 second or 0.0006 minute.

The MTM system allows a detailed description of any procedure to be made and its time requirement to be calculated. It follows that the best working method must already have been established under the given working conditions. MTM makes the assumption that there is only one standard time, so it is not necessary to evaluate the performance rating of each worker.

MTM systems have been developed especially for the requirements of the modern garment making industry (e.g. small batches, frequent style changes). Sector-specific programs allow rapid and flexible implementation. With the **MTM-Sewing Data** program, all of the tasks that are typical for this sector can be described and timed.

SDNVB Machine-sewing Standard Activity

PROCESS

Action	Item	Item	Precision	Code	TMU
Sewing	start	short stitching		SSSS	38
		first loop		SSSB	7
	end		rough	SER	5
			near	SEN	11
			tight	SET	21
		snip thread by hand		SEYH	22
			last loop	SEEB	7
		cut thread with knife		SEYK	11
Controls	lifter		single	CLS	35
		combined		CLC	40
	button			CB	20
	handwheel	needle	raise/lower	CHN	43
Handling	prepare	Part 1	near	HPFN	35
			tight	HPFT	45
		Part	near	HPSN	45
			tight	HPST	55
		turning		HT	40
		turn + place	near	HTPN	70
			tight	HTPT	80
	shape	fold + seam	near	HSFN	37
			tight	HSFT	47
		Part	fold in	HSF	27
	reposition	small part		HRS	43
		medium part		HRM	59
		large part		HRL	70
	push away			HP	22
	pick up		hand 1	HUF	17
			hand 2	HUS	22
	set down		rough	HDR	13
			near	HDN	27
			tight	HDT	37
Default value	reach, pause, transfer			DRT	6

pre/post Process | Process | Close

SDNVB Machine-sewing Standard Activity

PRE AND POST PROCESS

Action	Item	Item	Precision	Code	TMU
Offering	1 part	1 hand	rough	OFFR	31
			near	OFFN	58
			tight	OFFT	68
		2 hands	rough	OFSR	43
			near	OFSN	71
			tight	OFST	81
	2 parts	together	near	OSTN	91
			tight	OSTT	111
		sequen-tial	near	OSSN	137
			tight	OSST	157
Extras		gathering, per 10 cm		XG	24
Removing	push away	1 hand	rough	RPFR	22
	lay aside	1 hand	rough	RLFR	27
		2 hands	rough	RLSR	38
Handling	tools	scissors	near	HTSN	55
			tight	HTST	65
		clothes iron	rough	HTIR	69
Motion cycles	sequence	1 movement		MSF	5
		sequence		MSS	10
		transfer	tight	MSTN	30
			near	MSTT	20
Bodily motion	walking, per metre			BMA	25
	bending, stooping, kneel + rise			BMB	60
	sit, stand			BMC	110
Visual control				VA	15

pre/post Process | Process | Close

1: Computerised data charts from MTM-Sewing Data for the garment industry

11.4.1 Systems and Processes

Systems

A system is a collection of elements, all serving a defined objective. Three basic types of system have been suggested.

- **Technological systems** machines e.g. automated bed-sheet manufacture
- **Social systems** humans e.g. training classes
- **Socio-technological systems** humans + machines e.g. seamstress + sewing machine

Processes

A process (*Figure 1*) is any self-contained operation (sub-system) within a system. Processes are the building blocks for the organisation of the factory and for work study. They can be viewed on widely different scales.

- **microprocesses** are the smallest operations in the factory (sewing a collar)
- **macroprocesses** are departments or the whole factory (making a shirt)

Processes are usually socio-technological systems. They fulfil specific objectives by combining the potentials of humans and machines, moderated by environmental and organisational influences. Many processes can be analysed into the following seven process (system) elements.

1 Objective Assemble a shirt
2 Operations Actions to be taken
3 Inputs Materials, methods, standards, energy
4 Human Jane Smith
5 Equipment Sewing machine, table, storage space
6 Output Assembled shirt
7 Environment Working conditions

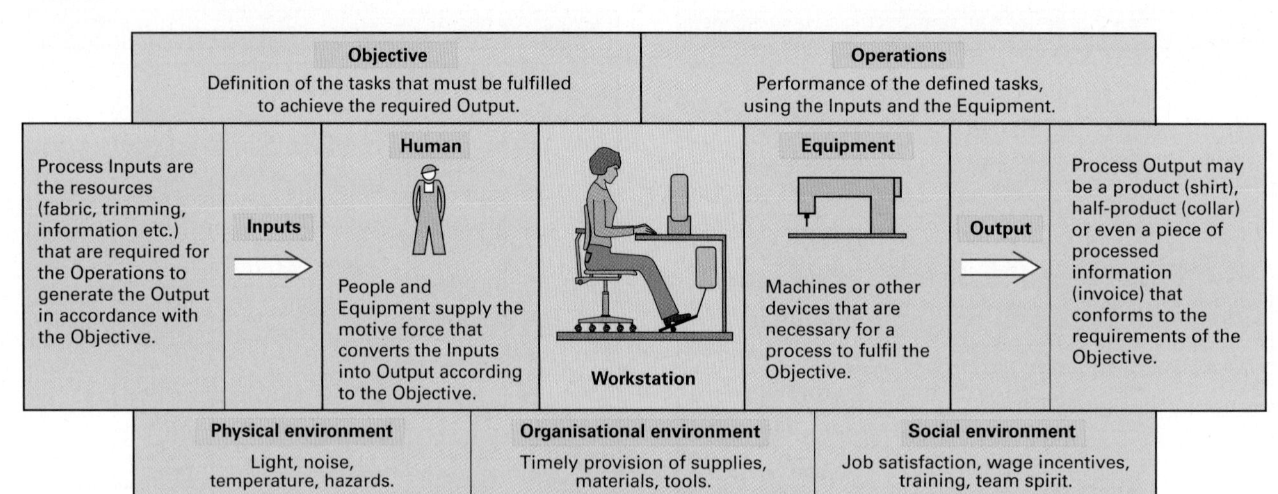

1: Sewing process

Total Process Shirt manufacture
Sub-process make a sleeve
Process stage finish sleeve opening

Procedure	Sewing
Sub-proc.	Attach trimming
Step	Position material
Action	Pick-up workpiece

2: Process analysis

Process Analysis

It is useful to analyse processes by classifying them into sub-processes of smaller scope (*Figure 2*).

The **total process** comprises all of the operations required to manufacture a given product (shirt making).

A **sub-process** comprises those operations required to produce an intermediate product or half-product (sleeves, bodies, collars).

A **process stage** comprises those operations required to produce the intermediate or half-product (finish sleeve, attach cuff).

A **procedure** is a working method or technique used in any process (e.g. sewing).

A **sub-procedure** comprises a small number of individual steps, that are considered as a group for analytical convenience (e.g. attach trimming).

A **procedural step** is a single stage in the sub-procedure, comprising only elemental actions (e.g. position the material for sewing).

An **elemental action** is one that, for practical purposes, can not be further subdivided (e.g. reach for the workpiece, pick up the work piece).

11.4.2 Method Study and Ergonomics (1)

Method study is the systematic investigation of a particular operation or function (process) with the objective of finding an improved way of achieving its objectives. It considers the interactions between people, equipment and environment and attempts to increase efficiency and productivity, whilst reducing the burden on the human operator.

System for Planning and Execution of Method Study

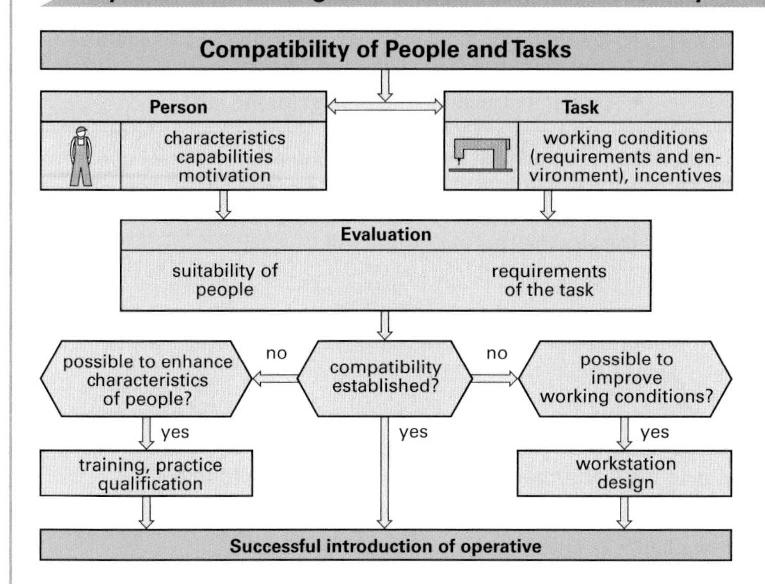

Method study investigations often make use of a six-step procedure.

Step 1: Analyse the situation, e.g. identify the key items

Step 2: Set objectives, define boundaries, e.g. precise targets

Step 3: Construct a process, e.g. develop procedures

Step 4: Elaborate the process, e.g. plan equipment and resources

Step 5: Introduce the process, e.g. acquire equipment

Step 6: Install the process, e.g. monitor success rate

Objectives of Method Study

Method study is concerned with the improvement, or development, of working methods, equipment, products, and working environments.

In studying **working methods,** one is attempting to improve the flow of products, to ensure better control of production, and to make the best use of equipment, e.g. transport of components by an overhead rail in trouser manufacture.

The study of **equipment** seeks to match the machinery and equipment to the particular task and the procedure, e.g. providing a larger working area for large components.

The study of **products** is often a collaboration carried out between the design and production planning departments e.g. to establish whether the existing profile-sewing jigs can be used, or whether new jigs have to be built, or whether the design can be changed to accommodate the existing jigs.

The study of the **workstation** is the section of method study which affects the operators most directly (*see page 223*).

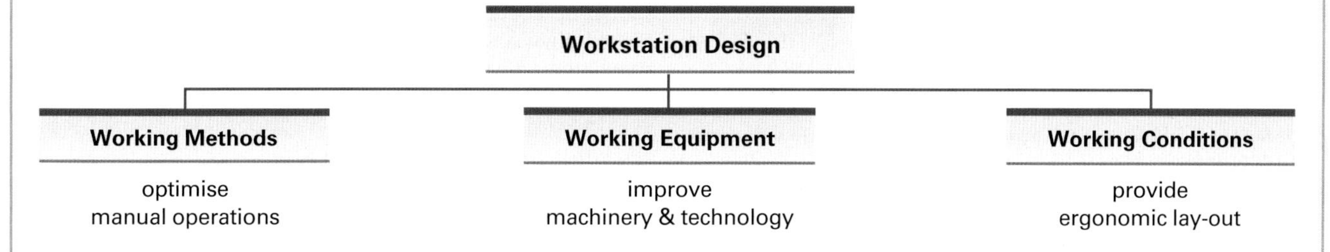

The **Working Method** means the sequence of manual operations performed by the operator. Picking and placing of components should be simplified and shortened. Manual operations can be condensed by using both hands or by overlapping operations e.g. the next part is prepared for feeding whilst one is handled automatically. Automatic devices can replace unproductive manual operations, e.g. thread cutters. As equipment gets ever more expensive, it has to be utilised more intensively, e.g. shift working for automatic cutting machines.

The **Working Equipment** includes the machinery and technology used to carry out a procedure. Possible technologies for closing a long seam include sewing with an automatic long-seamer or sewing followed by sealing with a welded tape.

The **Working Conditions** include the motivation and competence of the operator (internal conditions) and the physical environment of the workstation (external conditions). Both have a large effect on productivity.

11.4.2 Method Study and Ergonomics (2)

Ergonomics

Ergonomics is the study of the efficiency of the person in the working environment. Research is carried out on the influence of machinery and equipment design and disposition upon the comfort, health, productivity and production potential of the human operator, in order to be able to fit the person to the work or, better, to fit the work to the person.

Fitting the Work to the Person	Fitting the Person to the Work
• design of work station and equipment • comfortable working environment • sensible organisation of work	• rational personnel selection according to individual capabilities, age, constitution, etc. • proper instruction and training for the job

The objective of ergonomics is to measure stress, and to discover how to maximise the particular potential of human operators with the minimum of stress. Quite apart from any moral obligations, the fact is that when production conditions and equipment are designed to reduce stress in the operators, then the result is generally higher productivity, greater satisfaction, and a smoother pace of work. This is sometimes called humanisation of the workplace.

Human Productivity

The productivity of a person depends on his motivation and the way that he copes with stress. How a person copes with stress depends on his capability. Capability depends on education, training, experience, and practice. In addition, productivity depends on general disposition, current health, and fatigue.

Loading and Stress

Loading is determined by the physical nature of the work; it describes the heaviness of the work.

Stress is more to do with the individual response of a person to the loads imposed by a specific work environment.

Stress in a working person is analysed with respect to the loads which are placed on different bodily functions.

The following sources are distinguished:

1. Muscular loading, e.g. attaching a lining to a winter coat.
2. Sensory loading, e.g. computer-based pattern construction and grading.
3. Environmental loading, e.g. from steam and vapours.

Ergonomic Workstation Design

Ergonomically designed workstations can improve concentration, delay fatigue, and reduce accidents. An unsuitable seating position can lead to backaches. Other possible problems include neck and shoulder aches or discomfort in the thighs, seat, knees or feet.

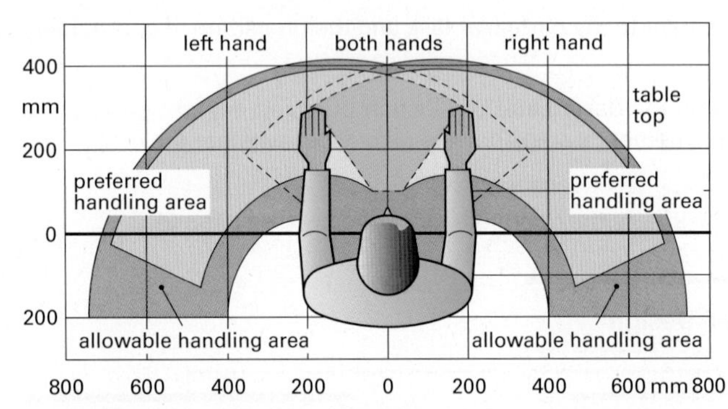

1: Seated workstation with handling areas according to ergonomic principles

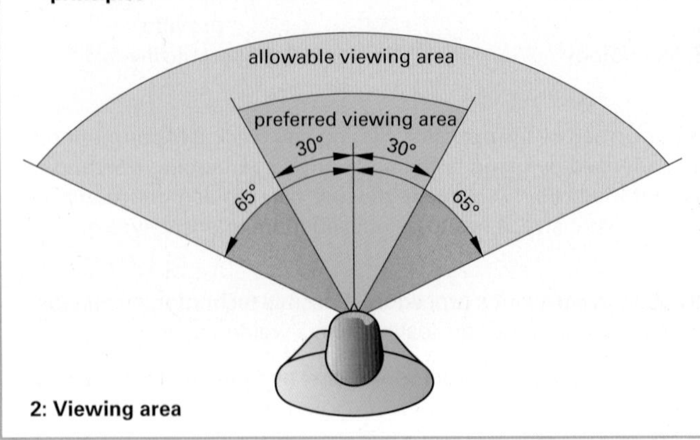

2: Viewing area

Anthropometry is the study of the sizes and proportions of the human body. **Anthropometric design** is the design of workstations in such a way as to conform to the natural dimensions of the human body. This includes the working height of tables and the lay-out of working areas. The space required for comfortable working depends on the operation to be performed and the technology. The seated posture should not be displaced by more than 20 cm away from the upright; the eyes should be about 40 cm from the working surface. The table should have a surface area sufficient for the task. *Figure 1* shows the appropriate dimensions. The small green area is suitable for hand movements that have to be controlled by eye. The larger yellow area is for the disposition of workpieces and tools.

Physiological design is concerned with the duration and the heaviness of the work. Attention is paid to the reduction and elimination of negative external influences such as noise, radiation, and waste materials. Lighting and air conditioning are also important in this connection.

Psychological design is concerned with providing a pleasant and comfortable environment, including colour, music, plants, etc.

Health and safety is an important part of work place design. Measures are taken to avoid work-related illness and accidents.

The **provision of information** is also subject to design considerations: easy-to-use forms, tabulated data etc.

11.4.2 Method Study and Ergonomics (3)

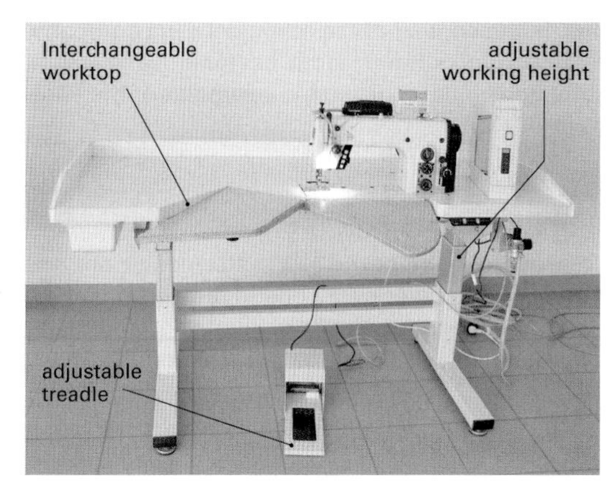

1: Configurable sewing station

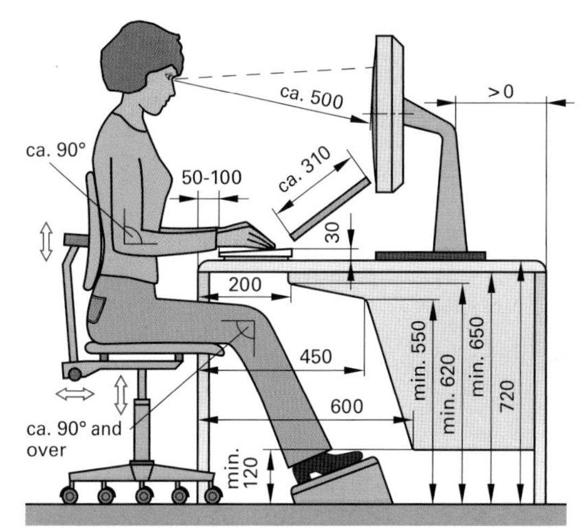

2: Ergonomically designed computer workstation

3: Standing workstation

Ergonomic Design of the Sewing Workstation

Sitting is more comfortable than standing and is always to be preferred. For the sewing operation, the seated position provides stability and allows better control of the fine movements that are required. A disadvantage is the restricted space for movement and the unbalanced muscular loading. Additional load is provided by the need to hold the legs in a fixed position during sewing to operate the foot pedal speed control.

Sewing workstations place **special requirements on people and equipment.**

Demands on the **operative** include visual requirements (sharp vision) manipulation skills (positioning, guiding) and precision of foot movements (foot pedal control).

So far as the **equipment** is concerned, it has to be possible to adjust the workstation to the individual operative in at least the following respects.

- height of seat and worktop
- angle of seat backrest
- inclination of the seat
- height and inclination of the foot pedal

The operative should ensure that the equipment is properly adjusted to suit her own body dimensions. All workers should be instructed in the importance of correct posture and the risks of neglecting this aspect.

Ergonomic Design of the Computer Workstation

There are particular ergonomic and safety considerations for computer workstations.

Arrangement of equipment

A computer workstation requires an adjustable, swivelling chair and a correctly placed footrest. All equipment must be placed centrally in the preferred handling area. Copy holder stands must be raised and angled in the preferred viewing area, for easy reading. To maintain the correct posture, the keyboard must be detached and should be placed in the preferred handling area

Lighting

Monitors must be raised and angled in such a way that there are no reflections to be seen on the screen. Large variations in ambient lighting conditions and high-contrast conditions (e.g. directly facing windows) should be avoided by appropriate positioning. Suitable conditions are when at least 500 lumens of diffused illumination are available.

Eyesight testing

Computer operatives should have their eyesight tested by a qualified ophthalmologist. The first test should be made before taking up the position. Follow up tests should be carried out every three years on persons over the age of 45.

Ergonomic Design of Standing Workstations

The height of the operative affects his posture. To maintain the correct posture, the height of tables and equipment should be adjustable. The design of standing workstations should pay regard to the following body dimensions:

Height, eye level, sternum level, stride length, elbow level, reach, shoulder width.

11.5.1 Fundamentals

Quality means the degree to which a product or service satisfies expectations. In the context of the manufacturing company, it means conformance to a product specification. The primary objective of quality management is total customer satisfaction, by prevention of faulty or substandard work. Its primary by-product should be efficient and profitable operation of the company.

Quality Management (QM)

Quality management is an important component of company management. It seeks to optimise product performance, process efficiency and costs. It affects company structure, customer relations, product planning and development, methods, procedures, resources and responsibilities. It seeks to engender a whole-company culture that is geared towards better and better interpretation and fulfilment of the requirements of its customers. There is a strong emphasis on the prevention of errors at all stages.

Basic quality management principles have been described in ISO 9001. For several industries, such as aerospace, medical technology, healthcare, pharmaceuticals, and food production, suitable quality management systems have already been described in some detail.

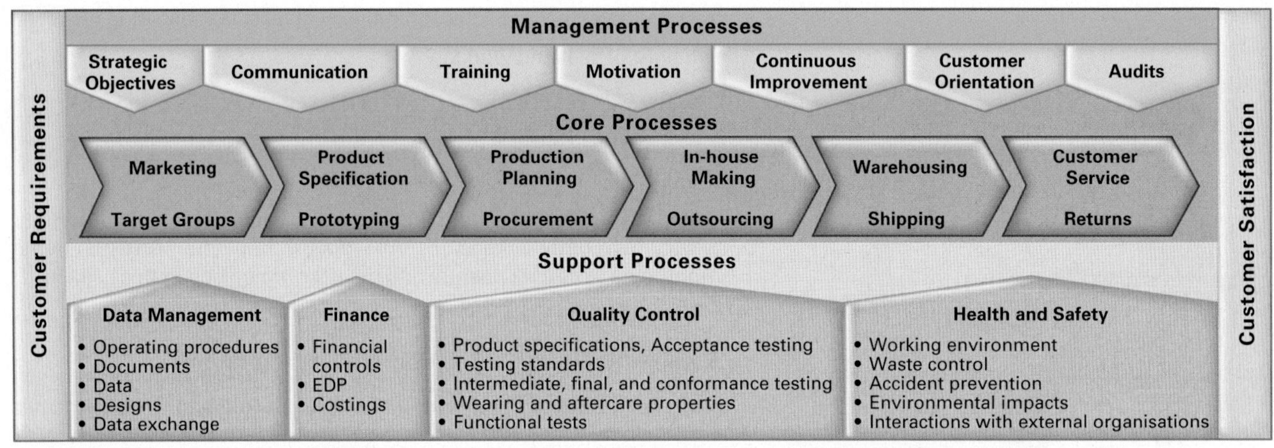

1: Process Oriented Management System

Figure 1 summarises a typical **quality management system,** comprising Core, Support and Management Processes.

- **Core Processes** (value-added processes) stand at the heart of any manufacturing operation and, therefore, are the central focus of a process oriented management system. These are the processes that progressively add value to the raw materials and that convert a customer requirement into a finished product.
- **Support Processes** are the necessary supporting systems that supply materials, information, controls and personnel to enable the core processes to function smoothly. Examples are product development, provision of materials and preparation of machinery.
- **Management Processes** provide planning and control services. For example, the future financing and investment plans are determined on the basis of the targets and strategies embodied in the forthcoming season's product range, or collection. Lines of communication and responsibilities have to be established; additional training may have to be organised, and remuneration has to be calibrated against additional responsibility. All processes are geared towards satisfying and even exceeding the customer's expectations.
- **Quality Audits** have to be carried out regularly. These assess the procedures and documentation already in place; check that the procedures are actually being correctly observed; and make recommendations for improvements or for further research.

Objectives and Advantages of a Quality Management System

- Optimal lines of communication
- Customer satisfaction and reputation enhancement
- Improved competitiveness
- Employee satisfaction & motivation
- Business expansion
- Efficient equipping of the work areas
- Self-esteem and lasting improvement
- Standardisation of working procedures, tendering, servicing and documentation
- Discovery of unnecessary costs
- Demonstration of potential for improvements
- Improvements in quality and productivity
- Transparency of technical and managerial procedures
- Avoidance of faults and insurance against product liability claims

11.5.2 Quality Assurance in a Clothing Company (1)

Requirements for a Quality Management System

Quality awareness has to be integrated into every activity, from design to delivery. An integrated approach to quality spans all departments. It has to derive from the company Directorate, who must ensure that the necessary resources are made available. The processes and procedures necessary for implementation of the QM system are approved by the company's senior management (*see pages 210 ff*). Methods and standards for operation and control of the core processes are elaborated, and the availability of the necessary finance, test methods, operatives and information is secured. The processes are monitored using prescribed control and measurement tools. Problems and faults are constantly evaluated to see if improvements can be made.

Documentation

The whole quality management system is laid out, together with a statement of the company's quality policy, in a Quality Management Handbook. This document serves as a reference point for all future quality activities. In principle, a standard procedure may not be altered without proper investigation by the quality assurance team and, once adopted, the new procedure must be recorded in the Quality handbook.

The handbook will include instructions on how processes are to be carried out and how they are to be monitored and controlled. Typical entries will include the following.

- Company policy
- Quality targets
- Managing documentation
- Managing designs
- Internal audits
- Managing faulty products
- Corrective measures
- Preventative measures

Management Processes

Dialog Textil-Bekleidung DTB Dialog schafft Partnerschaft

Product Profile
Woven fabric
January 2012

Internal Qual. No.
Supplier Qual. No.

Supplier:
Supplier No:
Supplier ID:
Town:
Street:
Contact:
Telephone:
Facsimilie

Season: *Date:* *Product sector (e.g. Ladieswear):*
Application in clothing industry: *Set programm Yes No* *Product area (e.g. trousers):* *Mill-wash: Yes No* *Process:*

Remarks	Supplier data	Test Standard
1. Construction		
Fabric construction		DIN 54200
Cloth description		
Fibre type	Staple ☐ Filament ☐	
Area weight	g/m² g/m	ISO 3801
Ave. Piece length	m	
Total width	cm	DIN 53851
Usable width	cm	DIN 53851
Ave. Fault rate	/10m	
2. Finishing		
Finish type (e.g. antistatic		
Coating/Type	no ☐ yes ☐ /	
Dyestuff class, all colours e.g. reactive dyes (mill wash)		
Cationic fixation (mill wash)		
Optical brightener	yes ☐ no ☐	
Fusing suitability	yes ☐ no ☐ Check ☐	
No fusing, sewn interlining	yes ☐ no ☐ Check ☐	
Can be permanently creased	yes ☐ no ☐ Check ☐	
3. Making up		
Uni	yes ☐ no ☐	
Stripes/squares	yes ☐ no ☐	
Repeat/panel length	cm	
Repeat width	cm	
Trimming, from fabric edge	R cm L cm	
Repeat matches both edges	yes ☐ no ☐	
Bias extensibility	%	
4. Aftercare labelling (ISO 6330) Washing, Bleaching (3175-2, 3175-3), Ironing, Dry cleaning, Tumble drying, Laundering (3175-4), Supplementary advice (e.g. iron on reverse)	°C; Supplementary advice:	
5. Fabric Properties		
Extensibility (stretch fabrics)	warp % weft %	DIN EN 14704-1
Extensibility (mill wash)	warp % weft %	DIN EN 14704-1
Permanent extension (stretch fabrics)	warp % weft %	DIN EN 14704-1
Permanent extension (mill wash)	warp % weft %	DIN EN 14704-1
Tear strength		DIN EN ISO 13937-1
Tensile strength (mill wash)	warp daN weft daN	DIN EN ISO 13934-1
Seam slippage		DIN EN ISO 13936-1
Abrasion resistance	cycles	DIN EN ISO 12947-2
Pilling (mod. Martindale)		DIN EN ISO 12945-2
Creasing/recovery		ISO 2313, DIN EN 22313
Water permeability/water head		DIN EN 2081, ISO 811
Water repellency/Spray test		

1: Product profile with testing requirements

The top cloth, linings, accessories and other components required to complete a garment all contribute to the final quality. The procurement department is responsible for securing quotations and selecting suppliers. However, only those suppliers may be used that have been evaluated and approved by the quality assurance team.

Fabric Testing

Inspection and testing are carried out in order to ensure consistent product quality. The range of tests, the methods, and the instruments used depend on the individual company and the application. Inspection of the fabric at the earliest possible stage serves not only for **quality control** but also to ensure **customer satisfaction** and **cost savings.**

Inspection of incoming goods (acceptance testing) is to check for conformance to the specification, so that a claim for compensation from the supplier can be made if deficiencies are found. Checks may be made on the fabric type, design, piece lengths and widths, repeat, weight per unit area, thread density, permeability and frequency of faults.

The test data are evaluated by the quality team who consult with Procurement whether to accept or reject the delivery.

The technical information is archived and documented in standard format as a **Product Profile** (*Figure 1*) which can be distributed to the relevant departments.

Technological Testing together with use and aftercare characteristics give an insight into the performance properties of clothing, such as durability, suitability, and aftercare requirements.

11.5.2 Quality Assurance in a Clothing Company (2)

Quality in Product Development

During **product development,** the required cutting plan is set up according to the design sketches and descriptions. The plan will have been influenced by past experience with similar models from earlier collections, as well as the fabric properties, especially in so far as they affect the garment fit. All of this information is sent to the **sample making** department.

The **prototype** garments are fully developed and, if necessary, improved in the sample making department. The final specification, including recommendations for improvements in cut, materials, fusing, etc. is embodied in suitable documentation, including measurements to provide **quality targets** for the subsequent manufacturing of this particular product. The test data from acceptance testing are also noted. The specification and targets are translated into information and instructions suitable for the manufacturing section.

As part of the **prototype testing** the prototype garments, plus accompanying documentation, are taken before a committee representing the Product Management, Design and Development, Quality Management, Marketing, and Production departments. This group provides an overall perspective which can request alterations and improvements before the model is approved and can be released for production.

Criteria that are considered, and included in a sample test report, include the following.

- Compatibility with the required image and range for the new collection
- Conformance of manufacturing instructions and accompanying paperwork to company quality policy
- Visual appeal of the component materials (top cloth, lining, interlining, accessories)
- Appropriate style and fit
- Adequate documentation
- Compatibility with available manufacturing time

Fashion AG	Pants/Skirt			Plant:
Prototype ☐	Production ☐			
Customer:	Style:			No. pieces:
Article:	Colour:			Pieces tested:
No.	Group:			No. faulty
Responsible:	Conformance tested with following sizes			
	Size:	check at	yes:	no:
	Size:	check at	yes:	no:
	Size:	check at	yes:	no:
	Conforms to specification		yes:	no:
Remarks:				
Test item	Value			Remarks
Appearance				
Waist girth				
Hip girth				
Hem/Bottom				
Inside leg				
Length				
Seat seam				
Waistband				
Loops				
Labels				
Tucks				
Folds/puckers				
Zipper				
Buttons				
Pockets/lapels				
Seams				
Lining				
Slits				
Hem				
Pressing:				
Surface				
Seams/hems				
Waistband				
Threads/spots/holes				
Technical:	☐ free ☐ limited			available in department:
Date:	☐ risky			Date
Symbols to be used:	1 = Good	2 = Within tolerance		3 = Outside tolerance

1: Acceptance Form

After constructing a cutting and grading pattern, a **sample series** is manufactured of, say, three examples per style in different sizes. The findings from these samples provide the basis for production planning and quality control for series production, and the samples themselves become the **reference standards.** When all of the quality requirements have been met, the new model is released for production, along with the standards.

The cutting plan, the materials, the accessories, the reference standards, and the documentation are then delivered to the Production department.

The product development exercise also produces documented production guidelines such as fusing conditions, tables of finished size measurements, technical measurements for sewing and stitching details, construction details such as belt loops, technical improvements for garment making, etc.

Quality in Manufacturing

This applies to the actual making-up operations, from cutting to delivery. The **manufacturing objective** is that the product shall conform to its written specification. The flow of data and information from Marketing / Purchasing through to Production / Sales has to be smoothly co-ordinated.

The **production schedule** provides the basis for management and control. It comprises the production plans, the material availability plans, calculations, and allocation of labour and responsibilities.

The work and time measurement analysis predicts the manufacturing time.

The quality assurance team supplies a schedule for **intermediate and final testing,** and watches over conformance.

All procedures that influence the quality have to be collected, evaluated and documented as current practice. Approved changes have to be implemented immediately

11.5.2 Quality Assurance in a Clothing Company (3)

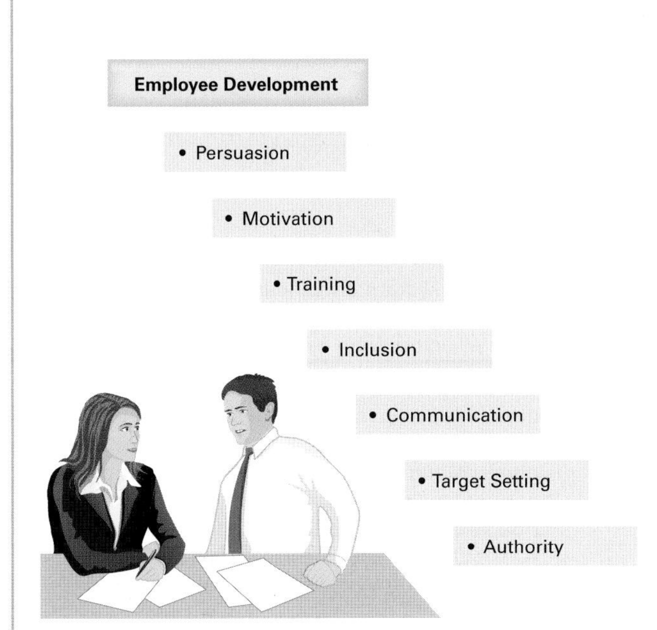

1: Employee Development

Promotion of Quality Awareness

One of the most important factors in the success of a company is a motivated workforce: when people are happy in their work, they are cooperative and productive. A highly competent workforce provides a formidable competitive advantage in the market.

Effective training and inspired leadership makes a workforce fit for purpose through enhancements of competence, skills and dexterity. Improvements can be made, for example, by introducing rationalised sewing techniques, special procedures or test instrumentation, improved methods for quality control, or leadership training.

Individual operatives should be made aware of the advantages of correct working, as well as the consequences of faulty work on their colleagues, on the production costs, the satisfaction of the customer, and hence the profitability of the company.

Additional incentives can be provided by bonuses for fault-free working and for suggestions for how to improve the operation (*Figure 1*).

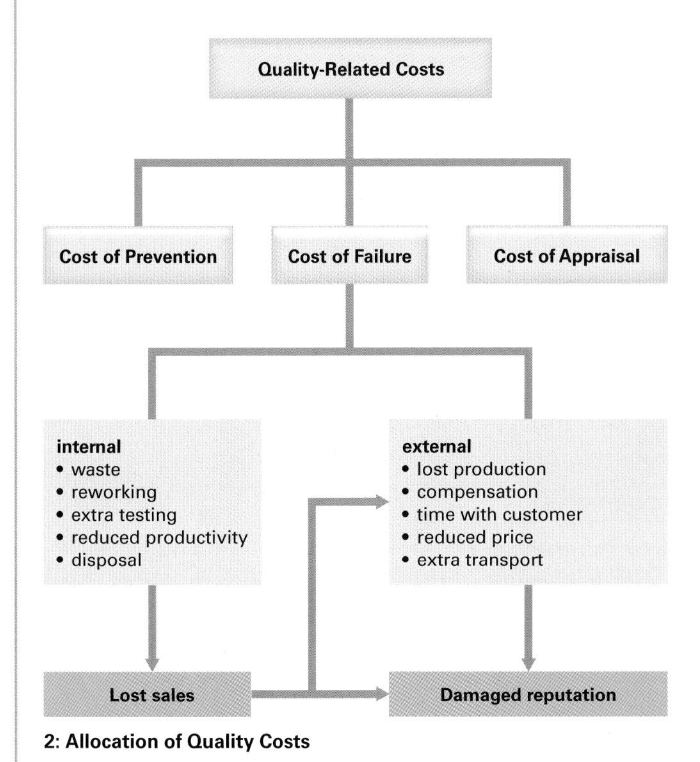

2: Allocation of Quality Costs

Quality Costs

The costs of planning, evaluation, control and management of quality are called **quality-related costs.** A primary objective of quality management is to improve the effectiveness of the quality system so as to reduce the total cost of quality.

Distinction is made between the costs of **Failure, Prevention,** and **Appraisal** (*Figure 2*).

Potential faults should be detected as early as possible in the production line because the further down the line an item is, the more costly are the consequences of a fault.

Cost of Failure

Failure cost is the cost that results from faults. Failure has both internal and external consequences. In any case, the result is reduced productivity, lost sales, and damaged reputation.

Cost of Prevention

Prevention cost is the cost of those activities geared towards process improvement and the prevention of failures.

Cost of Appraisal

Appraisal cost is the cost of routine quality control testing and inspection

Quality Management Control Loop

One of the most important objectives of quality management is continuous improvement – of both the core manufacturing processes and the quality system itself. The results of investigations and improvements are fed back in a **continuous improvement loop.**

- **Quality planning:** Boundary conditions, scope, concepts and procedures are developed.
- **Quality control:** The boundary conditions, concepts and procedures are implemented.
- **Quality assurance:** Monitoring and evaluation of the measured data and observations.
- **Quality improvement:** Optimisation of processes and procedures based on the evaluations.
- **Successful results** and information are publicised and used to design improved procedures.

11.6.1 Information Flow in a Clothing Company (1)

The clothing industry has particular requirements, having the challenge of continuous evolution of a standing collection. This imposes a need for transparent decision making criteria at all stages. Appropriate computer software lends support to management strategies.

Information Technology **(IT)** or Electronic Data Processing **(EDP)** can facilitate rapid **information exchange** between all company management departments, both internally and externally, thus enabling optimised operations. A strategy for realising these objectives is Product Lifecycle Management.

Product Lifecycle Management (PLM)

The **PLM system** encompasses the entire undertaking. Its data and procedures permeate and integrate all actors from designers to salesmen.

Thus PLM can serve as a central control system for the whole company. It includes support IT systems as well as methods, processes and the management of planning, construction, calculation and garment making, up to financial planning and control, sales and service. The strategic implementation of basic PLM functions and concepts may vary somewhat from company to company.

The basis for introducing a PLM system is **Product Data Management (PDM)** and **Enterprise Resource Planning (ERP)** systems. These two are tightly intermeshed.

Linked Industrial Information Systems PDM and ERP

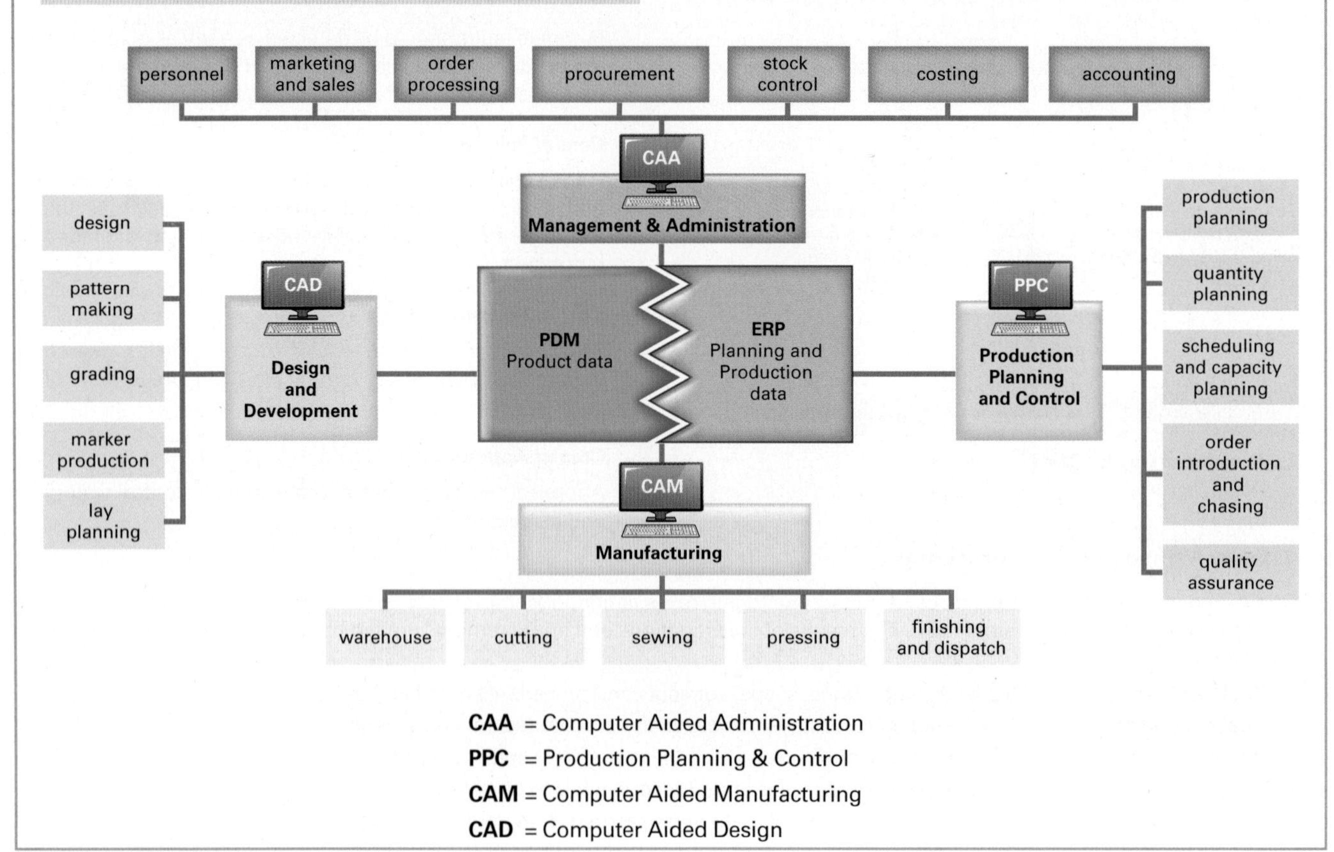

CAA = Computer Aided Administration
PPC = Production Planning & Control
CAM = Computer Aided Manufacturing
CAD = Computer Aided Design

11.6.1 Information Flow in a Clothing Company (2)

The increase in quantity of data requires a central data storage and processing facility, together with individual interfaces for each department. Implementation of **PDM and ERP systems** forms the basis for comprehensive **data exchange** and a higher potential for useful exploitation of the data.

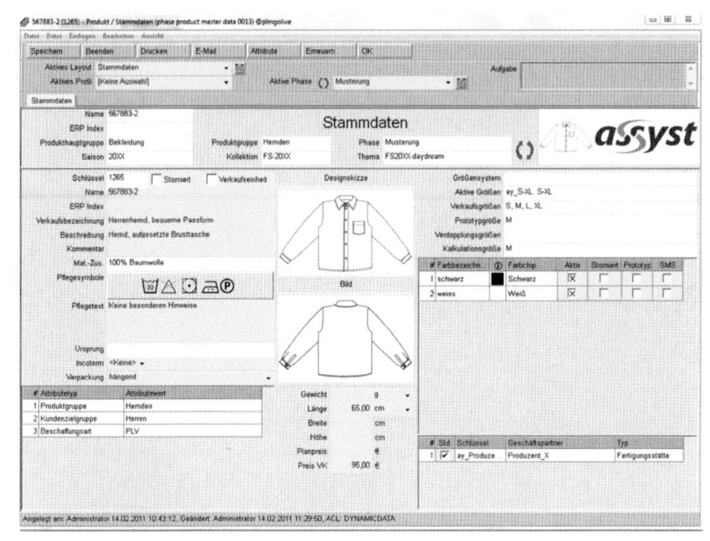

1: Product specification data

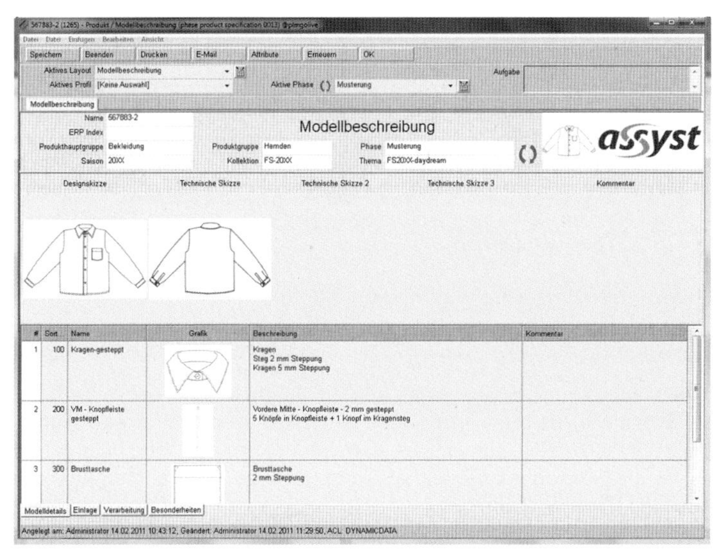

2: Product description

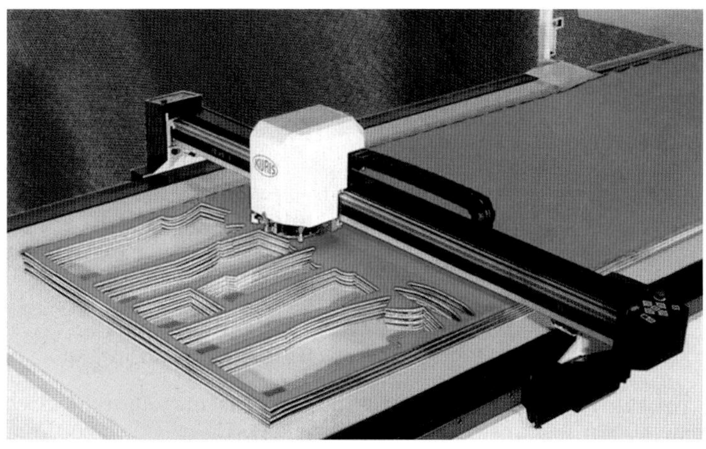

3: Computer-controlled cutting

Product Data Management (PDM)

PDM plays a central role in the introduction of PLM (Product Lifecycle Management). All data relating to a given model are linked through the EDP system. At the same time, various operations on a given model can be carried out, e.g. development of the cutting pattern, production of forms and making instructions. An integrated user interface allows access to all authorised co-workers. This allows production factors such as development, quality specification and costing to be optimised (*Figures 1 and 2*).

Enterprise Resource Planning (ERP)

The materials management systems in ERP use the in-house data from the PDM as well as data from the market.

The following areas are served.

- **Quantity planning**

  This is materials management processes such as disposition, availability and warehousing.

- **Scheduling and Capacity**

  Delivery times, production capacity (machines) and operator efficiency (personnel)

- **Progress chasing, control**

  Order taking, order planning, order introduction, deadlines and quality assurance. Oversight by finance and accountancy.

Computer Aided Manufacturing (CAM)

CAM systems are especially useful for series production and mass production, but are also used for large-scale made-to-measure operations.

- Monitoring and control of **material flow** in individual sections.
- **Laying-up and cutting** is performed by fully automatic (CNC[1]) laying and cutting machinery (*Figure 3*).
- **Computer controlled sewing** machine programs can be stored and automatically invoked.
- In the pressing department, programs for form presses, form finishers and tunnel finishers can be made available.

[1] CNC = Computerised Numerical Control

12.1.1 Basic Concepts

Proportion is the relationship of one part to a whole or to other parts. An appreciation of natural proportions is essential to the representation of the human figure, and therefore to clothing design. Two concepts which have proved useful in representing human body proportions are the Golden Section and Division into Eighths.

The Golden Section (Golden Mean)

When dividing a line into unequal sections, harmonious proportions can be constructed by using the golden section.

Principle:

The shorter section (a) is to the larger section (b) as the larger section (b) is to the whole line (a+b) (*Figures 1 and 2*).

$$\frac{\overline{BE}}{\overline{AE}} = \frac{\overline{AE}}{\overline{AB}}$$

Construction of the golden section:

1. The perpendicular $\overline{BC}$ is erected at B, with $\overline{BC} = ½\,\overline{AB}$.
2. C is joined to A.
3. D is marked on $\overline{CA}$ so that $\overline{CD} = \overline{CB} = ½\,\overline{AB}$.
4. E is marked on $\overline{AB}$ so that $\overline{AE} = \overline{AD}$.
5. E divides $\overline{AB}$ into the golden section.

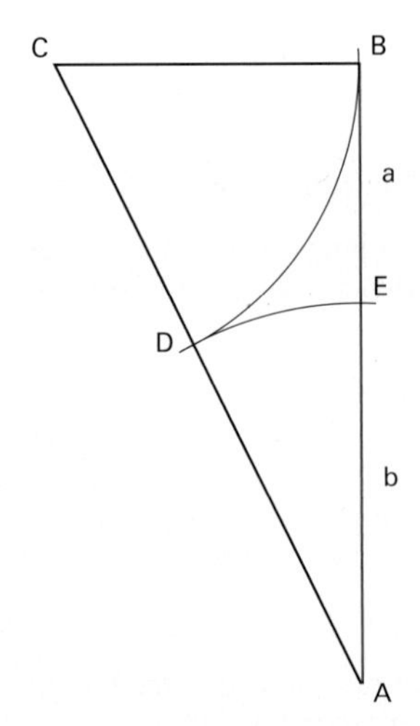

1: Division of a line into the golden section

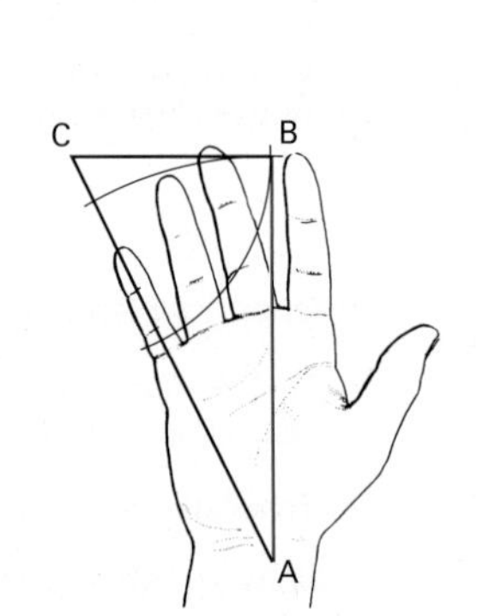

2: Proportion of a hand

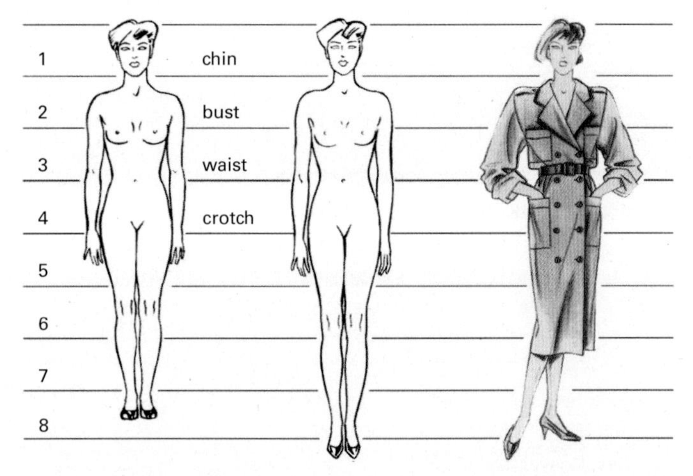

3: Female proportions

4: Ideal proportions for clothing

Division into Eighths

The ratio of the golden section works out in practice to 0.618 which is quite close to 5/8. The total height of a full-grown woman is about seven and a half times the vertical size of the head. Therefore, the body is provided with **ideal proportions,** and sketching of it is made easier, by dividing it into eight equal parts, whereby the waistline is placed at about 5/8 of the total height, and the crotch is at about half the height. For fashion sketches, the proportion is often extended to between eight and eight and a half times the head, with the extra length being given to the legs (*Figures 3 and 4*).

Departures from the Ideal Figure

Every individual has his or her individual body size and proportions. Large, small, slender, or stocky figures do not always have the ideal proportions. *Figure 5* illustrates the wide range of female body proportions found in a typical population.

Most of the women had a bust girth smaller than their hip girth. For about 37% of the population, this difference averaged about 5 cm; for a further 23% the difference averaged about 10 cm and for a further 25%, bust and hip girths were about the same. The total range of hip girth in that survey was from about 81 to 132 cm and, for a large portion of that range (86 to 122 cm), the range in bust size at constant hip size was 20 to 25 cm. Results similar to these have been found in a number of different countries, e.g. Britain, France, Germany, Sweden and the USA.

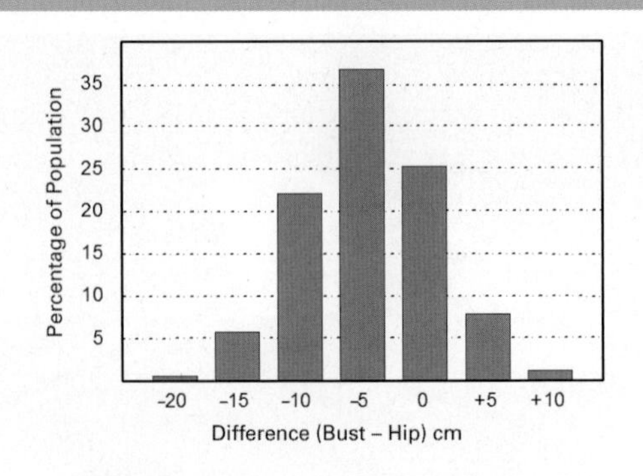

5: Difference between Bust girth and Hip girth

Clothing has to be made so that it fits the size and the shape of the body as well as possible, but industrial manufacturing does not allow for the economic production of a vast range of different garment shapes and sizes. Somehow, the data obtained from population measurement surveys have to be grouped into a manageable number of average body types and sizes.

12.2.1 Making Body Measurements

Measurements

Measurements made on real humans are the fundamental basis for garment sizing. Large numbers of people have to be measured to obtain reliable summary statistics.

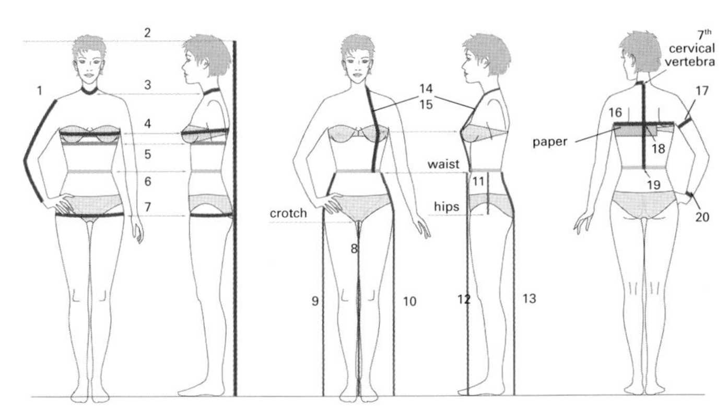

1 arm length
2 stature
3 neck base girth
4 bust girth
5 under-bust girth
6 waist girth
7 hip girth
8 crotch height
9 left waist height
10 right waist height
11 waist-hip height
12 front waist height
13 back waist height
14 chest depth
15 front length
16 back width
17 upper arm girth
18 scye depth
19 back
20 wrist girth

1: Locations of manual measurements

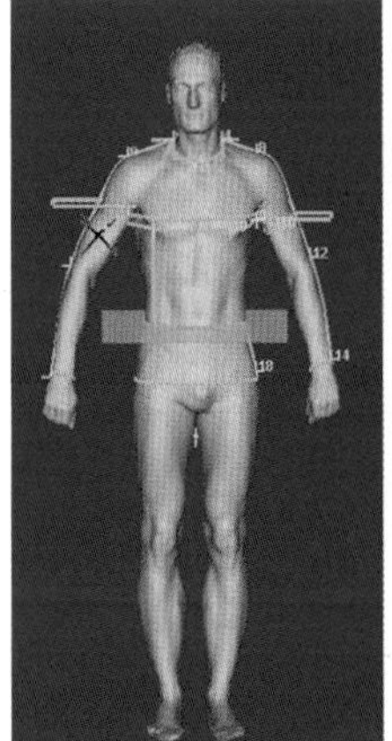
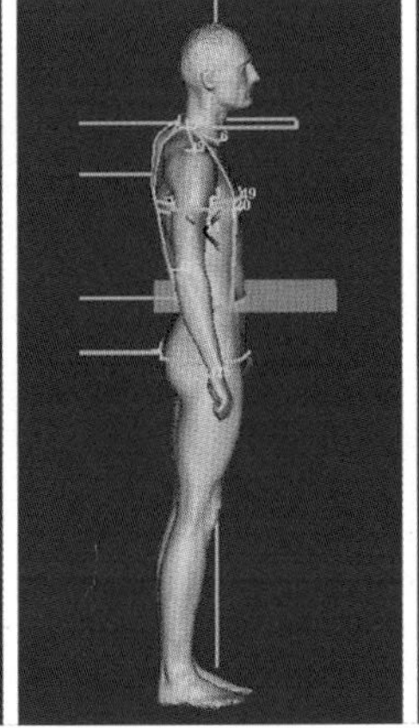
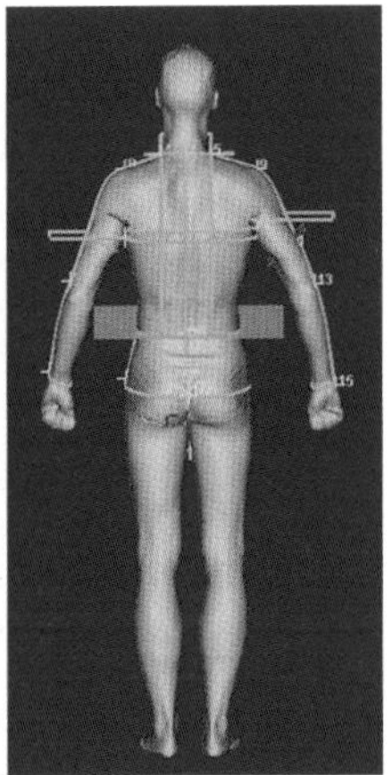

2: Virtual representation of a male body

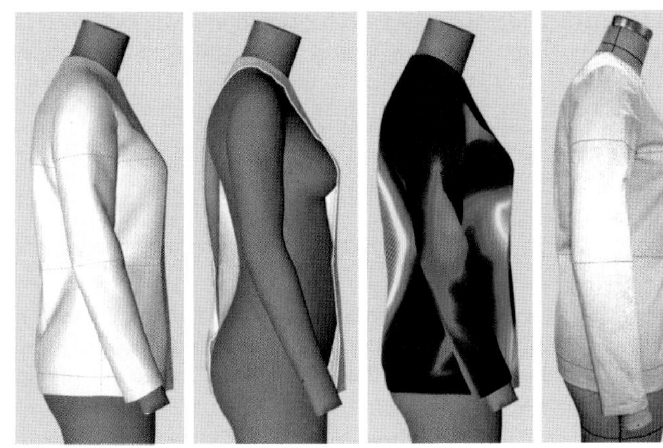

3: Virtual representation of women's outerwear

Manual Measurements

The parts of the body that are measured have been standardised (e.g. ASTM 5219) and are similar the world over.

Figure 1 shows examples of where some body measurements are taken, using a tape measure.

The population statistics are divided into distinct body types, e.g. according to height, chest girth and waist girth, and averages are calculated for the separate body types for inclusion in the final body measurement tables (e.g. ASTM 5585).

Automatic Measurements

An individual stands in a measuring booth which is equipped with scanning systems and software.

Not just the standard measurements but also the whole body shape are incorporated into a suite of up to 100 parameters that can later be recalled, either for entering into a comprehensive database for the whole population, or for the construction of made-to-measure garments (*Figure 2*).

Utilisation of the Measurements

Size Tables

Body size tables are constructed from the grouped average measurements. They form the basis for industrial garment sizing. Individual clothing companies construct their in-house, or customer-specific cutting patterns from the standard tables.

Three-Dimensional Pattern Development

A virtual body **(avatar)** can be generated from actual body measurements, so that digital product development is enabled. The avatar can be used to construct a mannequin, with which to test the fit and develop prototype garments.

In a simulation, the individual pattern pieces can be draped over a virtual body, so that different ways of cutting, fabric qualities, colours, and patterns can be evaluated. The simulation gives a good impression of the appearance and fit of the proposed garment, or part (*Figure 3*).

From the 2-D cutting pattern, a 3-D representation can be made. This can speed up the development of a new style, with a reduction in time costs.

Industrial Made-to-Measure

Individual measurements, obtained either automatically or manually (*see page 208*), can be transmitted directly to the manufacturer for use as input for a CAD system, to develop a custom-made cutting pattern and production recipe. A CAM system can then take over the garment making.

The customer can be provided with the output of the computer simulation so that she can approve the design before it goes into work.

12.3.1 Basic Considerations, Body Types, Control Dimensions

Basic Considerations

The division of statistical survey measurements into a manageable number of body types and sizes has usually been a largely empirical process. Therefore it is not surprising that different countries construct different body type and size groupings, even when starting from similar statistical data. In all cases, however, the construction of average body size tables stems from just a few basic concepts, such as the **percentage of the population** that has to be satisfied, the **control dimensions** which define different **body types** and the **size intervals** between different sizes within the same body type.

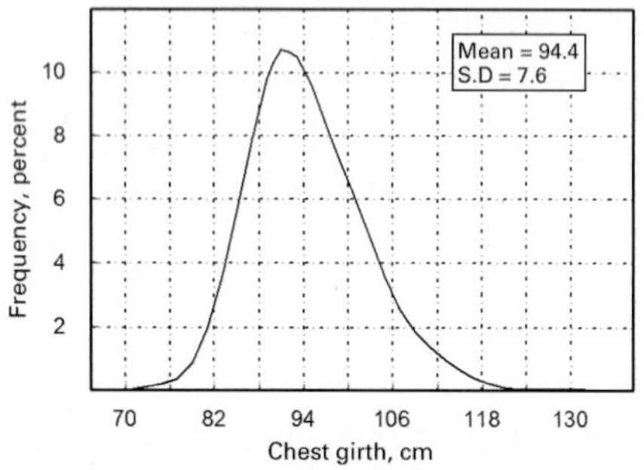

1: Distribution of adult male Chest Girth

Percentage of the Population

Within a given population, most body dimensions are distributed in a pattern similar to *Figure 1*. The standard deviation of that distribution was about 7.6 cm, which means that about 95% of the population could be accommodated by a range of chest sizes spanning about 4 x 7.6 = 30.4 cm.

In a different population the average girth and the standard deviation may both be different. Even within a single population the distributions may be different for different age groups. For example, in the population of *Figure 1*, the mean chest girth for men aged between 17 and 26 was 91.1 cm, but that for men aged between 26 and 65 was 96.5 cm.

Once the basic statistics are available, the range of measurements which covers a given percentage of the target population can easily be discovered.

Control Dimensions

In body measurement surveys, there may be more than 40 different body measurements made on each individual. It is clearly impractical to develop body size charts taking all of these measurements into account individually. It is necessary to select a few control dimensions which will serve to make the major distinctions between body types and sizes. The other dimensions have to be related to the control dimensions, usually by averaging. Thus, the control dimensions serve several functions:

- They provide the basis for establishing the **total range** in body measurements.
- They provide the basis for defining different **body types** (proportions) within the population.
- They provide the basis for creating the **size intervals** between different sizes within the same body type.

Obviously, the control dimensions which are selected must be ones which largely determine the fit of a garment to a given body size. For a skirt, the waist girth, the hip girth, and the length are dominant. The same control dimensions, which are used to divide population statistics, will later be used to specify the key dimensions of garments.

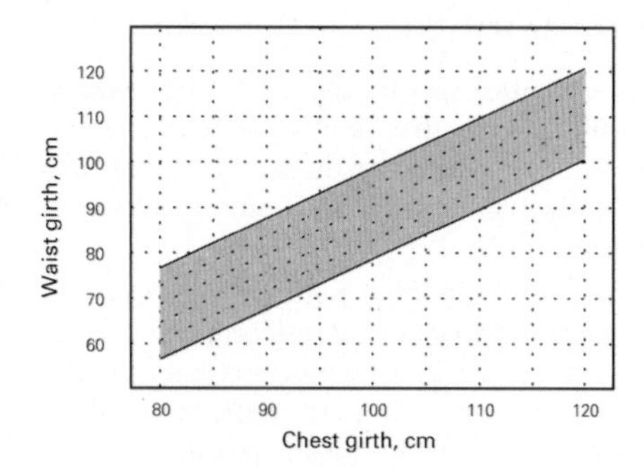

2: Adult male Waist Girth versus Chest Girth

Figure 2 illustrates the general relation between male chest girth and waist girth. It shows that, for any given chest girth, the waist girth may vary by up to about 20 cm, because of the differences in body proportions. An area of approximately constant body proportion is defined by a band which is parallel to the two lines which outline the total range. Different body types (different proportions) are found by moving vertically through the range of waist girths at a given chest girth. To delineate different body types, the total range can be divided into parallel, sloping bands. In this case, with equal size intervals of 4 cm for the waist girth, there would be five parallel bands, i.e. 5 different body types. Taking the average waist girth within a band to be representative of that body type then, over the whole range of chest girths, there will be a constant difference between chest girth and waist girth. This is called the **drop value.** Each body type would have a different drop value, representing the five different body shapes in the population. Thus a given body type can be specified by the chest girth and the drop value.

Example: Men's whole body outerwear garments

Body Type: Name	Athletic	Regular	Portly	Stout	Corpulent
Mean drop value (chest-waist), cm	16	12	6	0	–6

This is not the end of the matter, because the population is also distributed according to **stature** (total body height). Often, the total range of stature will be divided into three; "short", "medium", and "tall". In the male population illustrated in *Figure 1*, the average stature was about 174 cm with a standard deviation of about 7 cm. As an example, therefore, "short" could be defined as less than 167 cm; "medium" could be 167 to 181 cm; "tall" could be greater than 181 cm.

Following this classification, each of the 5 chest/waist groups may be divided into the three (or more) stature types to make 15 (or more) different chest/waist/stature body types, e.g. Tall-athletic, Medium-athletic and Short-athletic, etc.

12.3.2 Size Intervals, Size Charts, Size Codes

Size Intervals

Size intervals fulfil three major functions:

- They provide the basis for assigning the boundaries for the different body types.
- They provide the numerical basis for grading sizes, and hence garment cutting patterns (grading intervals).
- They provide the final purchaser of the garment with a guide for which garment, within a range on offer, is likely to be the most suitable for his/her figure.

To keep the number of different sizes to a manageable quantity, the size interval should not be too small. To serve the consumer, the size interval ideally would be small enough so that no one is expected to purchase a garment which is too large, or out of proportion. The ideal situation is not always achieved.

Size Charts

Once the population has been classified into major types and sizes according to the chosen control dimensions and size intervals, then all of the measurements from all of the individuals contained within each type/size group can be averaged to provide the basic set of body measurement tables for each body type and size. Minor adjustments to these raw tables may then be made to provide consistency within types and between sizes and to give practical numbers (whole numbers, even numbers). In the body size tables of ASTM D5586, there are 7 body type tables for women. Each table contains 45 body measurements for between 6 and 10 different sizes, making a total of 55 type/size groups.

To develop garment patterns using these tables, allowances must be applied to the basic body dimensions. These will depend on the style of garment and type of fabric to be used. For stable woven fabrics and loose styles in knitted fabrics space must be provided between the garment and the body to allow for movement and for changes in body dimensions (e.g. spreading of the hips when seated). This is called the **ease allowance** or **tolerance.** For close fitting garments or support styles using stretch fabrics, the allowance may be zero or negative. In any case an additional allowance is made for the width of the seams. Further modifications may also be made to allow for fashion and styling details.

Size charts are tables, which have been constructed from the basic body measurement tables, and which include ease allowance and other allowances necessary for the production of a particular type and style of garment.

Designation of Sizes, Size Codes

Each of the body type/size groups contained within the body size tables or size charts is given a simple size designation or size code to identify it. The **size code** performs two main functions.

- For the garment maker, it indicates which size table is to be used to construct the master cutting patterns for the garment in question.
- For the consumer, it indicates the body type and size which the displayed garment is intended to fit.

At present, there is no universal system for size designation that is used world-wide to indicate the same or similar body sizes in different countries. As an example of the differences in size designations between systems, the US standard size codes for women can be compared to those for Germany, for similar body measurements. A few of these are shown in the table, where the US body measurements are converted from inches and rounded to the nearest half centimetre.

Comparison of some US and German Size Designations

	Short				Medium				Tall			
Size Code	US 22½	G 25	US 12	G 19	US 22	G 48	US 16	G 42	US 22T	G 596	US 18T	G 588
Bust, cm	117	116	89	88	112	110	96.5	96	112	110	101.5	100
Hip, cm	119.5	119.5	94	94.5	117	114	101.5	101.5	117	120	106.5	111
Hip-Bust, drop	2.5	3.5	5	6.5	5	4	5	5.5	5	10	5	11
Stature, cm	160	160	162.5	160	168.5	168	165	168	179	176	176.5	176

Because of the lack of standardisation in size codes, the ISO has recommended that size designations for garment labels should refer primarily to body measurements[1] rather than size codes.

Example: Man's Suit (Control dimensions are Chest girth, Waist girth, and Height)

The ISO recommendation specifies the use of a pictogram showing the control dimensions and/or a box with the control dimensions for the recommended body size indicated in words and numerals. The control dimensions to be used for different types of garments are also specified. Additional information, such as other body dimensions, garment dimensions, or size codes may also be given but should be indicated separately and should not reduce the prominence of the main control dimensions.

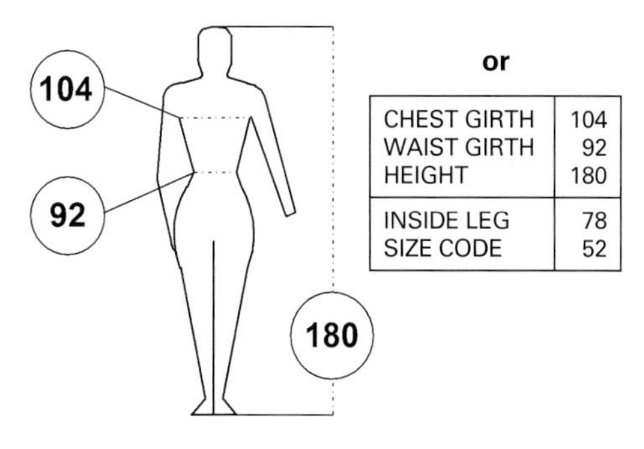

[1] see for example ISO 3636, 3637, 4415, 4416

13.1.1 Developing a Collection

A collection is a range of garment styles (models) designed with respect to current fashion trends and economic realities. It is put together by a collaboration between creative, sales and technical resources. Individual development steps may be undertaken sequentially or in parallel. The time required depends on the quality level and the size of the collection. Computer software is available for the design and the product data management aspects (*see page 228*).

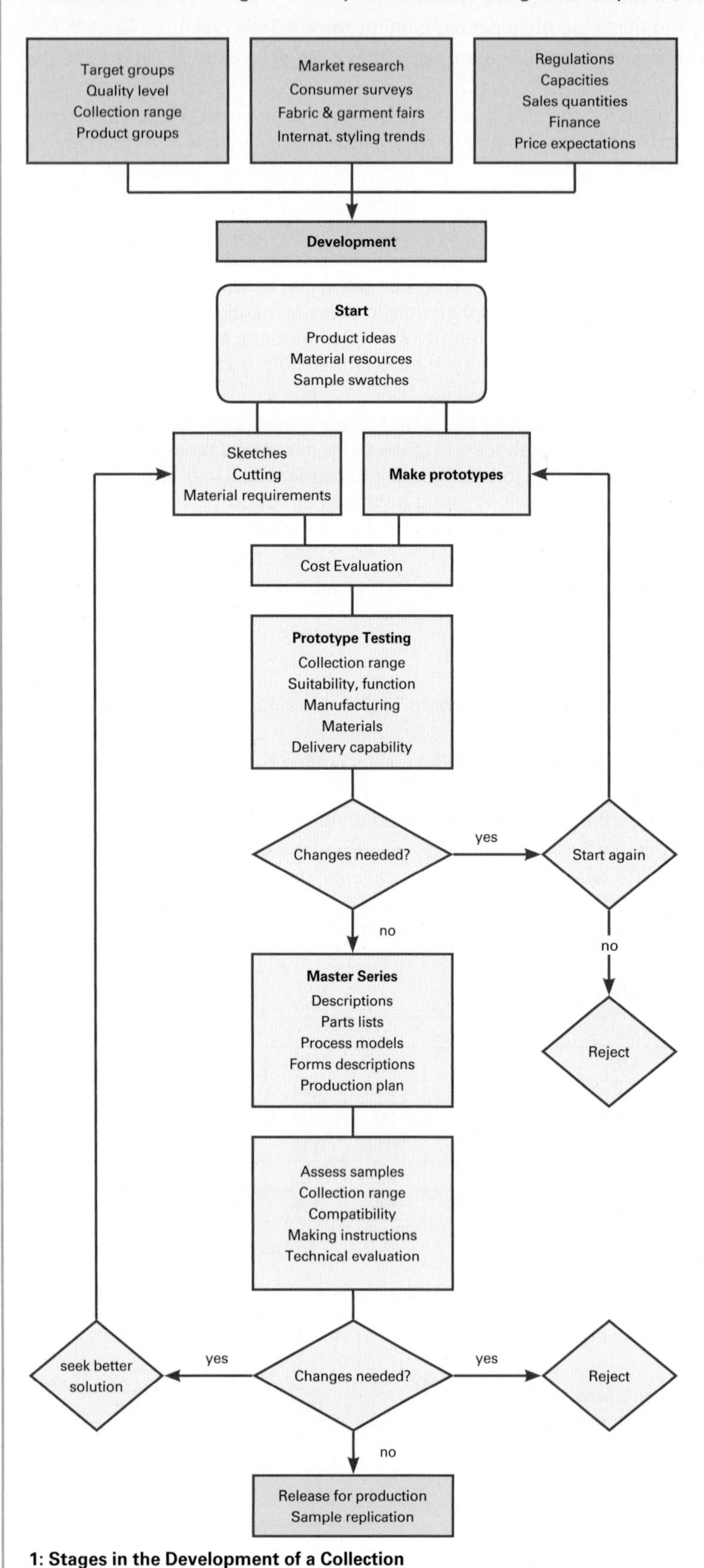

1: Stages in the Development of a Collection

Development starts with the assimilation of market intelligence. Seasonal trend information on colours, silhouettes, and materials is available from market research, textile and fibre companies, trade fairs, haute couture, and ready to wear. Inspiration is drawn also from social and cultural trends, previous history, and trade journals.

From this information, broad styling themes are distilled, refined and re-interpreted into specific styles suited to the requirements of existing customers and target groups. Preliminary **design sketches** are made and assembled together with selected materials and indications of fashion themes to create a **storyboard.**

These ideas are discussed at a **collection appraisal meeting** in which the scope, balance, and image of the collection is decided. Samples of each chosen style are cut and assembled in the sample room to create garment **prototypes.**

Preliminary **costings** for material, labour and appropriate profit margins are calculated and compared with established selling prices.

A detailed **prototype evaluation** checks the models for sales appeal, production requirements and materials compatibility. Cutting and making experience from the prototypes is translated into the normal factory production planning instructions using forms and software as appropriate. If a particular model is found not to conform to production requirements it is either modified or rejected.

Usually a **master series** of three sizes per style is manufactured. These garments will serve as the control series for reference purposes in production and quality control. The assembled models, together with the corresponding manufacturing instructions are documented in a collection specification, which will be reviewed and adjusted until it is considered to be ready for release into production.

A **manufacturing plan** is constructed for each individual model, and the **prototype collection** is submitted to the sales department for approval. If the collection is approved, all of the necessary resources are made available to production to enable its replication, so as to have **sample collections** for representatives, exhibitions, displays, and presentations.

Before full series production can begin, the production plan has to be geared to shop-floor conditions and detailed **procedure descriptions** have to be developed, consistent with large-scale production.

13.1.2 Planning a Collection, Quality Levels

1: Trend theme – Scottish look

2: Trend theme – Marine look

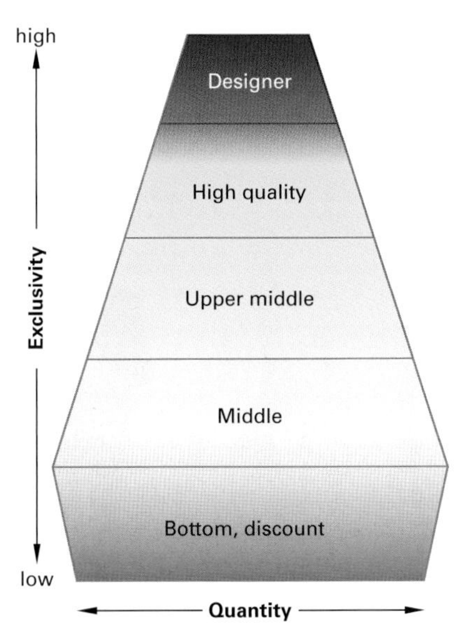

3: Clothing quality levels

Collection Plan

The **Collection Plan** concerns all those sections of the company that are involved in the development, making and selling of a collection. It is the organised framework for timely processing – from the acquisition of sample materials through to exhibition at the clothing fair and follow-up sales. A basic concept for the new season's collection is developed by the senior management together with product managers and designers. The collection plan contains all of the necessary information for those departments that will be directly or indirectly involved with realising the collection, for example:

- **Product concepts:** number of models, model groups, deadlines, production planning, themes
- **Design concepts:** general character and particular style, guidelines for the themes
- **Market:** target groups, price levels, sales plan, delivery schedules
- **Fabric concepts:** trend themes, fabric qualities, basic and fashion colours

The collection plan is drawn up as closely as possible in conformity with the conclusions of the planning discussions and the new concepts. Objectives are to relieve the design department of routine work, to ensure optimum and timely collaboration between technical, purchasing and production departments, and to deliver the sample collection to the sales department in good time.

The collection has to be co-ordinated to the seasonal and product requirements of the retail trade. Both Summer and Winter seasons are subdivided into individual segments. These segments are given theme names and each will be composed of a number of items according to style, fabrics and colours which form a **fashion trend.** Members of a theme will be grouped together in the retail store.

Quality Level

Quality level is the other factor that determines the market sector towards which a collection will be aimed. The quality level defines the rank of the product in the total range of offers in the market, so far as its design content and workmanship are concerned. The following factors, for example, have an influence.

- Fabric quality
- Fashion content
- Elaboration in the interior parts
- Precision of assembly
- Style and Fit
- Range of sizes and number of pieces

The following quality levels can be distinguished

Designer quality characteristics include unique designer labels, small numbers per style, the most exclusive fabrics – often with in-house designs – extreme fashion leaders, avant-garde designs.

High quality or **Model** fashions are characterised by very high levels of workmanship, exclusive designs and detailing, small series production, limited size range, up-to-date styling.

The **Upper middle** level uses good quality fabrics, provides optimum fit, and follows the latest fashions in style and colour.

The **Middle** level has strict price constraints, a comprehensive size range, but a limited range of styles.

The **Bottom** or **Discount** level has large quantities of limited styles. Fabric quality and workmanship are geared to low price levels. The style and fit are of comparatively lower importance.

13.1.3 Target Groups (1)

A **target group** is an identifiable sector of consumers with broadly similar characteristics, such as fashion consciousness, buying habits, types of shops used, brand awareness, brand loyalty and quality requirements. Thus there is a strong incentive for garment makers and the retail trade to finance extensive market research to identify and classify different target groups that can be reached by product promotion. Three such research-based classifications are outlined below.

Target Grouping Schemes

Dr. Leichum Retail Marketing Target System

Classification according to fashion and quality levels

This scheme presents a three dimensional classification based primarily on fashion and quality levels. The results are presented as sections of a **target cube** (*see page 237*).

The garment maker gathers data from retail sales in the form of number of items sold classified according to e.g. product type, colour and size. These data are analysed and the results are utilised for product management.

Target Groups based on Retail Sales

		Women	Men
1A	Avant-garde	2%	1%
1B	Fashion conscious	7%	6%
1C	Jeans type	8%	16%
2A	Business	7%	5%
2B	Modern	8%	10%
2C	Casual	11%	10%
3A	Strict classical	11%	7%
3B	Modern classical	19%	21%
3C	Middle of the road	19%	20%

The **numbers (1, 2, 3)** stand for the **fashion level.** The **letters (A, B, C)** stand for the **quality level** (*see page 237*).

Outfit 7.0 – Typology Spiegel Verlag 2011

Classification according to attitude to fashion

This scheme is based primarily on the needs, the habits and the attitudes of users towards clothing, fashion, brands, and purchasing experiences. The study yields information over how often a given type of clothing is purchased, how much is paid for it and who is most likely to buy it.

The results are based on a representative survey of persons between the ages of 14 to 69.

Target Groups based on the Spiegel study

Type structure for womenswear

Type	Description	%
Type 1:	Mainstream	26.4%
Type 2:	Trendy, brand-aware fashion followers	19.3%
Type 3:	Pragmatic, price conscious	17.0%
Type 4:	Independent thinker, individualist	16.0%
Type 5:	Purposeful, habitual	10.8%

Type structure for menswear

Type	Description	%
Type 1:	Price conscious, habitual	21.4%
Type 2:	Satisfied mainstream	19.8%
Type 3:	Market aware trendsetter	16.1%
Type 4:	Self-confident fashion follower	14.6%
Type 5:	Classical-elegant	14.1%

Sinus-Milieus Social Trend Analysis

Classification according to social status (milieu)

The Sinus Institute, in Heidelberg, is an independent research and consultancy organisation which looks at basic social and cultural trends.

The Milieu study has been running since 1980. It groups people according to attitudes and lifestyle. It is based on values, lifestyles, and preferences in the context of social status.

The results can be useful for targeted marketing in various product areas.

Examples of Classifications based on Sinus-Milieus

Higher status	
Conservative-establishment	10%
Liberal-intellectual	7%
Performing arts	7%
International creative	6%
Middle status	
Bourgeois	14%
Adaptable-pragmatic	9%
Socialist-green	7%
Lower middle status	
Traditionalist	15%
Insecure	9%
Hedonistic	15%

1: Examples of various target groups in menswear

13.1.3 Target Groups (2)

The Dr. Leichum Retail Marketing Target System[1]

This concept proposes a three-dimensional classification system of target segments. The first dimension stands for the fashion level, the second for the quality level, and the third represents aspects of the market.

These relationships are illustrated graphically in the **target group cube** (see below).

First Dimension: Fashion level		
Segment	**Style**	**Description**
Segment 1	**Trendy**	Trendsetter, highly fashionable, mostly young (14 to 29), lifestyle oriented; per-capita expenditure slightly below average.
Segment 2	**Modern**	Modern, fashionable, mostly aged from 30 to 50, lifestyle oriented; per-capita expenditure above average.
Segment 3	**Classic-conservative**	Classical, conservative fashions, mostly over 50 years, quality oriented; per-capita expenditure slightly below average.
Segment 4	**No style**	Price oriented, no interest in fashion trends, all ages; per-capita expenditure far below average.

Second Dimension: Quality level		
Segment	**Level**	**Description**
Segment A	**Upper**	Top model culture with corresponding demands on style and quality; per-capita expenditure well over average, expects high price.
Segment B	**Middle**	Bourgeois attitudes to style; mainstream market. Average per-capita expenditure; seeks good price-utility ratio. Desires exceed spending capacity.
Segment C	**Cheap**	Simple styles, one item at a time, price more important than quality; per-capita expenditure well below average.

Third Dimension
Analysis of qualitative and quantitative attributes e.g. sales outlets, end uses, demographics, habitual clothing, media usage, shopping behaviour, leisure activities, etc.

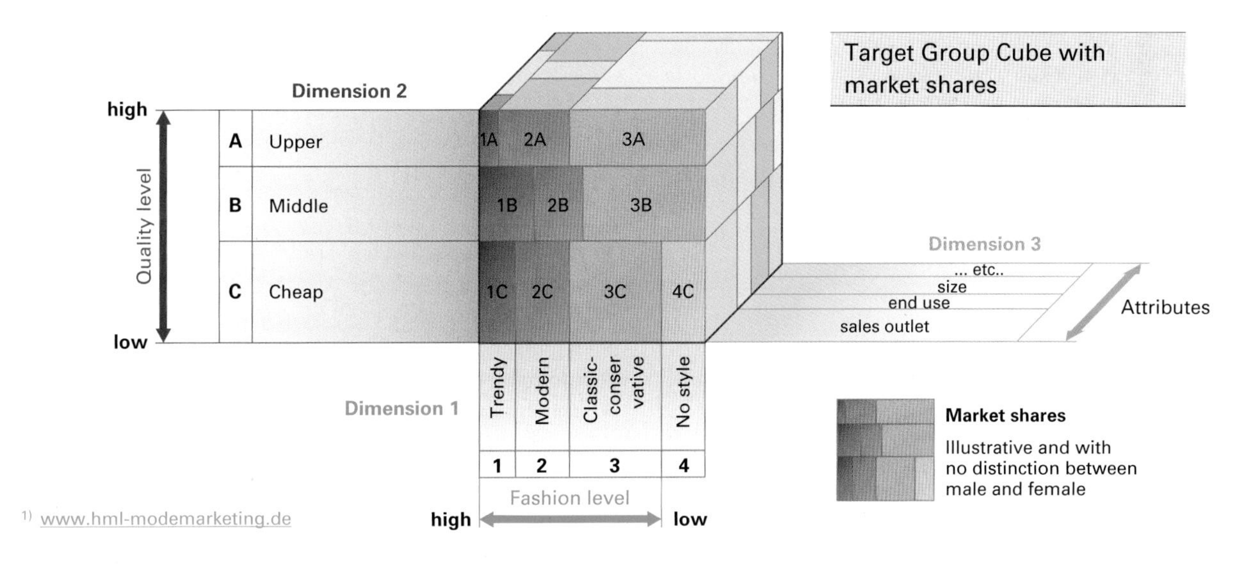

[1] www.hml-modemarketing.de

Examples of Target Group behaviours:

- A Group 1B consumer buys fashionable items, like Group 1A, but at a lower price.
- A Group 1C consumer buys items that are on-trend and highly fashionable at the lowest possible price. Fashion and price are more important than quality.
- Group 1A has a very small volume, though the per-capita expenditure is much higher than average.
- The largest share of the market is taken by Group C. These consumers prioritise modern and wearable fashions. Their per-capita expenditure is below average.

13.2.1 Elements of Clothing Design

Fashion is not the only consideration in developing a garment for a market. The overall appearance (style) as well as the utility value (fitness for purpose, aftercare) also have to be appropriate. The style, colour, decoration, material, trimmings and technique are fundamental elements of clothing design.

Styling

A fashionable cut, a good fit and comfort in wearing arise mostly from the structure of the design. This includes for example:

- position and direction of vertical and horizontal components
- length-width proportion
- shaping
- details, e.g. sleeves, collars, fastenings, pockets

Distinctive **silhouettes** are attained from particular designs. These are denoted by letters (*Figures 1 to 7*) or according to their shape (*Figures 8 to 11*) or after particular periods (*Figures 12 and 13*).

A distinct **sectioning** of the garment is obtained from the disposition of seam lines and edges (*Figures 15 to 18*).

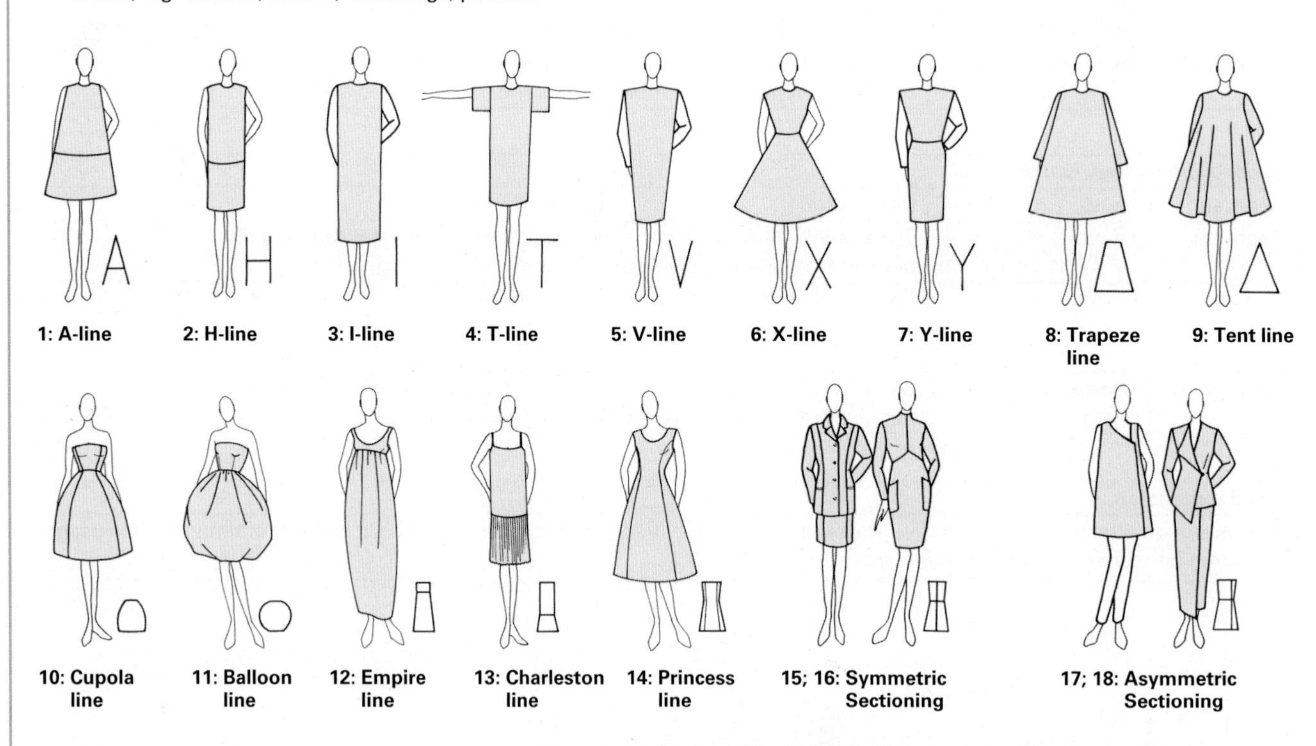

1: A-line 2: H-line 3: I-line 4: T-line 5: V-line 6: X-line 7: Y-line 8: Trapeze line 9: Tent line

10: Cupola line 11: Balloon line 12: Empire line 13: Charleston line 14: Princess line 15; 16: Symmetric Sectioning 17; 18: Asymmetric Sectioning

Decoration

Decoration can emphasise the **style** of a particular item of clothing and can, for example, give an elegant, casual, business-like, or romantic feel to the clothing.

Decoration can take the form of:

- decorative stitching and embroidery
- pleats and tucks
- frills and flounces
- piping and binding
- trimming and braid edging
- appliqué and incrustation

Material

The material greatly influences the **character** of an item of clothing and also determines its possible **end-use**.

On the one hand, the visual qualities such as how the material hangs, the colour, pattern and surface texture are important when choosing a material. On the other hand the comfort, wearing, and care characteristics, which depend on the fibres, type of yarn, fabric and finishing, must also be taken into account.

Trimmings and Technique

The trimmings and the technique considerably influence the **utility** or the functional performance of the clothing. Apart from the material, they are crucial to the overall **quality level** (*see page 235*).

Trimmings include the application of linings and interlinings, padding and fastenings.

Technique includes technical aspects of sewing, such as the quality and structure of the seams, reinforcement of edges, and securing of pockets and flies.

13.2.2 Design Influences

Many factors need to be considered when designing clothing. The major influences are the fashion and style trends, the purpose of the clothing and the characteristics of the wearer.

Fashion

Fashion sets the **accent**. The major features which are determined by fashion are:

- basic silhouette and accentuations
- length and width
- details and decoration
- colour, pattern and structure of the material

Style Trends

Clothing is an **expression of personality**. Clothes only feel good when they express the wearer's own attitudes. The great variety of styles which exist side by side in today's fashion clothing allows for individual expression. The style that is favoured at a given time depends on both the venue and the personality of the wearer.

Typical styles are:

- sporty
- casual, informal
- classic, timeless
- business-like, masculine
- conservative, formal
- romantic, pretty
- traditional, rustic
- casual, elegant
- refined, elegant
- feminine
- extravagant
- avant-garde
- frivolous
- nonconformist

1: Casual leisure wear

2: Formal dress

3: Sporty

4: Sporty-elegant

5: Classic-elegant

6: Romantic-pretty

7: Extravagant

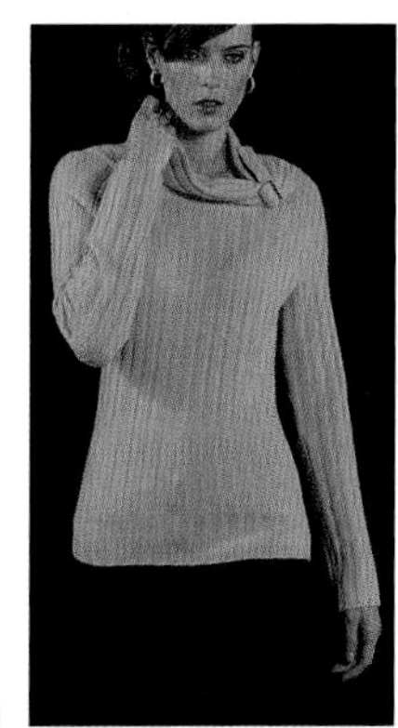

8: Feminine

Purpose

Clothing has different **requirements** according to its purpose.

Sport, leisure and work clothes are primarily functional. Formal dress should stand out from everyday clothes and appear elegant, dignified or festive.

Clothing for Summer wear will have different requirements, in terms of its ventilation and insulation capabilities, moisture absorption and transference, than clothing intended for Winter (*see page 49 ff*).

The Characteristics of the Wearer

The characteristics of the wearer include the combined aspects of figure, stature, age and personality.

For a satisfactory **overall effect** the clothing must be adapted not only to the individual body measurements but also to the different requirements of a particular age group. The bespoke tailor can accommodate these individual aspects whereas the ready-to-wear clothing industry must endeavour to consider the broad distinctions between particular target groups (*see page 236*).

14.1.1 Underwear, Nightwear (1)

Underwear

Underwear has several functions. It protects the body from harsh outerwear fabrics and it protects the outer fabrics from perspiration. In cold weather it provides extra warmth. Fabrics used include wovens and knits from cotton, viscose, silk, wool, nylon and polyester, as well as blends of these. Elastane fibres are included for stretchy fabrics. Open-work knitted fabrics are often used. Ladies' underwear will often include lace. Elegant ladies' underwear is called **lingerie.**

Underwear styles include briefs, undershirts, slips and bodys. The boundary between underwear and outerwear is becoming blurred. An underwear style worn as fashionable outerwear is no longer unthinkable.

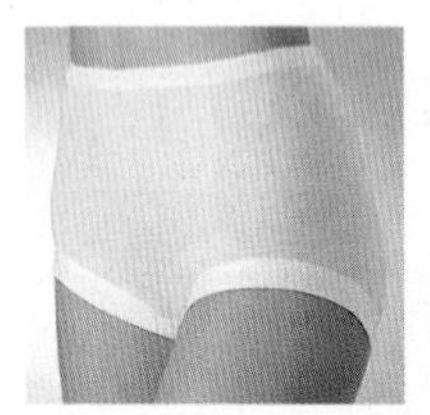
1: full brief

2: hipster

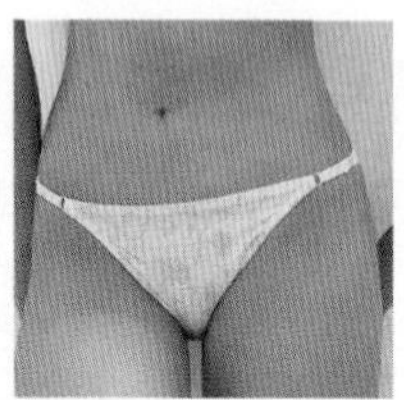
3: tanga

4: midi

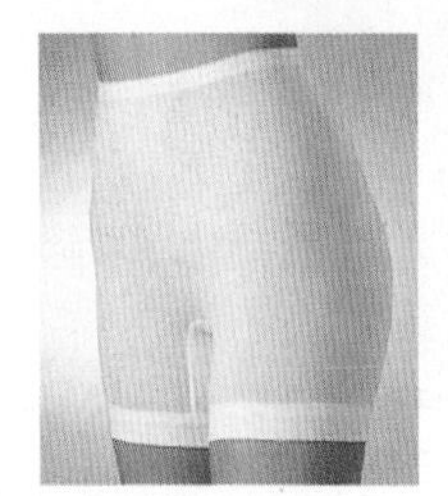
5: long knickers

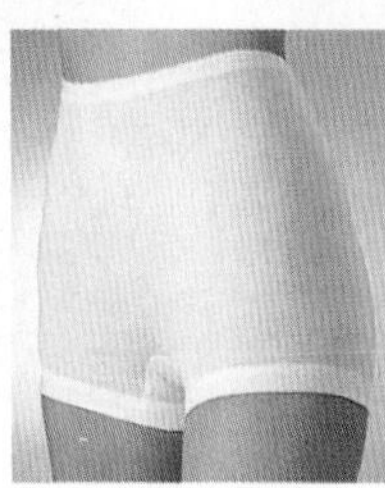
6: short knickers

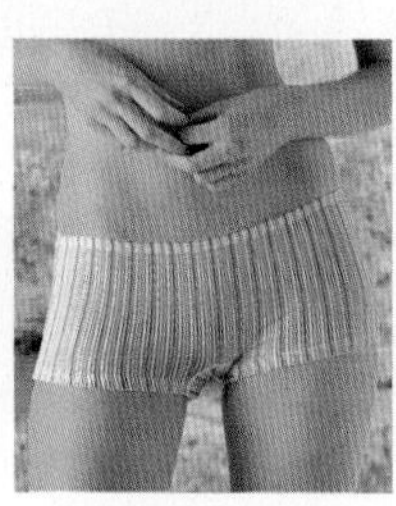
7: shorts

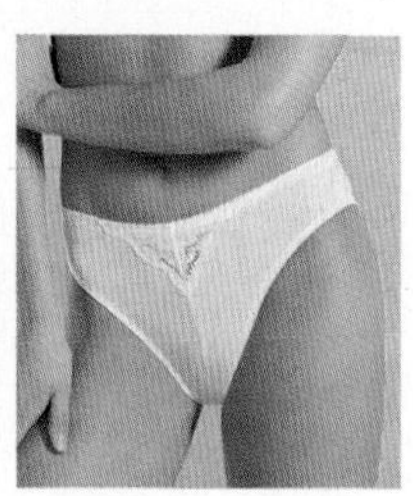
8: high-leg

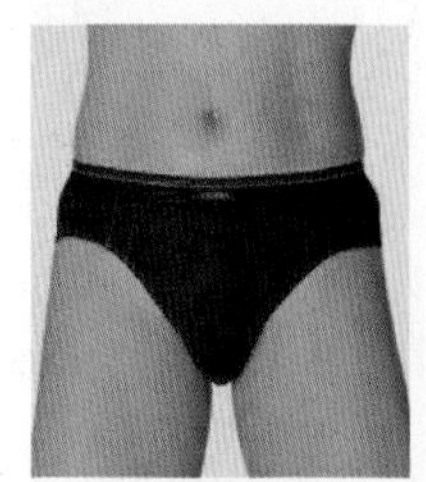
9: mini-slip

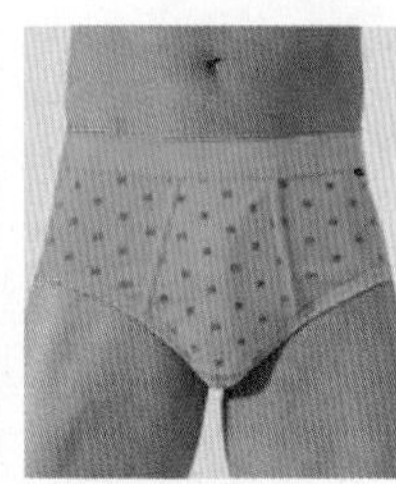
10: slip

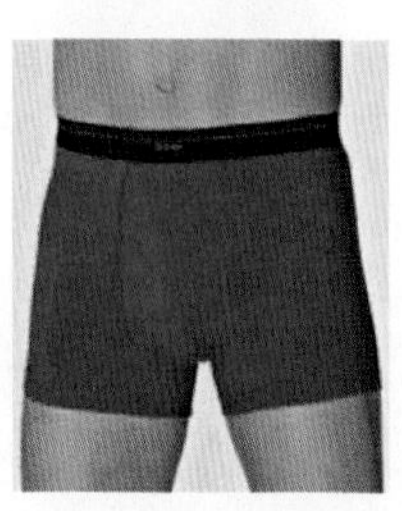
11: briefs

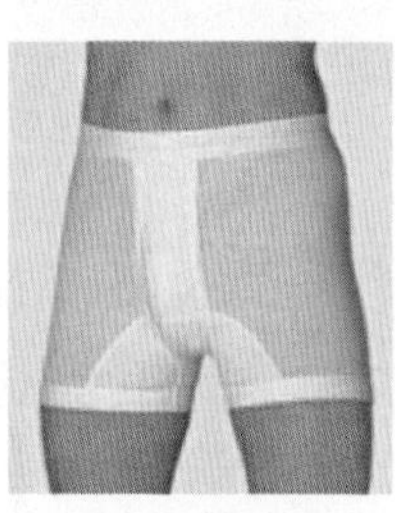
12: fly-front briefs

13: boxers

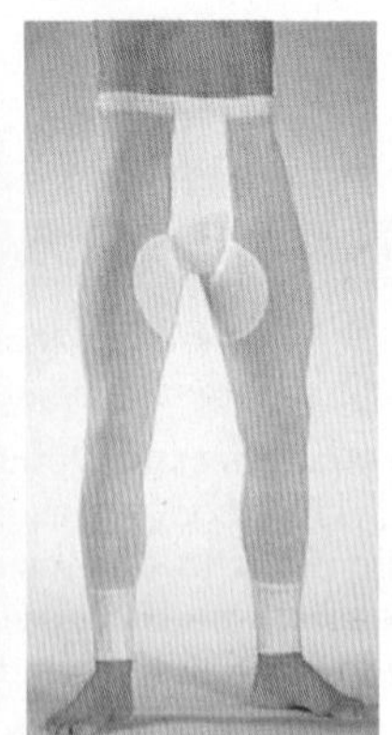
14: long johns

15: leggings, tights

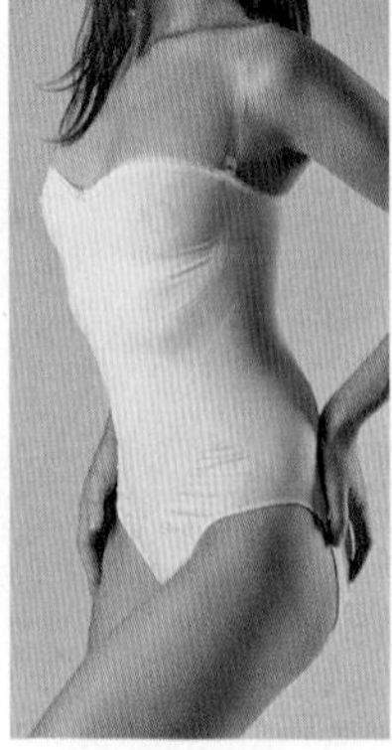
16: body

The **brief** has a cutaway leg opening. Different forms are distinguished by the extent of the cutaway and the height of the waistband. The **full brief** reaches to the waist (*Figure 1*), whereas the **hipster** rests on the hips (*Figure 2*).

The **rio** is a fashionable form with a deep V-shaped waistband and the **bikini** has high cutaway.

The **tanga** (*Figure 3*) is strongly cut away to hip level with quite small front and back pieces. The **thong** is an extreme form of tanga with scarcely any material – particularly at the back.

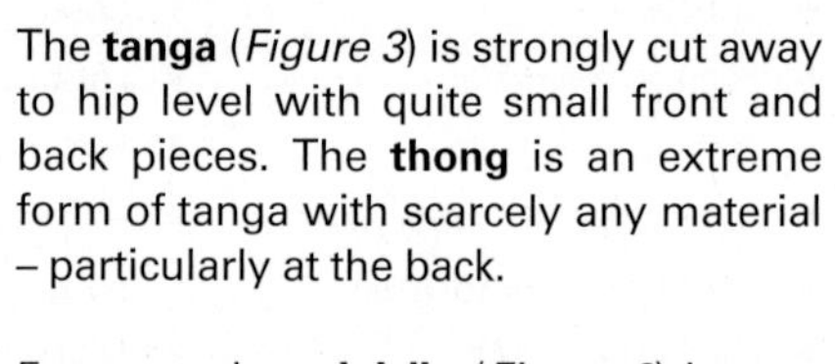

For men, the **minislip** (*Figure 9*) has no front opening but the **slip** (*Figure 10*) is made either with or without an overlapped front opening. **Briefs** (*Figures 11 and 12*) have a higher waistline and usually have an overlapped front opening.

Knickers (*Figures 5 and 6*) are waist-high with short, half length, or long legs The legs are not cut away but run straight across.

Close-fitting midis and shorts (*Figures 4 and 7*) are made from elastic material and usually have a straight cut across the legs. The **high-leg** (*Figure 8*) has a very high cutaway leg opening

Boxer shorts (*Figure 13*) are wide-cut, comfortable underwear with short legs, made from woven or knitted fabrics.

Full length undergarments are called **long johns** (*Figure 14*) or **leggings** (*Figure 15*).

A close fitting, one-piece undergarment is a **body-suit** or body (*Figure 16*). A **body former** fits like a second skin and helps to produce a flattering shape.

14.1.1 Underwear, Nightwear (2)

1: camisole

2: vest

3: sport vest

4: undershirt

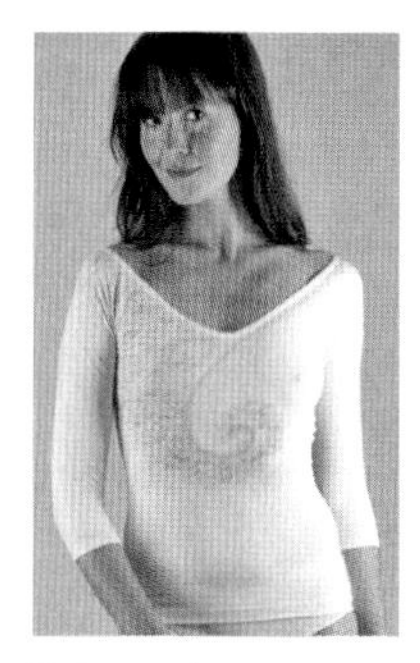

5: long-sleeve vest

6: bra-slip

7: crop-top bra

8: basque

9: underslip

10: nightdress

11: nightshirt

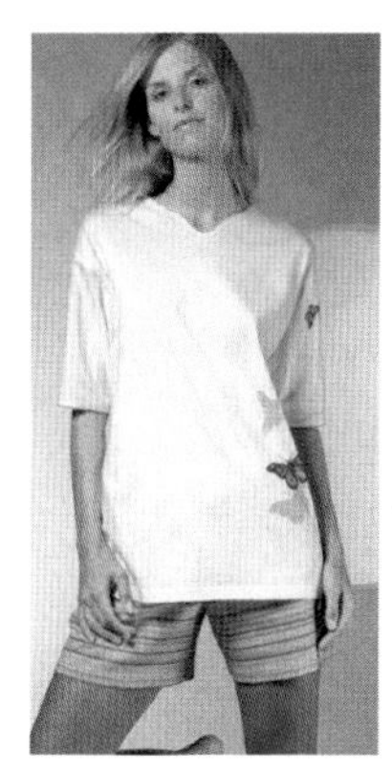

12: shorties

13: long-sleeve pyjamas

14: shorties

15: lounger

16: housecoat, dressing gown

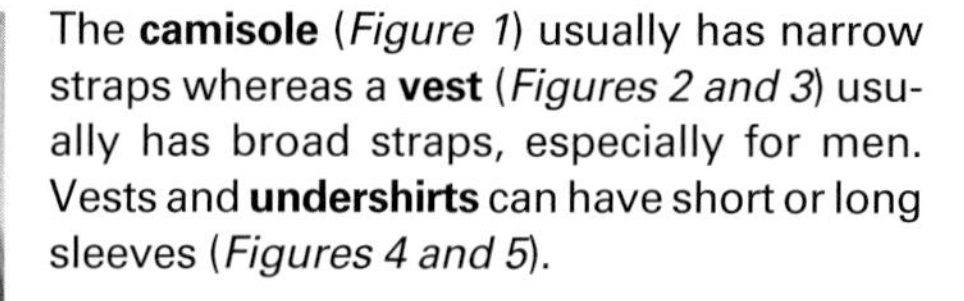

The **camisole** (*Figure 1*) usually has narrow straps whereas a **vest** (*Figures 2 and 3*) usually has broad straps, especially for men. Vests and **undershirts** can have short or long sleeves (*Figures 4 and 5*).

The overslip may be made from elegant material and may be decorated, so it can also be worn as an outerwear top. Ladies vests are often ornamented.

The **bra-slip** (*Figure 6*) is a one piece ladies underslip with bra top included, and the **crop-top bra** (*Figure 7*) is a close-fitting support garment which is deeper than a bra but does not reach the waist.

The thigh-length **underslip** (*Figure 9*) and the shorter, waist- or hip-length camisole are made of fine, smooth, fabrics.

Men's undershirts are generally plain or conservatively patterned but those for ladies may be made from fine, elegant materials and often are embellished with lace or fancy trimmings.

Some of the fancier undergarments (*Figure 8*) can also be adapted for fashionable outerwear.

Nightwear

Nightwear is made predominantly, but by no means exclusively from knitted fabrics. It is not only for sleeping but can be worn in the house, together with a housecoat or dressing gown. The boundary between nightwear and **housewear** can be rather fluid.

The **nightdress** or **nightshirt** (*Figures 10 and 11*) comes in various lengths. Nightdresses can be in any length, from floor to thigh. Nightshirts are from thigh to waist.

Shorties (*Figures 12 and 14*) are a combination of a hip-length shirt with thigh- to knee-length shorts. **Pyjamas** (*Figure 13*) are similar but with long legs.

Housewear is soft, informal, comfortable clothing for wearing indoors within the family. Examples are the **kaftan,** the **lounger** (*Figure 15*), and the **jogging suit.** They are often made from fleece, terry, or plush fabrics.

The **housecoat** or **dressing gown** (*Figure 16*) is a lightweight long coat, often in kimono style, for wearing over nightwear or underwear. An elegant, loose, flimsy style for ladies is the **negligée** which may be combined with a matching nightdress to form a set.

14.1.2 Foundation Garments, Swimwear

Foundation Garments

Foundation garments are close fitting ladies undergarments with shaping and support functions, such as bras, bodices, corsets, corselets and other body-shaping garments. They are mostly made from warp knitted fabrics containing elastomeric yarns. Shaping and support are effected by the particular cut and design of the garment panels and, in the case of bras, by appropriately shaped cups. Matching bra and briefs, in traditional white or in fashionable colours and patterns, are called a set.

1: soft bra

2: underwired bra

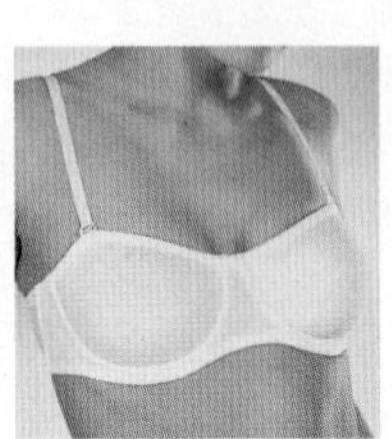
3: multiway bra

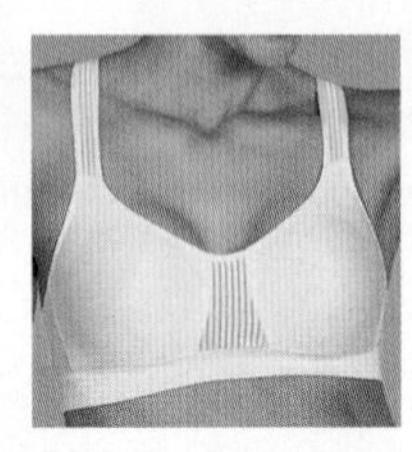
4: sport bra

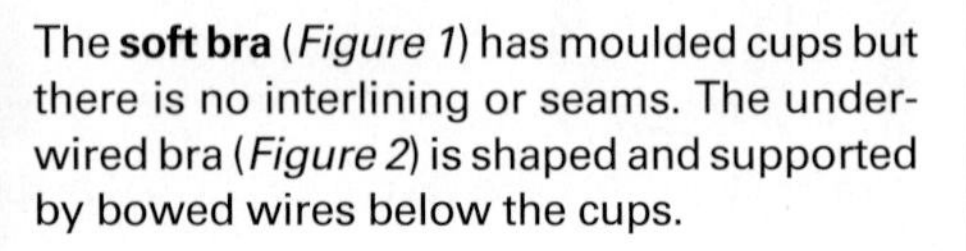

The **soft bra** (*Figure 1*) has moulded cups but there is no interlining or seams. The underwired bra (*Figure 2*) is shaped and supported by bowed wires below the cups.

Bras can have front or rear closings, fixed or removable straps (*Figure 3*). A **sport bra** (*Figure 4*) will usually have broad, padded straps, soft and generous cups, flat seams and net inserts for maximum comfort under stress.

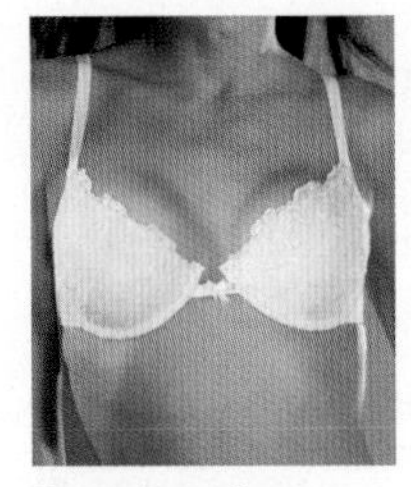
5: push-up bra

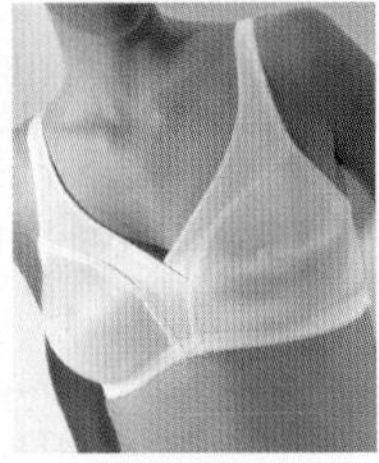
6: minimizer

7: support bra

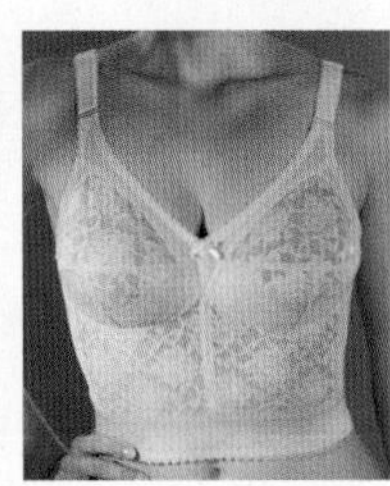
8: longline bra

The **push-up** (*Figure 5*) is constructed so as to raise the breasts, a **padded bra** gives augmentation through sewn-in pads, but the minimizer (*Figure 6*) gives an apparent reduction by spreading and flattening.

Additional support is provided by extra-wide straps to spread the load (*Figure 7*) or by deeper front and back panels, in longline or **bodice** style (*Figure 8*).

9: shaper

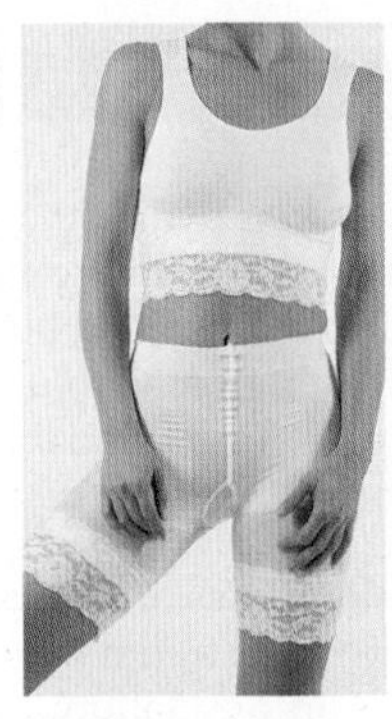
10: longline shaper with crop-top

11: corset

12: corselet

Shapers give more or less support and shaping to the stomach and hips according to their cut and stretch properties. Those without legs are called **shaper briefs** (*Figure 9*). With legs, they are **long shapers** or **longline shapers** (*Figure 10*).

The **girdle** is an elasticated tube that supports the waist and hips. It can have stocking suspenders built in. The **corset** is a one-piece combination of bra and girdle (*Figure 11*) offering both shaping and support. The **corselet** is a lighter and softer version, often with a closed crotch and no suspenders (*Figure 12*).

13: bathing suit with pareo

14: bikini

15: tankini[10)]

16: men's beachwear

Swimwear

Swimwear is mostly made from warp knitted nylon with elastomeric yarns. Colours and designs are very fashionable. The **swimsuit** (*Figure 13*) is a one-piece garment, here shown strapless with a pareo wrap. The **bikini** (*Figure 14*) is a two piece set, usually of much flimsier material. The tankini (*Figure 15*) is a swim-suit top cut off at the hips and a bikini bottom. For men, **swimming trunks** are close-fitting in a brief style (*Figure 16 below*). **Beach shorts** (*Figure 16 above*) have a wider and longer fit in lighter materials.

14.1.3 Babywear, Childrenswear

Clothing for babies, toddlers and children has to take account of the special needs of this age group. **Requirements** include freedom of movement, comfort, skin-friendliness, durability and easy care. Cotton and blends are the most common fibres. Blending with polyester improves easy care performance and durability. There is a tendency for next-to-skin garments to be produced according to the Ecotex 100 Standard.

Clothing for Babies and Toddlers

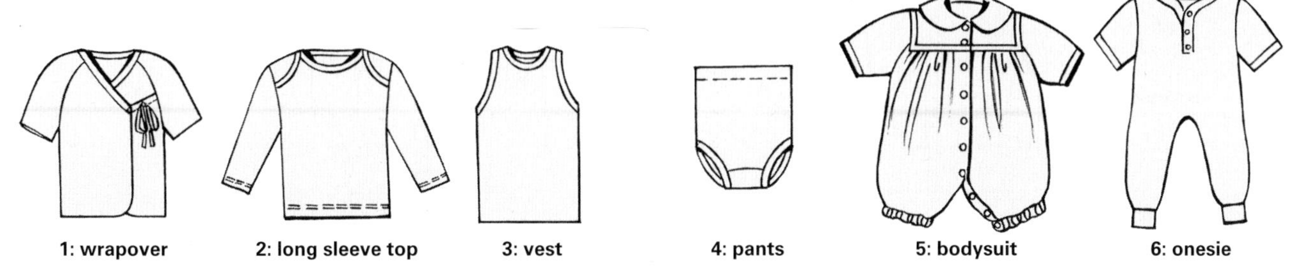

1: wrapover **2: long sleeve top** **3: vest** **4: pants** **5: bodysuit** **6: onesie**

Knitted **wrapovers** and ribbon-tie jackets are for very young babies. Long or short-sleeved **tops** have a comfortable neckline. **Vests** and **pants** are made in single jersey, fine rib, or interlock; printed or plain dyed. **Bodysuits** are one-piece garments used as underwear or outerwear. Fastenings at the crotch are simple and functional. They, and **onesies** may have long, short, or no arms. They are often made in terry or plush or interlock fabrics. They can also be made in single jersey or fine rib for sleepwear. **Outdoor coveralls** can be one-piece, or jacket and trouser combinations with hoods, mitts and shoes

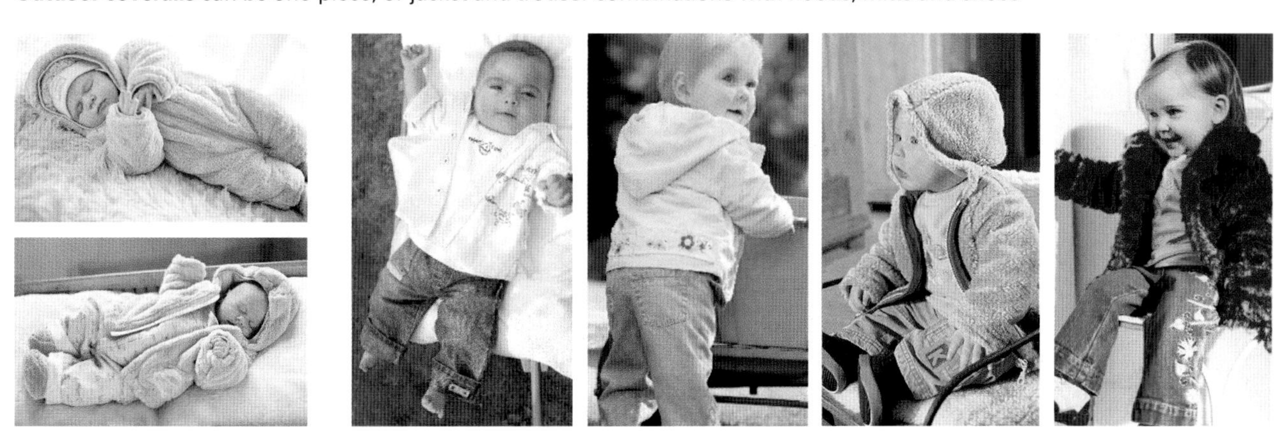

7; 8: Outdoor coveralls

9; 10; 11; 12: Clothing for toddlers

Childrenswear

Children's underwear and outerwear is largely similar to that for adults. The sizes are usually related to stature, ranging from about 104 to 182 cm in steps of 6 cm. The outerwear is usually functional, with bright colours and comfortable styles.

13; 14; 15: Girlswear

16; 17; 18: Boyswear

14.1.4 Men's Shirts

Men's shirts are produced in a wide range of colours, styles, and materials depending on the purpose, season and fashion trend e.g. business shirts, dress shirts, leisure shirts, etc. The distinguishing details are in the front and back styling, the collar and the cuffs.

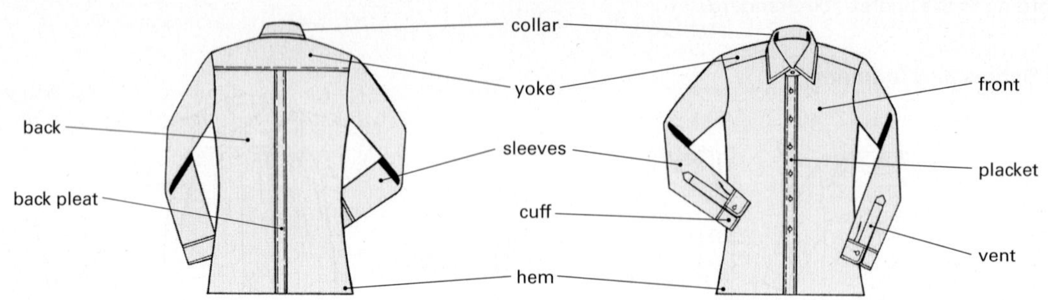

1: Parts of a shirt

Shirts are mostly made from woven fabrics such as poplin, flannel, batiste, oxford, madras, seersucker, hopsack, gingham. Some casual shirts are made from knitted fabrics such as interlock, rib and piqué. The most common fibres are cotton and polyester/cotton blends but shirts are also made from silk, linen, wool, viscose, lyocell and nylon either alone or in various fibre blends and yarn mixtures.

The main control dimension for shirts is the neck size, in inches or cm, with two neck sizes per body size.

37/38 = S, 39/40 = M, 41/42 = L, 43/44 = XL, 45/46 = XXL

The most important style variations are illustrated in the sketches below.

Front

Plain front with no button placket.

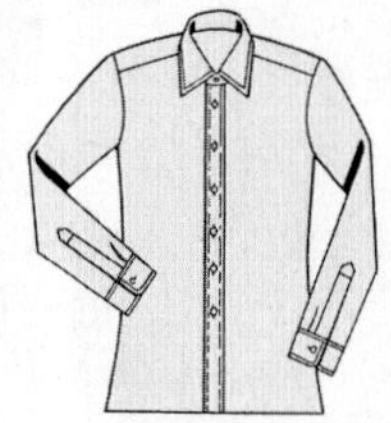

Standard front with button placket

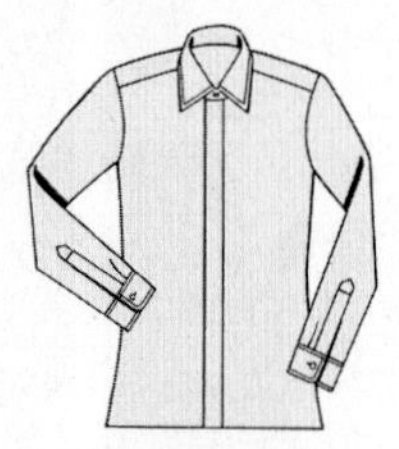

Covered button placket

Bib insert

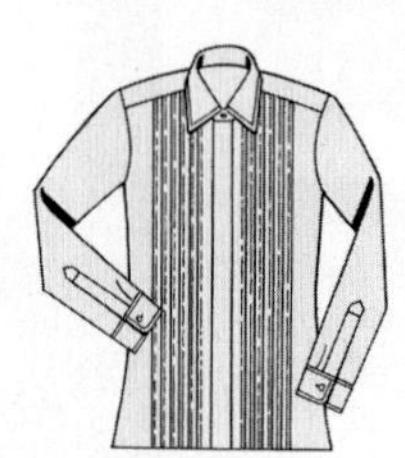

Pleated front

Cowboy yoke

Back

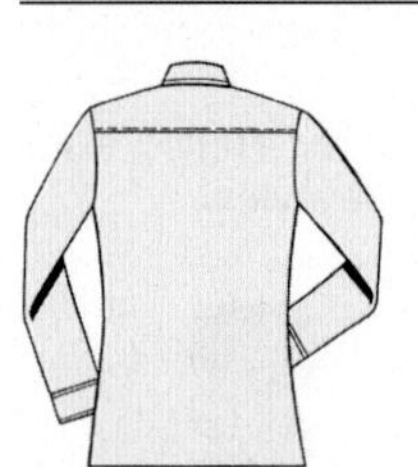

Straight back

Full pleat

Sectioned

Gathered pleats

Cuffs

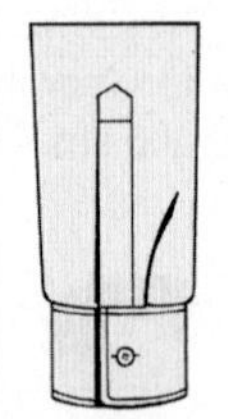

Plain cuff

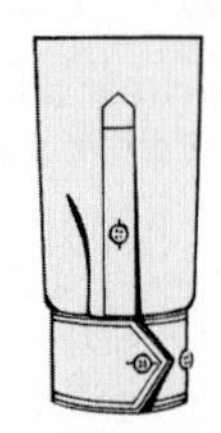

Pointed cuff

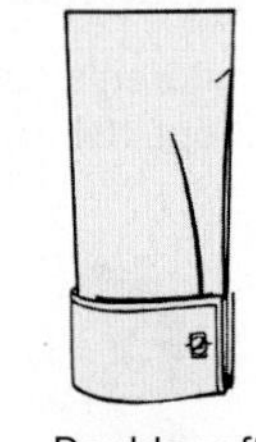

Double cuff

Collars

Classic, standard

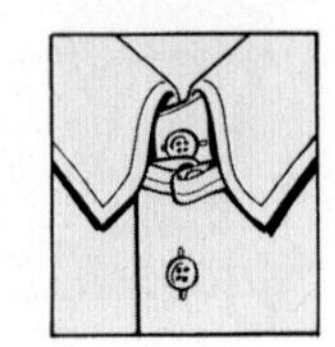

Tab (with press-stud)

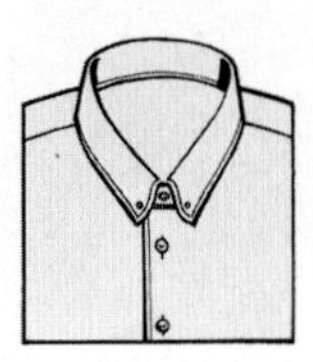

Piccadilly (with pin)

Button-down

Open

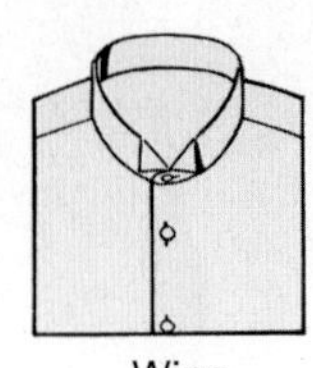

Wing (for dress shirts)

14.1.5 Workwear, Career Apparel

Workwear is clothing that is suited to workers in specific occupations, by its material, function, cut and details. It can also serve to identify particular occupations e.g. waiter, chambermaid. Certain categories of workwear are given soil resistant finishes. Functional details may include special loops and pockets for tools such as hammers and folding rules.

Protective clothing has additional requirements, depending on the occupational sector and the safety requirements. Protective clothing is seldom universally applicable – it is designed for the demands of a particular end use (*see page 51*).

Requirements for workwear include durability plus easy handling and appropriate, economic aftercare. These are provided through choice of fibres, processing, finishing and garment design. Workwear is made mostly from cotton, polyester, polyamide and blends.

1: protective suit with reflective stripes

2: work suit

3: overall (boiler suit)

4: guild uniform

5: bib and brace

6: tool-carrying waistcoat & trousers with holster-pockets

7: work coat

8: apron

9, 10: restaurant staff

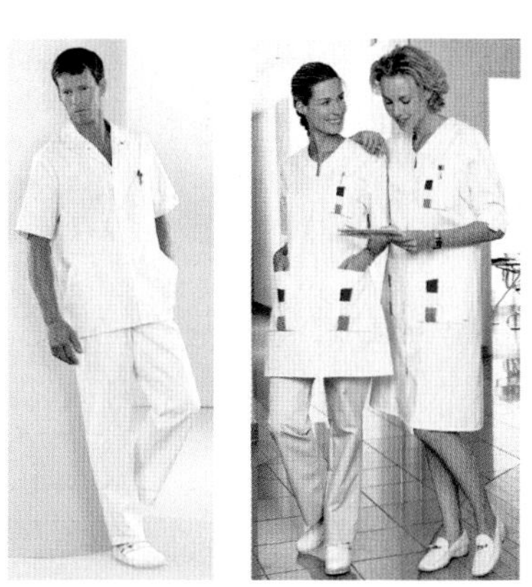

11, 12: medical staff

Work outfits can be a jacket and trousers (*Figures 1 and 2*) or a one-piece overall (*Figure 3*). They are made in durable weaves such as drill, canvas and cord. Typical details would be adjustable fastenings, knee reinforcement and divided pockets appropriately placed.

Work trousers are designed according to the workplace, with special features such as a bib with braces (*Figure 5*), protective padding, rule pocket, tool suspension loops (*Figure 6*).

Waistcoats specially designed for tradesmen have many pockets and loops suitable for storing hand tools (*Figure 6*). Waistcoats made from elegant fabrics e.g. satin, jacquard in the style of a classic men's waistcoat are used by waiters (*Figure 10*). Outdoor workers such as foresters and farmworkers use waistcoats or sleeveless jackets made from heavier, warmer, multilayered materials.

Jackets and smocks (*Figures 9, 11 and 12*) are made from medium weight plain weaves, twills or satins. They may be worn over other clothing. The design is specific to the end use e.g. painters, chefs, nurses, dentists.

Work coats in classic or fashionable cuts have buttoned fronts, functional pockets, and short or long sleeves (*Figures 7 and 12*). They are made from heavier fabrics like gabardine or workwear twill and are often worn over other work clothes.

Pinafores are made from lightweight fabrics e.g. calico, cretonne. They wrap around the whole lower body, may or may not have a waistband, usually have a bib with halter and are fastened by tapes rather than buttons. Versions for restaurant and cocktail waitresses are made from lighter materials such as batiste and can be ornamented with frills, trimmings and pleats. An **apron** (*Figure 8*) is a simple, sturdy one-piece construction with bib and halter. It also encloses the whole lower body and, depending on the end use, may be made from leather, strong woven fabric, or coated fabric.

Work shirts made from fine twill and flannel are usually chequered and raised (*Figure 7*). Smooth fabrics like poplin, fine gabardine and hopsack are usually plain dyed.

14.2.1 Skirts (1)

Nowadays, the term skirt is used for an item of clothing worn from the waist down and which is the basic element of women's and girls' clothing. A matching jacket with a skirt makes a suit, or costume. Many styles of skirt are subject to changes in fashion. Other styles are considered classics, or timeless. Individual styles are distinguished by length, width, silhouette, cut and details.

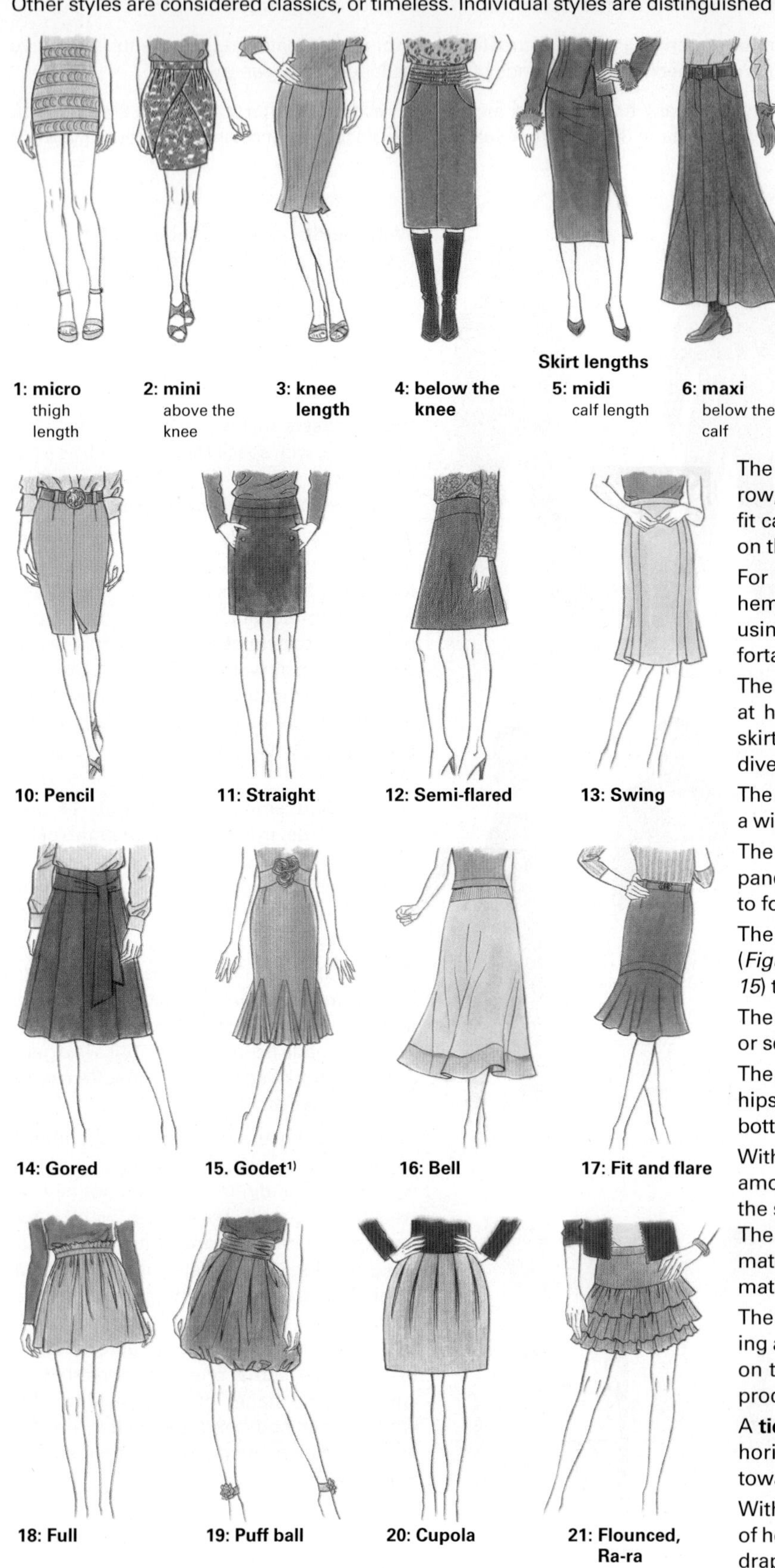

Skirt lengths

1: micro thigh length; **2: mini** above the knee; **3: knee length**; **4: below the knee**; **5: midi** calf length; **6: maxi** below the calf; **7: ankle length** above the shoes; **8: floor length** covers the shoes; **9: trailing** overlength

10: Pencil **11: Straight** **12: Semi-flared** **13: Swing**

14: Gored **15. Godet**[1] **16: Bell** **17: Fit and flare**

18: Full **19: Puff ball** **20: Cupola** **21: Flounced, Ra-ra**

[1] godet (Fr.) = flared, fluted

The elegant **pencil** skirt (*Figure 5*) is rather narrow, with a knee or midi length. A close, smooth fit can be effected by means of an elastic insert on the reverse.

For the closest fit (*Figure 10*), the width at the hem is made narrower than that at the hips using side seams. A slit at the hem allows comfortable walking.

The **straight** skirt (*Figure 11*) has the same width at hips and hemline, whereas the **semi-flared** skirt (*Figure 12*) has a wider hemline due to diverging side seams.

The **swing** skirt (*Figure 13*) is close at the hips with a wide hem obtained by shaped vertical panels.

The **gored** style (*Figure 14*) has symmetrical panels that become broader from waist to hem, to form a flared or semi-flared silhouette.

The **godet**[1] style has either shaped panels (*Figure 3*) or bell-shaped inserts (*Figures 6 and 15*) to allow the hem to swing out.

The **bell** skirt (*Figure 16*) is formed from circular or semi-circular panels.

The **fit and flare** style (*Figure 17*) is narrow at the hips, with a flared, gathered section near the bottom.

With a **full** or **full flare** style (*Figure 18*) the large amount of material, gathered at the waist, makes the skirt billow out to a greater or lesser extent. The **puff ball** style (*Figure 19*) is similar but the material is also gathered at the hem so that the material puffs out between waist and hem.

The **cupola** silhouette (*Figure 20*) is formed using a relatively firm top cloth and reinforcement on the reverse. A **tulip** shape (*Figure 2*) can be produced using special pleating or overlays.

A **tiered** skirt (*Figure 7*) is built from successive horizontal panels, which increase in width towards the hem.

With the **flounced** skirt (*Figure 21*) a succession of horizontal flounces is sewn onto the skirt and drape freely The very short version is called a **Ra-ra**.

14.2.1 Skirts (2)

Pleats and folds are comfortable and attractive. They are equally pleasant with sporty or elegant looks and are made in many different styles, such as the **centre pleat** (*Figure 22*), **side pleat** (*Figure 23*), **all-round pleat** (*Figure 24*), **furbelow** (*Figure 25*), or **bunched pleats** (*Figure 26*). Pleats can be soft, flared, or sharply pressed. Special types are **sunray** (*Figure 27*), **umbrella** (*Figure 28*), and **scissor** (*Figure 29*).

Pleats

22: Centre inverted pleat — **23: Side** inverted pleat — **24: All-round** accordion pleat — **25: Furbelow** — **26: Bunch** knife pleats — **27: Plissé** sun-ray pleats — **28: Umbrella** — **29: Scissor**

30: Box — **31: Zipper** — **32: Sporty, casual** — **33: Cargo**

34: Yoked — **35: Flounced** — **36: Layered** — **37: Draped**

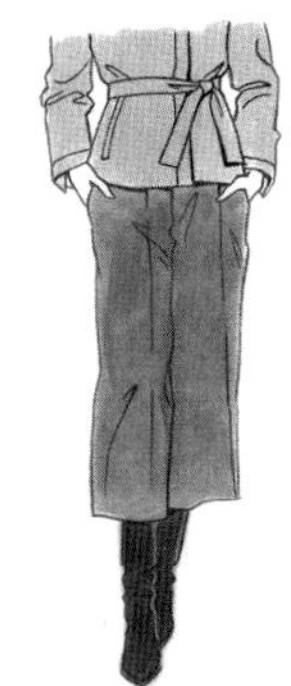

38: Wrap-around — **39: Handerchief** — **40: Slip-on** — **41: Culottes**

Inverted, accordion, and knife pleats are pressed sharp. **Sunray pleats** (*Figure 27*) and **umbrella pleats** (*Figure 28*) are formed from panels that widen towards the hemline.

Scissor pleats (*Figure 29*) are made from one or more deep gathers at the waistline which fall to a narrowed hemline.

The **box skirt** (*Figure 30*) is a straight, narrow cut with clearly defined panel seams and vertical details.

With the **zipper skirt** (*Figure 31*) one or more of the panels is joined wholly or partly by a long zipper, which can be simply a fashion detail but may also be functional. The **sporty casual skirt** (*Figure 32*) may have details such as patch pockets and a button-through style.

The **cargo skirt** (*Figure 33*) will have decorative stitching on large bag pockets and back pockets as well as side pockets.

A **yoke** is a flat section from waist to hip all around the top of the skirt. It can be straight, bowed, or pointed. The lower skirt may gathered at the yoke (*Figure 34*) or pleated, or straight with a slit or inserted pleats at the hem.

Flounced (*Figure 35*), **frilled,** and **tiered** skirts belong to the romantic and folkloric themes.

With the **layered look** (*Figure 36*) components of different lengths are superimposed. Often, the components are sewn at different angles or with different styles (gathered, frilled).

An elegant, sophisticated and feminine style is achieved with the softly-folded, **draped skirt** (*Figure 37*).

The **wrap-around** (*Figure 38*) has an open edge with a large overlap which is usually fastened only at the waist. The asymmetric or **handkerchief hemline** (*Figure 39*) gives an elegant, folkloric style.

The **slip-on** (*Figure 40*) has a broadened elasticated waist-band, which makes it quick and easy to put on and off.

Culottes (*Figure 41*) are shorts or trousers, but with legs so wide that the effect is of a skirt.

14.2.2 Blouses

The blouse is an outerwear garment, fitted or loose, for the upper body. It is worn either over or tucked into a skirt or trousers. A wide range of styles is created by differences in cut, collar, length, width, details, decoration and materials.

1: Shirt style 2: Blouson 3: Denim style 4: Knitted top

5: Tie neck 6: Peplum 7: Slip-on 8: Kimono sleeve

9: Romantic style 10: Sleeveless top 11: Frilly style 12: Carmen

13: Tunic 14: Cossack 15: Wrap-over 16: Jacket style

The **shirt blouse** (*Figure 1*) has the typical features of a man's shirt: collar, cuffs, button placket and breast pocket.

The **blouson** (*Figure 2*) has a very full cut but is brought together at the waist. The **denim style** (*Figure 3*) is a sportier shirt, usually in indigo fabric.

A **knitted top** (*Figure 4*) may also be called a jersey top or a **polo shirt,** depending on the fabric.

The elongated, voluminous collar bands of the **tie-neck** (*Figure 5*) are loosely knotted or tied in a bow.

The **peplum** (*Figure 6*) is a very feminine style with a short, loosely draped, pleated, flounced or gathered skirt (peplum) from the waist to about the hips.

Slip-on is a generic term for an item that has to be pulled on over the head (*Figure 7*).

The essential feature of a **kimono sleeve** (*Figure 8*) is a very wide arm opening at the side seam (armscye).

Elements of the **romantic style** (*Figure 9*) are a stand-up collar, decorative embroidery, lace, frills, ruffles and ruches.

A simple **sleeveless top** (*Figure 10*) can be made in knitted or woven material, in various lengths, with wide or narrow shoulder straps, loose or fitted.

Frills and ruches are elements of the romantic and folklore styles but may also be used as a simple decoration to soften a classic blouse (*Figure 11*).

The **Carmen** (*Figure 12*) is a folklore style featuring an off-the-shoulder, low-cut neckline with frilled or flounced trimmings.

The **tunic** (*Figure 13*) is long and loose, though it may be worn belted. Often it is embellished with ethnic or folkloric embroidery or printing.

The **Cossack** (*Figure 14*) is a straight-cut tunic style, usually worn belted.

The **wrap-over** (*Figure 15*) has overlapping edges and either is provided with attached ties or with a belt of the same fabric.

A long, unlined **jacket blouse** (*Figure 16*) is worn over a light slip-on, T-shirt, or sleeveless top.

14.2.3 Dresses

The dress is a basic item of female outer clothing. In its original form, a shift or smock, it was worn in ancient times. In the narrow sense, the term is used for a single piece of clothing comprising an upper body part and a skirt section, either cut from the same panels or sewn on. In a two piece the matching top and skirt are made separately (*see page 254*).

Individual styles of dresses differ in width, silhouette, cut, details and decoration.

The **shift dress** (*Figure 1*) is rather straight and loose but yet reveals the body shape below. Many variations are possible.

The **sheath dress** (*Figure 2*) shows off the figure but is not constricting. The shape is revealed by the cut or by the use of elastic material. With a small armscye and short sleeves it is practical and feminine.

The **loose dress** is a free-falling style with a wide hemline (*Figure 3*).

The **princess style** (*Figure 4*) has long, vertical seams (Viennese seams from the armscye or English seams from the shoulder). The upper body is close fitting but the skirt is flared and swinging.

The **pinafore dress** may have short, broad shoulder straps (*Figure 5*) or long narrow ones. Often it is worn over a jumper or top and with leggings.

The **dirndl** (*Figure 6*) is based on traditional Tyrolean dress, with a straight or laced low-cut bodice, puffed arms, a wide skirt, ruches, ruffles and an apron.

The **shirtwaister** dress is based on the typical men's shirt style. It may have a button placket just for the upper body or may be buttoned all the way through, with a belt. The **coat dress** (*Figure 7*) is similar but made from firmer material, styled on a trench coat and is always buttoned right through and belted.

The **wrap-around** (*Figure 8*) has open edges with a generous overlap. It is tied at the side and drapes in a very feminine style.

The **empire style** (*Figure 9*) is characterised by the high, figure-hugging, gathered, under-bust seam and the slim silhouette.

The **cocktail dress** or **party dress** (*Figure 10*) is for small semi-formal occasions. Often the upper body is close-fitting and strapless or with very thin straps.

The **folklore style** (*Figure 11*) exhibits features of the romantic style, such as embroidery, lace, ruches and flounces. However, it can also refer to **ethnic styles** (*Figure 12*) with e.g. Indian, Japanese, Chinese, or African influences.

14.2.4 Knitted Outerwear

Knitted outerwear is highly popular as it is very comfortable. It is indispensable in sportswear, leisure wear and casual clothing. Bulky knitted fabrics are particularly suited for warm outer clothing. Their resistance to wrinkling and creasing can also be an advantage.

1: Basic T-shirt

2: Polo shirt

3: Sweatshirt

4: Tunic with waterfall neckline

5: Round-neck pullover

6: V-neck pullover

7: Troyer fisherman's sweater

8: Boat-neck Parallelo

9: Tank top

10: Waistcoat

11: Jacket

12: Cardigan

13: Long pullover with open collar

14: Roll-neck jumper and waistcoat

15: Twinset

16: Two-in-One

The term **T-shirt** is used generally for casual tops with a narrow neckline, short sleeves and no collar, usually made from cotton (*Figure 1*).

The **polo shirt** (*Figure 2*) is similar to a shirt or blouse and is made from a light, knitted material in a slip-on design. It always has a collar and a short button placket. It can have either short or long sleeves.

The **sweatshirt** is a long-sleeved jumper usually made from cotton or cotton/polyester loopback or brushed fleece fabric. Many different styles of neckline, collar, closings and hoods are available (*Figure 3*).

Ladies' knitted tops, shirts and tunics come in many different designs with long or short sleeves (*Figures 4 and 13*).

Pullovers or **jumpers** can have long or short sleeves or no sleeves, with round necks, V necks, boat necks, turtle necks, roll necks or collars with zips or buttons (*Figures 5 to 9, 13, 14 and 15*).

The **troyer** or **fisherman's sweater** is a heavy, close-knit construction with a roll-neck or a stand-up collar with buttons or a zip (*Figure 7*).

The **parallelo** is a sweater with kimono style sleeves (*Figure 8*). The square look is accented by rib or cable patterning.

The **tank top** (*Figure 9*) is a sleeveless pullover, usually waist length and worn over a blouse or shirt.

The classic **waistcoat** is a sleeveless jacket, usually waist length (*Figure 10*). It can be provided either with buttons or a zipper. *Figure 14* shows a more fashionable development with cap sleeves.

Knitted jackets (*Figure 11*) are fastened by buttons or zips and often have a distinct waistband. The **cardigan** is a jacket with no collar (*Figure 12*).

The **long pullover** (*Figure 13*) can be close-fitting or very wide, often worn with a belt.

The **roll-neck** (*Figure 14*) is usually made of rather fine fabric, for wearing under a cardigan or jacket.

The **twinset** (*Figure 15*) is a classic combination of matching pullover and cardigan for women. The **two-in-one** (*Figure 16*) has the look of a twinset in a single garment.

14.2.5 Trousers

Trousers (pants) are a basic item in both male and female wardrobes. The various styles of trousers have developed mainly from different functional uses, but they are also influenced to a greater or lesser extent by fashion. Length, width and silhouette, cut and details distinguish the different styles.

1: Leggings **2: Skinny jeans** **3: Straight leg** **4: Flared** **5: Palazzos**

6: Shorts **7: Bermuda shorts** **8: Capri pants** **9: ³/₄ length** **10: ⁷/₈ length**

11: Pleated waist **12: Chinos** **13: Ski pants, stirrup pants** **14: Boot cut jeans** **15: Cargo pants**

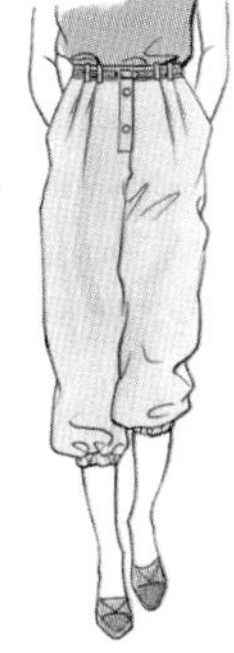

16: Knee breeches **17: Knicker-bockers** **18: Harem pants, (short)** **19: Harem pants, (long)** **20: Carrot pants**

Leggings (*Figure 1*) are tight fitting and made from elastic material. **Jeggings** are a combination of jeans and leggings.

Skinny pants have a very narrow leg. *Figure 2* shows an overlength style.

With **straight-leg pants** (*Figure 3*), the width at knee and bottom is the same whereas with **flares,** the leg widens towards the bottom (*Figure 4*).

Palazzos (*Figure 5*) have a very wide, straight cut.

Shorts (*Figures 6 and 7*) are available in various lengths. **Hot pants** are very short and close fitting; **Bermuda shorts** are just above knee length with a generous fit.

Capri pants (*Figure 8*) are just below knee length with fitted legs and, usually, a slit at the bottoms.

Three-quarter and **seven eights** trousers (*Figures 9 and 10*) may be wide or narrow, sporty or elegant.

A **pleated waist** (*Figure 11*) gives a comfortable width. The classical form has pressed pleats.

Chinos (*Figure 12*) are casual leisure trousers in soft cotton twill fabrics: lightweight for summer and heavier in winter.

Foot straps hold the **ski pant** style trousers tight and straight (*Figure 13*).

Jeans (*Figure 14*) are characterised by prominent decorative stitching, leather brand labels and the "five-pocket" details.

Cargo pants (*Figure 15*) have large bag pockets at the thighs with normal side and back pockets.

Knee breeches and **knickerbockers** (*Figures 16 and 17*) are knee- to calf-length trousers with buttoned cuffs. They hark back to traditional designs such as **plus-fours** for golf, walking and country sports, but are also adapted as modern fashion items.

Harem pants (*Figures 18 and 19*) are available in a wide range of lengths and widths, but all are relatively wide and gathered at the waist with a tight-fitting bottom cuff. **Aladdin pants, pump pants or salvars (chalvars)** also have a very deep, wide crotch seam.

Carrot pants (*Figure 20*) are wide at the hip with legs that taper to a fairly close fit at the bottom.

14.2.6 Jackets

The jacket is a basic item of outerwear worn by men, women and children alike. In matching fabrics, they turn trousers or a skirt into a suit. The distinguishing features between individual designs for example, length, width, silhouette, cut and details, as well as the material, production and finish are determined by the particular fashion style and the practical purpose.

1: Bolero; 2: Waistcoat, Gilet; 3: Spencer; 4: Short, cropped; 5: Janker; 6: Blazer; 7: Tailored; 8: Edge-to-edge; 9: Shirt jacket; 10: Blouson; 11: Lumber jacket; 12: Anorak; 13: Coat jacket; 14: Parka; 15: Pea coat, reefer; 16: Long waistcoat

The **bolero** (*Figure 1*) is a short, open jacket. Usually it has an open front with no collar and short or no sleeves.

The **waistcoat** (*Figure 2*) is modelled on the classic gent's waistcoat, with a lightweight, tailored construction, reaching to just below the waist and with a back panel of lining fabric. The **gilet** is a similar, sleeveless construction but may be a looser fit, less tailored and may also be a longer and heavier, padded garment for outdoors wear.

The **spencer** is a close-fitted, tailored jacket with long sleeves. The bottom hem is at or above the waist and can be straight or pointed (*Figure 3*).

The **short jacket** (*Figure 4*), or jacket top, is relatively short and loose in a straight cut.

The **janker** (*Figure 5*) is either collarless or has a short stand-up collar and a straight cut. It is often made of milled fabric, such as loden.

The **blazer** (*Figure 6*) is a sporty, elegant, tailored jacket in a masculine style. It can be single or double-breasted and may be embellished with nautical features such as embossed metal buttons.

A **tailored jacket** is a general term for any ladies jacket that has significant decorative tailoring work embodied. Usually it will be rather close-fitting (*Figure 7*).

With an **edge-to-edge jacket,** there are no front closings. The front edges may just meet (*Figure 8*) or may be more or less well separated.

The **shirt jacket** (*Figure 9*) is modelled on the man's shirt, but in heavier fabric. It can be tailored or straight and usually is unlined.

The **blouson** (*Figure 10*) has a comfortable, wide fit whereas the **lumber jacket** (*Figure 11*) is narrower. Both have close-fitting waistbands.

The **anorak** (*Figure 12*) or **windcheater** is an all-weather, windproof jacket with a hood. It may have a waistband or the waist can be drawn in with a cord built into the hemline.

The **coat jacket** (*Figure 13*) is in the style of an overcoat, but reaches only to the crotch or just below.

The **parka** (*Figure 14*) is a long, voluminous, weatherproof jacket with roomy pockets, a hood and draw-strings at the waist and hem.

The **pea coat or reefer** (*Figure 15*) is modelled on a sailor's heavy, double breasted short coat.

The **long waistcoat** (*Figure 16*) is like an overlength cardigan, usually without closings at the front.

14.2.7 Coats

The coat is an item of outer clothing and is an essential part of women's, men's and children's clothing. It is longer than a jacket and is also more generously cut. The cut and material determine different styles, which in turn are fitted to different functions. The various styles are distinguished by the length, width, silhouette, cut and details.

1: Straight 2: Swing, flared 3: Cape 4: Redingote

5: Raincoat 6: Duffle coat 7: Trench coat 8: Wrap

9: Raglan

10: Ulster, greatcoat

11: Chesterfield

12: Blazer style

The **straight coat** (*Figure 1*) hangs straight from the shoulders, or is very slightly flared.

The **swing or flared coat** (*Figure 2*) features narrow shoulders and a wide swinging hem.

The **cape** (*Figure 3*) is a wide, sleeveless cloak of various lengths. The coat-style design usually has holes for the arms.

The **redingote** is a fitted women's coat with lapels and long vertical seams which widen to provide a flared or semi-flared hem. The long seams may be Viennese style, from the armscye (*Figure 4*), or English style, from the shoulder.

Figure 5 shows a standard style of **raincoat** or **overcoat** with concealed buttons, a shoulder yoke and a straight or slightly tailored fit.

The **duffle coat** (*Figure 6*) is a casual short coat with a box-like cut, large patch pockets, toggle fastenings and a hood.

The **trench coat** (*Figure 7*) is an all-weather coat with a double-breasted, loose cut, with broad lapels and a shoulder yoke. It is worn belted. Shoulder straps, shoulder pads and wrist straps are typical details.

The **wrap** generally has a comfortable width with a wrap-over construction and is held together simply by a belt. Popular details are raglan sleeves and shawl collars. There are both sporty (*Figure 8*) and elegant styles.

The **raglan** coat (*Figure 9*) has the characteristic raglan sleeve, whose seam extends all the way to the collar. It is most commonly seen in men's raincoats with concealed buttons and a broad collar.

The **Ulster** or **greatcoat** (*Figure 10*) is a heavy, warm, winter overcoat with a straight cut, usually double-breasted.

The **Chesterfield** (*Figure 11*) is a heavy, thick men's coat with wide, suit-style lapels and flap pockets. They are usually double-breasted.

The **blazer style** ladies coat (*Figure 12*) is in the style of a man's suit jacket, has a fitted cut with lapels and is single or double breasted with flap pockets.

14.2.8 Women's Outfits

Since the end of the nineteenth century, putting together several items of clothing to form a whole outfit has been part of the sophisticated female wardrobe. Whilst the earlier classic combinations such as the **ensemble**[1] and the **complet**[2] always formed a complete outfit and were also mainly made of the same material, today's unconventional combination fashion allows outfits to be put together according to individual taste.

1: Tailored suit

2: Chanel suit[3]

3: Traditional look

4: Trouser suit in safari look

5: Jacket dress

6: Two-piece

7: Complet[2]

8: Composé[4]**, Ensemble**[1]

9: Three piece, ensemble

10: Trouser-ensemble, co-ordinates

11, 12: Separates in a mix of denim and folklore styles

The **suit** or **costume** consists of a skirt and jacket, possibly accompanied by a waistcoat. A strong, masculine finish, as well as high quality classic material, are characteristics of the **tailored suit** (*Figure 1*). The fitted jacket with lapels is single or double-breasted, has double-seamed sleeves and fitted pockets. The skirt has a narrow cut and is always made of the same material as the jacket.

Fashion suits generally have a less severe finish and have popular technical details in the cut. Trimmings, embellishments and decoration are frequently used. Trousers can be substituted for the skirt. The suits are usually described according to the design of the jacket or the style (*Figures 2, 3 and 4*).

The **jacket dress** (*Figure 5*) combines a one-piece dress with a jacket whilst the **two-piece** (*Figure 6*) is a suit that consists of a matching skirt and top. Combination of a matching jacket and two-piece gives a **three-piece** costume (*Figure 9*).

The **complet**[2] (*Figure 7*) is a combination of a skirt, dress, suit, or trouser suit with a coat or long jacket, all of matching materials, whereas with the **composé**[4] (*Figure 8*) the individual components can be of different, though complementary fabrics, which can also be trimmed or decorated.

The **ensemble**[1] (*Figures 8 and 9*) puts together items of clothing which complement each other in style, colour and material to form a whole outfit.

The term **co-ordinates** is used for combinations which are made out of co-ordinating materials, e.g. the same pattern on a different fabric; the same pattern on a different scale or in different colours; a different pattern in the same colouring (*Figure 10*).

Separates (*Figures 11 and 12*) are co-ordinating garments, displayed and sold as separate items. The purchaser selects from the range to produce an outfit.

[1] ensemble (Fr.) = together, harmoniously
[2] complet (Fr.) = complete
[3] Coco Chanel: French couturier
[4] composé (Fr.) = combined

14.2.9 Men's Outfits

The basic men's outfit consists of a combination of **jacket** and **trousers.** Material, cut and details are chosen according to the purpose. Conventional designs dominate but the influence of fashion is nevertheless evident.

The two-piece outfit can be supplemented with a **waistcoat** to form a three-piece. If the same fabric is used for all pieces, then the result is a **suit.** If not, then the individual parts will normally be chosen to be complementary in colour, pattern, cut and details. However, modern fashions allow strong contrasts in style and colouring such as a black velvet jacket with blue jeans.

1: One-button jacket

2: Two-button jacket

3: Three-button jacket

4: Four-button jacket

5: Double-breasted suit

6: Business suit

7: Traditional look

8: Smart-casual

9: Blazer

10: Summer jacket

11: Leisure outfit

12: Blouson

A jacket which has only one row of buttons is described as **single-breasted.** The row can include one, two, three or (occasionally) four buttons. The lapels usually point downwards (*Figures 1 and 2*) but can also point upwards (*Figure 3*). Their width and depth vary according to fashion. The pockets are either integral (flap pockets) or sewn on (patch pockets) according to the style. The single-breasted suit appears more elegant with a waistcoat.

The **double-breasted** suit can have one, two or three pairs of buttons on the jacket (*Figure 5*). The lapels generally point upwards (pointed design) and the pockets are always integral. The double-breasted suit is normally worn fastened and this design is rather smart and formal.

Suits and outfits are named according to the material, style, cut, and details. For a **business suit** (*Figures 5 and 6*) classical styles and fabrics are used in sober colours.

Traditional (folklore) styles (*Figure 7*) include e.g. short, upright collars, contrasting lapels, cuffs and pocket edgings, embroidery, trimmings, fancy waistcoats, and decorative buttons.

Smart-casual wear can include jacket and tie with jeans, cords, or chinos (*Figure 8*) and lightweight, often unlined or part-lined **summer jackets** (*Figure 10*).

Typical of a smart but sporty style is the club **blazer** (*Figure 9*), with metal buttons and possibly even a breast-pocket badge. The so-called **sports jacket** derives originally from country sports, in rustic tweeds with details such as prominent, oversewn seams, yokes, patch pockets, leather buttons and elbow patches. (*Figure 1*) is a modern derivative.

Leisure wear (*Figures 11 and 12*) comes in many styles, colours and weights according to fashion and season.

14.2.10 Formal Dress

Formal dress describes men's and women's clothing for official or festive occasions. Distinctions are made between the wardrobes for the day and the evening.

Apart from the classic or formal styles of clothing, modern or unconventional styles have developed. Although these styles are not as severe, they are nevertheless clearly distinguishable from normal day wear.

1: Morning suit

2: Shawl-collar costume

3: Formal suit

4: Formal party outfit

5: Bride and groom

6: Formal party outfit

7: White Tuxedo

8: Trouser ensemble

9: Black-tie outfit (dinner jacket)

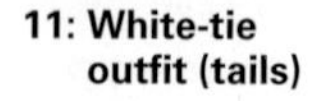

10: Evening dress

11: White-tie outfit (tails)

The **cutaway** or **morning suit** (*Figure 1*) is the very formal daytime attire. The tails of the black jacket are cut back in a curve from the single, fastened button. It is worn with striped trousers, a grey waistcoat, a broad silver-grey silk tie or cravat and a grey top hat. Alternatively, the whole outfit can be grey.

The **formal day suit** (*Figure 3*) consists of a dark jacket, striped trousers without turn-ups and a grey waistcoat.

Women wear an elegant costume (*Figure 2*), a two-piece or an ensemble (*see page 254*) for special occasions.

For weddings and other special festive occasions, the most stylish outfit for men is a three-piece suit made from fine, elegant fabrics. The waistcoat and accessories will be either in matching (*Figures 4 and 5*) or contrasting (*Figure 6*) tones.

The black single-breasted **dinner jacket (tuxedo)** (*Figure 9*) is part of the classic **(black-tie)** evening dress suit. The characteristics are silk-covered, straight or pointed lapels and silk stripes **(galloons)** down the sides of the trousers without turn-ups. The suit is traditionally worn with a white-on-white embroidered or fancy-woven dress shirt, a cummerbund (broad silk waistband) and a black bow tie. The formal tuxedo (*Figure 7*) can be black, white or cream and single or double-breasted but, nevertheless, is always worn with dark trousers and (mostly) a black bow tie.

The very formal **(white-tie)** evening suit is the **black tail coat** (*Figure 11*) which has tails on the back beginning from the side seams. The front is only waist length, the pointed lapels are covered with silk and the trousers have a silk stripe down the sides. The tail coat is worn open and is accompanied by a white waistcoat with broad lapels, a dress shirt with a wing collar and a white bow tie.

Women choose a party suit or **ensemble** (*Figure 8*), a party dress, a cocktail dress, or **evening dress** (*Figure 10*) according to the occasion. The women's very **formal evening dress** is always full length.

An invitation to a formal or semi-formal occasion will usually state the **dress code:** white tie, black tie, lounge suit, informal or casual.

14.3.1 Requirements for Sport and Leisure Wear

1: Clothing system comprising undershirt (1), shirt (2) and jacket (3)

Extremes of climate are found around the world – desert, tropical, arctic etc. In addition, seasonal and short-term weather fluctuations cause large changes in local conditions.

According to the conditions, the human body will produce warmth or perspiration, or it will begin to cool. To remain comfortable and functionally active for sporting or leisure activities, in the most varied weather conditions, requires clothing that has been designed specifically for the purpose. Such clothing is named **functional clothing, active wear** or **active clothing.**

"Active" clothing is selected for the end purpose and can be built up of several layers (*Figure 1*) according to requirements. The layers have to be made from mutually compatible materials (*see page 258 ff*).

Requirements

- **Physiologically oriented design**

  Appropriate fibres and textiles are needed to maintain efficient physical activity in difficult climatic conditions. Examples are membrane systems, fleece fabrics, microfibre fabrics, double layer fabrics.

- **Functional, comfortable design**

  Comfort is maintained by: appropriate design and cut; pre-formed elbows, knees and seat; individual adjustment through drawstrings and adjustable fastenings; collars with integrated hoods; purpose-built pockets; adjustable ventilation openings that can be closed to keep out the cold and wind (*Figure 2*).

- **Strength and durability**

  First-class, strong and abrasion resistant materials and sewings are needed for clothing that will suffer heavy loading. Durability can be enhanced by reinforcement at the elbows, knees and seat.

- **Form stability and ease of care**

  Active sport clothing needs to be well fitting, extensible and elastic. The fabric surface should not be susceptible to pilling or felting.

  Easy care fabrics from synthetic fibres allow simple and economic aftercare.

- **Low weight and small packing volume**

  For lightweight outdoor clothing the ability to roll up into a small volume is an advantage.

- **Easy disposal**

  Recycling is made easier by using only one fibre type per garment.

- **Visibility**

  Depending on the application (e.g. motorsport, cycling, jogging) the clothing may need to be reflective. This can be achieved with luminous colours or reflective coatings.

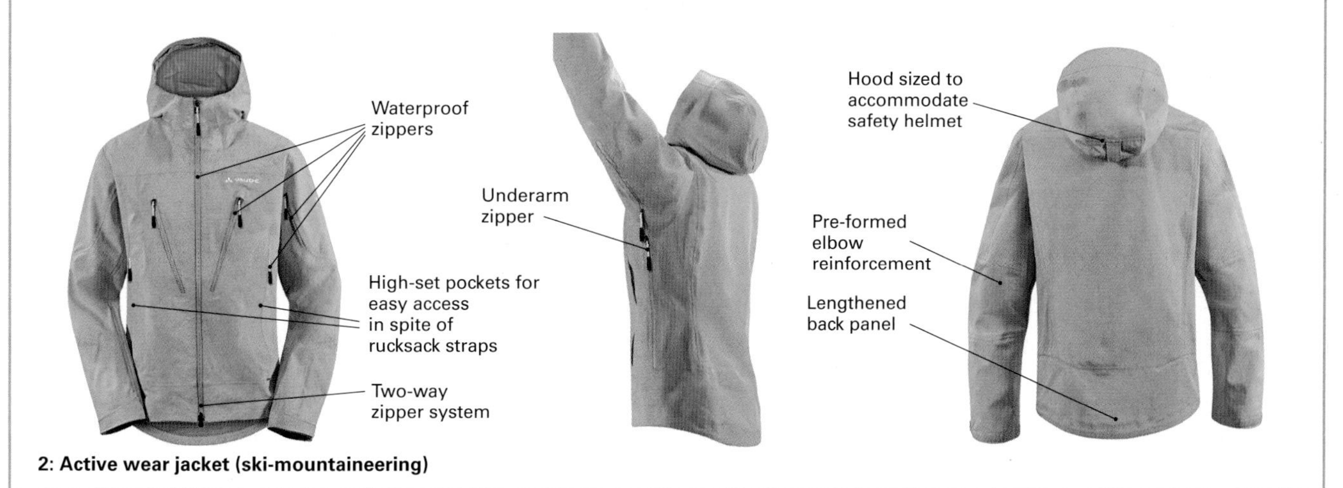

2: Active wear jacket (ski-mountaineering)

14.3.2 Construction and Materials (1)

Active Clothing Systems

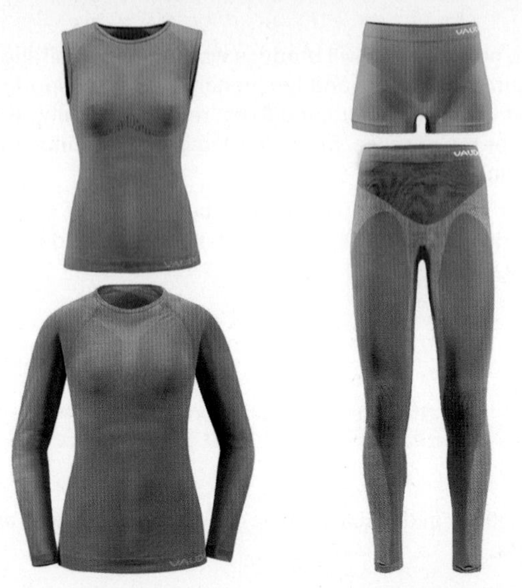

1: Active underwear (seamless)

2: Cotton top with integrated bra

3: Ventilating top with mesh inserts

4: Polyester flannel shirt

5: Warm pullover

6: Knitted sweater

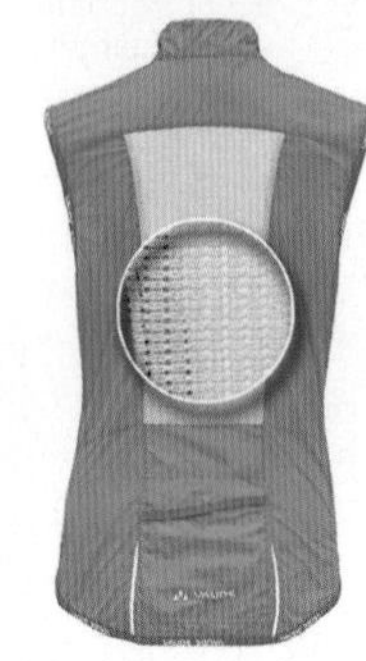

7: Windcheater vest with mesh inserts in the back

An **active clothing system** encompasses the various functional layers of clothing that are designed for a particular sporting activity.

The number of layers, and the material from which they are composed, depends on the season, the type of sporting activity and the consequent levels of heat and sweat production (*see page 48*).

The **first layer** must transport the sweat outwards to be dispersed by, or transmitted to the next layer. The **second layer** transports the sweat further, if necessary. According to the outside air temperature, this layer may have an insulation function and may comprise several clothing items. The **third layer** protects the body from cold, wind and weather.

First Layer: Underwear

They should keep the body warm and dry by ensuring efficient transport of moisture to the next layer. They should be soft and dimensionally stable.

Often these are seamless garments (*Figure 1*) so as to reduce irritation and pressure.

Suitable materials:

- Single-face materials from polyester, nylon, polypropylene (microfibres, staple fibres or filaments) in combination with a second layer of absorbent material.
- Double-face knits e.g. body side polyester; outer side cotton, modal.
- Knitted fabrics made from hollow fibres e.g. acrylic, polyester.
- Stretch knitted fabrics including elastomeric fibres for close-fitting garments.

Second Layer: Tops, Shirts, Pullovers

They should keep the body comfortably dry through efficient moisture transport and maintain an equable temperature by appropriate exchange of heat and air between body and environment. They should be easy-care and stable.

Suitable materials:

Depends on whether they are worn next to the skin or in combination with an inner layer.

- Smooth wovens and knits from polyester, nylon, or blends
- Wovens and knits from cotton, modal, wool, silk
- Raised wovens and knits of microfibres (mainly polyester) e.g. fleece.
- Raised microfibre fabrics (e.g. fleece), combined with smooth microfibre fabrics
- Raised wovens and knits of cotton or wool
- Three-layer fleece with Microporous membrane as a "windstopper"
- Stretch fleece for body-hugging items (stretch fabric on the outside, smooth fleece on the inside).

14.3.2 Construction and Materials (2)

1: Hiking pants

2: Rain pants

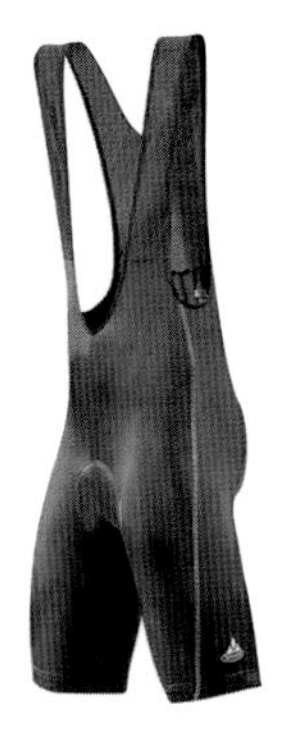
3: Biking pants

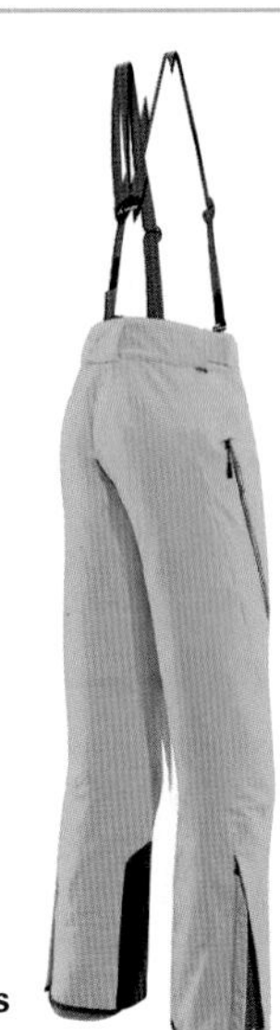
4: Ski pants

Second Layer: Trousers

Trousers (or leggings) may be worn next to the skin or over short or long underwear, depending on the particular sport. For cycling or jogging or gymnastics, they have to be close fitting and elastic. Hiking or ski pants need a more comfortable fit.

The **hiking pants** (*Figure 1*) have zippers at about knee level so they can convert into shorts.

The **rain pants** (*Figure 2*) have two layers with a mesh lining.

The **biking pants** (*Figure 3*) have an integrated, seam-free seat pad.

The **ski pants** (*Figure 4*) have three layers with an integral membrane. They are elastic and weatherproof.

5: Ultra-light wind jacket

6: Soft-shell jacket with hood

7: Double jacket

8: Quilted parka

Layer 3: Jackets

The jacket has to insulate against wind and cold, snow and rain, and must allow evaporation of moisture transported from the interior. The materials should be strong, abrasion resistant and easy-care. **Double jackets** are constructed with a wind and water-proof outer shell and a warm inner. The two can be worn either separately or as a combination (*Figure 7*).

Suitable materials for jackets and trousers

- microfibre fabrics of polyester or polyamide with a microporous coating
- filament polyester or polyamide fabrics with a hydrophobic finish
- polyester/cotton blends with a water repellent finish
- two or three-layer membrane systems (liner or laminate) with or without a microporous coating (*see page 115*)
- quilted fabrics
- woven or knitted polyamide/aramid
- aramid fabrics for motorsport
- patches of Kevlar or high strength polyester

9: Sun hat with neck shade

10: Storm helmet for extreme cold and wind

11: Climbing gloves with free fingers

12: Waterproof heated gloves

Accessories

Various accessories are available for the protection of the head and hands, e.g. caps, headbands, scarves, neck and face masks, gloves.

Suitable materials:

- microfibre fleece
- microfibre fabrics
- Neoprene®
- membrane systems.

14.4.1 Headwear

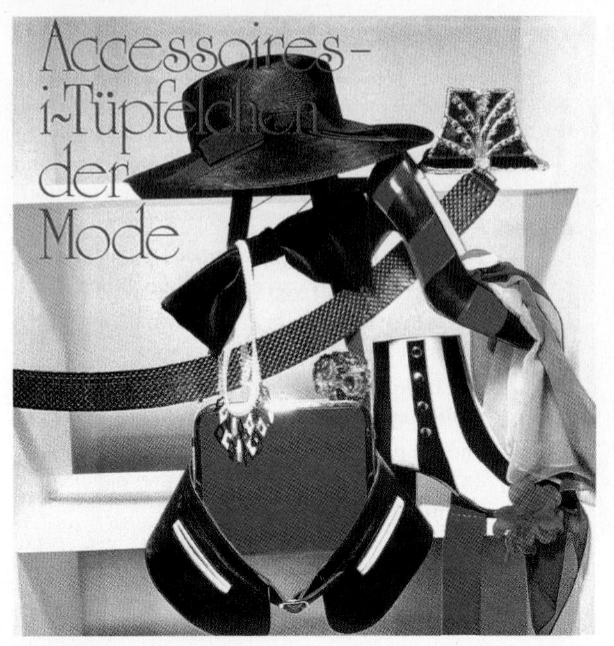

1: Fashion accessories for women

Accessories are those additional items of adornment which extend and round-off an image. They have played an important role in every fashion age and were often as characteristic as designs or colour.

Even though today's fashion allows for combinations of different styles and contrasting accessories, nevertheless a clever and appropriate choice of accessories is still of great importance.

Only a few accessories offer **decoration** alone, for example, jewellery and flowers. Above all shoes, but also headwear, handbags, scarves and belts have a specific **function** to fulfil.

Every season the fashion industry offers co-ordinating accessories in current colours and materials for different fashion themes.

Headwear

Style, material and trimmings are aimed at the occasion.

The headbands and brims on hats can be greatly varied in design and embellishment. Caps and woolly hats are generally not reinforced and have no brims, but sometimes do have a peak.

Materials may be: felt, exotic straw wickerwork (sisal, raffia, panama), wheat straw, viscose, sinamay (abaca cloth), mottle (twisted straw), hemp, ramie, paper, leather, fur, woven and knitted fabrics, fleece, etc.

Possible **trimmings** are ribbons, feathers, leather and felt strips, cords, flowers, veils, sinamay, buttons, buckles, eyelets.

2: Fancy straw hat

3: Viscose hat with ribbon-flower decoration

4: Straw hat with sisal crown and sinamay decoration

5: Turned-up brim with contrasting wool materials

6: Felt fedora with repp headband

7: Felt cloche hat with contrasting decoration

8: Sisal hat with repp headband

9: Panama straw hat and leather band with buckle

10: Western style fabric hat

11: Safari hat with leather braid headband

12: Classic trilby with ribbon headband

13: Classic fabric hat

14: Straw mottle with tied cloth square

15: Ladies lacquered flowerpot hat

16: Men's shower-proof flowerpot hat

17: Soft, leather-look peaked cap

18: Baseball cap with ear flaps

19: Peaked Mao cap in corded fabrics

14.4.2 Other Fashion Accessories

Ties

The current, elongated form of tie was introduced in the middle of the 19th century. It has steadily gained in popularity and is now the primary decorative element in men's clothing, having largely replaced the bow tie. Ties are distinguished by their width, the fibre material, the fabric type, and above all by the patterning. Width is according to fashion trends, silk is the highest quality, and woven fabrics are most common. Patterns are heavily influenced by current trends in art and fashion as well as tradition and the intended end use. They range from sober and formal to bold, artistic fantasy designs.

1: Straight and bow ties

Squares and Scarves

Squares can be made from woven silk, fine synthetics, cotton or wool. They are worn mostly as decorative accessories either on the head or around the neck. They often have a single design covering the whole square. Long scarves are made from flat-knitted or woven fabrics. They often have fringes at each end and are frequently co-ordinated with headwear or gloves and sold as a set.

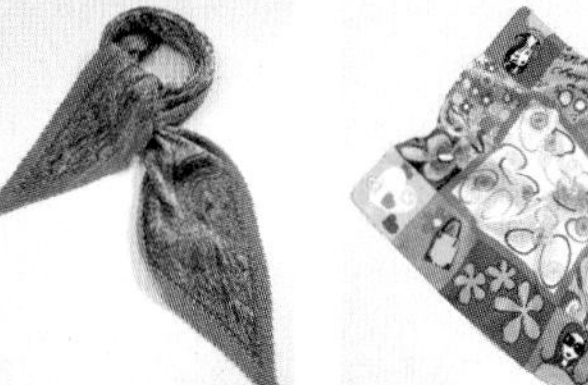
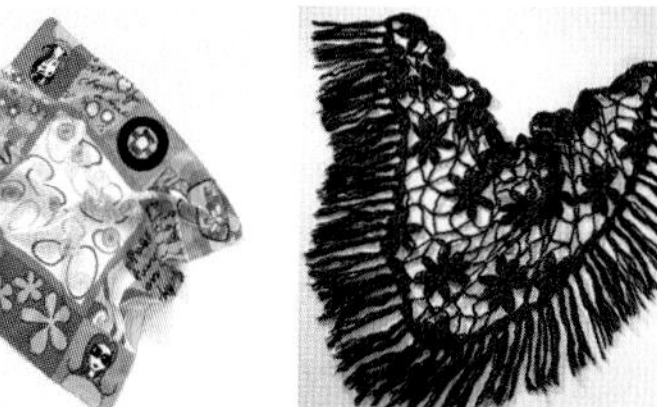

2 to 7: Scarves and squares

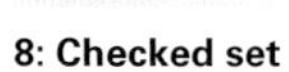

8: Checked set **9: Fleecy set** **10: Imitation fur set** **11: Flat-knitted set**

Gloves

Fashion gloves are primarily functional, for protection of the hands, but they are also co-ordinated with the rest of the outfit. Mittens are a type of glove in which only the thumb has a separate enclosure. Glove and mitten materials are leather and knitted or woven fabrics from cotton or wool.

Socks, Stockings and Tights

Socks are usually either ankle or calf length. Stockings are either knee or thigh length. Tights (panty hose) are waist length. Colours and materials are according to the style and function of the rest of the outfit. Men's sock sizes are normally according to the shoe size. Ladies stocking sizes are according to stature; tights are according to stature and hip girth.

15.1.1 Style Periods

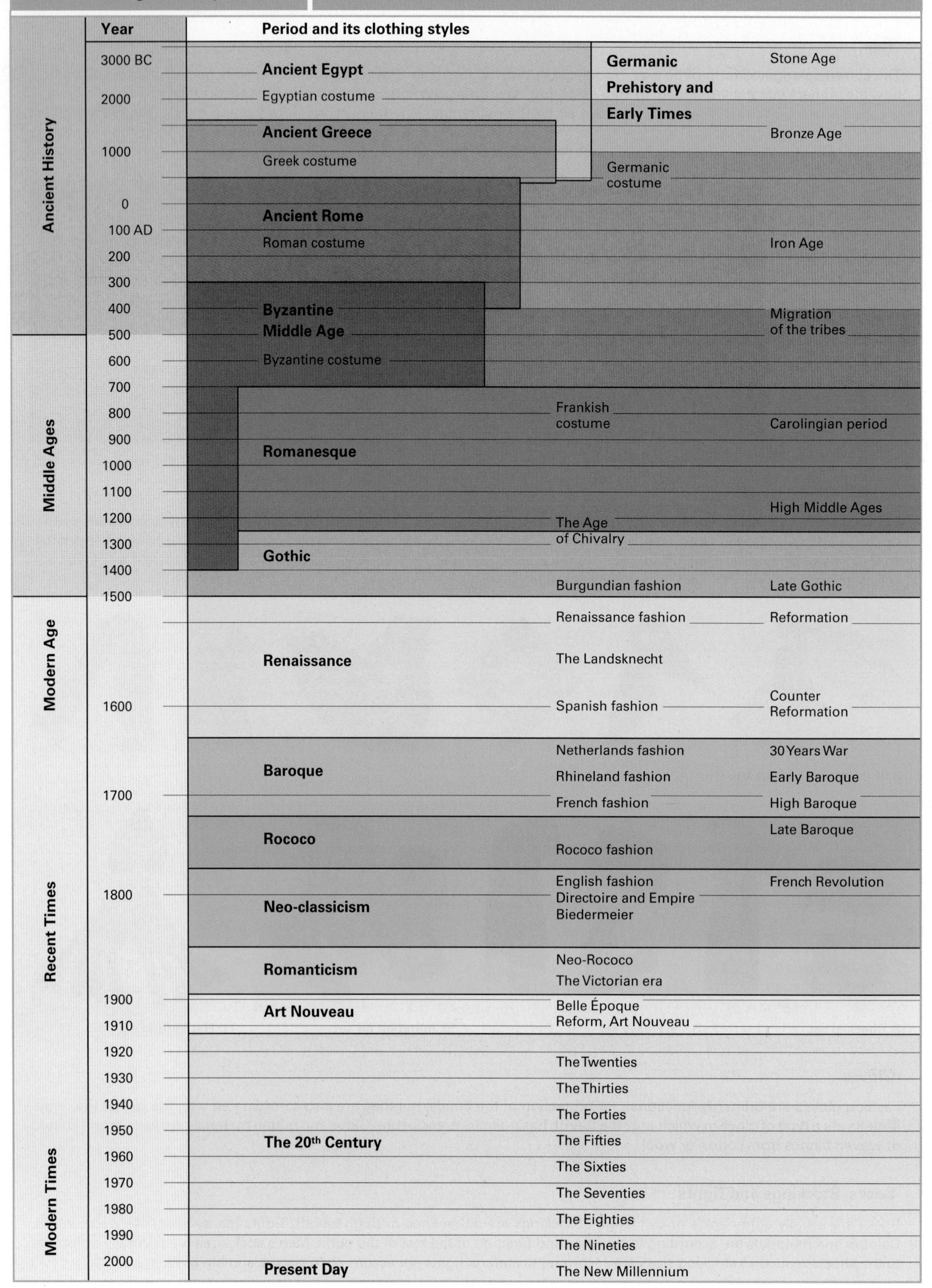

15.1.2 Fashion

The term **fashion** describes the current prevailing trends in a society, for example concerning a particular way of dressing, lifestyle, pattern of thought, and the development of the arts.

Fashion in the narrow sense of the word means the changing forms of clothing. These originate from people's need to be adorned and admired but also allow the opportunity to enhance personal style or indicate a position in society e.g. membership of a particular group.

Originally, the term fashion was used for a very short-lived trend, whilst something which prevailed over a longer period and developed on a cultural and artistic level was described as style.

Today, many of the terms used to describe the various trends in clothing generally mean, more or less, the same; for example **"fashion", "style" "look", "line".**

In the past, power and wealth, social distinction and belonging to a particular class were emphasised by clothing.

Customs and moral conventions were often more important than practical utility in shaping clothing styles. Conversely, aesthetic ideas could be expressed or a sense of sexuality could be displayed through clothing.

Until the middle of the nineteenth century, the aristocracy and the courts, or the sophisticated bourgeoisie determined fashion styles. After this, **haute couture** took on the leading role. Fashion designers or fashion houses created **exclusive models** for a chosen look. Paris was the centre of women's fashion, whereas for men the English style was the most popular.

Industrialisation and the emergence of **ready-to-wear** clothing, as well as the development of **synthetic fibres** enabled the gradual participation of all classes of society in the fashion scene. However, the dictates of haute couture still dominated in the mid 1950's as they were imitated by the bespoke tailors and the ready-to-wear clothing industry. An increasing number of fashion centres grew up alongside Paris. One of the strongest influences was the Italian haute couture, the Alta Moda, challenging the French women's fashion and the English men's fashion.

1: Court clothing, mid 15th Cent.

2: Leading citizen, 16th Cent.

3: Bourgeois fashions, about 1840

4: Ladies fashions, 1950

During the 1960's, as an unconventional style of clothing gained acceptance and clothing was seen less as a status symbol but rather to serve as a means of self-expression, the fashion industry began to adapt to the changing situation. The ready-to-wear fashion industry moved to the forefront, driven by consumer demand.

Developments in fashion are based on the desire for change, variety or emulation and are influenced by the structure of society, by technical and cultural development as well as political and economic events.

Fashion designers and Couturiers are inspired, take hold of trends and make suggestions for a forthcoming fashion season. If these suggestions are taken up by a significant section of the population, they become the fashion.

International fashion fairs, with **trend shows,** are held regularly in a number of cities around the world, e.g. Paris, Milan, Münich, London, New York, Hong Kong and Tokyo. Fashion houses, designers and the ready-to-wear clothing industry present their collections for each Spring/Summer season and Autumn/Winter season.

These shows are held immediately before the season for haute couture fashion and six months earlier for the ready-to-wear clothing industry.

The **themes** for a fashion season include the cuts, patterns, details, materials, colours and designs as well as the accessories. The interested public is kept informed of fashion events through the news media and glossy magazines.

A fashion appears, is accepted and then disappears again **(fashion cycle),** but very often a fashion may be revived from the past. Styles of clothing which achieve long lasting acceptance are described as classic (timeless).

Every change in fashion has an associated risk for the clothing industry as something new must succeed over that which is already established. The correct prediction of **fashion trends** is therefore of crucial importance. Those with **"avant garde"** tastes have an enthusiasm to assimilate unusual new ideas. This can help predict how a general trend may develop.

15.2.1 Ancient Egypt (1)

ca. 3000 to 300 BC

Characteristics of the Age

1: Egyptian building style (Sphinx and Pyramids of the Pharaohs, Giza)

The ancient Egyptians had a well-developed culture. Their architecture, in particular, was technically highly advanced. Large temples and powerful pyramids, the tombs of the Pharaohs (kings), have survived to the present. Characteristics of the Egyptian **style** were a strong regularity and rhythmic repetition. Wall paintings, reliefs, sculptures, and hieroglyphics (pictographic writing system) yield information about the life and customs of the Egyptians. Religion and tradition were very important. There was enormous interest in life after death in another world.

Only light **clothing** was necessary because of the mild climate. Originally, all levels of society dressed the same but later clothing became an indicator for social standing and wealth.

Men and women wore similar items of clothing. The preferred material was fine white linen. However, fabrics with colourful patterns or with gold thread incorporated were also popular. The garments were often transparent and finely pleated.

2: Kalasiris in both pleated and narrow styles

3: Shenti and narrow kalasiris

Women's Clothing

Originally, the women wore a simple linen cloth that was wrapped around the lower body and knotted together at the waist. The upper body remained uncovered. Only members of the upper class wore a cape, which came down to the elbows and was gathered into crossways folds.

The **kalasiris** appeared later and was worn in many different ways. Worn as a calf or ankle length garment, it was close-fitting on the body leaving the breasts uncovered and was secured by a shoulder band or broad straps. They were often richly decorated.

The kalasiris in shift form came up to the neck or had different necklines. It was either sleeveless or was provided with sleeves. It was worn loose or belted, and was usually transparent and finely pleated.

Under the influence of Asia, a sort of coat was developed. A broad piece of fabric, double the length of the body, had a neck opening and side seams from the waist to the hem. It was gathered under the breasts so that the top was like a cape. A sash was often added.

15.2.1 Ancient Egypt (2)

ca. 3000 to 300 BC

1: Narrow women's kalasiris and different styles of the shenti (shown on gods; a mixture of human, animal, plant and the forces of nature)

2: The men's pleated kalasiris, women's tight kalasiris

Men's Clothing

The men wore a loin cloth or hip cloth, the **shenti.** The cloth was wrapped around the lower body and was tied in front or kept up by a belt. Kings and dignitaries wore cloths which were gathered, had many pleats and were decorated. Several cloths were often worn one on top of the other. The outermost was the longest and was similar to a skirt.

Originally, the shenti was the only item of clothing and the upper body remained bare. Later men also wore a shift-style **kalasiris** usually over, seldom under, the loin-cloth.

The wide, coat-like drape, which was pulled on over the head, was held at the waist by a knot. The **haik,** a transparent coat wrapped around the body, was reserved for the ruler.

3: Men's and women's wigs

4: Crown head-dress

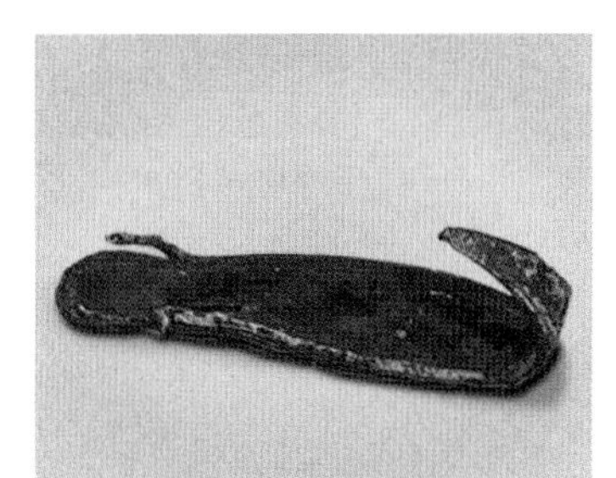

5: Egyptian sandal

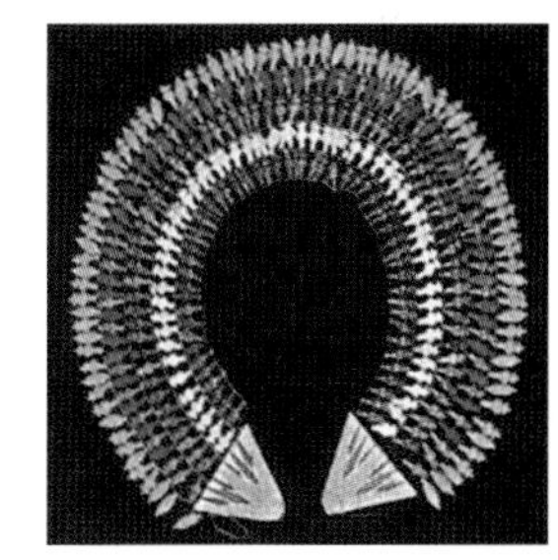

6: Shoulder collar

Accessories

Natural hair and the large **wigs** had a straight chin-length cut and were smooth or braided into many small plaits.

As symbols of power, the rulers wore **headbands, crowns** and elaborate **head-dresses,** for example the snake diadem **(uraeus)** or the sphinx head-dress **(khat).**

The Egyptians generally went barefoot. Only the upper class wore **sandals** with toe straps and long points.

Circular or shoulder collars were worn as jewellery and as protection from the sun and were a permanent part of Egyptian clothing. They were made out of leather, metal or fabric and were painted in many colours or were studded with precious stones.

Men and women wore expensive jewellery made of gold and precious stones, enamel and ivory: armbands, necklaces, ankle bracelets, earrings, finger rings, belts. Great value was placed on cosmetics.

15.2.2 Ancient Greece (1)

ca. 1600 to 100 BC

Characteristics of the Age

1: Greek architecture (Erechtheum, Acropolis, Athens)

The ancient Greeks had a high level of culture. They made significant achievements in the areas of architecture, art and craft. Greek philosophy is considered as the foundation of scientific thought. Their highest ambition was to achieve harmony of body, soul, and lifestyle.

The characteristics of Greek **architecture** were serenity, clarity, balanced proportions and a strict order. Vertical sections of buildings stood in harmony with the horizontal sections.

Clothing was airy and wide. It consisted of pieces of fabric elaborately draped around the body. Individual gathering and the arrangement of the belt were the main forms of decoration. Men and women wore similar clothes.

The woven fabrics were made of linen and wool, then later out of cotton. Rich strong colours and edges decorated with braid trimming were valued highly.

2: Noble Greek women; a priestess in the background

3: Belted Peplos

4: Chiton

5: Chiton and himation

Women's Clothing

The **peplos** consisted of a rectangular woollen cloth which was laid around the body, under the arms, and then lifted over the shoulders where it was secured by brooches, clasps **(fibula),** buttons or knots. The upper edge of the fabric was folded over, down to the waist or the hips; the right side remained open. This long straight garment was often worn unbelted although sometimes it was belted at the waist either under or over the folded-down material.

The lighter **chiton,** made from linen, was usually sewn up at the sides. The narrow design, reaching from elbow to elbow with outstretched arms, was simply placed on the shoulders and, consequently, was sleeveless.

The wide chiton stretched from fingertip to fingertip and had sleeves of a sort. They resulted from gaps in the sides (arm holes), or the uppermost edges were knotted over the arms. The top drape could be greatly varied, for example cut unevenly or round. The typical chiton was arranged with a multiplicity of pleats and folds produced by one or several belts at the waist, or the hips, or under the breast.

In later times, both types of garments were combined. They were also worn together, the chiton as an under garment, the peplos as an outer garment.

The **himation,** a large rectangular woollen cloth wrapped around the body, was worn as a coat. Sometimes it also covered the head.

15.2.2 Ancient Greece (2)

ca. 1600 to 100 BC

1: Men's chiton 2: Exomis 3: Himation 4: Himation 5: Chlamys

6: Men's long chiton

Men's Clothing

The men's **chlaina** corresponded to the women's peplos. The rectangular woollen cloth was placed over the back and shoulders and held together at the front, or on the right shoulder, by a clasp.

The men's **chiton** ended, like the chlaina, above the knee and was belted at the waist. The ankle-length chiton, which was belted under the chest, was put on only for festive occasions and was reserved for high-ranking men and priests.

The short garment which left one shoulder bare was called the **exomis.** It gave more freedom of movement.

The **himation** was elaborately draped around the body and sometimes was the only item of clothing.

Horsemen, travellers and soldiers preferred to wear the **chlamys** as a coat. This short, woollen drape was put over the left shoulder and pinned over the right shoulder, so that the right arm was free.

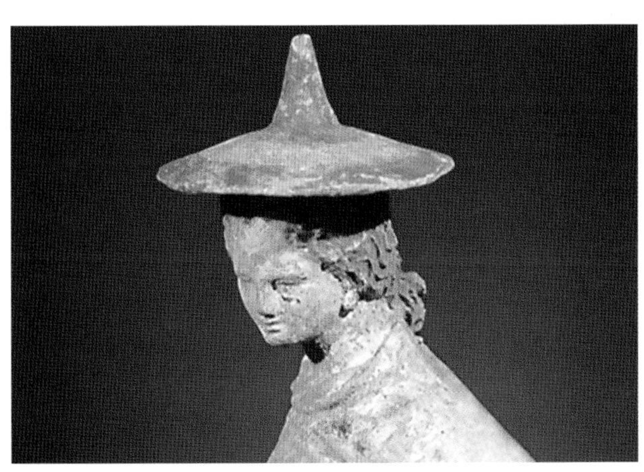

7: Disc shaped hat with pointed top

8: Petasos

9: Pilos

10: Greek garment clasps

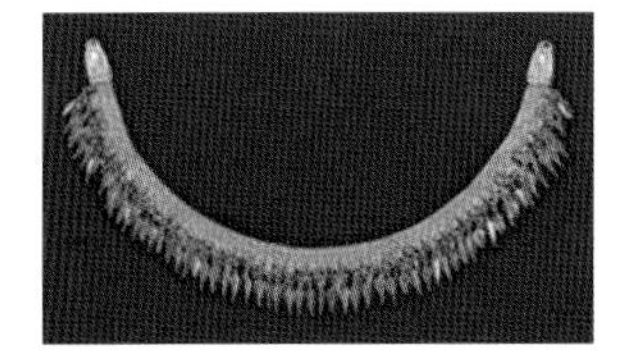

11: Greek necklace

Accessories

Headwear was worn by the Greeks only when travelling. The most popular was the **petasos,** a flat round felt hat with a brim. Men also wore the **pilos,** a tight fitting cap made of leather or felt. The elaborate wavy and often knotted hair of the women was secured by **hair bands, circlets** and **ribbons.** Occasionally, head scarves were worn. The round hat with a pointed top presumably offered protection against the sun.

The Greeks went barefoot in the house; sandals were worn in the streets. These were often laced up high. Women's sandals were decorated.

Tasteful jewellery was made out of precious metals. Necklaces, rings, earrings, diadems, decorative brooches and bangles were produced from very fine filigree made out of gold wire.

15.2.3 Ancient Rome (1)

ca. 500 BC to 400 AD

Characteristics of the Age

1: Roman architecture (The Colosseum, Rome)

The Romans made significant advances in the organisation of government and in town planning. Their supremacy and high level of self-confidence was also reflected in their lavish lifestyle and imposing buildings.

The style of **architecture** was characterised by the sympathetic blend of prestige and functionality. Monumental and functional buildings, such as palaces, theatres, aqueducts, and viaducts, were constructed with arches and domes.

The influence of Greek culture was particularly evident in **clothing** which, however, was governed more by tradition than by individuality. Clothing sometimes appeared rather formal and impersonal but, nevertheless, was very lavish and imposing – often even luxurious and elaborate. Design, colour and decoration were indicators of rank and status.

Originally the garments were made of natural-coloured wool with decorated edges. Later, more showy and colourful garments were favoured. Women generally preferred lighter materials such as cotton and the expensive silk.

2: Noble Roman women and slave (right)

3: Roman woman in a stola and palla

4: Roman woman in a stola and palla

5: Roman woman in a stola and palla

Women's Clothing

The **tunic,** a shift-like, floor length house dress or under-dress, was two pieces of material sewn together with a slit for the head and openings for the arms. Sleeves were occasionally sewn on or cut out. The tunic was usually belted under the bust and decorated on the shoulders with buttons or brooches. Early versions were made of wool; later fine linen, cotton or even silk was used.

The outer garment, the **stola,** had the same cut as the tunic and was similar to the Greek chiton. It was wide and often trailing. The **strophium,** a kind of bust-bodice, was put on before the stola. Belts were worn under the breast, at the waist or at the hips.

Occasionally the stola was worn with no belt. Expensive materials were used and decorations such as pearls, fringes, gold spangles and embroidery were added.

For outdoors wear, the **palla,** a rectangular woollen cloth, was draped around the body. This usually covered the head although occasionally it was only wrapped around the hips.

The **paenula,** an oval or diamond-shaped drape made from thick woollen material or fine leather, was worn in bad weather. It was either worn open at the front or closed all around. It often had a hood.

15.2.3 Ancient Rome (2)

ca. 500 BC to 400 AD

1: Roman emperor (centre) and nobleman (right)

2: Roman in tunic and toga

3: Roman in tunic and the earliest style of toga

Men's Clothing

The men's **tunic** reached to just below the knees and was belted at the hips. Later, and on ceremonial occasions it was ankle length. Several tunics were often put one on top of the other. Many had insignia on them, for example purple bands. In these cases, the tunic was worn without a belt.

The **toga,** the impressive state and honorary dress of the Roman people, was draped over the body in elaborate folds and occasionally covered the head.

It consisted of an oval woollen cloth which was folded lengthways. The length corresponded to the height of three men, the width about two men.

The **pallium** was more practical and comfortable than the toga. The rectangular robe was wrapped around the body. Later it was draped only over the left shoulder and fastened at the right shoulder.

When travelling or in bad weather, the men also wore the **paenula.**

4: Roman sandal

5: Roman boots

Accessories

The women wore a **veil** outdoors. Their elaborately curled hair was put into **nets** woven from gold and silver and secured by clasps and tiaras. Men rarely wore headgear and then only for a specific purpose. Farmers, hunters and workers wore a close fitting **cap.** The free citizens preferred a **hat** with a narrow rim. The upper class citizens used the toga to cover their heads.

Footwear also indicated to which class a Roman belonged. The occasion determined the footwear. There were many variations of **sandals,** enclosed and slipper-like shoes and also **boots** for men. Women's shoes made out of fine leather were richly decorated.

Tiaras, rings, armbands, ankle bracelets, necklaces and earrings were worn as jewellery. These were manufactured from precious metals, enamel, ivory and pearls.

15.2.4 Germanic Prehistory and Early Times (1)

ca. 2000 BC to 600 AD

Characteristics of the Age

1: Architecture in the Bronze Age (pile buildings by lake Constance)

The ancient Germanic (Teutonic) tribes originally inhabited the central and northern areas of Europe. With their advance to the Alps, after about 800 BC, they came into contact with the ancient people of the Mediterranean and their highly developed culture. During the period of the migration of the tribes in the second to the sixth centuries AD, the Teutonic peoples contributed to the decline of Roman power in southern and western Europe.

Very few **buildings** survive from this time. Those that do had been built from logs.

Techniques for spinning, weaving and basket work were already known during the **Stone Age,** the earliest known age of human cultural development (up to about 1800 BC). Clothing was made with the aid of flint and bone tools.

Clothing from the **Bronze Age** (about 1800 to 800 BC), with its own distinctive character, has been found preserved in graves. In the **Iron Age** which followed (about 800 BC to 600 AD), an ancient influence was evident, particularly in women's clothing, as indicated by relics recovered from peat bogs.

The **clothing** of the Teutonic peoples was suited to the cold northern climate. Wool, linen, and especially animal skins were used. Woven patterns, coloured borders and edgings, as well as fringes enlivened the simple garments.

2: Bronze Age Teutons

3: Bronze Age girl's clothing; smock, cord skirt

4: Iron Age Teutons, 3rd to 4th century AD

Women's Clothing

Women's garments during the Bronze Age consisted of a **skirt** and **blouse.** The wide skirt was ankle length and came up to just under the breast. The skirt was gathered at the waist, secured by a braided fringed belt or cord and decorated with an ornamental belt disc. The blouse had kimono-like sleeves, was made out of one piece of material and had an opening for head and neck. It was worn inside the skirt and fastened with a decorated brooch.

Young girls wore a knee length **cord skirt,** which consisted of numerous, closely packed cords suspended from a waistband.

The Iron Age brought the **tunic dress** which was put on over the head, held together on the shoulders by pins or clasps and belted once or twice. It draped in many folds and was sleeveless but was often worn under or over a blouse with sleeves. Later, it was provided with short or long sleeves.

Chest, leg and thigh bindings were worn under the dress.

A large cloth served as an outer garment. It was wrapped around like a cloak, covered the head, and was held together by pins or clasps **(fibula).**

15.2.4 Germanic Prehistory and Early Times (2)

ca. 2000 BC to 600 AD

1: Bronze Age men's clothing

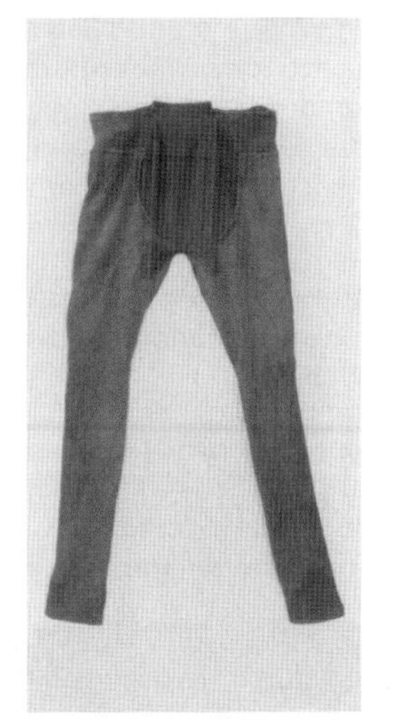

2: Iron Age trousers

3: Iron Age smock

4: Iron Age men's clothing

Men's Clothing

During the Bronze Age, the men wore a **tunic** wrapped around the body and belted at the waist. It reached from the armpits to the knee and was held by a strap which ran over the shoulder and was secured at the back by a button. Under the tunic, a rectangular belted loincloth was commonly worn.

Trousers were developed in the Iron Age. The long style of trouser might be tied at the lower leg.

Short trousers were extended by leg pieces or bindings. The trousers were held up by a belt which ran through loops.

A knee length **smock** which was put on over the head was worn with the trousers. It was originally sleeveless, although later it was provided with short or long sleeves. It was usually belted and occasionally had a hood.

A **cloak** was worn over the smock; a linen **shirt** was worn under.

5: Thonged shoe

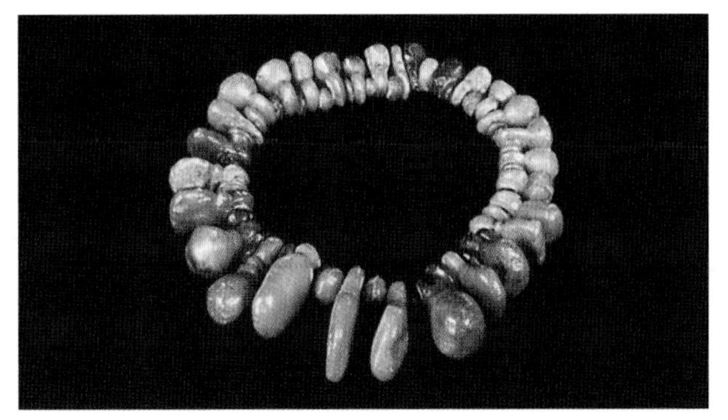

6: Amber necklace

Accessories

Women put their hair, which was pinned up or knotted, into **nets**. Girls wore their hair loose held by a circlet. Squares, veils and caps served as headwear. Men mostly had long hair which either was worn loose, or was knotted or tied into a bunch. Helmets with animal heads were common in battle, otherwise tall or hemispherical **caps** were made out of hide or knotted wool.

Thonged shoes were usually worn on the feet. These were made out of a piece of hide with the fur on the inside. The network of straps was held together by a shoelace.

Richly decorated jewellery was also regarded as part of the clothing. The magnificent belt discs, garment clasps, arm and leg bangles, ear and finger rings were made out of bronze or precious metal and decorated with precious stones, glass beads, enamel or amber.

15.3.1 Byzantine Middle Ages (1)

ca. 300 to 1400 AD

Characteristics of the Age

1: Byzantine architecture (Hagia Sophia, Istanbul – formerly Constantinople or Byzantium)

After the division of the Roman Empire around 300 AD, Byzantium, the capital of the Eastern Empire, became the economic and cultural centre. Christianity became the state religion. The Greco-Roman culture developed a new form, shaped by both Christian and oriental influences. From then on the Church had a crucial role not only in cultural life but also in society; the emperor was head of everything both secular and spiritual.

The Byzantine style of **architecture** represented wealth and power. Characteristics were round arches and domes, as were gloriously colourful mosaics which covered the insides of the powerful churches.

Clothing developed into a sumptuous formal costume which enveloped the body completely, covering its natural shape. The ruling class preferred heavily coloured silk fabrics and brocades, richly embroidered with precious stones and pearls. Insignia were important. The ordinary people, however, wore unobtrusive wool and linen materials.

Even today the vestments of the Church are based on Byzantine clothing. For a long time, the coronation robes of emperors and kings also followed the Byzantine model.

2: 6th century Byzantine court costume: Empress and retainers

3: Byzantine Empress and princess, servant in the background

4: 6th century Byzantine nobles

Women's Clothing

A white ankle length **tunic** served as an under garment. This was belted, had long sleeves and was often made of silk.

The outer garment, the long or short sleeved **stola,** originally reached to the floor but was later shortened to reveal the under garment. It was worn either belted or loose, depending on the weight of the material.

The **paenula** served as a top garment. The front edge of the circular cut, closed robe was often lifted up and placed over the shoulder.

Members of the ruling house wore a **shoulder cloak** secured on the right shoulder by a decorated clasp.

15.3.1 Byzantine Middle Ages (2)

ca. 300 to 1400 AD

1: Byzantine Emperor and Empress

2: 6th century Byzantine court costume

3: Byzantine Emperor and noble youth

Men's Clothing

The long sleeved **tunic** was either knee or ankle length and was usually belted. Length, width, colour and material revealed rank and status. The tunic was normally worn over close-fitting leg-wear.

The **dalmatic,** a long unbelted robe with wide sleeves was reserved as an outer garment for rulers and high ranking dignitaries. Colourful lengthways stripes, called **clavi,** decorated the front and back as well as the hem of the sleeves.

The cloak was either rectangular or rounded and was fastened with a clasp at the front or on the right shoulder. A fabric appliqué, the **tablion,** was sewn on at chest height to show rank. For the ruler, it was gold and richly decorated; for high-ranking officials, it was Tyrian purple.

The **paenula,** a robe which was put on over the head, was adopted by the Church and became the **chasule.**

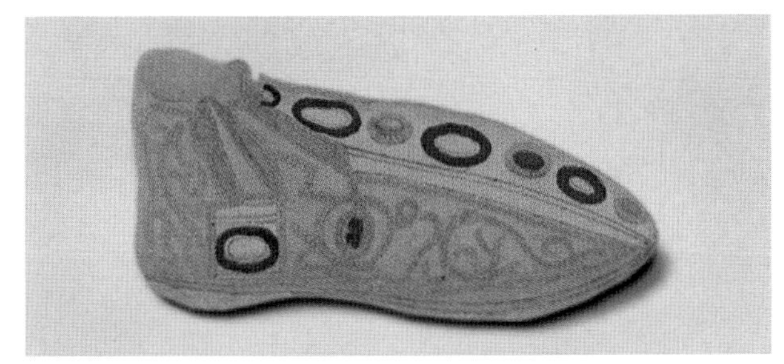

4: Coronation shoe of the German Emperor

5: Collar necklace

Accessories

Women combed their hair into a sort of **rolled style** and adorned it with a **tiara** onto which a veil was secured. **Head-dresses** and turban-like caps were popular, as was the caul, a cap of silk or wool covered with a net of coloured silk, wool, gold, or silver thread, sometimes jewelled at the intersections. Men usually wore nothing on their heads. Members of the ruling class occasionally wore a flat **cap.** The emperor wore a **crown.**

Footwear also depended on status and the occasion, and was always determined by the garment. Apart from **sandals** with an enclosed heel and pointed toe, richly decorated **slippers** were common. Men often favoured high, laced shoes and **leather socks.**

The diverse and luxurious jewellery made out of different metals and enamel was richly studded with pearls and precious stones. Large earrings, collar-like necklaces, finger rings and striking ornamental brooches were worn.

15.3.2 Romanesque (1)

ca. 700 to 1250 AD

Characteristics of the Age

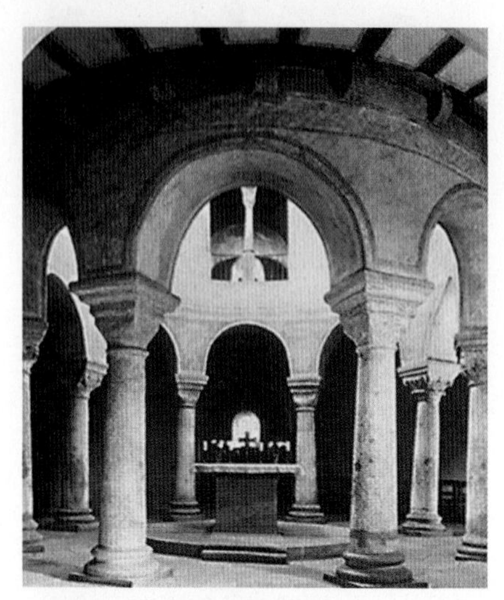

1: Romanesque architecture (St. Michael, Fulda)

The cultural period of the Romanesque Middle Ages was characterised by the strong display of power by the ruling nobility and the struggle for power between Church and State. The founding of cities contributed to the development of business and trade.

The Romanesque style of **architecture** developed from a fusion of Teutonic elements and the art of the Romans. The characteristics were clear, calm execution, round arches, powerful masonry, supporting columns and pillars.

During the **Carolingian** period (about 700 to 1000 AD) France under Charlemagne gained supremacy over central Europe. The clothing of this period, **Frankish costume,** was derived from Teutonic or Roman clothing. It was also influenced by the Church, which demanded that the body be covered up.

Chivalry, or **Knighthood** played a significant political and cultural role in the twelfth and thirteenth centuries. Lifestyles improved and clothing became more worldly; it disguised the body less.

The clothing of the courts was colourful. Delicate linen, fine cotton, velvet, silk and brocade were valued. The borders of the garments were decorated with expensive trimmings. However, the clothing of the ordinary people was prescribed by decree. Only coarse fabrics in dark colours were to be used; trimmings and jewellery were to be avoided.

2: 10th century Frankish noblewomen

3: 12th century German noblewomen and female citizen

4: 13th century German prince and noblewomen

Women's Clothing

Until the 11th century, the women's dress had a tunic-like cut and was generally long sleeved, belted and richly decorated with trimmings. The shift-like, pleated under garment was often visible at the neckline and sleeves. It reached the floor and had long, narrow sleeves. In time, the outer dress was shortened and made narrower which emphasised the female figure. The sleeves, however, became very wide at the wrists.

A piece of material, placed around the shoulders and fastened at the side or front with a clasp, served as a cloak.

In the 12th century, the top part of the dress, called the **cotte,** was made to fit closely to the body. This was achieved by the shaped cut of the front and back sections, and by lacing on the side or back. The skirt trailed and an inserted gusset maintained a wide hem. A belt accentuated the low waist.

Noblewomen often wore a luxurious outer garment over the cotte, called a **surcot.** This was usually unbelted and sleeveless. In the 13th century it was excessively long and was held up when walking. The cotte also became very long, and less closely fitted and then also worn without a belt.

The shoulder cloak, cut in a semi-circle, was fastened at the front with a clasp, or with a cord or chain between two decorative discs **(tassels).**

15.3.2 Romanesque (2)

ca. 700 to 1250 AD

1: 9th century Frankish court costume

2: 10th century Frankish royal couple

3: 11th century Frankish royal couple

Men's Clothing

The **Frankish costume** for men consisted of a shirt, hose, tunic and cloak. The knee length tunic had long straight sleeves and a round or square neckline. The shirt worn underneath was wide and long. The hose consisted of two long legs with bindings wrapped around the lower leg. Short hose were also common. The legs were secured onto a belt.

The rectangular shaped and usually long cloak was placed round the left shoulder and pinned on the right with a clasp.

During the age of chivalry, from the 11th until the 13th century, men's clothing differed very little from courtly women's clothing. It simply had fewer folds and was always above the feet. The shorter and sleeveless surcot was worn over the **cotte,** the long-sleeved and belted shift-like dress. The **surcot** was slit at the front or at the side, was often lined with fur or had fur trimming around the neck. The tight, stocking-like hose or **netherstocks** served only as under clothes. Men also wore the **cord** and **tassel cloak** as an outer garment.

4: Shoe from around 1000 AD (reconstruction)

5: Frankish gold foil clasps

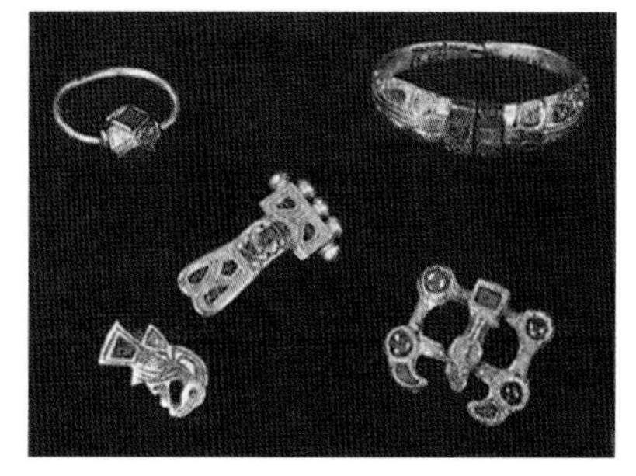
6: Jewellery from the tribal migration period

Accessories

Married women had to cover their hair in public. They pulled the cloak over their head or wore the **headrail** (or couvrechef = coverchief = kerchief), a shoulder length or longer draped head square, with or without a headband. Later, the **wimple** appeared. This was a linen strip wrapped around the chin and head and was often topped by a crown. Young girls decorated their loose or plaited hair with a **fillet,** a brow or head circlet made of metal or flowers.

Originally, men seldom wore headgear, except when at war.

Later they wore caps, turban-like hats and a hat with a tall point. Young men also wore the fillet or circlet on their chin-length hair.

Footwear included ankle high **thonged shoes, slippers** and **leather socks.** The pointed shoe with no heel appeared in the 12th century.

Jewellery consisted of belts, clasps, chains, sword decoration and circlets. These were made out of gold or enamel and richly studded with precious stones, real pearls or glass beads.

15.3.3 Gothic (1)
ca. 1250 to 1500

Characteristics of the Age

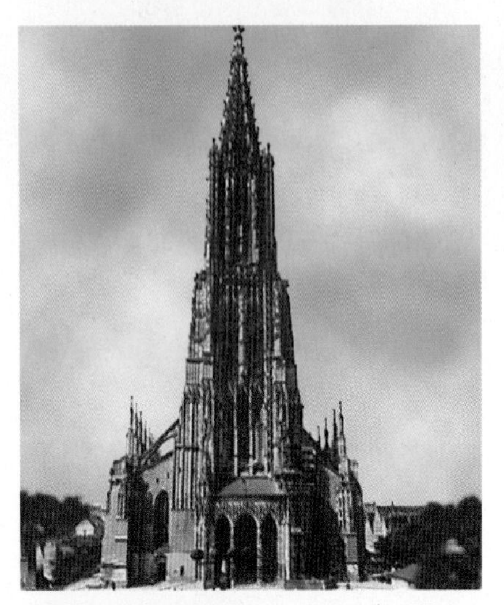
1: Gothic architecture (Cathedral, Ulm)

Culture in the late Middle Ages was determined not only by the church and the nobility but also by the rising bourgeoisie and the city states. The German Empire crumbled, and France gained political and cultural superiority in Europe. The Gothic style of **architecture** also originated in France. Characteristic features were towering spires, pointed arches, strong vertical divisions and delicate tracery.

Clothing was graceful and elegant, but also complicated and lavish. It was then made by "garment tailors". Typical characteristics were long, slender designs with an emphasis on the waist and bright colours. Men's clothing lost its similarity to women's clothing.

The 14th century saw the emergence of relatively rapid changes in fashion. Fashion was spread by travelling bards and traders.

Around 1450 a peculiar **exaggerated fashion** emerged from the court of the wealthy dukedom of Burgundy. Apart from exaggerated designs of headwear and shoes, the most conspicuous features of **Burgundian fashion** were deeply-serrated garment borders, called **dagges,** decorations of small bells and diamonds, padding and quilting. The **mi-parti**[1] or parti-coloured fashion was also very popular: different coloured legs, or garments in which differently-coloured fabrics were joined together.

2: 14th century princess and noblewoman

3: German noblewoman, early 15th century

4: 14th century knight and noble maiden

Women's Clothing

In the 13th century, the women's **cotte** was still close fitting and was worn either loose or belted. It was gently waisted and the skirt was very long, with many gathers and folds. The sleeves were narrow for the full length, or became very wide at the wrists.

In the 14th century the top of the dress became tightly laced, with a very wide neckline and button fastenings. The skirt widened from the hips, which were often accentuated by a belt. Short sleeves with long, trailing strips of material secured at the back, called hanging sleeves, also came into fashion.

The garment was gradually divided into a skirt and top or bodice.

The bodice could then be made very tight-fitting. The join with the long trailing skirt was covered by a belt.

The sleeveless **surcot** was popular as an outer garment. The deeply cut armhole, which often reached the hips and allowed the waist to be visible, was called the **devil's window.** Sometimes the surcot would be only hip length, with fur-trimmed edges.

The **houppelande,** a cloak-like outer garment, also became fashionable. It was open at the front or closed all round and was usually worn belted. It had various styles of sleeves, which were often dagged around the edges.

The circular-cut **clasp cloak** was fastened at the front by a decorative clasp.

[1] mi-parti : divided in half

15.3.3 Gothic (2)

ca. 1250 to 1500

1: Early 15th century German court costume

2: Burgundian fashion, around 1450

3: Burgundian court costume, around 1450

Women's Clothing at the time of Burgundian Fashion

In the late Gothic period, the **silhouette** of the women's dress became **slender.** The tight bodice had a very deep pointed neckline. The waist seam and the belt moved up to just under the breasts. The **train** at the back of the skirt became very long.

The front of the bodice was often provided with a breast bib and a shawl collar. Tight-fitting pipe sleeves, wide at the wrists were popular, as were bag sleeves with arm slits, very long loose sleeves and open hanging sleeves.

4: English Court clothing, around 1400

5: Burgundian men's clothing, around 1450

6: Late 15th century French court costume

Men's Clothing

The tunic became narrow and short and was provided with a fastener at the front. The front and back sections, the skirt part descending from the waist, and also the long, narrow sleeves were tailored to fit.

The outer garment, which was originally calf length, developed into the **doublet,** a jacket that reached only to the hips.

The doublet was narrow at the waist, tight fitting at the front, buttoned up or deeply cut. The back and skirt section were gathered in folds. The chest section and the upper sleeves were well padded. The collar came up to the chin. Open sleeves often had long falling folds of cloth, whilst the closed sleeves were often widened at the wrist. The belt sat on the hips and became an item of decoration.

15.3.3 Gothic (3)

ca. 1250 to 1500

1: English court clothing, around 1400

2: 15th century English court clothing

3: Late 15th century French men's clothing

Men's Clothing (continued)

The stocking-like **hose** made of leather or stretchy fabrics were often **parti-coloured.** These were fastened behind the skirt of the doublet. Towards the end of the 14th century they were joined at the top so they created trousers which now covered the stomach. The **codpiece** was developed, both for protection and for emphasis.

Over time, the doublet became very short; older men preferred long over-garments, especially for formal occasions.

The **houppelande** was gathered into the waist and was belted. It was often slashed at the sides and usually had a stand-up collar. The long, wide conical sleeves and also the puffed sleeves were often provided with additional arm slashes. The long, or knee length **tabard** (a rectangular garment adapted from crusader knights' armour covering) was worn draped loosely back and front over the tunic.

Cloaks of various lengths were worn; sometimes long and trailing, sometimes only hip length.

4: Chaperon hood and shoulder cape

5: Piked shoe and patten

Accessories

Married women always covered their hair, which was plaited or worn up, when in public. Apart from **headrails,** many different kinds of **head-dresses** were popular. These were very important at the time of the Burgundian fashion. The **steeple,** a tall conical head-dress with a long flapping veil, the rolled **heart-shaped** head-dress and the stiffened **frilled** head-dress were particularly characteristic of this period.

Young girls and boys wore a circlet over loose hair. In the course of time, long hair for men went out of fashion. However, hair crimped with tongs was popular. The preferred head covering in the 14th century was the **chaperon,** a close fitting hood with collar-like shoulder pieces and tail. Today this is a part of a jester's clothing: a fool's or trickster's cap. Apart from caps and tall felt hats, the **turban** and the **silk roll,** a flat cap or a roll of fabric with trailing strips of material, also came into fashion.

The typical footwear of the late Middle Ages included shoes with long, extended (piked) toes, known as **poulaines**[1]. Their toes were often so long that they had to be tied up when walking. In addition, undershoes made of wood, called **pattens** were worn outdoors. Short boots with turned-over cuffs were introduced for men.

Gloves and fans completed women's clothing. Gold necklaces set with precious stones, clasps and belts as well as gold and silver bells, buttons and bangles were worn as jewellery and decoration.

[1] Poulaine (Fr.) = Poland; hence Polish style shoes

15.4.1 Renaissance (1)

ca. 1500 to 1640

Characteristics of the Age

1: Renaissance architecture (Old castle, Stuttgart)

The beginning of the **Modern Age** marked a turning point in all areas of life and culture. A humanistic philosophy of life promoted individual personality and sought a freer spirit reminiscent of Greek and Roman culture. Meanwhile the Reformation started a movement towards the renewal of the Church. **Architecture** also was influenced by ancient models. Greek columns and Roman arches were combined. In contrast with the vertical lines of the Gothic, an emphasis on horizontal structuring was favoured.

Clothing of the early Renaissance or Reformation period reflected the individual taste of the newly influential, self-aware and prosperous bourgeoisie. The colourful garments made from expensive materials, such as brocade, damask and velvet were richly patterned and lavishly decorated with ribbons, braids, trimmings, embroidery and lace. The striking costume of the **Landsknecht** (mercenaries), with puffs and colour-contrasting slashes, had a strong influence.

Around the middle of the 16th century, Spain rose as a strong political power after the discovery of America and the establishment of a colonial empire. Consequently, the Spanish court also set the trend for styles of clothing.

Spanish fashion expressed the austere spirituality of the Counter-Reformation and dictated colours, designs and details quite precisely. Although the clothes were sometimes elegant and showy, they were also stiff, uncomfortable and often in sombre colours.

2: German patricians, early 16th century

3: German patricians, early 16th century

4: German patricians, early 16th century

Women's Clothing during the Reformation

The **tight bodice** was separate from the skirt, often laced-up at the front and provided with a breast bib. The round or square neckline was broadened and was usually filled with a fine pleated undershirt, with a ruche close to the neck. The **sumptuous sleeves** were tied on and were therefore interchangeable. By using draw strings and inserting strips, numerous subdivisions and puffs were obtained. They were also often provided with slashes which were lined with differently coloured fabric. The cuffs and ruched edges often covered half of the hand.

The wide **trailing skirt** was gathered in folds and was accented crossways by braid and other trimmings.

Whilst walking, the skirt was held up to reveal the pleated underskirt. Occasionally a long and richly embroidered **apron** was worn which later also served as a replacement for the outer skirt.

The **partlet,** a round shoulder collar, was placed on top of the low-cut bodice. It usually had a stand-up collar, was made out of velvet or silk and was often decorated with embroidery.

Laced bodices, partlets and aprons are still seen today, in traditional rural costumes.

The long, wide **chamarre** with a broad collar and arm slits was worn as a coat.

15.4.1 Renaissance (2)

ca. 1500 to 1640

1: German Landsknecht (mercenaries), early 16th century

2: German magistrate and knight, early 16th century

3: French court costume, 16th century

Men's Clothing during the Reformation

The tight-fitting doublet reached just to the hips. A shirt with finely pleated neckline and cuffs was worn underneath. A knee length coat, with a gathered and pleated lower section was worn over, or instead of the doublet. It could either be open to the belt or high-necked. The **doublet and skirt** had **broad bulging sleeves,** which could be exchanged, had slashes with coloured linings, and were bound many times to create puffs.

The legs were clothed in **wide knee breeches** and stockings which were either fastened or sewn on. Often, the tight hose were secured to a belt.

Many of them were differently coloured or **parti-coloured.** Later, baggy breeches with puffs and slashes, called **slops** or **pluder hose** or **trunk hose** were borrowed from the Landsknecht mercenaries costume.

The typical outer garment of the Reformation was the **chamarre**[1)], a decorative coat with a shawl collar. It was open at the front and usually unbelted. It was often lined or trimmed with fur. Sometimes it was ankle length, sometimes just above the knee. The wide sleeves often had additional openings for inserting the arms. The chamarre is worn today as a robe or gown by judges and protestant priests.

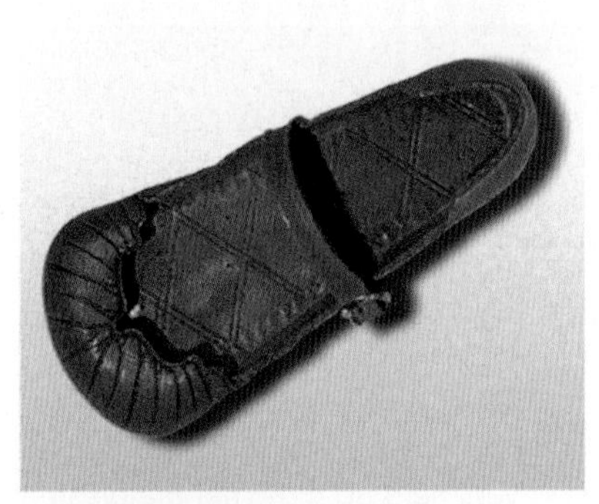

4: Duck bill shoe (reconstruction)

Accessories during the Reformation

The flat **biretta,** richly decorated with feathers and cords, was the typical headwear for men and women during the Renaissance period. This was usually secured onto a **calotte,** a tight fitting skull cap. Men preferred their hair to have a round cut with no parting. The women wore their hair up, and often would use a net of gold and silver cords as the calotte. Apart from the biretta, head-dresses also came back into fashion.

The flat shoes were very broad but were supported by a raised heel. The **duck bill** shoe was round at the front and excessively broad. The **horn shoe** had padded pointed toes.

Heavy rings, chains, medallions and gold circlets were popular as jewellery. While the men wore wide leather belts, fashionable accessories for women were gloves and lace edged ornamental handkerchiefs.

The Spanish Fashion in Women's Clothing

The tight **bodice** was always high-necked and reinforced by bone and wire to press the upper body flat. At the front it had a pointed or rounded lengthening, the **stomacher.** The waist was laced very narrow by a corset worn underneath.

The neck ruche of pleated white linen or lace developed gradually into a circular **ruff.** The Stuart[2)] collar, or **collet monté,** made from stiffened lace surrounding the head in a fan shape, also became fashionable.

1) chamarré (Fr.) = bedecked, gaudily decorated
2) after Mary Stuart, Queen of Scotland

15.4.1 Renaissance (3)

ca. 1500 to 1640

The Spanish Fashion in Women's Clothing (continued)

A white ruff was also formed at the ends of the long sleeves. Wide over-sleeves, and emphasis of the upper arms by puffs and rolls were popular.

The floor length underskirt was stretched over a conical frame. The first **hoop skirt** of fashion history was called a **"farthingale"**[1].

The top skirt lost all its folds, was usually open at the front and decorated with trimmings on the edges. The hips were broadened by means of padding which was tied on.

Occasionally, a coat-like over-dress with a straight cut, the **ropa** was also worn.

1: Spanish fashion in France, 16th century

2: Spanish nobles, late 16th century

3: Spanish fashion in England, 16th century

The Spanish Fashion in Men's Clothing

The **doublet** was kept very short, was tight-fitting and deeply padded. The padding on the chest created a ridge running all down the middle of the chest, called a **peasecod-belly.** The high-necked doublet had a long, stiff stand-up collar over which projected the shirt ruff. The neck ruff grew increasingly larger and stiffer and eventually became a separate item of clothing. The long sleeves were padded, puffed and slashed, and were provided with shoulder pads; they also had stiff ruffs at the ends.

Sleeveless doublets were often provided with loose decorative sleeves.

The full, well-padded breeches, which sometimes had slashes, were short and extended only to the middle of the thighs. They had tight bands at the waist and on the legs. The front flap, or **codpiece** was also padded. Below these **trunk hose,** tight fitting **netherstocks,** or leggings fastened with ribbons were worn.

The very short, bell-shaped **Spanish cape** of velvet or silk was only placed around the shoulders. It had a high standing collar and occasionally a hood.

4: Shoe in the Spanish fashion

The Spanish Fashion in Accessories

The high neck ruff of the Spanish fashion meant a shorter haircut for men. The women combed their hair into severe upswept hairstyles. Headwear was stiff. The **toque,** a small hat with or without a narrow brim was popular, as was the **Spanish hat,** a tall felt hat with a narrow brim.

The soft, close fitting **leather shoes** often had rich decorations of holes or embossed patterns. The women's shoe was often of brocade or embroidered velvet and sometimes was even provided with a high sole. These stilted shoes were known as **chopines.**

The exquisite jewellery consisted mainly of rings and necklaces. Fringed sashes placed over the chest, gold chains worn around the waist, as well as **fine gloves, decorative handkerchiefs** and **fans** were also popular.

[1] farthingale: from verdugo (Sp.) = hoop of pliant wood

15.4.2 Baroque (1)
ca. 1640 to 1720

Characteristics of the Age

1: Baroque Architecture (Monastery Church, Ottobeuren)

A struggle for European supremacy developed during the **Thirty Years War** (1618 to 1648), fuelled by differences in religious doctrines. Spain lost her leading role and for a short time, the Netherlands became the dominant economic and trading power.

However, under the dictatorship of Louis XIV (from about 1670), France determined the political and cultural scene. The splendid court of the "Sun King" at Versailles had a leading role. The strong need for display was exemplified in the **architecture.** Magnificent palaces, churches and parks were constructed. Behind curved and ornate façades, the buildings had richly decorated interiors. Further features of the architecture were complete symmetry, twisting columns, onion towers and domes.

After the bourgeois **Netherlands fashions** of the early Baroque the **French fashion** of the High Baroque period was once again very elegant and luxurious. Men's clothing was even extravagant and pompous. Heavy fabrics such as damask, velvet and brocade were preferred and garments were lavishly trimmed and embroidered. Lace became the most important fashion accent. From then on, the people of the courts had to be dressed "à la mode"[1] – according to the French dictate. News of the latest fashions, the way of dressing and the latest luxuries, now changing faster than ever before, was spread by the first fashion magazines, and by means of dolls, dressed according to the latest "ladies' fashion" and "gentlemen's fashion".

2: Mid 17th century Netherlands Fashion

3: Late 17th century French aristocrats in court costume

4: Court costume in the Fontange period, late 17th – early 18th century

Women's Clothing

When fashion was led from the **Netherlands,** the bodice had a comfortable width. It was kept short or had divided skirts. The wide neckline was framed or covered by a flat lace collar. The shortened puffed sleeves ended with lace cuffs and were sometimes decorated with ribbons. The skirt, under which many underskirts were worn, fell in soft folds and trailed. The small decorative apron came into fashion.

With the arrival of **French fashion,** the waist was once more tightly laced. The reinforced **stomacher,** with a pointed lower edge, was held together at the front over a richly decorated insert called a **tucker** or **modesty piece.**

The low neckline, the **décolletage,** was edged with trimmings and lace, and the short sleeves also were sometimes provided with several lace flounces **(engagéantes).** The long trailing outer skirt was made of the same material as the bodice. Together they made a complete outer garment, called the **manteau** or **robe.** The skirt was open at the front and the edges were folded over and pulled back at the sides. Later the sides were pulled up high at the back and were puffed out over seat padding **(bustle)** into the so-called **French tail.** The visible underskirt **(jupe)** was made from material of a different colour and was richly decorated with e.g. braid, cord, lace, ribbons and embroidery.

[1] à la mode (Fr.) = in the style (current fashion)

15.4.2 Baroque (2)
ca. 1640 to 1720

1: Late 17th century German aristocrats

2: Court costume and Rheingrafen fashion; France, late 17th century

3: French aristocrats at the court of Louis XIV, early 18th century

Men's Fashion

During the Thirty Years War, the loose fitting **doublet** and skirt had a high neck. The open seams of the wide sleeves allowed the richly decorated shirt to be seen. A flat lace collar **(falling band)** and also lace cuffs on the sleeves were popular. At first the calf-length trousers were wide and fastened under the knee. They later became narrow at the bottom. Occasionally, a leather jerkin served as an outer jacket. This was either sleeveless or had sleeves fastened by cords.

Around 1650, men's clothing became more feminine. The fashion of the Rhineland Counts **(Rheingrafen)** consisted of a short open jacket with short sleeves and wide skirt-breeches, the **petticoat breeches** or, later, the **rhinegraves,** which were narrow at the hips, fastened under the knee and provided with lace cuffs.

The shirt which was embroidered and decorated with lace bulged out at the chest, waist and sleeves. Everything was lavishly decorated with ribbons and bows.

The knee-length, tight fitting outer coat, or **justaucorps**[1)], came into fashion around 1670. It was made out of velvet, silk or brocade and decorated with gold or silver braids and metal buttons. The lavish lace shirt cuffs were visible under the broad cuffs of the straight coat sleeves. The vest worn underneath was a little shorter and had the same cut. The coat covered almost all of the fairly wide knee length trousers, the **culottes.**

With the introduction of the justaucorps, the falling band gave way to a loosely tied, fancy lace cravat.

4: Woman's shoe

5: Man's shoe

Accessories

Originally, men and women wore the soft felt hat with a broad brim and ribbons or feather decoration over chin-length curled hair. Later, women piled their hair high and decorated it with the **fontange** which was typical of those times. This headdress had stiff pleated lace ruches on the front which stood up like organ pipes.

When wigs came into fashion, men wore the tricorn hat over the **full-bottomed wig,** which was piled high and had long falling curls.

After the wide bucket-top and goblet boots, which were often filled out with lace cuffs, **shoes with heels** came into fashion for men. They were often made like those for women, of brocade or damask, fastened with a buckle and decorated with interchangeable rosettes or bows. The coloured silk stockings were secured with ribbons.

Both men and women wore expensive bracelets, necklaces and earrings. **Long gloves, muffs** and **canes** all were part of the fashionable image. Apart from these, fans and beauty spots were important items of decoration for ladies.

[1)] justaucorps (Fr.) = close to the body

15.4.3 Rococo (1)

ca. 1720 to 1785

Characteristics of the Age

1: Rococo Architecture (Falken House, Würzburg)

The Rococo period concluded the style of Baroque in the 18th century. Lifestyles became more refined. Composure and gestures revealed a serene, gallant and rather affected character. Aristocratic society was only slightly influenced by the great spiritual movement of this period, the Enlightenment.

Architecture kept the basic curved shape of the Baroque period. However, the lines were softer, lighter and more elegant. The characteristics were mainly shown in the decorative, dainty and proliferous decor and the lavish interiors of the buildings. Grandeur became cluttered. Shell ornaments and Asian subjects were popular.

Clothing also moved away from the stiff showy Baroque fashions to a lighter, graceful and occasionally frivolous style. The luxurious silk fabrics were in single colours, delicately patterned or elaborately embroidered, and in the typical pastel shades of the time. Women's robes were extravagantly full and decorated with flounces, ruches, bows, lace and artificial flowers.

Towards the end of the Rococo period, the influence of English fashion began to be felt. Clothing became more bourgeois and more practical.

2: "Madame Pompadour" by François Boucher

3: "The declaration of love" by Jean-François de Troy

Women's Clothing

Women from all levels of society wore the **hoop skirt**. It was originally dome-shaped. The graduated hoops of wire or wood were secured with oil cloth. They were later flattened at the front and back to give the typical ellipse shape and were constructed from whalebone. The framework or **panier** became so large that it was only possible to go through doors sideways.

The under skirt **(jupe)** lay quite flat over the hoop skirt and was richly decorated with flounces, bows, garlands and flower arrangements. The outer skirt was of a different colour, open at the front in the shape of a triangle and with elaborated edges. From about 1775, when it became fashionable for skirts to be above the feet, they were gathered up at the sides and back and puffed out over a frame or padding – the **bustle**.

The **stomacher** was pointed at the front and had a deep neckline which was often decorated with frills. The **modesty piece** was lavishly decorated. The narrow elbow-length sleeves were provided with many frills, **engagéantes,** and bows.

The outer skirt and bodice were of the same material and together comprised the manteau. The desired wasp waist was obtained by a laced under-bodice.

The **contouche,** the bourgeois and comfortable indoor, outdoor and travelling dress, had a straight cut and fell loosely over the hoop skirt. It was held together at the front by ribbons. At the back there were deep inserted folds, called **Watteau pleats** (supposedly named after the painter, Watteau).

15.4.3 Rococo (2)

ca. 1720 to 1785

1: Woman in a hoop skirt, mid 18th century

2: Fashion around 1780

3: French fashion around 1780

Men's Clothing

The elegant **justaucorps** with decorated borders reached the knee and usually allowed the long **vest** to be seen. Pockets with slashes were provided at the sides and at the back. The richly decorated shirt, with a lace frill (jabot) at the front and wide lace cuffs, was also visible. As time went by, the skirts of the coat and vest were stiffened with whalebone and horsehair so that they stood away from the hips.

The semi-wide knee breeches, the **culottes,** were usually made of velvet. These were originally worn with white knee-length stockings. Later the trouser legs were provided with buttonholes at the side and were fastened with a clasp over the stockings.

Overcoats were uncommon in this period. Short, sleeveless cloaks were worn when the need arose.

The cravat evolved into the **stock,** a wrapped neck-cloth fastened or tied at the back.

4: Woman's shoe

5: Man's shoe

Accessories

Women wore a **lace head-dress** or a small confection of feathers, flowers and lace on their decorative curled hairstyles. Later, hair was styled over tall frames and was richly decorated. Men twisted the hair on the sides of their wigs into rolls, back-combed the hair on the crown very high, and wore the hair at the back in a net or plaited. The **tricorn** was carried under the arm. It was seldom worn.

Heavy powdering and make-up as well as men's wigs were a privilege of status. Grey or white powdered hair was a characteristic of the Rococo period.

Women preferred the **stiletto shoe** with a very pointed toe and curved high heels. They were usually made out of embroidered fabric and provided with interchangeable buckles and bows. Embroidered slippers with heels were worn indoors. The men's **buckled shoe,** usually made of leather, had heels and was rounded at the front.

Whilst the women's décolletage was often decorated only with a ribbon ruche or ribbons with lockets, the dress and hairstyle were studded with pearls and precious stones. Multi-stranded pearl bracelets and diamond-studded earrings were also popular. **Fans, gloves,** drawstring purses and a **muff** were essential. The men arrayed themselves with long watch chains. The rapier became an essential part of the cavalier's clothing.

15.5.1 English Fashion, Directoire and Empire (1)

ca. 1785 to 1815

Characteristics of the Age

1: Neo-classical architecture (The Brandenburg Gate, Berlin)

The **French Revolution** (1789) created the preconditions for a bourgeois society, after the abolition of the feudal system and the pronouncement of human and civil rights.

Art turned towards Classicism. The clear and simple designs of ancient Greece and Rome were revived. **Architecture** was characterised by columns and strong symmetrically structured facades. Museums, theatres, residences and monuments were built.

Clothing also expressed a striving towards a new freer lifestyle. This was made possible through the abolition of classes and therefore also clothing dictates. Before and after the period of the Revolution, the bourgeois and functional **English fashions** came to the fore, influencing also the **Werther costume**[1] developed later in Germany.

At the time of the **Directoire**[2] (around 1795), women's clothing developed classical overtones. Pre-eminent were the finest cotton fabrics in fashionable white. In the following **Empire**[3] period, clothing returned to greater ostentation. Robes were of velvet and heavy silk and had the typical high waistline. Men's clothing, originally unobtrusive and made of dark woollen fabrics or leather, also gradually became more sophisticated for the ruling classes. The uniform played a significant role.

2: English Fashion around 1790

3: French Fashion around 1800

4: Empire Fashion, early 19th century

Women's Clothing

For the **English fashion,** the long, wide skirt fell in soft folds and, instead of a hoop skirt, a bustle was tied on. A bodice top or the **caraco,** a short jacket of a similar style to the tailcoat, was worn with the skirt. The long coat, or **redingote** (riding coat), had the skirt cut away at the front. The neckline was covered with a small shawl, the **fichu.**

The light **chemise** appeared in the **Directoire** period. The waistline moved up to below the breast and was held, like the large neckline, by a gathered seam. The transparent garment with many folds, either sleeveless or with short sleeves, had a long train. Underneath was simply a skin coloured knitted shift. Sumptuous cashmere shawls were draped around the body when it was cold or in bad weather.

Top dresses reappeared later. They were worn open over the long, trailing under garment which was a different colour. Otherwise they ended at the knee as a tunic. The edges were decorated with embroidered trimmings. The décolletage was covered by a small, long sleeved, spencer-style jacket, the **canezou.**

During the **Empire** period, the high bodice was separated from the skirt and was shaped into a corsage to fit the body very closely. The neckline was often emphasised by a tall lace collar. The sleeves were usually short and were puffed or slashed.

The skirt became stiffer, narrower and shorter. By 1808 it was above the feet, by 1810 even above the ankles. The hem was often decorated. The train was still worn at court and was fastened on the back as a separate item of clothing.

[1] Werther: hero in a book by Goethe
[2] Directoire (Fr.) = Directory: post-revolutionary French government executive
[3] Empire: Napoleonic Empire

15.5.1 English Fashion, Directoire and Empire (2)

ca. 1785 to 1815

1: German Werther costume, late 18th century

2: German Empire fashion around 1800

3: French court costume and carrick, early 19th century

Men's Clothing

At the time of the Revolution, the dark frock coat was given a high collar, broad tails and long, narrow sleeves. It gradually developed into the **tailcoat** and became the main item of clothing for the bourgeoisie. The two rows of buttons were fastened, or it was worn open. The waist moved upwards with time.

Bright colours were preferred for the trousers. Long breeches, the **pantaloons,** gradually replaced the tight-fitting knee-length trousers with a fastener at the side. They originally came down to the calf. Later they reached the feet and were held tight by stirrups and braces (suspenders).

The trousers were very narrow with a high waist, and knitted fabric was preferred.

The close-fitting short waistcoat, the **gilet,** was sleeveless and was often worn with a high collar, as was the open shirt. Large neck-cloths (stocks) were worn loosely or knotted under the chin. The sash appeared.

The long, double-breasted **redingote,** with overlapping front pieces, and the **carrick,** with several shoulder layers, served as overcoats. The short sleeveless **spencer** was also sometimes worn over the tailcoat.

4: Woman's shoe

5: Escarpin[2]: Man's dancing shoe

Accessories

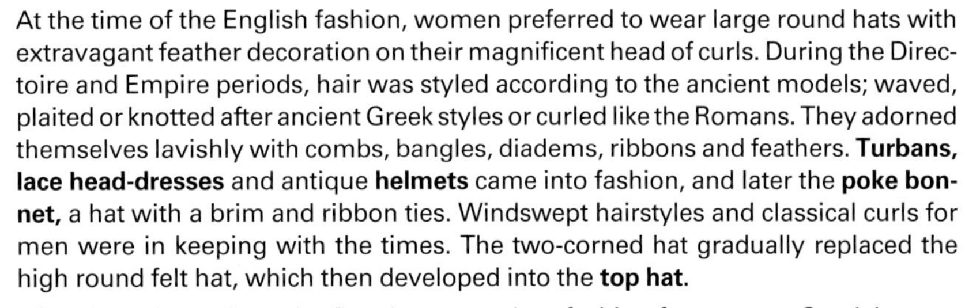

At the time of the English fashion, women preferred to wear large round hats with extravagant feather decoration on their magnificent head of curls. During the Directoire and Empire periods, hair was styled according to the ancient models; waved, plaited or knotted after ancient Greek styles or curled like the Romans. They adorned themselves lavishly with combs, bangles, diadems, ribbons and feathers. **Turbans, lace head-dresses** and antique **helmets** came into fashion, and later the **poke bonnet,** a hat with a brim and ribbon ties. Windswept hairstyles and classical curls for men were in keeping with the times. The two-corned hat gradually replaced the high round felt hat, which then developed into the **top hat.**

After the stiletto shoe, the flat shoe came into fashion for women. Sandals were appropriate to the long flowing robes. However, soft **slipper** shoes (pumps) with low fronts were worn in preference. These were covered in fabric and the colour was matched to the clothes. Later, when skirts rose above the ankles, they were provided with crossed ribbons. The main footwear for men was soft boots, with or without tops. However, flat, low-fronted shoes were also common. **Gamashes**[1] were worn as protection from the weather.

Long gloves were essential for women with short-sleeved dresses. **Muffs, shades** and **reticules,** a kind of small hand bag, were important accessories when going outside. Necklaces of many strands were worn with the low décolletage. Bracelets, rings and large earrings were also popular. Men wore a watch on a chain and would not go out of doors without **gloves.** Decorated cane handles and tobacco pouches were much esteemed.

[1] gamashes : stiffened fabric or leather item, usually with buttons, placed over the shoe and lower leg.
[2] escarpin (Fr.) = dancing shoe, pump

15.5.2 Biedermeier (1)

ca. 1815 to 1850

Characteristics of the Age

1: Biedermeier room (Düsseldorf)

After the political defeat of Napoleon, the **Vienna Congress** tried to create a new order in Europe and restore the earlier relationships. During this time of the **Restoration,** there was a growing interest in past cultures, revealed particularly in art and literature (romanticism).

Architecture retained its classical forms but a new, more bourgeois style, the **Biedermeier,** developed in the design of living rooms. A homeliness and idyllic atmosphere was attained by simple, clear and soft curving designs.

Clothing fashion was shaped according to the ideas of the **Romantics** and suited the needs of the bourgeois lifestyle. It was highly imaginative and colourful. In contrast to the lavish women's fashion, men's clothing was unobtrusively elegant and functional. Distinctions were made between day clothes and formal dress, Summer and Winter clothing, and materials and colours were chosen accordingly. Stripes, checks and floral patterns, combined with white linens were typical of the Biedermeier period.

2: German Fashion around 1820

3: Biedermeier Fashion around 1830

4: Biedermeier Fashion around 1830

Women's Clothing

For a while, the slim silhouettes of the Empire fashion were retained, although they were modified. The stiff, narrow skirt was ankle length, sewn on under the breast, belted, and accented around the lower part by flounces, frills, gathers and ribbons. The small neckline of the tight bodice was framed by a high ruche. The tops of the long, narrow sleeves were puffed.

Around 1820, the waistline moved down once more to its natural place and was tightly laced by a corset. Several underskirts supported the wide skirt, which came above the feet. A collar or a **bertha,** a deep collar or trimming, surrounded the broad neckline of the tight fitting bodice. The enormous **leg-of-mutton** (gigot) or **elephant sleeves** had to be supported by a whalebone frame. They were set deeply into the dress and were usually narrow from the elbows to the wrist. Later they were narrow at the top and puffed out below.

Widened shoulders, full sleeves, narrow **stomachers** and wide skirts produced the so called **hour-glass silhouette.** The dress was also richly decorated with ribbons, bows, embroidery, flounces and artificial flowers.

Around 1840 the floor length skirt returned, but this time stiffened around the circumference by horsehair. Originally, it had only a single flounce at the hem, but gradually it developed many rows of flounces. Sometimes several skirts were worn over each other in graduated lengths.

The **crinoline**[1)], a hoop skirt originally stiffened by horsehair then later with wire hoops, developed from the stiffened underskirts. The sleeves became narrow once more.

Because of the bulky sleeves on dresses, shawls and capes were popular. The **pelerine**[2)] was like a broad, fringed scarf, the **mantilla** was a triangular shawl. Shoulder collars were developed from the **canezou,** a short, long-sleeved jacket. The long and very wide cloak was called the **rotonde** or **wrap.**

[1)] crin (Fr.) = horsehair
[2)] pèlerine (Fr.) = pilgrim; hence pilgrim's cape or shawl

15.5.2 Biedermeier (2)

ca. 1815 to 1850

1: Cloak fashion around 1830

2: Crinoline fashion 1847

Men's Clothing

The coat jacket or double-breasted **frock coat** became the day suit. The **tailcoat** with rounded or cornered lower jacket front served as a formal suit or upper class street wear. The frock coat and the tailcoat were made of dark or colourful woollen fabric. The knee-length flared tails were sewn on at the waist. The chest and shoulders were padded. Sometimes the men would even wear a corset to attain the required slim waist. The tops of the sleeves were puffed. Later they were sewn flat.

Lighter, or differently coloured knitted material was always preferred for the long trousers called **pantaloons.**

The trouser legs were very narrow at the bottom, partly covered the foot and were held taut by a **stirrup.** The colourfully patterned or embroidered waistcoat was also tightly fitted. The tall, stiffened **pointed collar** (cut-throat) and the cuffs of the white shirt were visible. Neck-scarves or stocks would be wrapped loose, tied according to individual preferences, or tied into a bow.

The fashion of the cloak was very varied. The **carrick** was worn loose and had several shoulder collars. The **redingote** was fitted in the cut of the frock coat but somewhat longer. The **paletot** was a new design with a straight cut and high neckline, sometimes with a flared skirt.

3: Woman's boot

4: Man's buttoned boot

Accessories

Women's coiffure was highly imaginative and varied. Elaborate hairstyles with pinned-up plaits, tufts of curls, corkscrew curls and kiss-curls were characteristics of the Biedermeier period, as was the **poke bonnet.** This was made out of straw, felt, or cloth and was richly decorated with flowers, fruit and bows. The broad brim often jutted out over the face and it was tied under the chin with ribbons. The typical headwear for men was the tall **top hat,** both with day clothes and formal dress. Curled hair and mutton-chop side-whiskers were fashionable.

The women's shoe had a thin sole and no heel. It was very soft and invariably covered with fabric. **Cross-band** shoes were popular and were often tied up to the calf. Later the women's **short boot** with low heels and laces appeared. The shortened skirts allowed light coloured, often decorated stockings to be seen. The men's laced or buttoned **half boots** also had low heels. Fabric and leather were often combined.

Gloves, reticules[1)], **shades, fans** and **muffs** were important accessories for women. Necklaces with lockets, long earrings, brooches and lavish belt buckles were popular. Men were equipped with **gloves** and a **walking stick** or **umbrella.** The pocket watch was worn on a long chain, and expensive tie pins and signet rings were favoured.

[1)] reticule: dainty fabric handbag, often with a draw-cord

15.6.1 Neo-Rococo, and the Victorian Era (1)

ca. 1850 to 1890

Characteristics of the Age

1: Architecture of the Romantic period (Textile factory, Ochtrup)

The second half of the 19th century was a period of rapid **industrialisation.** Mechanisation of spinning and weaving and the arrival of the ready-made clothing industry, supported by the invention of the sewing machine, now enabled more classes of society to dress fashionably.

However, there were no really new developments in the style of either fashion or architecture, rather a reworking and mixing of earlier styles. The renewed interest in ideas and designs of previous ages was known as **Romanticism.** Elements of especially the Renaissance, Gothic, and Rococo periods were incorporated into churches, civic and prestigious buildings, as well as functional buildings such as factories and railway stations.

The **clothing** of middle-class women presented their status and image, and was lavish with the material and trimmings. However, men's clothing was distinguished by functional, classic and practical designs in unobtrusive dark colours.

From 1860 to 1870, women's fashion copied the style at the French Imperial Court of Napoleon III, where the Rococo was popular again **(Neo-rococo).** Later, derivatives of the Baroque were more popular.

The **Victorian era** in general, and in Germany especially the period after the Franco-Prussian war of 1870/71 and the founding of the German Empire **(Founding Years),** was a time of great industrial expansion.

2: Crinoline fashions (Neo-rococo) 1860

3: Visiting dress 1879

4: Formal dress 1882

Women's Clothing

During the **Neo-rococo** period, the dome-shaped skirts, supported by a **crinoline,** became enormous. To add to this, the width was emphasised by flounces, frills and embroidery. The **stomacher,** usually buttoned all the way up, was high necked and had a lace collar during the day. For evenings, it was deeply cut and richly embellished. The pagoda sleeves, which were narrow at the top and widened into a bell shape from the elbows, were often overloaded with frills, flounces and lace trimmings. Puffed under-sleeves were often worn.

Shawls, capes, mantillas, and jackets with a masculine cut served as over garments.

After 1860, the skirt was flattened at the front, became wider at knee height and trailed at the back in many folds. The bodice emphasised the body line down to the hips.

The sleeves were also long and tight. The over skirt was eventually lifted up and puffed out at the back over a frame. This **bustle,** or improver, was extravagantly decorated with e.g. cords, braids, bows, flounces and lace.

This fashion also continued during the **Founding Years** until about 1875, when it was replaced by the **slim line.** Skirts became very narrow, the bodice fitted very tightly and the length was emphasised by stripes and seams. The length of the train was determined by the formality of the occasion. Day clothes eventually lost their train.

The costume (suit) appeared, accompanied by a blouse. Colour and material combinations, as well as contrasting trimmings were popular.

Around 1880, once again a drape was attached to the back of the skirts, the **Cul de Paris** (Paris tail).

15.6.1 Neo-Rococo, and the Victorian Era (2)

ca. 1850 to 1890

1: Outer garments of the crinoline period

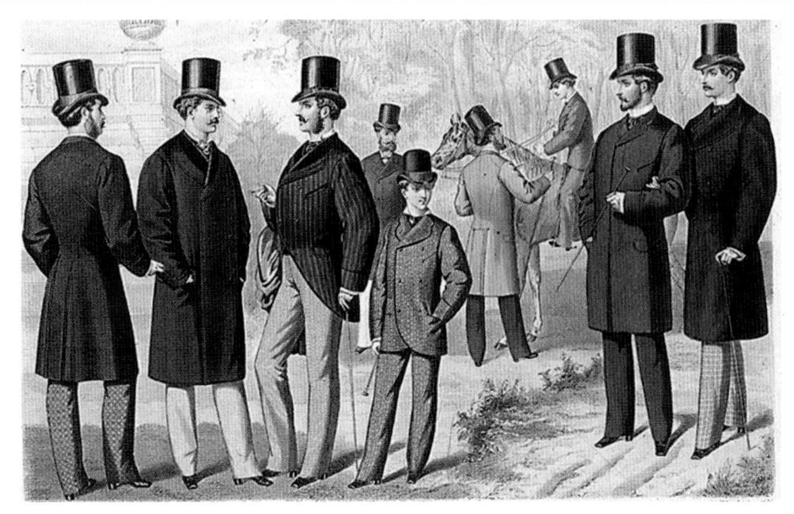

2: Men's fashion 1875

Men's Clothing

Men's fashion was completely modelled on the English example and was suited to the professional or social occasion. For a while, outerwear was dominated by the **frock coat** and **tail coat** but, gradually, the more comfortable jacket, the suit jacket, became accepted. The front and back parts had a straight cut and were not very fitted. The double-breasted style and trimmed edges were popular.

Stirrups went out of fashion. Trousers became wider, with a higher waist, and were often striped or checked. Initially, the waistcoat was still individually coloured but, when the **suit** appeared, around 1860, jacket, trousers and waistcoat were all made from the same colour and material.

The black tail coat, combined with striped trousers, was worn only for particular occasions. The black tail coat with a white waistcoat was worn only as formal dress.

The **paletot** with a straight cut was the preferred style of overcoat.

Shirts were often embroidered. Stand-up collars and turned down collars were gradually replaced by stiff buttoned-on collars. Depending on the type of outfit, a narrow tie, a broad cravat or a neckband would be worn.

3: Woman's boot

Accessories

Women's headwear continued to evolve with the appearance of **spoon** and **gipsy** bonnets. They were lavishly decorated and sat directly over the forehead or on the back of the head. The sometimes smooth but also sometimes elaborate hairstyles were decorated with fine hairnets, pearls and precious stones, ribbons, feathers and flowers. Men wore tall **top hats** on their slicked down parted hair to go with the tail coat and frock coat. The **bowler,** a felt hat with a stiff rounded top and a small stiff brim, came into fashion for wearing with the suit. The **boater,** a flat straw hat, was worn with the summer suit.

The women's wardrobe was completed by low or calf-length **boots** with a medium heel, so no part of the leg was to be seen. The boots were often embroidered or had stitched decoration. **Pumps** began to be worn with ball dresses, as skirt lengths became shorter. Laced or buttoned **boots** were also fashionable for men. Only the formal shoe was lower.

Women favoured conspicuous jewellery; large lockets, earrings, brooches and bracelets studded with precious stones and pearls. **Gloves, handbags** and **shades** were necessary when going outdoors. Men displayed prominent tie pins and cuff links. The gold watch was worn on a heavy chain. The correctly dressed man always wore **gloves** and carried a **cane** or walking **umbrella.**

15.7.1 Belle Époque[1], Reform, Art Nouveau (1)

ca. 1890 to 1914

Characteristics of the Age

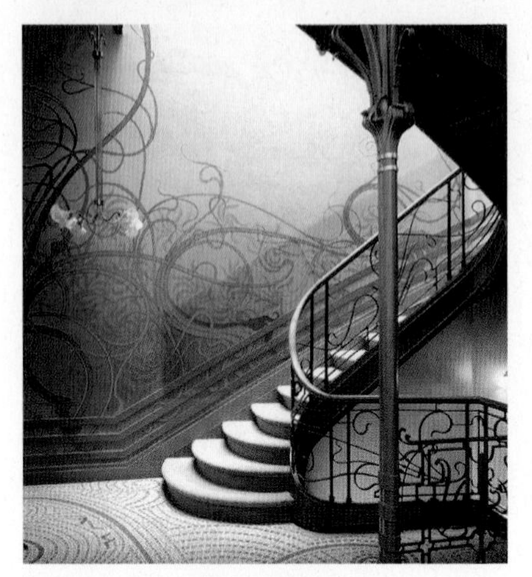

1: Tassel House (Brussels)

Lifestyles were influenced by the tremendous developments in science and technology that occurred during the periods before and after the turn of the century. The fabric, colour and cut of men's and women's clothing was now suited to its purpose and the occasion. Jobs, sport and free time were influential. Attempts at **reform and emancipation** by doctors, artists and women's groups towards the end of the century, meant that women's clothes had to be more functional and easier to wear. They also had to reflect the increased status of women in society.

The English style with a formal business-like design and subdued colours and patterns was still of prime importance to men's fashion.

Women's fashion in the period before the turn of the century, known as the **Belle Époque** was luxurious and extravagant with the material, the cut, and the finish. Discreet colours were nevertheless retained. The **clothing reform** at the beginning of the 20th century brought simplified designs, lively colours and new decorative patterns, inspired by the **art nouveau.** This art trend (about 1895 to 1914) attempted to harmonise the functional with the natural and aesthetic. This included architecture and above all, craft. Basic characteristics of this style were soft, flowing lines, simple ornaments inspired from nature, and designs which were suited to the materials.

2: Women's fashion around 1898

3: Turn of the century women's fashion

4: Women's fashion, early 20th century

5: Dance dress 1914

Women's Clothing

In 1890, skirts with a **slim silhouette** were preferred. They were narrow at the front and trailed in folds at the back. The panelled, flared skirt appeared. It was tight-fitting at the hips and flared out in many folds from the knee. Lining and underskirts, both silk and trimmed with flounces, gave a fullness to the dress and produced the popular rustle. The long and pointed bodice was always high necked and had a high stand-up collar for day wear. It gradually became more like a blouse and was decorated with a false collar. Generously puffed sleeves, in particular the leg-of-mutton sleeve, were popular.

A skirt and blouse with a belt to emphasise the waist were often worn. The **bolero** allowed the attractive finishings of the blouse to be visible. The **costume,** with a masculine style of jacket, also became firmly established. Straight or fitted coats and longer jackets replaced the cape.

Around 1900, the princess cut came into fashion and the very long sleeves became narrower. The front was made straight and the breasts were emphasised by lacing the body and hips into a corset. From the side, the body then resembled an S-shape. This unhealthy fashion was counteracted by the **reform dress,** which flowed softly to the floor from the shoulders or the breast. At first, it found favour only as formal wear but, gradually daywear also began to be less tightly constricted and higher in the waist. Around 1910, skirts became so narrow that walking became difficult. However, this **hobble skirt** was as unpopular as the trouser skirt.

Around 1914, the shoe-length straight skirt, often with a draped over-skirt **(tunic),** combined with a blouse-like top dominated day wear. An oriental style was preferred for extravagant evening wear.

[1] belle époque (Fr.) = beautiful age

15.7.1 Belle Époque[1)], Reform, Art Nouveau (2)
ca. 1890 to 1914

1: Riding outfits 1890

2: Formal dress 1910

3: Formal dress 1910

Men's Clothing

Men wore the **suit** in a moderately fitted style with a fairly high front at work and outdoors. Gradually the suit became more fitted and the lapel became longer. The ankle length trousers tapered towards the bottom and had turn-ups (cuffs) and pressed creases.

On formal occasions, in the day time, the frock coat was replaced by the **cutaway** (tail coat) with rounded tails. This was worn with striped trousers with no turn-ups.

The **dinner jacket** (smoking jacket, tuxedo) appeared in formal evening dress and, from then on, tails were not worn in the evening except for large, official occasions.

The overcoat was chosen according to the suit. Apart from the elegant **Paletot** or **Chesterfield,** the casual **Ulster,** the comfortable **Raglan** and the **short coat** were favoured. With the arrival of sporting fashions, knickerbockers and plus fours became popular.

4: Woman's strap shoe

5: Man's short boot

Accessories

Women preferred small hats on their tightly waved hairstyles with a knot at the nape of the neck. When the piled up, protruding hairstyles came into fashion, the hat also developed into a **"picture hat"** and was richly decorated with feathers, flowers, ribbons and bows. For men, a soft felt hat, a stiff **bowler,** a smart **top hat** or a summery **boater** was worn, depending on the occasion or the suit.

With the shortening of skirts, the women's shoe entered the fashion arena. The low fronted shoe, the **pump,** gradually replaced the boot which had been the standard daytime footwear. The pumps were pointed, had curved, medium height heels and often a strap. Men wore ankle high **laced** or **buttoned boots** or dark shoes, over which they wore fabric gaiters. Lacquered (patent) shoes had to be worn with formal evening dress.

Hats, gloves and **handbags** were essential outdoor accessories for women. In addition, a **sunshade** was required during the Summer and a **muff** in Winter. Highly imaginative jewellery, feather boas and fans completed the evening dress. **Breast pocket handkerchiefs, gloves** and **canes** completed the men's outfit. In addition, tie pins, shirt buttons and cuff links made of expensive materials were displayed. The wristwatch appeared.

[1)] belle époque (Fr.) = beautiful age

15.7.2 The Twenties (1)

1920 to 1929

Characteristics of the Decade

1: Bauhaus (School of Design, Dessau)

After the First World War (1914 to 1918), women's clothing in particular underwent revolutionary changes. One of the most important influences was the movement towards **equal status for women;** in the work place, in private and political life and, increasingly, in sport. A newer, more business-like type of woman emerged and made corresponding demands on **clothing.** The constriction of a corset was no longer desired. Exaggeration of the female form was abjured and more freedom for the legs was demanded. The result was simplified styles and short skirts. Above all, day wear was practical and comfortable. Casual fabrics in muted colours were preferred. On the other hand, evening dress was composed with striking materials in bright colours and extravagant decoration. The new leaders of fashion were to be theatre and movie stars.

The fashion industry began to boom. Art, theatre and music also flourished. Evening entertainment made the pressures of inflation, political unrest and unemployment more bearable. The years from 1924 to 1929 were described as the "roaring twenties".

The Bauhaus, a school of design founded in 1919, heavily influenced the trends in **architecture** in the 20th century. Its goal was the fusion of art and technology. Function and efficiency were most important. Concrete and metal, glass and plaster were the building materials. In contrast, the fantastic ornaments and interior design of the **Art Deco** were reminiscent of Art Nouveau.

2: Sport suit and jumper fashions 1926

3: Evening wear 1925

4: Afternoon wear 1929

5: Formal dress 1929

Women's Clothing

After the wartime fashions, with an emphasised waist and a wide skirt, the narrow, loose, shift dress emerged. The length of the skirt became shorter; by 1920 the mostly one-piece dresses were scarcely calf-length. The loosely swirling dropped waist was emphasised by a belt or sash. Comfortable knitted fabrics and affordable "artificial silk" fabrics appeared. Long jumpers or pullovers were also popular.

By 1924 the skirt was at the knee and by 1927 it had risen above the knee. The lengthened top of the dress had a straight cut so that the bust and waist disappeared. The fashion ideal was the **garçonne**[1], a boy-like figure.

Formal dress had the same cut as day wear although the **décolletage** was larger and there were more feminine details such as swinging flared or pleated skirts and trimmings of pearls, sequins or fringes **(Charleston dress).**

At the end of the decade clothing became more figure hugging and skirts lengthened to the calf. Biased cuts, drapings, flounces, asymmetrical and uneven hems were popular.

A **masculine cut** was often chosen for costume jackets and day coats. The wrap-around coat with a shawl collar dominated the elegant style of clothing. Fur coats and fur trimmings came into fashion, as well as the **ensemble** (dress and coat).

[1] garçon (Fr.) = boy

15.7.2 The Twenties (2)

1920 to 1929

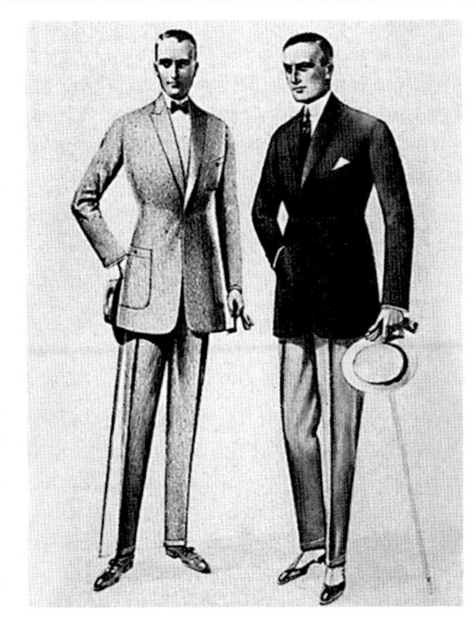

1: Men's fashion 1920

2: Men's fashion 1925

3: Men's fashion 1928

Men's Clothing

Men's day wear was either business-like or sporty. The discreetly coloured fabrics had various patterns, such as checks, stripes and small designs. At first, the **jacket** retained its stiffened front and high waist and was usually single breasted with pointed lapels. The **trousers** became narrower at the bottom.

Around 1925, the suit jacket became less fitted and was not so stiff. The trousers had an even leg width.

Around 1929, the shoulders became well padded. The suit jacket was fairly fitted and close on the hips. Trousers with turn-ups and a wide, straight cut appeared.

Knickerbockers and the sports jacket were no longer worn only for sporting occasions. The waistcoat, essential when dressed correctly, was often replaced by a pullover or cardigan during the day.

The **trench coat** appeared as a casual overcoat. The **Chesterfield** was preferred when more elegance was required.

Formal dress remained similar. The **cutaway, dinner jacket**, or **tails** were chosen according to the occasion. The **Stresemann**[1]), a combination of a dark jacket and striped trousers, emerged as a semi-formal outfit for day wear.

4: Woman's shoe

5: Man's shoe

Accessories

Women wore the bell-shaped **cloche hat** pulled right down over the forehead over their smoothly styled or wavy short (bobbed) haircuts. The **turban** decorated with feathers was preferred for formal occasions. Men combed their parted hairstyle smooth and slicked it down. Headwear included the soft felt **Trilby,** the elegant stiff **Homburg** or various **sporty caps,** chosen according to the occasion.

Women's shoes were quite pointed, whether elegant **pumps,** high heeled **strap shoes,** or casual **flat shoes.** Short skirts revealed the legs and therefore the stockings. Skin-coloured silk or artificial silk stockings were often decorated. The men wore ankle length **boots** or **shoes;** the latter with gaiters or spats in winter.

Gloves, handbags, shawls, shades and **hats** provided splashes of colour. **Ties,** now colourful and patterned, were also fashion items. Women favoured multi-strand pearl necklaces, bracelets and earrings. Costume jewellery appeared alongside genuine jewellery. The long cigarette holder was also essential. The men wore wristwatches and signet rings as decoration.

[1]) Stresemann: German politician of the time

15.7.3 The Thirties

1930 to 1939

Characteristics of the Decade

The beginning of the decade was marked by the aftermath of the economic crisis (1929). Frugality was enforced by unemployment. **Socialism, Communism,** or **Fascism** were strengthened in many countries as a reaction to social and economic difficulties.

Art developed very little. Architecture was functional and plain. Public buildings were constructed in the **Neo-classical** style.

Women's fashion was very **feminine.** The emphasis on natural forms was in keeping with the conservatism of the times. With the rise of militarism, daywear became severe and acquired masculine details.

Men's clothing remained conservative, although the everyday fashions became gradually more sporty and casual.

1: Formal dress 1932

2: Coat and Ensemble 1933

3: Evening dress

4: Winter coat 1936

5: Costume 1939

6: Afternoon dress 1939

7: Chesterfield and Great coat

8: Men's casual fashions

Women's Clothing

Dresses were made of flowing fabrics, were calf length, accented at the **waist,** narrow at the hips and had a flared hem. Biased cuts, draping, and the wrap-over effect emphasised the elegant line. The shoulders were accentuated by pads and strongly gathered sleeve settings. Formal evening dresses were low-cut and often had a train.

Jackets and coats were also slim-fitting. By the end of the decade, shoulders had become heavily padded. Skirts just covered the knee. Coats were often 7/8 length. Details from **uniforms** such as shoulder straps, large sewn-on pockets and broad lapels were typical.

Men's Clothing

The fitted jacket would lie on the hips, had emphasised shoulders and short, broad lapels. The straight trousers with **turn-ups** (cuffs) had a comfortable width. The **double-breasted** suit was popular for special occasions during the day.

The **Norfolk jacket**[1] and **knickerbockers,** or blazer and belted slacks were popular casual combinations. Beside the fitted Chesterfield and the straight great coat, trench coats and raincoats were worn.

Accessories

Women favoured **small** decorated **hats** or close-fitting caps on their chin-length curled hair. Shoes with high heels, wedge heels and thick soles appeared. White trimmings, fabric flowers and decorative belts provided the finishing touches.

Soft or stiff felt **trilbys** or sporty **peaked caps** completed the men's wardrobe. Narrow, two-tone shoes were common.

[1] Norfolk jacket: casual sporty jacket with golfing pleats, oversewn belt, bellows pockets and shoulder saddle yoke.

15.7.4 The Forties

1940 to 1949

Characteristics of the Decade

During the **Second World War** (1939 to 1945) and the immediate **post-war years,** few developments of clothing fashion were possible. The shortage of fabric and official rationing necessitated frequent alterations and patching. The motto was "waste not – want not". **Women's clothing** was simple and functional but nevertheless flattering.

Muted colours were used and expensive trimmings were excluded. In 1947, **haute couture** was revived in Paris and took up the fashion leadership once more. Christian Dior rose to be "fashion king" with his new, feminine fashion for women, known as the **New Look.**

Women's fashion of the early forties

1: Day and afternoon dresses **2: Day wear** **3: Suit, costume**

Women's fashion 1949

4: New Look costume **5: Pencil line** **6: Bolero suit** **7: Afternoon dress**

8: Casual coat 1949 **9: Elegant day coat 1949** **10: Men's fashion**

Women's Clothing

Narrow designs with emphasised shoulders and **knee-length** skirts were typical during the war. The dresses stressed the waist; jackets and coats had details echoing uniforms.

In contrast, the New Look brought calf-length, wide **flared skirts** and tops with rounded shoulders which flattered the figure. An alternative to this youthful, bouncy style was provided by the **pencil line** with its elegant and feminine close-fitting top and long, narrow skirts.

Formal evening dress acquired drapings, tunic and peplum effects, and a stylish décolletage. The **tight waistline** brought a revival of the corset and stiffening of the bodice.

Jackets and coats were tailored to fit the figure or had a flared back.

Men's Clothing

Men's fashion changed very little and remained conservative in colours and patterns. The standard suit was **double-breasted** which made the waistcoat unnecessary.

In the post war years, the **suit jacket** became longer, and broader on the shoulders, but remained narrow at the hips. **Trousers** were given a wide cut and turn-ups. The casual **duffle coat** appeared.

Accessories

Caps or draped **headscarves** were worn on the long and wavy or upswept hairstyles. Shoes were often heavy, with thick soles. The New Look brought short curled hairstyles and elegant **hats** with either no brim, or a broad brim.

Men wore soft felt **trilbys, peaked caps** or berets. The crêpe sole for shoes first appeared in the post war years.

15.7.5 The Fifties

1950 to 1959

Characteristics of the Decade

Tremendous developments were made in the clothing industry due to a boost in the economy and the consequent rise in living standards. The exclusive ideas of haute couture were converted into wearable fashion and made accessible to all levels of society. Position in society was underlined by clothing. Affordable, easy-care synthetic fabrics promoted a consumer society.

While **men's clothing** remained conventional, the fashion trends for **women** began to change from season to season. Silhouettes were labelled by letters or shapes. Skirt hems rose from the calf to below the knee.

Apart from **sports** and **leisure** clothing, a separate and uncomplicated fashion developed for the younger generation based on knits, cords, and leather clothing but, most of all, the popularisation of blue denim jeans. Fashion was modelled on film stars and pop idols; many of the trends came from the USA.

1955: tulip, cupola, and I line
1957: trapeze, A, H, and sack line
1958: barrel line

1: Fashion lines

Women's Clothing

Slim skirts, narrow waists and styled hips were the elegant, feminine fashions. Typical examples were the **pencil line, tulip line, Y line** and **Empire line.** The youthful, swinging styles were typified by the **X line** with a princess cut, **cupola** and **balloon** lines with bouncing skirts and **petticoats,** and also the flared **trapeze** and **A lines.** Emphasis on the hips, a fluid waist line and a blouse-like top were features of the **H line** and **wave line.** The **sack line** was a completely loose cut, which concealed the figure and later developed into the barrel line.

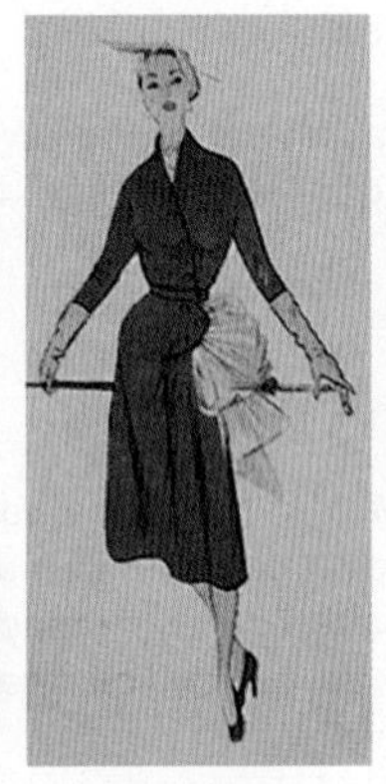

2: Coats in X and V lines, 1951

3: Afternoon dress, 1951

4: Blouson suit, 1959

5: Cupola line, 1959

Men's Clothing

Jackets and coats had a wide cut, broad **padded shoulders** and **no waist.** The trousers were comfortably wide at the top and became narrower towards the bottom.

Around 1955, the suit jacket became **more fitted** and acquired more rounded shoulders. The single-breasted jacket with a short, broad lapel and the elegant double-breasted jacket were both popular.

6: Tailored suit and double-breasted suit

7: Single-breasted suit, 1954

8: Sport and leisure wear, 1954

Accessories

Headwear, handbags and gloves were carefully matched to the clothing. Broad brimmed or decorative hats sat upon short curly hairstyles. Pointed low-front shoes with **stiletto heels** and whisper thin nylon stockings were in demand. Young girls preferred ponytails and the **ballerina slipper.**

Soft **felt hats** or **sporty caps,** narrow **shoes** or **slip-ons** were worn by men. The **breast-pocket handkerchief** and narrow tie or bow tie were required for correct dressing.

15.7.6 The Sixties

1960 to 1969

Characteristics of the Decade

Clothing in the sixties was characterised by a liberation from constraints and taboos. Young people were allowed to adopt unconventional clothing styles, and the textile industry adapted accordingly. The catchword for advertisers and the media was **"youth"**. The prime example of the trend was the **miniskirt fashion.** Jeans, sweaters and T-shirts became universal dress for the young in their late teens and early twenties, who modelled themselves mainly on pop stars. Towards the end of the decade long hair came into fashion.

Space travel and **abstract art** also influenced the fashion scene. Loud colours and new types of materials such as plastic film and coated fabrics appeared. However, there was also an **anti-fashion** movement which expressed the protest of youth against social and political events. The so-called "nostalgic" and "hippy"[1] fashions were directed against the achievement-orientated consumer society just as the deliberately careless "drop-out" look was against the conventional style of dress.

Women's fashion of the early sixties
1: Princess dress **2: Fitted dress** **3: Chanel suit** **4: Shirtwaister**

Fashion after 1964
5: Op-Art **6: Courrèges look**[4] **7: Op-Art** **8: Trapeze line**

9: Maxi-coat and trouser combination **10: Mini-coat** **11: Leisure suit 1964** **12: Single-breasted suit 1964**

Women's Clothing

The **sporty casual** style, with loose jumpers and shirtwaister dresses, was popular alongside feminine and figure-flattering lines such as the decorative princess and fitted styles. Blousons, long waistcoats and pinafore dresses also were popular; the Chanel suit, **miniskirt** and ladies trousers became accepted once and for all.

Op-art[2] and the **space look** brought a futuristic fashion with geometrical patterns and designs in black and white, white and silver. Dresses and coats in the **trapeze** line stressed contrasting trimmings and clearly defined seams.

Trousers with extremely wide flares appeared. Hot pants[3], maxi-coats and the transparent look were unusual variants.

Men's Clothing

At first, suit jackets and coats had a **straight** and comfortable cut. However, after 1965 the silhouette became more **tailored.** Occasionally, the suit jacket was even very strongly waisted. Narrow trousers without turn-ups and knee length coats were preferred. Leisure jackets and pullovers were combined with tight fitting belted trousers.

Accessories

Broad shoes with **large heels** appeared. Fine tights (panty hose) made the miniskirt more acceptable, and it was worn with **boots** of all lengths. Women's hats were seldom to be seen. Large back-combed hairstyles were therefore popular, as were short hair cuts, false hairpieces and wigs.

Apart from colourful shirts, thin polo neck jumpers came into fashion for men. The broad ties were colourfully patterned.

[1] Hippies: flower children; hip (USA) = well informed, stylish
[2] Op-art: optical art, geometric-abstract patterns
[3] Hot pants: skin tight ladies shorts
[4] André Courrèges: French fashion designer

15.7.7 The Seventies

1970 to 1979

Characteristics of the Decade

Fashion was extremely wide ranging, allowing people to compose their own **individual look. Combinations** of separately-purchased items were popular (separates), as were mixtures of materials and patterns (mix-and-match).

Skirt lengths fluctuated and settled on **midi** style. A wave of **nostalgia** brought back the feminine styles of the thirties as an alternative to the sporty, casual style. The **romantic/folklore** look also was a new trend.

In men's fashion, a rich selection of **leisure** or **casual** clothing developed alongside the conservative and formal.

Young people preferred denim and jeans. Trainers became the most popular footwear. Disco fashion appeared with loud colours and shiny materials. Punks[1] gave vent to their non-conformist feelings through skin tight leather clothing and shocking hairstyles.

1: Blazer fashions 1972

2: Mix and match combinations 1977

3: Denim fashion 1976

4: Nostalgia fashion 1978

5: Romantic/folklore style 1978

6: Exotic look 1977

7: T line 1979

8: Party fashion 1975

9: Single and double-breasted suits 1972

[1] punk (USA) = worthless, naive

Women's Clothing

Day wear was dominated by **mini length** pleated skirts and shirtwaister dresses, trousers with **wide flares,** blousons and **fitted** blazers. Many different styles of blouses, trousers and jackets appeared with the fashion for **combinations.** Skirt hemlines fell to below the knee.

For the new **feminine line** dresses of flowing fabrics had fitted tops, longer skirts and a belt to emphasise the waist.

Frills, flounces and embroidery characterised the **romantic/folklore** look. There was a strong exotic influence in evening wear.

Finally, a more business-like style arose with the **T line,** which had a straight cut and emphasised shoulders. **Over-size** styles were a clear reflection of the trend towards more casual fashions.

Men's Clothing

For a while, men's fashion was exemplified by the **closely fitted** suit with narrow shoulders and **broad lapels,** together with trousers that were close fitting to the thighs but with **broad flares.** Later came a new style which, though it **looked very slim,** was more comfortable. Typical features were broad shoulders, long lapels and narrow trousers.

Accessories

Bell-shaped and veiled hats came in with the **nostalgia** trend. Shoes with thick soles and heavy heels were popular for a short time. Otherwise many different styles of **boots** dominated footwear.

Men's shirts had discreet small patterns, stripes and checks. Scarves and cravats were sometimes worn instead of ties. The **handbag for men** (manbag) appeared.

15.7.8 The Eighties

1980 to 1989

Characteristics of the Decade

Clothing fashion was highly **diverse and differentiated.** This was a reflection of the range of different and individualistic lifestyles as well as the multiplicity of opportunities for wearing different styles of clothes at work, during the day, and at a wide range of leisure pursuits. Awareness of fashion was generally high, and clothing was an expression of higher living standards. Good quality fabrics, high-grade garment making, decorative details and a great **diversity of style** were typical.

In **menswear** the traditional suit had to be elegant, with a classic cut, and comfortable. In casual clothing, light materials, a casual cut and elaborate functional details were required.

In **womenswear** the inspiration was the active, self-aware woman. Styles were both classic/elegant as well as casual/functional. Feminine fashion persisted, however, with refined, seductive and extravagant styles. **Nostalgic influences** were reminiscent of fashions of past decades and led to the style mix, a combination of greatly contrasting silhouettes. **Skirt lengths** varied from knee length to ankle length according to the style; the miniskirt returned.

Youth fashions showed a distinct tendency to move away from punk and the tattered look towards a neater, more wholesome style which, nevertheless, was combined with original ideas.

1: Feminine fashion

2: Layered look

3: Suit with new proportions

Women's Clothing

Daytime clothing was predominantly casual with a simple, comfortable cut. The swirling, slim silhouette and the voluminous, very wide layered look competed with each other. The **casual, elegant** city style, with masculine shape and details was retained for suits and coats.

Evening wear was **feminine and elegant**: softly flowing or figure-fitting with a tight, or flared, or full skirt.

The waist was accented or raised or lowered. Sleeves were cut generously for freedom of movement. The **shoulders** were very often **emphasised,** and the combination of very different lengths and widths gave rise to **new proportions.**

4: City style

5: Casual, elegant men's fashion

6: Party fashion, "after six"

Men's Clothing

The suit jacket changed very little. The waist was slightly fitted, shoulders were lightly padded, and lapels were not very broad. **Belted, pleated trousers** were the most common. Quilted and light shell coats were popular. Evening wear was a broad and lively mixture of **party fashions.**

Accessories

There was a great **diversity of accessories.** Fashionable and functional were often combined. The colours, designs, and materials of the latest fashion themes could be used to reinforce a given style, or to contrast with it.

15.8.1 The Nineties

1990 to 1999

Characteristics of the Decade

The discussion of fashion and ecology criticised environmentally damaging production processes, chemical residues in clothing and overconsumption of textiles. However, the resulting **eco-trend** and natural-fibre trends were not long lasting.

The **techno wave**[1] brought a comeback for high-tech fabrics, with shiny synthetic fibres. Fleece, microfibres and membrane systems provided high value, lightness, functionality and easy care especially to **outdoor fashions.** Stretch fabrics were comfortable but also allowed a close fitting, provocative and sexy **bodyfashion.**

For classical styles **purism** and **minimalism** were the keywords. With the motto "less is more" styles were simple and direct in neutral tones but nevertheless made with high quality fabrics and expert tailoring.

Retro fashions revived the feminine looks of the 30's, 40's and 50's. **Youth** fashions were more interested in the styles of the 60's and 70's. The layered look developed out of **grunge** – an anti-fashion trend, which sought out old styles and distressed looks from flea markets and second-hand shops. **Casual elegance** combined comfort and chic and was derived from loose, sporty, oversize **casual wear.**

1: Natural look

2: Transparent look

3: Legging fashion

4: Layered look

5: Sexy fashion

6: Purism

7: Feminine fashion

8: Flares

9: Casual look

10: Broken suit

11: Microfibre coat

12: Colour and high-tech

Women's Clothing

Narrow trousers or leggings were combined with long upper garments. The re-emergence of femininity brought a close, flowing line and the **comeback of the dress.** The **bodyfashion** abolished the distinction between under and outerwear. Bodys were used as a substitute for blouses. Youth fashion demanded the baring of the navel, with hipster pants and short tops **(girlie fashion),** over-length pants and stretch minis.

Men's Clothing

Apart from the free and comfortable casual look, a simple masculine style emerged that was casual but nevertheless **business-like.** Sport and leisurewear had increasing influence on suit fashions, where the totally matching formula was abandoned. With the **broken suit** the jacket, trousers and waistcoat still had exactly the same colouring but were made of different fabric weaves and patterns. Now suits had higher buttons and a softer shoulder line.

High-tech materials were introduced into overcoats. In sport and leisurewear, **colour** was more important. The boundary between leisure shirt and classic shirt was blurred. Fine knitwear became acceptable with the business suit.

Accessories

The female leg gained prominence with decorative, colourful fine stockings and leggings. Underwear and lingerie was more elegant. The **rucksack** became popular for any occasion. Footwear included trainers with profiled soles, jumping boots, **platform shoes,** and **super-high heels,** according to the outfit. Baseball caps were worn back-to-front. Ties began with lively colours and designs but later became more modest.

[1] techno: electronic dance music

15.8.2 The New Millennium

2000 onwards

Characteristics of the Period

In the new millennium clothing has to reflect what is expected from life in general: function, fun, and **lifestyle** – an all-embracing term signifying particular styles and manners of living, independent of age group. The boundaries between styles are disappearing. The city look gets more sporty and sportswear is acceptable in the city. A smart **natural look** confronts the puritan minimalism, which plays down fashion influences.

The old target group mentality has been overturned by changed consumer attitudes. On the one hand, the differences between social classes have largely disappeared. On the other hand fashion trends play a large role even in children's clothing.

Designer labels are displayed to gain notice and status. Nevertheless, there is a strong emphasis on price and performance due to the effects of two major economic recessions and consequent cutback in fashion consumption. Quality conscious consumers go for a basic collection, which can be continuously enhanced and varied with individual new pieces.

Youth fashion maintains its own identity of sporty chic without too much embellishment. It is modern and "cool" but also aggressive and progressive with intensive colours and designs or maybe romantic flavours. **Cross-style**[1] and **free-style** dressing has become common for both men and women.

1: A-line

2: Over-length pants

3: Layered look

4: Empire line

5: Overcoat

6: Transparent look

7: Shiny fashion

8: Unconstructed suit

9: Jacket with "inner life"

10: Casual look

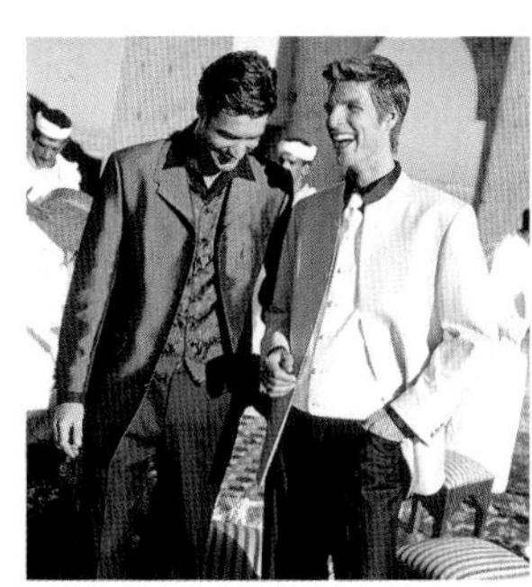

11: Unconventional formal fashions

Women's Clothing

The overemphasised sex symbol has given way to a more appropriate and **elegant** theme with the emphasis on **femininity,** fantasy and romance but also a strong **city fashion** bias and elements of **sportswear.**

The trend is to a less showy fashion with simple, slim lines from interesting fabrics which, nevertheless, have to be comfortable, functional, and business-like. In **playing with contrasts** soft, rustic fabrics are juxtaposed with shiny fabrics, lace and embroidery. Muted tones are offset by dazzling colour highlights. Skirt and trouser lengths range from the knee to the ankle.

Men's Clothing

The trend is to **timeless elegance** and **smart fashion.** The so-called "unconstructed" suits have a close fit with a comfortable width. Variations include narrow trousers and jackets with no lapels or short, wide lapels. In leisure wear, blousons, zip-ups, and shirt-jackets are popular. Materials may be **traditional** or **high-tech.**

Accessories

Lingerie is stylish and sophisticated for the transparent look. "Wellness" is the watchword for underwear, stockings and tights.

In shoes and handbags textile materials are meticulously combined with technically perfect detail effects. The muff hand warmer appeared briefly as a gimmicky joke; jackets, coats and handbags are provided with a mobile 'phone pocket.

Shoes for daily and business wear are light, sporty, functional, super-soft, and comfortable. For festive occasions, they can be extravagant.

[1] cross-style: combination of garments that traditionally do not go together

15.9.1 Special Terms in Clothing History (1)

Term	Description	Style Era
Berthe, Bertha	Loose collar or neckline insert for women	Biedermeier, Neo-rococo
Biretta	Flat cap, decorated with feathers and cords	Renaissance
Bustle	Wire or whalebone frame over which the rear of the skirt was gathered; also "Cul de Paris"	Baroque, Rococo, Neo-rococo, Victorian
Canezou	Short small jacket, spencer type, for women; later with a wide shoulder collar	Empire, Biedermeier, Neo-rococo
Caraco	Short tailed jacket for women, similar to a tail coat	English
Carrick	Coat with several stepped shoulder layers	Empire, Biedermeier
Chamarre	Decorative loose coat with large collar and broad sleeves	Renaissance
Chaperon	Close fitting hood with shoulder collar and tail	Gothic
Charleston	Women's dress for evening wear with a straight unwaisted line, often with fringes; named after the fashionable dance	Twenties
Chemise	Light women's dress with high waist, puffed sleeves, décolletage, train	Directoire, Empire
Chiton	Women's and men's belted linen robe, gathered into many folds and secured at the shoulders	Ancient Greek
Chlaina	Simple woollen men's robe, draped over the back and shoulders, clasped at the right shoulder	Ancient Greek
Chlamys	Short woollen men's cloak, thrown over the left shoulder and clasped at the right	Ancient Greek
Circlet	Ring of metal or flowers etc., worn around the head or brow	Romanesque, Gothic
Clasp cloak	Circular cut shoulder cloak, held at the front with a clasp	Gothic
Clavi	Decorative strips used as edge trimmings, mostly purple dyed	Ancient Rome, Byzantine
Codpiece	Pouch in the crotch of men's breeches	Late Gothic, Renaissance
Contouche	Women's outer garment for house, street and travel wear; fully tailored with deep folds at the back (Watteau pleats)	Rococo
Cotte	Long women's dress or men's long tunic	Romanesque, Gothic
Crinoline	Underskirt stiffened with horsehair or wire	Biedermeier, Neo-rococo
Cul de Paris	Emphasised rear of a women's outer dress, using a frame or padding; also "Paris tail", "French tail", "bustle"	Baroque, Rococo, Neo-rococo, Victorian
Culottes	Knee breeches; at first quite broad, later close fitting	Baroque, Rococo
Dagges	Cut out or sewn-on flaps of fabric at the edges of a garment	Gothic
Dalmatic	Unbelted outer robe for the ruling classes with wide arms and coloured lengthways strips (clavi)	Ancient Roman, Byzantine
Doublet	Term for the men's close fitting, buttoned jacket; worn over the shirt and under the coat, or as an outer garment	Gothic, Renaissance, Early Baroque
Engagéantes	Multiple lace flounces or ruches at the sleeve ends	Baroque, Rococo
Exomis	Short robe, used mainly as men's working clothing, which left the right shoulder bare	Ancient Greek
Farthingale	Earliest hoop dress; a conical frame of thin, flexible switches was worn below the underskirt	Spanish
Fibula	Pinned clasp for holding robes together	Ancient, Middle Ages
Fichu	Cloth square for covering the décolletage	English
Fontange	Head-dress with stiff, folded lace ruches at the front, standing up like organ pipes	Baroque
Full-bottom wig	High, long, curly wig for men	Baroque
Head-dress	Various confections made from stiffened cloth, veils, padded rolls, wire flowers, nets, jewels, brooches, etc.	Burgundian
Headrail	Women's kerchief, headsquare or head-dress	Romanesque, Gothic
Himation	Large, rectangular woollen outer robe for men and women	Ancient Greek
Hobble skirt	Long, very narrow skirt; very difficult to walk in	Art Nouveau
Houppelande	Cloak-like outer garment for men and women; long and heavily folded, mostly open at the front and belted	Gothic
Jupe	Underskirt, made visible by gathering up the overdress (manteau); usually of a different colour and richly decorated	Baroque, Rococo
Justaucorps	Elegant, knee length, close fitted men's coat of velvet or brocade and decorated with cords; later with flying tails	Baroque, Rococo
Kalasiris	National robes for men and women; narrow shell with straps, richly ornamented, shift style, transparent and finely pleated	Ancient Egypt

15.9.1 Special Terms in Clothing History (2)

Term	Description	Style Era
Manteau	Courtly women's outer robes; bodice and usually open skirt from the same material	Baroque, Rococo
Mantilla	Shawl, usually triangular covering the shoulders and sometimes the head	Biedermeier, Neo-rococo
Modesty piece	Decorated, triangular insert for the neckline of a bodice	Baroque, Rococo
New Look	Post-war women's fashion revival from Paris couturier Christian Dior	Forties
Paenula	Oval or diamond shaped cape with head opening, closed all round or slit at the front; often with a hood	Ancient Rome, Byzantine
Palla	Rectangular woollen cloth used as a robe by women out of doors; often covered the head	Ancient Rome
Pallium	Men's rectangular woollen cloth outer robe, wrapped around the body, over the tunic	Ancient Rome
Panier	Framework for 18th century hooped skirt; typically very wide, but flattened at the front and back	Rococo
Pantaloons	Originally calf or ankle length narrow breeches, later full length and held with stirrups	Directoire, Empire, Biedermeier
Parti-coloured	Hose of different colours, or garments with panels of different colours	Gothic, Renaissance
Partlet	Women's broad shoulder collar used to cover a wide neckline	Renaissance
Peasecod-belly	Doublet with heavily padded breast, with a ridge down the middle	Spanish
Pelerine	Collar-shaped shawl or large shoulder collar on a cape	Biedermeier
Peplos	Women's rectangular woollen cloth robe, wrapped around the body and fastened over the shoulders	Ancient Greece
Petticoat	Stiff, dome-shaped underskirt, usually layered and decorated	Fifties
Poke bonnet	Richly decorated bonnet-hat with a broad brim; tied with ribbons under the chin	Empire, Biedermeier, Neo-rococo
Poulaine	Shoes with extended (piked) toes	Gothic
Redingote	Waisted coat with full skirts or a back vent, usually double breasted; riding coat	English, Empire, Biedermeier
Reform dress	Loose, freely draping dress, worn without a corset	Art Nouveau
Rhinegraves	Wide men's breeches, close fitting at the hips and tied under the knee; richly decorated with loops of ribbon	Early Baroque
Robe	Term for women's overdress, also called a manteau	Baroque, Rococo
Ropa	Fully tailored overdress, resembling a coat	Spanish
Rotonde	Long, circular cut cape for women; also called a wrap	Biedermeier
Ruff	Projecting frill of several layers of starched, pleated fabric worn around the neck	Spanish
Shenti	Loin cloth or hip skirt, highly pleated and decorated	Ancient Egypt
Slops	Baggy, overhanging knee or calf length breeches, often having lengthways slashes with protruding lining	Renaissance
Spencer	Short, narrow-waisted jacket with lapels; sleeveless or short sleeved	Empire
Spoon bonnet	Small bonnet tied under the chin with a ribbon	Neo-rococo, Victorian
Steeple	Tall, conical women's head-dress with a flowing veil	Burgundian
Stola	Women's outer robe in the form of a shift, worn belted over the tunic	Ancient Rome
Stomacher	Lengthening of the lower bodice front into a pointed or rounded peak	Spanish, Baroque, Rococo, Biedermeier, Victorian
Surcot	Women's or men's over-garment, usually sleeveless and unbelted, often trimmed with fur	Romanesque, Gothic
Tabard	Men's knee or ankle length closed outer robe, draped in many folds, usually unbelted	Gothic
Tassel cloak	Semi-circular shoulder cape closed at the front by a cord or chain on a pair of decorative plates (tassels)	Romanesque
Toga	Outer robe of the Roman ruling class; an oval woollen cloth folded lengthways and draped artistically around the body	Ancient Rome
Toque	Small flat hat with a narrow brim or brimless	Spanish
Trunk hose	Short, heavily padded breeches tied at the thigh, often with differently coloured slashes	Spanish
Tunic	Women's or men's shift style robe sewn from two pieces of fabric	Ancient Rome, Byzantine
Wimple	A band of linen wrapped around a woman's head and chin, supplemented with a brow band (fillet) or crown	Romanesque

Bibliography

The following works have been consulted in making the translation from German into English.

Handbook of ASTM Standards, Section 7
ASTM International, West Conshohocken, PA, USA

Cassel's New German Dictionary
H.T. Betteridge, *Cassel*, London, 1970

Circular Knitting
C. Iyer, B. Mammel & W. Schach, *Meisenbach*, Bamberg, 1992

Cotton
R.J. Kohel & C.F. Lewis, *American Society of Agronomy, Crop Science Society of America, Soil Science Society of America,* Madison, 1984

Cotton: World Statistics
International Cotton Advisory Committee, Washington

Dictionary of Art & Artists
P. & L. Murray, *Penguin Books*, Harmonsworth, 1968

Dyeing of Cellulosic Fibres
C. Preston, *Dyers Company Publications Trust,* Bradford, 1986

Encyclopedia of Fashion Details
P.J. Ireland, *Batsford*, London, 1993

Encyclopaedia of World Costume
D. Yarwood, *Batsford*, London, 1988

Fachwörterbuch der Maschenwaren-Produktion
E. Lesykova, *Meisenbach*, Bamberg, 1991

Fachwörterbuch Textil
J. Lösch, *Josef Lösch*, Frankfurt am Main, 1975

Fachwörterbuch Textil
D. O. Michelson, *Deutscher Fachverlag*, Frankfurt am Main, 1967

Fairchild's Dictionary of Textiles, 7th Edition
P.G. Tortora & R.S. Merkel, *Fairchild Publications*, New York, 1996

Fashion in the Western World
D. Yarwood, *Batsford*, London, 1992

Fusing Technology
G. Cooklin, *Textile Institute*, Manchester, 1990

Handbook of Textile Fibres, Vol 1 Natural Fibres
J.G. Cook, *Merrow Publishing*, Watford, 1968

Handbook of Textile Fibres, Vol 2 Man-Made Fibres
J.G. Cook, *Merrow Publishing*, Watford, 1968

History of Art
H.W. Janson, *Thames and Hudson*, London, 1968

Illustrated Dictionary of Fabrics
M. Hardingham, *Studio Vista*, London, 1978

Illustrated Encyclopaedia of Costume and Fashion
J. Cassin-Scott, *Studio Vista*, London, 1994

Introduction to Clothing Manufacture
G. Cooklin, BSP Professional Books, Oxford, 1991

Introduction to Clothing Production Management
A.J. Chuter, *BSP Professional Books*, Oxford, 1990

ITMF Conference Papers
International Textile Manufacturers Federation, Zürich, 2006

ITMF Textile Machinery Statistics
International Textile Manufacturers Federation, Zürich, 2006

ITS Textile Dictionary
International Textile Service Ltd., Zürich, 1989

Knitting Technology
D.J. Spencer, *Pergamon Press*, Oxford, 1989

Leather Clothing, Its Manufacture and Maintenance
British Leather Confederation, Harrogate & Fabric Care Association, Northampton, 1989

Leather Technician's Handbook
J.H. Sharphouse, *Leather Producer's Association*, Northampton, 1989

Lexikon der Textilen Raumausstattung
D.C. Buurman, *Deutscher Fachverlag*, Frankfurt am Main, 1992

Man-Made Fibres
W. Meyer-Larsen, *Rowohlt Taschenbuch Verlag*, Reinbeck bei Hamburg, 1972

Man-Made Fibres
R.W. Moncrieff, *Heywood Books*, London, 1969

Manual of Textile Technology, Short-Staple Spinning Series, Vol 1 to 5
W. Klein, *Textile Institute*, Manchester, 1987 & 1993

Materials Management in Clothing Production
D.J. Tyler, *BSP Professional Books*, Oxford, 1991

Metric Pattern Cutting, 4th Edition
W. Aldrich, *Blackwell Publishing*, Oxford, 2004

Modern Sizing and Pattern Making for Women's and Children's Garments
P. Kunick, *Philip Kunick Publications*, London, 1984

Oxford-Duden German Dictionary
W. Scholze-Stubenrecht & J.B. Sykes, *Clarendon Press*, Oxford, 1993

Practical Introduction to Fibre and Tow Coloration
G. Clarke, *Society of Dyers and Colourists*, Bradford, 1982

Practical Introduction to Yarn Dyeing
J. Park, *Society of Dyers and Colourists*, Bradford, 1981

Reverse Dictionary
Readers Digest, London, 1989

Story of Art
E.H. Gombrich, *Phaidon Press*, London, 1964

Technisches Taschenwörterbuch
H.G. Freeman, *Max Hueber Verlag*, Ismaning, 1995

Technology of Textile Properties
M.A. Taylor, *Forbes Publications*, London, 1990

Technology of Threads & Seams
J & P Coats Ltd., Glasgow

Textile Printing
L.W.C. Miles, *Society of Dyers and Colourists*, Bradford, 1994

Textile Terms and Definitions
Textile Institute, Manchester, 2002

Watson's Textile Design and Colour
Z. Grosicki, *Newnes-Butterworths*, London, 1975

Watson's Advanced Textile Design
Z. Grosicki, *Newnes-Butterworths*, London, 1977

Wirkerei- und Strickerei- Fachwörterbuch
G. Sammler, *Prost & Meiner-Verlag*, Coburg, 1976

Wool Handbook, Vol 1
W. von Bergen, *Interscience Publishers*, New York, 1963

Wool, Its Chemistry and Physics
C. Earland, *Chapman & Hall*, London, 1963

Woven Cloth Construction
A.T.C. Robinson & R. Marks, *Textile Institute, Manchester*, 1973

Acknowledgements

The authors would like to thank the companies, associations, publishers and museums who have collaborated in discussing or reviewing various parts of this book and for supplying various materials and illustrations.

Special thanks are due to the staff of Europa Lehrmittel: Mr Maier and Mrs Picasso for the production of illustrations, graphics and pictures, and Mr Freitag for liaison and coordination.

The new fashion drawings in the section on Product Groups were provided by Mr Hannes Döllel, Aufkirchen bei Erding.

Many micrographs and photographs have been provided by Mr Hans Mengel, Eningen.

We are also grateful to Mrs Sonja Langer-Korsch and Mrs Susanne Kolb-Wachtel for a critical review of the section on Leather and Fur.

We thank the following named companies and persons (in alphabetical order) but also many others who have given support in the form of pictorial material, photos, literature, advice, and sources.

Companies

Baekert, Deutschland GmbH, Bad Homburg
Basler, Goldbach
Bayer AG, Chemiefasern, Leverkusen
Big Pack GmbH, Bissingen/Teck
Bundesverbandes des Deutschen Textileinzelhandels e.V. (BTE), Köln
British Leather Confederation, Northampton, England
Cotton Technology International, Stockport, England
DOB-Verband, Köln
East West Textilrecycling, Kursun GmbH, Langen
Efka (Frankl & Kirchner), Nähmaschinenmotoren, Schwetzingen
Eisele Apparate- und Gerätebau GmbH, Schwäbisch Gmünd
Freudenberg Vliesstoffe KG, Weinheim
Gerber Scientific Europe S.A., Bremen
Gütermann, Nähgarne, Gutach, Breisgau
HAKA-Verband, Köln
HB Schutzbekleidung, Neuwied
Hoechst AG, Chemiefasern, Frankfurt a. M.
Hoffman, Bügelmaschinen, Köln
Industrieverband Garne e.V., Frankfurt a. M.
Industrievereiningung Chemiefaser e.V., Frankfurt a. M.
Instut für Textiltechnik der RWTH Aachen, Bereich: Lifescience und Smart Textiles, Aachen
Interactive Wear AG, Starnberg
Internationales Woll-Sekretariat, Düsseldorf
Kampe Gunhild PR, Bad Homburg
Lectra Systèmes, München
London College of Fashion, London, England
Manchester Metropolitan University, Department of Clothing Design & Technology, Manchester, England
Marc O'Polo International GmbH, Stephanskirchen
Mayer, Wirkmaschinenfabrik, Obertshausen
Meyer, Herbert, Maschinenfabrik, Roetz
Peter Gilles KG, Düsseldorf
Prym-Werke, Nähnadelfabrik, Stolberg
Singer, Nähnadelfabrik, Würselen
Sirel AG, Langendorf, Switzerland
Steinhöfer, Niedernhall
Strauss, engelbert strauss GmbH & Co. KG, Biebergemünd
Südwesttextil Stuttgart
SW-Agentur Schirmers & Welsing, Bochum
Tempex GmbH, Schutzausrüstungen, Heidenheim
Terrot, Strickmaschinenfabrik, Stuttgart
Texaid, Richterswill, Schweiz
Vastema-Maschinenfabrik, Veringenstadt
Verband der Knopfindustrie, Waldkraiburg
Verlag textil-praxis international, Leinfelden-Echterdingen
W.L. Gore & Associates GmbH, Feldkirchen-Westerham
Winkelmann Euro-Edition, Frankfurt

Persons

Aplas, Thomas, CHT Tübingen
Bartsch, Stefan, Erima Pfullingen
Baumgärtel, Theo, DTB Heimstetten
Becker, Matthias, Gewerbliche Schule Metzingen
Berndt, Rainer, CHT Tübingen
Bobrowski, Steffi, Trevira GmbH
Burg, Jürgen, Freiwillige Feuerwehr Kaufbeuren
Buschmann, Dr. Hans Jürgen, DTFZ, Krefeld
Doser, Prof. Dr. Michael, ITV Denkendorf
Engelhard, Dr. Stefan, IHK Reutlingen
Friedrich, Dr. Kerstin Grafis Viersen
Geiger, Roland, Mey Albstadt
Grynaeus, Dr. Peter, Freudenberg Weinheim
Gutknecht, Ursula, Lichtenstein-Göllesberg
Haid, Hartmut, ITV Denkendorf
Hegemann, Dr. Dirk, Empa St. Gallen
Hehl, Jörg, ITV Denkendorf
Hehl, Rudolf, Albstadt
Hepner, Gudrun, Aulendorf
Horter, Hansjürgen, ITV Denkendorf
Jehle, Dr. Volker, Rieter AG
Knecht, Willi. Nehren
Knick, Anja, Rieter AG Winterthur
Kolb, Rudi TVU Leutershausen
König, Sabine, VAUDE, Tettnang
Koslowski, Hans J., Melliand-Textilberichte
Krattenmacher, Birgit, IHK Reutlingen
Krause, Michael, Hessnatur Butzbach
Lang, Alexandra, Human Solutions
Messerschmidt, Irina IVC, Frankfurt
Mittermayr, Johann, Woolmark International
Moskopp, Anke, Bremer Baumwollbörse
Müller, Heinz, ITV Denkendorf
Müller, Sonja, 2-some, Boxmeer (Holland)
Nebel, Kai, RRi Reutlingen
Niess, Anna, DTB
Pass, Susanne, DTB
Renner, Ingrid, Gewerbliche Schule Metzingen
Rissek, Anke, Human Solutions Kaiserslautern
Schenek, Prof. Dr. Anton, Hochschule Reutlingen
Schindler, Dr. Stefan, ITV Denkendorf
Schneider, Christine, Südwesttextil
Seidel, Adolf, ITV Denkendorf
Seidel, Alexandra, Human Solution Kaiserslautern
Stegmaier, Dr. Thomas, ITV Denkendorf
Tomanin, Lorena, MS SRL Bergamo (Italien)
Van Mol, Pierre, Fedustria Brüssel und Gent
Vois, Jörg, Fuchshuber Techno-Tex, Lichtenstein
Werminghaus, H. Peter, DTB
Wizemann, Gustav, Groz-Beckert

In the past, it has not been a requirement to cite the sources of pictures in school books. Therefore, this list of accreditations refers only to those illustrations that appear in the 10th German and 6th English editions.

Illustrations

Source	Pages
© dpa-Report – dpa Picture Alliance GmbH, Frankfurt a. M.	294-1
© Gemeindeverwaltung Gutach (Schwarzwaldbahn), Gutach	48-3
© Maier Sports, Michael Müller	37-3
© Otto (GmbH & Co KG), Hamburg	59 ECO
2-some, Textile Consulting & Marketing Conception, MS Boxmeer	109-1; 2; 3; 7
Alte Pinakothek, München	284-2
Amann & Söhne GmbH & Co. KG, Bönnigheim	71-5
Arbeitsgemeinschaft Pflegekennzeichen, Frankfurt a. M.	All aftercare symbols
Archäologisches Landesmuseum, Schleswig	271-2, 3
Assyst Bullmer GmbH, Kirchheim bei München	231-2, 3
Benninger Zell, Webereivorbereitungsmaschinen, Zell	77-2, 3, 4
Betty Barclay, Gil Bret, Vera Mont, Heidelberg	299-9; 300-1 to 7; 301-1, 2, 3; 302-1 to 7; 303-3, 4, 6, 7
Bierbaum-Proenen GmbH & Co KG, Köln	245-9 to 12
Bildarchiv Monheim	286-1
Blicker, Wilhelm Blicker GmbH & Co KG/Eres, Karlsruhe	302-9,11; 303-5
bluesign technologies ag, St. Gallen, Schweiz	59-3 Bluesign
Boss, Hugo Boss AG, Metzingen	301-4; 302-12; 303-8
Bremer Baumwollbörse, Bremen	11-3
Busche, Nähmaschinenhandel, Stuttgart	182-1
Bussmann, Elza, Bernd-Blindow-Schule Friedrichshafen	235-1, 2
Charmor, Vertriebs GmbH & Co KG, Pocking	241-10 to 12; 241-15, 16
CHT R. Breitlich GmbH, Tübingen	112-1, 2, 3, 4, 6, 113-1, 2, 3, 4, 5, 6, 114-1, 2, 3, 4, 5, 6
Continental Clothing Company GmbH, Berlin	59-8 Earth positive
Cotton Technology International, Stockport	230-5; 232-1, 2; 233-2
Dastex, Muggensturm	51-4
Deuter, Bernd, Reischmann Mode + Sport/Marc O'Polo, Ravensburg	239-1
Deutsche MTM-Vereinigung, Hamburg	219
Deutsches Pelzinstitut, Frankfurt	145 to 149
Deutsches Schuhmuseum, Offenbach	265-5; 269-4, 5; 271-5; 273-4; 275-4; 278-5; 280-4; 281-4; 283-4, 5; 285-4, 5; 287-4, 5; 289-3, 4; 291-3; 293-4, 5; 295-4, 5
Digel – the menswear concept, Nagold	54-2
Döllel, Hannes, Aufkirchen bei Erding	150-1, 2; 153-4, 5; 230-2, 3, 4; 243-1 to 6; 246 to 256 all pictures
Dr. Leichum, Handelsmarketing, Frankfurt	237-1
DressMaster GmbH & Co KG/Stones, Herne; S/W-Agentur Bochum	302-10; 303-9, 10
DTB Dialog Textil Bekleidung, Heimstetten	225-1, 226-1
Du Pont, Luxemburg	39-4
Dürkopp & Adler, Bielefeld	165-13, 14; 172-1, 2, 3, 4, 6, 7, 8; 173-4, 5, 6; 191-1, 2, 3, 4; 206-4, 216-5
Eastman, Zuschneidemaschinen, New York	158 straight knife cutter
Enka AG, Chemiefasern, Wuppertal	31-2
ENKA International GmbH & Co. KG, Wuppertal	30-1
Erima GmbH, Pfullingen	35-1
European Ecolabel	59 Ecolabel
Europäische Seidenkommission, Düsseldorf	21-4, 5, 6; 24-1
Fair Wear Foundation, Amsterdam	57-2
Fairwertung, Dachverband FairWertung e.V., Essen	58-1
Fotolia.com © Composer	15-8 coir
Fotolia.com © cstyle	57-4
Fotolia.com © emer	15-4 ramie
Fotolia.com © Firma V	48-1 right
Fotolia.com © Inzyx	15-6 sisal
Fotolia.com © krizz7	57-3
Fotolia.com © lulu	9-2
Fotolia.com © MIKYIMAGENARTE	8-5
Fotolia.com © peht	15-1 kapok
Fotolia.com © siwi1	57-2
Fotolia.com © smereka	57-1
Fotolia.com © Yuri Arcurs	50-1
Fred's World by Green Cotton, Denmark	59-9 Green Cotton
Freiwillige Feuerwehr, Kaufbeuren	48-1 left
FUCHSHUBER TECHNO-TEX GMBH, Lichtenstein	35-2
Gardeur Dieter Janssen, GmbH & Co KG, Möchengladbach	303-1, 2; 302-8
GermanFashion, Modeverband Deutschland e.V., Köln	all aftercare symbols
Grafis-Software Dr. K. Friedrich GbR, Viersen	150-5; 152-3; 154-1, 2, 3
Green Cotton Ikast, Dänemark	59 Green Cotton
Groz-Beckert, Albstadt-Ebingen	169 all pictures
Handelsmarketing Dr. Leichum (HLM)	227
Hessnatur Butzbach	13-1
Hofenbitzer, Guido; Kerschensteinerschule Stuttgart	231-1
Hohensteiner Institute, Bönnigheim	53-3; 54-4

Human Solutions GmbH, Kaiserslautern	151-2, 152-1, 2, 229-1, 2
IBF Innovative Bio Fibre Corp. AG – Schweiz	15-5 jute
Institut für Textil- und Verfahrenstechnik, Denkendorf	53-2, 54-1
Internationaler Verband der Naturtextilwirtschaft, Selzen	59 Naturtextil, 59 GOTS
Internationales Baumwoll-Institut, Frankfurt a. M.	8-2, 3, 4; 9-1, 3, 4, 5
Kannegiesser, Herbert Kannegiesser GmbH, Vlotho	202-1, 2, 3, 4
Kanz, Josef Kanz GmbH & Co. KG, Neufra	243-7 to 13; 243-16, 17
Kelheim Fibres GmbH, Kelheim	30-4
KS-Formteile, Paul Kessler, Kempen-Tönisberg,	53-5
Kübler, Paul H. Bekleidungswerk GmbH & Co. KG, Plüderhausen	245-1 to 245-8
Kuris (Krauss & Reichert), Zuschneidegeräte, Fellbach	158 circular cutter, 229-3
Leinen-Kontaktburo, Düsseldorf	12-4, 12-5, 13-2
Lenzing Aktiengesellschaft, Lenzing, Österreich	30-2, 3; 31-1
Lutz, Edmund Lutz KG, Strumpf- und Trikotagenfabrik, Erlangen	240-15, 16; 241-5; 242-10
Mayer & Cie. GmbH & Co. KG, Albstadt	96-1
Mayser GmbH & Co. KG Produktbereich Hut, Lindenberg	260-2 to 19; 261-8, 9
Messe Frankfurt, Tech Textil, Essen	55 pictograms
MEV Verlag GmbH, Augsburg	268-1
Mey, Gebrüder Mey GmbH & Co. KG, Albstadt	241-1 & 4
MS SRL, Caronno Pertusella, (VA) Italien	108-2; 108-4
Mustang-Werke (Lossen-Foto, Heidelberg)	209-1, 2; 216-1, 2
Nationalmuseum, Kopenhagen	270-3
NATURANA, Dölker GmbH & Co. KG, Gomaringen	240-8; 242-1, 3, 4, 5, 8, 9, 11, 12
Nina von C., Karl Conzelmann GmbH & Co., Albstadt	240-2; 241-6 to 9
Normenausschuss Textil- und Textilmaschinen (DIN), Berlin	Textile & clothing standards
Novotex, DK-Ikast, Dänemark	59 Green Cotton
Passigatti, Georgio Passigatti GmbH, Neu-Ulm	261-2 to 7; 261-10, 11
Pfaff, Nähmaschinenfabrik, Kaiserslautern	166, 167, 176-1, 178-1, 179-1, 180-1, 190-1, 193-1, 2, 3
Ploucquet GmbH & Co., Schutzkleidung, Heidenheim	51-1, 2, 3
REFA-Verband, Stuttgart	218
Reiner Lautwein – Artur Images, Hamburg	292-1
Rieter Textile Systems, CH-Winterthur	65-2, 65-5, 66 Compact yarn, Siro-yarn, air-jet yarn
Robuso Stahlwarenfabrik, Solingen	162 & 163 all pictures
Rowenta-Werke, Bügeleisenfabrik, Offenbach a. M.	196-1, 2, 3
RRi Reutlingen Research Institute, Hochschule Reutlingen	13-4, 5; 15-2 hemp, 15-3 hemp, 15-7 manila
SANETTA Textilwerk, Gebrüder Amann GmbH & Co. KG, Meßstetten	243-14, 15; 243-18
Schäfer Textil GmbH/Götzburg, Ceceba, Margret, Tom Tailor, Balingen	240-9 to 14; 241-12, 13
Schärer Schweiter Mettler AG, Spulmaschinen, CH-Horgen	77-1
SCHIESSER AG, Radolfzell	241-3, 14
Schmetz, Nähnadelfabrik, Herzogenrath	195-1, 2, 3
Schoder Offsetdruck, Gersthofen (Textil- und Bekleidungs-Berufsgenossenschaft, Augsburg)	206-1, 2, 3, 5; 207-1, 2, 4, 5
Schoen-Sandt, Stanzanlagen, Pirmasens	158 die cutter
Schöneberger Systemtechnik GmbH, Landsberg	216-3, 7
Schweizerischer Pelz-Fachverband, Zürich	145 to 149
Sirtl, Helmut (Privataufnahme)	279-1
Spannagel, Barbara, Gewerbliche Schule Metzingen	49-1, 2, 4
Speidel GmbH Lingerie, Bodelshausen	240-1, 4 to 7; 241-2, 7; 242-2, 6, 7
Spiegel-Verlag, Hamburg	236-1
Staatliche Antikensammlungen und Glyptothek, München	266-3, 4, 5; 267-7, 8, 10, 11; 268-4, 5
Staatliche Museen preußischer Kulturbesitz, Berlin	265-3, 4; 267-5, 6; 271-6; 273-5; 284-4; 294-2; 295-1, 2, 3; 296-3, 7, 8, 297-10
Stadtfeuerwehrverband Kaufbeuren	48-1 left
Stäubli AG, Einziehmaschinen, Horgen, Schweiz	77-5
Steinhardt, Andrea, Fachschule für Bekleidung, Frankfurt	238-1 to 18
Stoedtner, Dr. Franz, Lichtbildverlag, Düsseldorf	264-1; 266-1; 272-1; 274-1; 276-1; 282-1; 284-1; 288-1; 290-1
Stoll, H.Stoll GmbH & Co. KG, Reutlingen	96-3
Strobel, Nähmaschinenfabrik, München	183-1
Sunflair Beachfashion, Bayreuth	242-12 to 16
Textil- und Bekleidungs-Berufsgenossenschaft, Augsburg	223-1
Textile Exchange, USA	59-5 Textile Exchange
Textilmuseum Neumünster	271-1
Textilveredlungsunion TVU, Leutershausen	106-1
Topcut-Bullmer, Mehrstetten	150-3; 158 band knife & auto cutter
Trevira GmbH, Hattersheim	37-5; 45-3: 2 pictures; 53-4
Trevira Institut, Hoechst AG, Frankfurt a.M.	299-11, 12; 300-8, 9
VAUDE Sport GmbH & Co. KG, Tettnang	257-2; 258-1 to 7; 259-1 to 12
Veit, Brisay, Kannegießer, Bügelgeräte, Landsberg	196-4 to 8; 198-1; 199-1 to 9; 200-1 to 4; 202-1 to 4; 216-6
Verband der Deutschen Lederindustrie e.V., Frankfurt a. M.	141 to 144
Verlag Europa-Lehrmittel Haan, Europa-Buch 53812; Prof. Schmid	227-1
Verlag Handwerk und Technik, Hamburg; Voigt, Hans Dietrich	227-2
Wahlenmeier, Sandra, Remseck-Neckargröningen	208-1
Wilvorst-Herrenmoden GmbH/AfterSix, Northeim	48-2; 239-2; 301-6; 303-11
Woolmark Company, Düsseldorf	16-2, 3; 19 WOOLMARK®, WOOLMARK Blend®, WOOL-Blend®
Yuppie, Sportswear in Leather; Bodnegg	144-5
Zucchero GmbH, München	239-3 to 8

Index of Technical Terms

A

Acceptance testing 225
Accessories, activewear 259
Accessories, fashion 260 ff
Accessories, garment making 137 ff
Accessories, pressing 197
Accidents 204
Acetate 7, 32, 41 ff
Acetate process 26, 27, 28
Acrylic 7, 27, 33, 38, 41 ff
Active clothing 257, 258
Addition polymer 26, 33
Adhesive bonding 75
Adhesive fusing 201
Adhesive lamination 115
Afghalaine 118
Afine 13
Aftercare characteristics 46 ff
Aftercare labelling 46 ff
Aftercare symbols 46 ff
After-treatments, finishing 103 ff
Aida 99
Air exchange 49
Airjet spinning 60 ff, 64, 65
Airjet texturing 67
Airjet weaving 78
Ajour 99, 116, 118
Alcantara® 118
Alginate fibres 7, 28
A-line 238, 298, 303
All-over effect 116
All-weather clothing 42, 50, 193
Alpaca 7, 20
Alternating compound feed 171
Amaretta® 118
Amazon 123
Amorphous regions 25, 26
Ancient Egypt 264 ff
Ancient Greece 266 ff
Ancient Rome 268 ff
Angora 7, 20
Animal fibres 6, 7, 16 ff, 41, 57
Anorak 252
Anthropometric design 222
Antibacterial 53
Anti-fashion 299, 302
Anti-felting treatment 18, 112
Anti-pilling 112
Anti-redeposition agents 46
Anti-shrink finish 10
Antistatic 113
Antron® 35
Apparel fabrics 6, 11, 14, 19, 24
Applied temperature, fusing 201
Apron 279
Arachne 98
Aramid fibres 7, 33 ff
Art Deco 294 ff
Art Nouveau 292 ff
Artificial silk 24, 28, 33, 294
Assembled yarns 60
Assembly, fur clothing 148
Astrakhan, imitation 128
Atlas warp knitting 97
Atom 25
Australian wool 17
Automated sewing equipment 192
Automatic cutter 158
Automatic fabric feed 190
Automatic fabric guiding 190
Automatic looper 165
Automatic measurements 231
Automatic presser foot 190
Automatic sewing machines 191
Automatic sewing stations 171
Automatic spreading 157
Auxiliary chemicals 105
Avant-garde 236, 263
Avatar 231
Awl 163
Azlon fibres 7, 28

B

Baby cord 118
Babywear 243
Back loop 91 ff
Backed cloths 86
Bacteria protection 51
Bacterial resistance 113
Bacteriostatic properties 53
Bag sleeves 277
Balance plan 215
Balanced twill 81
Balanced twist 69
Ballerina slipper 298
Balloon line 238, 298
Band knives 158
Bandages 53
Bar tacking 190, 191
Baroque 282
Barré 116
Barrel line 298
Baseball cap 260, 302
Basic time 218
Basic weaves 79 ff
Basket weave 80, 131
Bast fibre 7, 12 ff, 62, 64
Batch dyeing 106
Batch processing 103, 106
Batch production 209
Bathing suit 242
Batiste 80, 99, 118
Batt 98
Bavarian linen 127
Bayer-Perlon® 35
Beach shorts 242
Beamhouse 141
Beaming 77
Bearded needles 90 ff
Bedford cord 89, 121
Belle époque 292 ff
Belseta® 129
Belt drive 189
Bemberg silk 28
Beret 297
Berthe, Bertha 288, 304
Bespoke clothing production 208
Bias binding 139
Bib, Breast bib 277, 279
Bibliography 306
Bicolor 117
Bicomponent fibre 27
Bicomponent yarns 68
Biedermeier 288 ff
Bilateral structure 17
Biocotton 57
Biological resistance 43
Biophyl™ 57
Biopolymer fibres 28, 57
Biotechnology 53
Birdseye 136
Biretta 280, 304
Blaze 21
Blazer 252, 253, 255
Bleaching agents 46 ff
Bleaching, aftercare 47
Bleaching, finishing 104, 114
Blend ratios, fibres 44
Blind stitching 71, 165, 168, 178, 183
Blister 121, 127
Blister effect 88
Block copolymer 26, 33, 39
Block pattern 150, 151, 153
Block print 107
Blouses 248, 270
Blouson 248, 252, 255
Blouson suit 298
Blue jeans 114, 298
Boater 291, 293
Bobbed hair 295
Bobbin lace 100
Bobbin, weaving 78
Bobbinet 100
Bodice 280
Body lining 138
Body measurements 150, 152, 231 ff
Body types 232 ff
Bodyfashion 302
Bolero 252, 292
Bolero suit 297
Bond strength 202
Bonded fabrics 98
Bonded fibre 101
Bonded membrane 115
Bonded webs 74 ff
Bonding 75, 115, 201
Bonding fibres 75
Boot cut 251
Boots 269, 291, 293, 295, 299, 300
Bouclé 70, 117, 119
Bourette silk 22 ff, 62, 64, 119
Boutonné 117
Bow ties 261
Bowler hat 291, 293
Boyswear 243
Bra slip 241
Braid, Braiding 101, 139
Braided fabrics 74
Brand names 45
Brassiere, bra 242
Breaking extension 43
Breaking, flax 13
Breeds, sheep 17
Briefs 240
Broad ribs 94
Broad twill 81
Brocade 70, 119
Broché fabrics 86, 116, 119
Brodé 116, 119
Broderie anglaise 100
Broken suit 302
Broken twill 82
Bronze age 270
Brush 197
Brushed twill 124
Brushing 87, 110
Buckled shoe 285
Buckles 140
Buckram 137
Buffalo horn 140
Bundling 159
Burgundian fashion 276 ff
Burning test 11, 14, 19, 24, 30, 32, 35, 37, 38, 41
Burn-out 69, 87, 99, 100, 109, 116, 118
Burn-out printing 109
Business suit 255
Bustle 282, 284, 286, 290, 304
Button sewing machine 165, 191
Buttonhole scissors 163
Buttonhole sewing machine 165, 191
Buttonhole tape 139
Buttonholes 71, 191
Buttons 140
Byzantine Middle Ages 272, 273

C

Cabled yarn 69, 73
CAD system 150
Calendering 111
Calfskin 143
Calico 127
Calotte 280
Cambric 80
Cam-controlled sewing machines 191
Camel hair 7, 20
Camisole 241
Cane 283, 291, 293
Canezou 286, 288, 304
Canvas 119
Cape 253, 290
Cape wool 17
Capillary transport 49, 52, 113
Caps 269, 271, 273, 297
Caraco 286, 304
Carbon fibres 7, 33, 40
Carbonisation 40
Carbonising 16, 18, 104
Carded fibre yarns 60
Cardigan 250
Cardigan stitch 94
Carding 61 ff
Care symbols 11, 14, 19, 24, 30 ff, 35, 37, 38, 46 ff
Career apparel 51, 245
Carolingian 274
Carpet wool 17
Carré 116
Carrick coat 287, 289, 304
Cashgora 7, 20
Cashmere 7, 20
Casual elegance 301 ff
Casual wear 300
Cattle hair 7, 20
Caul 273
Cavalry twill 81, 134
Cellular effects 89
Cellulose 6, 9, 10, 13, 25, 28 ff, 41
Cellulose acetate 28
Cellulose nitrate 28
Cellulosic fibre fabrics 112
Cellulosic fibres 6, 7, 25, 26, 28 ff, 41, 57
Ceramic fibres 33
Chain stitch, sewing 95, 165, 174, 175, 178 ff
Chain stitch, warp knitting 97
Chalk stripe 128
Chamarre 279 ff, 304
Chambray 84
Chamois 142
Changeant 84, 117, 119, 138
Channel suit 254, 299
Chaperon 278, 304
Chardonnet silk 28
Charleston dress 238, 294, 304
Charleston line 238
Charmante 86
Charmelaine 120
Charmeuse 98, 120, 137, 138
Chasule 273
Check spring 166
Cheese cloth 127
Chemical compounds 25
Chemical finishing 31, 102, 110, 112 ff
Chemical protection 51
Chemise 286, 304
Chenille 70, 120
Chesterfield 253, 293, 295, 296
Cheviot 120
Chevron 82
Chiffon 70, 85, 120
Chiffon velvet 87
Childrenswear 243
Chiné 109, 116, 120
Chinos 251
Chintz fabric 111, 120
Chiton 266 ff, 304
Chivalry, age of 274 ff
Chlaina 267, 304
Chlamys, Chlamis 267, 304
Chlorofibres 7, 33, 39
Chopines 281
Circlet 267, 271, 275, 278, 304
Circular cutter 158
Circular knitting 90, 96
Ciré 117, 120
CITES 145
City fashion 303
City style 301
Clamp feed 171
Clasp cloak 272, 276, 304
Clasps 140
Classing 16
Clavi 273, 304
Clean room 51
Cleaning, hazards 207
Climbing gloves 259
Clip spot 86, 99, 128
Cloak 271
Cloche hat 260, 295
Cloqué 88, 117, 121
Closed lap 97
Cloth construction 79
Clothing and personal protection 204
Clothing comfort 10, 13, 18, 23, 29, 31, 34, 36, 48, 49
Clothing design elements 238
Clothing history, special terms 304 ff
Clothing manufacture 150 ff, 208 ff
Clothing manufacture, safety in 206 ff
Clothing physiology 48, 49
Clothing styles 238 ff

Clothing system 257
Clothing, functions of 48 ff
Clothing, history of 262 ff
Clutch types 189
CNC sewing machines 191, 192
Coarse fibres 42
Coarse wool 17
Coating 51, 102, 115
Coats 253
Cocoon 21 ff
Codpiece 278, 281, 304
Coir 7, 15
Collar anvil 197
Collection appraisal 234
Collection plan 235
Collection, developing 234 ff
Collet monté 280
Coloration 30, 102, 105 ff
Coloration, fur 147
Colour effects 70, 117
Colour fastness 105
Colour woven 84
Combed fibre yarns 60
Combination tanning 142
Combined fabric 115
Combined feeding systems 171
Combing 63, 64
Comfort, next to skin 10, 13, 18, 23, 29, 34, 36, 49
Comfort, of clothing 48 ff
Commercial descriptions 116 ff
Commercial quality 9
Common emergencies 204
Communication 211
Compact spinning 60 ff
Compactor 111
Company management 208 ff
Components list 215
Compound feed 171
Compound needle 90 ff
Compressive shrinkage 111
Computer Aided Manufacturing (CAM) 229
Computer aided pattern construction 150
Computer based grading 152
Computer controlled warehouse 216
Computer workstation 223
Computerised lay planning 154
Condensation polymer 26, 33, 34, 36
Condensed notation 79
Condenser spinning 60 ff
Conditioning, fur 146, 149
Conductivity 113
Cone winding 77
Construction, active wear 258
Construction, woven fabrics 79 ff
Constructive design 151
Constructive grading 152
Continuous coating 137
Continuous dyeing 106
Continuous filaments 67
Continuous processing 103
Contouche 284, 304
Control dimensions 232
Converter spinning 62, 64
Conveyor fusing press 202
Coolmax® 37, 52
Co-ordinates, clothing 254
Copolymer 26
Cord skirt 270
Cord weaves 89
Corded velvet 121
Corded velveteens 87
Cords, braided 139
Corduroy 87, 121, 153
Core processes 224
Core yarn 69
Core-spun yarn 60, 69, 71
Corozo nut buttons 140
Corporate fashion 51
Corselet 242
Corset 242, 288 ff, 297
Cost of quality 227
Costing 234
Costume, suit 290, 292
Costume, traditional 48
Côtelé 117, 121
Cotte 274 ff, 276, 304
Cotton 6 ff, 41 ff, 57
Cotton batiste 112
Cotton count 72
Cotton emblem 11, 45
Cotton fabric finishing 103 ff
Cotton fabrics 11, 104
Cotton finishing 111, 112
Cotton interlinings 137
Cotton spinning 62, 64
Cotton type fibres 27
Cotton yarn 71
Cottonisation, flax 13
Count, of yarn 72
Courrèges look 299
Course 91
Court clothing 263, 272 ff
Couturier 263
Couvrechef, coverchief 275
Covering stitches 175, 182
Cowhide 143
Crash 117, 121
Cravat 283, 285, 291
Cravattes 116
Creasing 10, 13, 23, 30, 35, 36
Creasing, 3-D 114
Creel 77, 216
Crêpe fabrics 70, 85, 88, 119, 121, 122
Crêpe sole shoes 297
Crêpe yarn 70, 85, 88
Crepon 70, 85
Cretonne 128, 153
Crimp, fibres 17
Crinkle 121, 127
Crinoline 288 ff, 290, 304
Croisé 122, 138
Cropping 110
Cross-band shoe 289
Crossbred wool 17
Cross-sections, fibres 11, 13, 14, 19, 30, 35, 37, 41, 103
Cross-style 303
Cross-tuck, piqué 93
Crown 265, 273
Crushed velvet 87
Crystalline 22, 29
Crystalline regions 25, 26
Crystallinity 34
Cuff styles 244
Cul de Paris 290, 304
Culottes 247, 283, 285, 304
Cultivated silk 7, 21 ff
Cupola line 238, 298
Cuprammonium process 26, 28, 32
Cupro fibres 7, 28, 32, 41
Curved needle 168
Cut pile fabrics 87
Cut plush 93
Cutaway 293, 295
Cutter's linen 137
Cutting 95, 153 ff, 158, 162 ff
Cutting pattern, pelt 147
Cutting points 169
Cutting tools, leather 144
Cutting wires 87
Cutting, fur 147, 148
Cutting, hazards 206
Cutting, leather 144
Cutwork 100
Cyclodextrins 54
Cylinder bed sewing machine 164

D

Dacron® 37
Dagges 276, 304
Dalmatic 273, 304
Damaged stitches 95
Damask 83, 122
Damassé 122
Danufil® 30
Darned lace 100
Darning needles 161
Data exchange 213, 228 ff
Data Interchange 154
Data sources 213
Draw frame 61
Dead wool 17
Deburring, fur 147
Decatizing 18, 111
Decitex, dtex 42, 72
Décolletage 282 ff, 294
Decoration 48, 139, 238
Decoration, seam types 187
Decorative buttons 140
Découpé 99, 116
Deerskin 143
Dégradé 116
Degumming 23
Demand for textile fibres 6
Denier system 72
Denim 81, 114, 122, 300
Denim jeans 114, 298
Design 150 ff
Design concepts 235
Design influences 239
Design sketches 234
Designer fashion 208, 263
Designer labels 303
Desizing 103
Detergents 46
Development of a collection 234
Devil's window 276
Dévoré 99, 100, 116, 118
Dewatering 104, 142, 146
Diagonal 122
Diagonal, weave 81
Die cutter 158
Differential drop feed 170
Digital printing 108
Dimensional stability 111
Dinner jacket 256, 293, 295
Diolen® 37
Direct beaming 77
Direct coating 115
Direct numbering systems 72 ff
Direct printing 109
Directoire fashion 286 ff
Discharge printing 109
Discontinuous dyeing 106
Disperse dyes 105
Disposal 6, 56 ff, 58
Division into eighths 230
Documentation 225
Doeskin 83
Dolan® 38, 45
Donegal 70, 80, 122
Dope-dyeing 105
Dorlastan® 39
Dot coating 137
Double breasted suit 296 ff
Double cloth 88, 89
Double face 123
Double jacket 259
Double jersey 94
Double piqué 94
Double plain fabrics 88
Double plush weaving 87
Double rib 122
Double-faced interlock 95
Double-layer fabrics 52
Doublet 277 ff, 280 ff, 283, 304
Doubling 61
Doupion, Doupioni 123
Dr. Leichum 236 ff
Dralon® 38
Dralon-Microfibre® 42
Drapé 123
Draw textured yarns 68
Draw texturing 67
Drawframe 64
Drawing and Measuring tools 160
Drawing, filaments 26 ff
Drawing, spinning 61, 63, 64
Drawing-in 77
Dresses 249
Dressing gown 241
Dressing, pelt 146
Dressmaker's thimble 161
Drill 81
Drill marker 159
Drop feed 170
Drop value 232
Dropped waist 294
Dry cleaning 47
Dry pressing 196
Dry spinning, bast fibres 64
Dry spinning, man-made fibres 27, 32
Drying 9, 13, 47, 104
Drying, leather 142
Drying, pelt 146
Dry-laid webs 74
Duchesse 83, 123, 138
Duck bill shoe 280
Duvetine, duvetyn 87, 110, 123
Dye marker 159
Dyebath 105, 106
Dyeing 102, 105 ff
Dyeing and Finishing 102 ff
Dyeing, leather 142
Dyestuff classes 105

E

Ease allowance 150, 233
Easy-care, finish 10, 13, 30, 31, 112
Eco-labelling 59
Ecology and Textile production 56 ff
Eco-trend 302
Edge allowance 156
Edge anvil 197
Edge detection 190
Edge interlooping 181
Edge trimming 190
Effect print 109
Eight month wool 17
Eighties 301
Elastane 7, 33, 39, 41 ff, 69
Elastic tape 139
Elasticity 10, 13, 23, 30, 32, 35, 36, 39, 43, 66
Elastodiene 7, 33
Elastomeric fibres 7, 26, 33, 39
Electric iron 196
Electronic control 189
Electrostatic charge protection 51
Electrostatic charge 10, 13, 18, 23, 30, 32, 35, 36, 113
Electrostatic flocking 109
Elegant fashion 303
Elephant cord 121
Elephant sleeve 288
Embossed fabric 115, 125
Embossing 85, 111
Embroidered lace 100
Embroidery lace 39, 100, 118
Embroidery needles 161
Embroidery scissors 163
Emerising 110
Emissions, control of 56
Empire fashion 286 ff
Empire line 238, 298, 303
End allowance 156
End-on-end 84, 124
Energy efficiency 56
Energy generation 58
Engagéantes 282, 284, 304
English cotton count 72 ff
English fashion 286
Enka-Perlon® 35
Enka-Viskose® 30
Ensemble 254, 294, 296
Enterprise Resource Planning (ERP) 228, 229
Environmental protection 55, 56, 102
Enzymes 114
Equipment, arrangement of 223
Ergonomics 221 ff
Escarpin 287
Etamine 123
E-textiles 54
Evening dress 256
Exaggerated fashion 276
Exomis 267, 304
Extensibility 66
Extra warp and weft 86
Extruded filaments, terminology 27
Extrusion 26 ff
Eyesight testing 223

F

Fabric concepts 235
Fabric damage 195
Fabric descriptions 116 ff
Fabric dyeing 102
Fabric finishing 102 ff
Fabric guides 172, 173
Fabric inspection 156
Fabric manufacture, woven 76
Fabric presentation 156
Fabric properties 74, 75
Fabric testing 225
Fabric trolley 216

Fabric utilisation 156
Fabric, definition of 116
Fabrics, comparisons 101
Fabrics, nonwoven 74
Face loop .....91 ff
Façonné 83, 116, 123, 138
Faille 123
Fake fur 93
Fallen wool 17
Falling band 283
False-twist texturing 67
Fancy yarns 60, 70
Fans 283, 285, 289
Farthingale 281, 304
Fasciated yarn 65
Fashion .....235 ff, 239, 263 ff
Fashion accessories .....260 ff
Fashion lines, shapes 298
Fastenings 140
Fastness 105
Faux uni 116
Fedora 260
Feed dog .....167, 170 ff
Feed dog teeth 170
Feeding pucker 194
Feeding systems .....170 ff
Felt 74
Felting 17, 18, 111
Festoon steamer 104
Fibre batt 74, 98
Fibre blends 11, 14, 19, 24, 31, 37, 38, 40, 44
Fibre bundle 13
Fibre composition .....25 ff, 29, 32, 34, 36, 38
Fibre crimp 17
Fibre cross-sections 11, 13, 14, 19, 22, 24, 27, 30, 35, 37, 41, 103
Fibre density 43
Fibre elasticity 17, 18
Fibre extensibility 10, 13, 18, 23, 30, 31, 35, 36
Fibre extraction 13
Fibre fineness 9, 10, 13, 17, 18, 23, 30, 31, 35, 36, 42, 43
Fibre identification 11, 14, 19, 24, 30, 32, 35, 37, 38, 41
Fibre impurities 9
Fibre length 9, 17, 43
Fibre manufacture 29, 31, 32, 34, 36, 38
Fibre preparation 9
Fibre production .....6, 8, 12, 15, 16, 20 ff, 28, 33, 34
Fibre properties .....9, 10, 13, 15, 17, 18, 20, 23, 25, 29 ff, 34 ff, 41 ff
Fibre recovery 58
Fibre strength 9, 10, 13, 18, 23, 30, 31, 35, 36
Fibre structure 10, 17, 22, 25, 31
Fibre type 43, 66
Fibre-forming materials .....25 ff
Fibreglass® 40
Fibres .....6 ff
Fibres, applications .....11, 14, 17, 19, 20, 24, 30 ff, 34, 35, 37 ff, 40, 42, 51
Fibril 10, 17, 22, 25, 26
Fibrillation 31
Fibroin .....21 ff, 41
Fibula 266, 270, 304
Fichu 286, 304
Fifties 298
Figuré 116
Figured jacquard 83
Figured purl 95
Fil-à-fil 84, 124
Filament yarns .....27 ff, 29, 35, 37, 39, 40, 60, 67 ff
Filaments .....21 ff, 26, 34
Filet lace 100
Fillers 46
Fillet 275
Filling yarn .....76 ff
Final cutting 157, 158
Finance 210
Fine fibres 42
Fine rib 124
Fine wool 17
Fineness, of yarn 72
Finette 124
Finger protection 161
Finishing .....110 ff
Finishing processes .....102 ff
Finishing, fur clothing 149
Finishing, leather .....141 ff
Finishing, of garments 137
First aid 203, 204
Fishbone 82, 124
Fisherman's sweater 250
Fixation 104
Flammability 18, 51, 112
Flammé 70, 117
Flammé bicolour 117
Flannel 110, 124
Flat bed knitting machines 96
Flat bed press 202
Flat bed sewing machine 164
Flat filament yarns 60
Flat knitting 90, 96
Flat multi-filament yarn 68
Flat press 200
Flat pressing 197
Flat screen printing 107
Flat seam sewing machine 165
Flat seam stitches .....95, 182 ff
Flat shoes 295
Flat-drawn filaments 40
Flattened twill 82
Flax .....6, 7, 12 ff, 41 ff, 62, 64
Fleece fabric 37, 42, 93, 124
Fleece, knitted 125
Fleece, sheep 16
Fleshing, leather 141
Fleshing, pelt 146
Float .....79 ff
Float loop 91
Flock print 124
Flock printing 109
Floconné 117
Florentine lace 100
Floss 21
Flowerpot hat 260
Fluorofibres 7, 33, 39
Foam laminate 115
Folded yarns .....60, 69 ff, 73
Fontange 283, 304
Formability 18, 35, 36
Formal clothing 256
Forties 297
Foulé 125
Foundation garments 39, 242
Founding years 290
Frankish fashion .....274 ff
Freestyle fashion 303
French fashion 282
French tail 282, 304
Fresco 70, 80, 125
Friction calendering 111
Fringes 139
Frisé 70, 117, 125
Frock coat 287, 289, 291
Frotté 70, 117, 125
Full bottomed wig 283, 304
Fulling 18, 74, 111
Fully fashioned 96
Functional clothing .....48 ff, 50, 257 ff
Functional finishing 113
Functional level 211
Functional organisation 211
Functional textiles 55
Functions of clothing .....48 ff
Functions of textiles .....48 ff
Functions, seam types .....187 ff
Fur .....145 ff
Fusible interlinings 137, 201
Fusing .....137, 201 ff
Fusing, hazards 206

G

Gabardine 81, 82, 110, 125
Gaiters 293, 295
Galloon 139
Gamashes 287
Garçonne 294
Garment assembly, fur clothing 149
Garment dyeing 105
Garment finishing 137
Garment knitting 96
Garment making .....208 ff
Garment manufacture, leather 144
Garment printing 108
Garment processing 102
Garment processing: Jeans 114
Garment sizing .....230 ff
Gas singeing 103
Gaufré 117, 125
Gauze 99
Georgette rayé degrade 99, 116
German Empire 290
Germanic prehistory 270, 271
Gilet 252, 287
Gingham 136
Ginning 9
Gipsy bonnet 291
Girdle 242
Girlie fashion 302
Girlswear 243
Glacé 117, 125
Glass fibres 7, 40
Glazed batiste 126
Glazing 111
Glazing, leather 142
Glen check 84, 126
Glitter effects, yarn 70
Glitter print 109
Glossary of special terms .....304 ff
Gloves .....259, 261, 278 ff
Gluing leather 144
Goat hair 7, 20
Goatskin 143
Goblet boots 283
Golden section 230
Gore-Tex® 39, 50, 193
Gothic .....276 ff
Grade rule 151
Grading increments 150, 151
Grading points 151
Grading .....151 ff
Grain leather 143
Granité 126
Great coat 253, 296
Green linen 137
Greige silk 22
Gripper 78
Grunge fashion 302
Guanaco 7, 20
Guide bar .....97 ff
Guides, sewing 173

H

Hackle, Heckle tow 13
Hackled flax 64
Hackling, Heckling 13
Haik 265
Hair fibres 7, 20, 42
Hair side 143
Hairbands 267
Haircloth 137
Half crêpe 85
Half garment lay 155
Half Milano 94
Half-boots 289
Half-cardigan 94
Hand buck 197
Hand iron 202
Hand printing 107
Hand ruler 160
Hand scissors 162
Hand sewing tools 161
Hand stitch 175
Handbags 291, 293, 295
Handkerchiefs .....280 ff
Handle 66
Handle, fabric 85
Handle, fibre 9, 10, 13, 18, 23, 24, 27, 30, 35, 36
Handle, modification 113
Handling systems 216
Hangers 216
Hard fibres 15
Hardness 66
Harris tweed 126
Harvesting 9, 13
Hats 259, 260, 269, 293, 295
Haute Couture 263, 297
Hazard warnings 203
Hazardous materials 205
Hazards 206
Head, needle loop 91
Head-dress .....265 ff, 304
Headrail 275, 278, 304
Headscarves 297
Headwear .....260, 264 ff
Health and safety .....203 ff, 222
Health and wellbeing 113
Health monitoring 54
Heat insulation 49
Heat setting 35, 104
Heated gloves 259
Heels 283, 299
Held loop 91
Helmets 271, 287
Hem marker 160
Hem tacker 160
Hemp 7, 15, 62, 64
Herringbone 82, 124
Hides 141
High heeled shoes 295
High heels 302
High speed sewing machines 190
High-leg 240
High-tech fabrics 302, 303
High-tech textiles .....53 ff
Himation .....266 ff, 304
Hippy fashions 299
Hipster 240
History, of clothing .....262 ff
History, of fibres 8, 12, 16, 21, 28, 33
H-Line 238, 298
Hole punch 163
Hollow fibres 54
Homburg 295
Homespun 126
Homopolymer 26
Honan 80, 126
Honeycomb 85, 89, 136
Hooks and eyes 140
Hooks 174
Hopsack 80, 131
Horizontal continuity 153
Horizontal hook 174, 176
Horn buttons 140
Horn shoe 280
Horse hair 7, 20
Hose 278
Hosiery 39
Hot air welding 193
Hot edge welding 193
Hot notcher 159
Houndstooth check 84, 126
Houppelande 276, 278, 304
Hour-glass silhouette 288
Housecoat 241
Household textiles 6, 11, 14, 19, 24, 115
Housewear 241
Human ecology 58
Human productivity 222
Human resources 210
Hydroentangled fabrics 75
Hydrophilic 54
Hydrophilic finish 113
Hydrophobic 17, 18, 54
Hydrophobic finish 50, 113
Hygroscopic 17, 18, 23, 49
Hygroscopic, membranes 50
Hypothermia 48, 50

I

Ideal proportions 230
Identification, function of clothing 48
Ikat 109
I-line 238, 298
Imitation Astrakhan 128
Imitation terry 125
Impregnation zone, sizing 77
Imprimé 117
Impurities 9
Indigo dyeing 114
Indirect coating 115
Indirect systems .....72 ff
Individual production 209
Industrial clothing manufacture 208
Industrial made-to-measure 208, 231
Inflatable chambers 52
Information 222
Information exchange 228
Information flow .....228 ff
Information technology (IT) 228
Ingeo® 57
Ingrain yarn 70
Injury protection 51

Inkjet type printer 108
Inlay 93, 125
Inlay, warp knitting 97
Inorganic fibres 40
Insect resistance 113
Inspection 225
Insulation 48, 49, 52
Integrated drug delivery 54
Integrated fully fashioned 96
Integrated monitoring 54
Intelligent textiles 54
Interchanging double cloths 88
Interlacing 79
Interleaving, fur clothing 148
Interlinings 75, 137, 144, 201
Interlock 92, 95, 127
Interlocking lay 155
Intermediate treatments, finishing . . . . 103 ff
Intermeshing point 91
Iron Age 270
Ironing 47, 196
Ironing boards 197, 199
Ironing, fur 147

J

Jabot 285
Jackets 245, 250, 252, 255, 259, 290
Jacquard knitted fabric 93, 94, 127
Jacquard weaving 76
Jacquard woven fabric 127
Jägerleinen 127
Janker 252
Jaspé yarn 70, 117
Javanese 127
Jeans . . . . 114, 251, 298 ff
Jeggings 251
Jersey fabric 92
Jet dyeing 106
Jet weaving 78
Jig 171
Jig dyeing 106
Jogging suit 241
Joining textile fabrics 193
Joining, seam types 187
Jumbo cord 87
Jumper 250, 294
Jupe 282, 284, 304
Justaucorps 283, 285, 304
Jute 7, 15
Jute spinning 62

K

Kaftan 241
Kalasiris 264, 304
Kapok 7, 15
Kelheim fibres 30
Keratin 17, 41
Kevlar® 35, 51
Khat 265
Kilotex, ktex 72
Knee breeches 251, 280
Knickerbockers 251, 295, 296
Knickers 240
Knit-de-knit texturing 67
Knitted fabrics . . . . 74, 90 ff, 101
Knitted loop 91
Knitted outerwear 250
Knitted plush . . 93, 98, 110, 126, 130, 138
Knitted terry 126
Knitted top 248
Knitted velour 93, 98
Knitting machines 96
Knitwear styles 250
Knop yarn 70
Kuralon® 39

L

Labelling . . . . 45 ff, 58, 59, 159
Labelling of chemicals 205
Lace 100
Lace collar 283
Lace fabrics 74
Lace, warp knitted 98
Lacquer printing 109
Laid yarns 98
Lambskin 143
Lambswool 17
Lamé 40, 70, 117, 128
Lamination 50, 102, 115
Lancé 86, 99, 116, 128
Landsknecht costume . . . . 279 ff
Lapping 97
Latch needles . . . . 90 ff
Laundering . . . . 46 ff
Lawn 128
Lay plan, printing 154
Lay plans . . . . 153 ff
Layered look . . . . 301 ff
Layering 49, 137, 257
Laying up 153
Leaf fibres 7, 15
Leather and fur . . . . 141 ff
Leather buttons 140
Leather cloth 118
Leather socks 273, 275
Leggings 240, 251, 302
Leg-of-mutton sleeve 288, 292
Leisurewear . . . . 54, 55, 92 ff, 257, 300
Leno 99
Lenzing Modal® 30
Lenzing Viscose® 30
Liberty 128
Life-cycle analysis 56
Lifestyle 303
Lifting pattern 79
Light test 14
Lighting 223
Liming 141
Line, fashion 238, 263, 298
Linear density 42, 72
Linear polymer 25, 33
Linen . . . . 12 ff, 128
Linen fabrics 14, 104, 137
Linen seal 14, 45
Lines of authority 211
Lingerie 240
Linings 138
Linking 95, 96, 165
Lint 9
Linters 9
Liquor ratio 106
Llama 7, 20
Loading and stress 222
Locknit 98, 120, 137, 138
Lockstitch . . . . 175 ff
Lockstitch needle 168
Lockstitch sewing machine . . . . 165 ff
Lockstitch, rotary hooks 174
Lockstitch, shuttles 174
Lockstitch, types of 177
Loden 74, 128
Loin cloth 265
Long Johns 240
Long staple spinning 62
Long waistcoat 252
Long wool 17
Long-chain polymers 25, 26
Long-staple spinning 61
Look, fashion 263
Loop 129
Loop characteristics 91
Loop fabric 125
Loop formation . . . . 90 ff
Loop yarn fabric 86
Loop yarn 70
Loopback 93, 125
Loopers, chain stitch 174
Looping wires 87
Loop-pile fabric 86
Loose fibre dyeing 102
Lumen 10, 13
Lurex® 40, 70
Lustre 129
Lustre effects 40, 70, 117
Lustre print 109
Lustre, fibres . . 9, 13, 23, 27, 30, 32, 35, 36
Lycra® 33, 39
Lyocell . . . . 7, 26, 28, 31, 41 ff

M

Macromolecule 10, 17, 25, 34
Macroprocesses 220
Madeira lace 100
Made-to-measure 152, 231
Madras 129
Making instructions 214
Making plan 215
Making-up department 213
Malimo 98
Maliwatt 98
Management . . . . 208 ff
Management processes . . . . 224 ff
Manbags 300
Manila 7, 15
Man-made fibre fabrics, finishing 103, 104
Man-made fibres . . . . 6, 7, 25 ff, 67
Man-made fibres seal 45
Man-made fibres, spinning 27, 29, 62, 64
Manteau 282, 284, 305
Mantilla 288, 290, 305
Manual lay planning 154
Manual measurements 231
Manual spreading 157
Manufacturing objective 226
Manufacturing plan 234
Mao hat 260
Marengo 70, 129
Marker length 156
Market 235
Market intelligence 234
Market research 236
Marketing 210
Marking 157, 159, 160
Marks 159
Marl yarn 70
Marquisette 100
Masculine cut 294
Mass production 209
Master series 234
Matching, stripes, checks 153
Matelassé 88, 117, 129
Material feed . . . . 170 ff
Material flow 216
Material for hats 260
Material selection 238
Materials for activewear . . . . 258 ff
Materials handling 216
Materials handling, hazards 207
Materials list 215
Matt effect 70
Matt weave 80
Measurements, body 231
Measuring tools 160
Mechanical entanglement 75
Mechanical finishing . . . . 31, 102, 110 ff
Mechanical pressing 200
Mechanical processes 102
Mechanical properties, yarns 70
Medium wool 17
Melange yarn 70, 117
Melt spinning 27, 34, 36
Melton 74, 129
Membranes 50, 52, 115
Men's shirts 244
Mending, pelt . . . . 146 ff
Menswear 255
Meraklon® 39
Mercerizing 10, 13, 103
Metal buttons 140
Metal fibres 7, 40, 70
Method study . . . . 220 ff
Metric number . . . . 72 ff
Microclimate 49
Microfibre fabric 129
Microfibre spun-laid nonwovens 75
Microfibres 37, 42, 50, 302
Microfibril 10, 22, 25, 26
Micromodal® 42
Microporous membranes 50
Microprocesses 220
Microscopy 11, 14, 19, 24, 30, 35, 37
Middle Ages . . . . 272 ff
Midi length 246, 300
Mille fleurs 116, 129
Mille point 116
Mille rayé 116, 118
Milled 125
Milling 74, 111
Mineral fibres 7, 40
Mineral pigments 105
Mineral tanning 142
Mini length 246, 300
Minimalism 302
Minimals 116
Minimiser 242
Mi-parti fashion 276
Miss loop 91
Mix and match 300
Mixed multi-size lay 155
Mixture yarn 70
Mock leno 99, 130
Mock linen 128
Mock velvet 87
Modacrylic 7, 38
Modal . . . . 7, 28 ff
Modern age . . . . 279 ff
Modern times . . . . 302 ff
Modesty piece 282, 284, 305
Mohair 7, 20
Moiré 111, 117, 130
Moiré ribbon 139
Moisture absorption . . . . 43, 48 ff
Moisture transport . . . . 48 ff, 52
Molecules . . . . 10, 25 ff
Moleskin 110, 138
Molleton 86
Momie cloth 126
Monofilament yarns . . 27, 35, 60, 67 ff, 71
Monomer 26
Mother of pearl 140
Mothproofing 18, 112
Mottle yarn 70
Moulded buck 197
Moulding . . . . 196 ff
Moulding press 200
Mouliné 70, 117, 130
Mousseline 130
Move number 79
MTM system 219
Muffs . . . . 283 ff
Mulberry silk . . . . 21 ff
Mull 99, 130
Multicolor 117
Multi-component yarns 69
Multifilament yarns . . . . 27, 60, 67 ff, 71
Multiple guide bar fabrics 98
Multiple ply 156
Multi-size lays 155
Multi-thread chain stitch 165, 175, 179, 182
Muslin 80

N

Names of fabrics . . . . 116 ff
Nanotechnology 53
Nappa leather 143
Natté 99, 117, 130
Natural colouring materials 105
Natural fibres . . . . 7 ff, 41 ff
Natural polymer . . . . 7, 28 ff
Navajo 116
Neckband 291
Needle 167
Needle bar 97
Needle bed, pressing 197
Needle cord 87, 121
Needle damage 195
Needle felting 75
Needle loop 91
Needle points 169
Needle positioning device 190
Needle size 194
Needle stripe 130
Needle thread loop 168
Needle thread 166
Needle with needle eye 166
Needle-point interlooping 181
Needles, hazards 206
Needles, knitting . . . . 90 ff
Needles, sewing machine . . . . 168 ff
Needles, sewing 161
Negligée 241
Neo-classical style 296
Neo-classicism . . . . 286 ff
Neo-rococo . . . . 290 ff
Net 100
Net fabrics 74
Net silk . . . . 22 ff, 67 ff
Net, warp knitted 98
Netherlands fashion 282
Netherstocks 275, 281
Nets, hair 269, 271
New Look 297, 305
New millennium 303
New wool 19
New Zealand wool 17
Nicki plush 130
Nightwear 241

Nineties .302
Noil silk .22, 23, 62, 64
Nomex® .35, 51
Non-flammable .112
Nonwoven fabrics .74
Nonwoven interlinings .137
Noppé .117
Norfolk jacket .296
Nostalgia . 300
Notation, weave .79
Notcher .159, 163
Nubuk leather .142, 143
Numbering and labelling .159
Numbering systems, yarn .72 ff
Nylon .7, 27, 33, 34, 35, 41 ff
Nylon buttons .140
Nylon stockings .33, 298

O

Observed time .218
Occupational clothing .51
OE rotor spinning .9, 61, 62, 65
Oil tanning .142
Oil test .14
Oiling .142, 146
Oil-stained appearance .114
Olefins .39
Ombré . 116, 117
Ondé .117
Opal .130
Opaline .130
Op-art .299
Open lap .97
Open width processing .106
Open-end rotor spinning . . .9, 61, 62, 65
Open-work fabrics .74, 99, 118
Optical brightening .46, 104
Organdy, Organdie .99, 112, 131
Organic cotton .57
Organisation, company . . .209, 210, 212
Organza .131, 137
Orientation .26
Oscillating looper .178
Oscillating shuttle .174
Ottoman .80, 131
Outlast® .52
Overall continuity .153
Overedge chain stitch . 175, 180 ff
Overedge sewing machine .165
Overedge stitch .95, 180, 181
Overknit .94
Overlock .181
Overprinting .109
Over-size . 300
Oxford .84, 131

P

Package dyeing .106
Packaging .45, 55, 71
Packaging machinery, hazards .207
Pad mangle .106
Padded shoulders .296, 298
Paenula . 268 ff, 272 ff, 305
Pagoda sleeve .290
Paisley pattern .116, 134
Palazzo .251
Paletot .289, 291, 293
Palla .268, 305
Pallium .269, 305
Panama .260
Panel knitting .96
Panier .284, 305
Panne velvet .87, 131
Pantaloons .287, 289, 305
Panty hose .261, 299
Paper shears .162
Parallelo .250
Parchmentising .112
Pareo .242
Paris tail .290, 304
Parka .252
Parti-coloured . 276 ff, 305
Partlet .279, 305
Parts list .215
Party fashions .301
Patch pocket maker .192
Pattens .278
Pattern construction .150 ff
Pattern development, 3D .231
Pattern draft .79 ff, 150
Pattern effects .116
Pattern grading .151 ff
Pattern matching .153
Pattern set .151
Pattern shears .162
Pattern square .160
Pattern wheel .160
Pea coat .252
Peaked cap .260, 296
Pearl print .109
Peasecod-belly .281, 305
Pelerine .288, 305
Pelts . 141 ff, 145 ff
Pencil line .297, 298
Pepita .84, 131
Peplos .266 ff, 305
Peplum .248
Performance rating .218
Performance requirements,
linings .137 ff
Perlé .117
Permanent creasing .18
Persian lamb .147
Personal health monitoring .54
Personal protection .203
Personality .239
Perspiration .48 ff, 52
Petasos .267
Petticoat .298, 305
Petticoat breeches .283
Phase-change materials .52
Photosynthesis .6
Physiological design .222
Physiological properties, yarns .70
Physiological requirements,
clothing .48 ff
Pickling .146
Pictogram .233
Picture hat .293
Piece dyeing .105
Piece goods .96, 102
Pigment printing .109
Pigments .105
Pigskin .143
Piked shoe .278
Pile fabrics .86, 87, 93
Pillar stitch .97
Pilling .112
Pillow lace .100
Pilos .267
Pin stripe .84, 130
Pinafores .245
Pincord .87, 121
Pinking shears .162
Pins .161
Pipe sleeves .277
Piping .139
Piqué, knitted .93, 94, 131
Piqué, woven .89, 117, 132
Plaid .133, 138
Plain jersey .92, 134
Plain net .100
Plain stitch .97 ff
Plain weave .79 ff
Plastic-head pins .161
Plated yarn .93
Platform shoes .302
Pleated waist .251
Pleats, types of .247
Plied yarns .60, 69 ff, 73
Plissé .85, 117, 127
Pluder hose .280
Plush, warp knitted .98, 132
Plush, weft knitted . 93, 110, 126,
130, 132, 138
Plush, woven .87, 132, 138
PMTS .219
Pocket maker .192
Pocket sewer .165
Pocketing .138
Pockets, marking .159
Point paper design .79
Point stitching .137
Pointed collar .289
Pointillé .116
Poke bonnet .287, 289, 305
Polar fleece .42, 124
Polishing .147
Polo neck sweaters .299
Polo shirt .248, 250
Polyacrylic .7, 26, 33, 38, 41
Polyamide .7, 26, 33, 34, 41
Polycaprolactam .33, 34
Polyester . 7, 26, 27, 33, 36 ff, 41 ff, 50
Polyester blend fabrics .103
Polyester buttons .140
Polyester yarn .71
Polyethylene .7, 39
Polymerisation .26, 34, 36, 38
Polymers .6, 7, 25 ff
Polyolefin .7, 33, 39
Polypropylene . 7, 26, 33, 39, 41 ff
Polytetrafluoroethylene (PTFE) . . .39, 50
Polyurethane .33, 39, 41
Polyvinylalcohol (PVA) . . 7, 28, 33, 39, 77
Polyvinylchloride (PVC) .26, 33, 39
Pompons .139
Pongé .132, 138
Poplin .80, 132
Population .6
Position marking .159
Post bed sewing machine .164
Poulaines .278, 305
Pre-aged jeans .114
Precision cutting .153
Preparation, dyeing and
finishing .102 ff
Preparation, fibres .9
Preparation, leather .141
Preparation, pelt .146
Preparation, sewing .159
Preparation, weaving .77
Preparation, worsted spinning .63
Presentation of fabrics .156
Press studs .140
Presser foot . 167, 170 ff
Pressing and fusing .196 ff
Pressing hazards .207
Pressurised jet .106
Pre-washed jeans .114
Princess cut .292
Princess line .238
Printing .102, 107 ff
Printing block .107
Printing techniques .109
Printing, lay plan .154
Problems in sewing .194 ff
Procedure descriptions .234
Process analysis .220
Process design .210
Process management .210 ff
Processes and systems .220
Processing department .213
Processing tools .213
Processing, sustainability .57
Product concepts .235
Product Data Management (PDM) . .228
Product description .214
Product design .238 ff
Product development . . . 213, 226, 234 ff
Product groups .240 ff
Product labels .47
Product Lifecycle Management
(PLM) .228
Product profile .225
Product specification .214
Product traceability .58
Production management . . 210 ff, 213 ff
Production method .90
Production of fibres . 6, 8, 12,
15, 16, 20 ff, 33
Production organisation systems . . .209
Production schedule .226
Production systems, types of .209
Production time .217
Professional cleaning . 11, 14, 19, 24,
30, 31, 32, 35, 37, 38, 47
Profile sewing .165, 192
Progress control .229
Progressive bundle system .209
Prohibitions .203
Projectile weaving .78
Proportion .230
Prostheses .53
Protection equipment .204
Protection .48, 50, 51, 53
Protective clothing . 35, 39 ff,
50, 51, 55, 245
Protein fibres .6, 7, 22, 25
Protein molecules .17, 25
Prototype .226
Prototype collection .234
Puckering .194
Puller feed .171
Pulling, flax .13
Pullover .250
Pumice stones .114
Pumps .287, 291, 293, 295
Punk fashion . 300
Purism fashion .302
Purl fabric .92, 95
Purpose .239
Pyjamas .241

Q

Quadrillé .116, 117
Qualitative division of labour .209
Quality control fused assemblies . . .202
Quality level .235, 238
Quality management .224 ff
Quality marks .44, 45
Quality planning .229
Quality related costs .227
Quality requirements,
sewing threads .71
Quality specifications .215
Quality targets .226
Quantitative division of labour .209
Quilt lining .138
Quilted parka .259
Quilting .89

R

Rabbit hair .7, 20
Radiation protection .51, 53
Raglan .253, 293
Raincoat .253
Rainwear .37
Raised bed sewing machine .164
Raising .18, 87, 110
Ramie .7, 15
Rapier weaving .78
Raschel knitted fabric . . .90, 98, 100, 137
Rateening .110
Ratiné . 110, 117, 132
Raw denim .114
Raw linen .137
Raw silk .21 ff
Rayé .116, 138
Rayon .28
Reactive dyes .105
Reactive monomer .26
Ready-made clothing .290
Ready-to-wear .263
Rearranging, fur clothing .148
Recent times .292 ff
Recovered wool .17, 62
Recycling .55, 56, 58
Redingote . 253, 286 ff, 289, 305
Reed .78
Reeled silk . 22 ff, 67 ff
REFA system .217 ff
Reference standards .226
Reform dress .292 ff, 305
Reformation .279 ff
Regenerated cellulose 29, 32, 33, 41
Regularity .66
Relax dryers .104
Relief effects .89, 117
Renaissance .279 ff
Renforcé .132
Repeat, weave .79
Resist printing .109
Resistance . 35, 36, 105, 112 ff
Restoration .288
Resultant yarn number .73
Reticule .287, 289
Retro fashion .302
Retting, flax .13
Reversible fabric .86, 88, 132
RF welding .193
Rheingrafen fashion .283
Rhinegraves .283, 305
Rho-Sport .35
Rhovyl® .39
Rib fabric, knitted .92, 94, 122, 124
Rib fabric, woven . 80, 89,132
Ribbed tape .139
Ribbons .139, 267
Rick-rack .139

Riding coat .286
Ring shuttle .174
Ring spinning 9, 61 ff
Ring spun yarns .60
Ring-dyed yarn 114
Rio .240
Ripper .163
Ripple fabrics .94
Robe 282, 305
Rock fibres .7
Rococo 284 ff
Rodier .94
Roica® .39
Roll handling .216
Roller feed .171
Roller printing .107
Romanesque 274 ff
Romantic 288 ff
Romantic look 300
Romanticism 290 ff
Ropa 281, 305
Rope washing .103
Rosettes .139
Rotary hook 167, 174
Rotary screen printing .107
Rotonde 288, 305
Rotor spinning 9, 60 ff
Rough cutting 157, 158
Roughing out, flax .13
Round point, needles .169
Roving formation .61
Roving frame .61
Royal rib .94
Rubber fibres 7, 28
Rubbing test .19
Rucksack .302
Ruff 280 ff, 305
Ruler, hand .160

S

S twist .60
Sack line .298
Safari hat .260
Safety at work 203 ff
Safety in Clothing Manufacture 206 ff
Safety measures .206
Safety signs and symbols .203
Safety stitch 165, 180, 181
Sailcloth 119
Sample collection .234
Sample making .226
Sample series .226
Sand crêpe 85, 133
Sandals 265, 267, 269, 273, 287
Sanding 110
Sanforizing® 111
Sateen weave .83
Satin carré 116
Satin crêpe 122
Satin quadrillé 117
Satin rayé 117
Satin stripe chiffon 83, 99
Satin stripe .83
Satin weave 79, 83
Satin-batiste carré .99
Satin-rib barré 116
Sawdust drumming .146
Saxony .133
Scales, wool .17
Scalloping .139
Scarf, scarves, squares .261
Schappe silk 22 ff, 62, 64, 71
Scheduling .229
Schoeller®-PCM™ .52
Schreinering 111
Scissors .162
Scissors, hazards .206
Scouring 16, 103
Scraping 114
Screen printing .107
Scroop .23
Scutcher tow .13
Scutching .13
Sealed seams .193
Seam diagrams 184 ff
Seam pressing .196
Seam puckering .194
Seam types 182 ff
Seaming tape .139
Seamless garments .258
Seams 193 ff
Second grade garments .156
Second-hand clothing .58
Sectional lay .155
Sectional warping .77
Seed fibres 7 ff, 15
Seersucker 85, 133
Segmenting .141
Selection .147
Semi-continuous dyeing .106
Semi-worsted spinning .63
Sensitivity .23
Sensor plate .159
Separates 254, 300
Seralit® .57
Serge 81, 133, 138
Sericin 21 ff
Set square .160
Set temperature, fusing .201
Seventies 300
Sewing faults 95, 195
Sewing leather .144
Sewing machine construction .166
Sewing machine drives .189
Sewing machine needles 168 ff
Sewing machines 164 ff
Sewing machines, automatic .191
Sewing needles 161, 168
Sewing quality .71
Sewing terminology .188
Sewing threads 37, 69, 71, 73
Sewing tools .161
Sewing workstation .223
Sewing, hazards .206
Sewing, knitted fabrics .95
Sewing, preparation for .159
Sewing, problems in 194 ff
Shades 287, 289, 291, 295
Shadow print 109, 116, 120
Shadow stripe .99
Shaft, weaving .76
Shantung .133
Shaper .242
Shaping fur clothing .149
Shaving leather .142
Shaving pelt .146
Shawl collar 277, 280
Shawls 286, 288, 290, 295
Shearing finishing 110
Shearing fur .147
Shearing sheep 16, 17
Shears .162
Sheeting .81
Shenti 264, 305
Shepherd's check 84, 131
Shetland wool .17
Shetland .134
Shift .274
Shirts 244, 271 ff
Shogging .97
Short boot .289
Short staple spinning 61, 62
Shorties .241
Shorts 240 ff, 251
Shot silk 119
Shoulder cloak 272, 274
Shoulder emphasis .301
Shrinking, finishing 111
Shuttle weaving .78
Shuttleless looms .78
Shuttles, sewing .174
Side bed sewing machine .164
Sigrafil® .40
Silhouettes .238
Silk 6, 7, 21 ff, 41 ff, 67
Silk fabrics, finishing 103, 104
Silk roll .278
Silk seal .24
Silk spinning 62, 64
Silk weighting .23
Silk yarns .71
Silver 53, 113
Singeing .103
Single breasted .255
Single guide bar structures .97
Single jersey 92 ff, 134
Single ply .156
Single size lay .155
Single thread chain stitch .178
Single yarns 60, 72
Sinker loop .91
Siro spinning 60 ff, 65
Sisal 7, 15
Sisal hat .260
Six month wool .17
Sixties .299
Size 77, 114
Size charts 150, 233
Size intervals 232, 233
Size tables 231, 233
Size, sewing needle 168, 194
Sizing, weaving .77
Skin quality, leather .141
Skin wool .17
Skinny jeans .251
Skirts 246 ff, 270 ff
Slashing .77
Sleeve board .197
Sleeve lining .138
Sleeveless top .248
Slim line .290
Slim silhouette .292
Slipper 273, 275, 285, 287, 298
Slipping resistance .112
Sliver knit .93
Sliver 61, 64
Slops 280, 305
Slub yarn .70
Slubbing .61
Smart clothing .54
Smart fashion .303
Smocks 245, 271
Smoking jacket .293
Snippers .163
Soaking 141, 146
Social systems .220
Socio-technological systems .220
Socks 261, 273
Softening agents .113
Soft-shell jacket .259
Soielaine 116, 134
Soil release finish .18
Solubility test 11, 19, 24, 30, 32, 35, 37, 38, 41
Solvent spinning process .28
Sorting leather .144
Sorting pattern pieces .159
Sorting pelt .147
Sources of textile fibres .6
Soutache .139
Space look .299
Spandex .39
Spanish cape .281
Spanish fashion 279 ff
Spanish hat .281
Spats .295
Special fabrics 99 ff
Special groups 240 ff
Special terms – Clothing history 304 ff
Specific volume .66
Specification .214
Speckled appearance .114
Spencer 252, 287, 305
Spindle cell .17
Spinneret 21, 26 ff
Spinning machine .65
Spinning systems 27 ff, 61 ff
Split leather .143
Spoon bonnet 291, 305
Sport and Leisure clothing 54, 55, 257 ff, 298
Spreading 95, 156 ff
Spreading, hazards .206
Spun silk 22 ff, 62, 64, 71
Spun yarns .60 ff
Spun-laid .74, 75
Squares, scarves .261
Stabilised yarn 67, 68
Stain removal, hazards .207
Stain resistance .112
Staking leather .142
Stamped tape .139
Standard time 217, 218
Standing workstation .223
Staple (man-made) fibres 27 ff, 30, 34, 35, 37 ff
Staple fibre yarns 9, 29, 60 ff
Staple length 9, 43
Stature 232 ff
Steam dolly 200
Steam pressing 196, 197
Steel pins .161
Steep twill .82
Steeple 278, 305
Stenter drying frame .104
Stepped lay .156
Stiffened linen .137
Stiffening fabrics .137
Stiletto shoe, heels 285, 298
Stitch bonded 74, 98, 137
Stitch compression .190
Stitch cutter .163
Stitch formation parts .167
Stitch formation 175 ff
Stitch types, applications 177 ff
Stitch types, sewing 164, 175 ff
Stitched double cloth .88
Stitching damage .95
Stock dyeing 102, 105
Stock, neckwear 285, 287, 289
Stockings 33, 261, 283 ff, 289
Stola 268, 272, 305
Stomacher 280, 282, 284, 288, 290, 305
Stone age .270
Stonewashing 114
Storm helmet .259
Story board .234
Straight knives .158
Straight shuttle .174
Straight ties .261
Straight-line system .209
Stranding fur clothing .148
Straw hat .260
Strawcloth .127
Strength, fibres 9, 10, 13, 18, 23, 30, 31, 35, 36
Strength, yarns .66
Strengthening, seam types .187
Stresemann .295
Stress measurement .222
Stretch fabrics .39
Stretch yarns .68
Stretching and recovery .113
Stretching pelt 146, 147
Strophium .268
Structural effects, yarn 70, 117
Structural pucker .194
Structuré 117
Stuart collar .280
Stuffer box texturing .67
Style periods, historical .262
Style trends .239
Style, fashion 263 ff
Styling .238
Styling themes .234
Suede leather 142, 143
Sueding 110, 142, 147
Suits 254, 255, 289 ff, 293, 300
Sun hat .259
Sunshade .293
Support processes .224
Supports, textile .53
Surah .134
Surcot 274 ff, 305
Surface structure .66
Surface texture .85
Sustainability 56, 57
Sweaters 250, 299
Sweatshirt .250
Swimming suit .242
Swimming trunks .242
Swimwear 39, 242
Swinger .253
Swiss rib .122
Swivel fabrics 86, 116, 119
Symmetry, pattern cutting .153
Sympatex® 50, 193
Synchronised system .209
Synthetic buttons .140
Synthetic dyes .105
Synthetic fibre finishing 111
Synthetic fibres 6, 25, 26, 33 ff, 41, 57, 113
Synthetic polymers 7, 33 ff
Systems .220

T

Tabard 278, 305
Tablion .273
Tactel® 35, 50, 129

Taffeta 80, 117, 134, 138, 139
Tailcoat. 287, 289, 291
Tailor's shears 162
Tailor's thimble 161
Tailored suit. .254
Take-up lever. 166, 167
Tanga 240
Tank top. 250
Tankini 242
Tannery 141
Tanning . . . . 141 ff
Tape measure 160
Tapes 139
Target groups . . . . 236 ff
Target population 232
Target time 218
Tartan. 84, 133
Tassel cloak 274, 275, 305
Tassels 139
Tearing test 11, 14, 30, 41
Technical terms, fabrics . . . . 116 ff
Technical textiles 6, 11, 14, 19, 24, 39, 55, 115
Technique 238
Techno wave .302
Technological systems 220
Technological testing 225
Teflon ironing shoe 196
Teflon® 39
Temperature protection 51
Tenacity 13, 23, 43
Tenax® 40
Tencel Micro® .42
Tencel® 31
Tension discs. 166,167
Tent line 238
Terminology, leather. . . . . 141 ff
Terminology, sewing needles 168
Terminology, warp knitting 97
Terminology, weft knitting. 91
Terminology, yarns 60
Terry, warp knitted 98
Terry, weft knitted. 93, 126
Terry, woven 86
Testing 225, 226
Tex system. . . . . .42, 72 ff
Textile Production and Ecology. . . . 56 ff
Textiles, functions of . . . . 48 ff
Textured yarns. . . . .27, 34 ff, 60, 67 ff, 71
Themes, fashion 263
Thermal bonding 75
Thermal insulation 10, 13, 18, 23, 29, 34, 36
Thermal regulation. . . . . 48 ff, 52
Thermal welding. 193
Thermolite® 37
Thermo-mechanical finishing . . 102, 111
Thermoplastic. 27, 32, 35, 36, 38
Thermoregulation. 52
Thimbles 161
Thirties. 296
Thong. 240
Thonged shoe 271, 275
Thread cutting. 190
Thread guide. 166
Thread marker. 159
Thread tension pucker 194
Thread wiper. 190
Three or more yarn systems . . . . . . 86 ff
Three-cylinder spinning 64
Three-thread overedge machine 180
Throat plate. . . . . 167, 170 ff
Tiara. 273
Ticket number. 73
Ties. 261, 291, 295, 299
Tights. 261, 299
Time analysis . . . . 217 ff
Tinting 114
Titre 72
T-line. 238, 300
Toga 269, 305
Toile de soie. 134
Toile travers. 117
Tolerance 233
Top cloths . . . . 118 ff
Top hat. 287, 289, 291, 293
Top pressing 196, 197
Tops, activewear. 258
Toque 281, 305
Total time. 218
Tow 27
Tow flax 13
Traceability 58
Tracing wheel 160
Trade descriptions. . . . . 116 ff
Trademarks, Trade names. . . . 11, 14, 19, 24, 30, 31, 35, 37 ff, 44, 45
Traditional dress 254, 255
Train 277, 290
Trainers 300, 302
Transfer printing 108
Transparent fabrics 99
Transparent look. 302, 303
Transport systems 209, 216
Trapeze line 238, 298, 299
Travers 116, 117
Trench coat 253, 295, 296
Trend shows .263
Trevira Finesse®. 42, 50, 129
Trevira Micro® .42
Trevira® 37, 45
Triacetate. 7, 28, 32, 41
Tricorn 283, 285
Tricot stitch . . . . 97 ff
Tricotine. 81, 82, 134
Trilby. . . . . .260, 295 ff
Trimming fur clothing. 148
Trimmings . . . . 137 ff, 238
Trimmings hats 260
Tropical 134
Trouser suit 254
Trousers. . . . . 251, 259, 271, 278 ff
Troyer. 250
Trunk hose. 280, 281, 305
T-shirt. 250, 299
Tuck loop 91
Tuck stitch 91
Tucker. 282
Tulip line 298
Tulle 135
Tumble dryer. .47
Tunic . . . . 250, 268 ff, 271 ff, 274, 277, 292, 305
Tunnel finisher. 200
Turban 278, 287, 295
Turn ups. 296
Tussah silk. . . . . 7, 21 ff, 136
Tuxedo 256, 293
Twaron® 51
Tweed. .70, 81, 135
Twelve month wool 17
Twenties . . . . 294 ff
Twill fabric . . . . . . 79, 81 ff, 122, 135, 138
Twinset 250
Twist 60, 66, 69, 135
Twist contraction 73
Twist direction 60
Twist level 60
Twist liveliness 69
Twist, twisting 61, 85
Twisted filament yarns. 60
Twistless yarn .69
Two-piece 254
Two-thread chain stitch 179
Two-thread fleece 93
Tyvek® 39, 51

U

Ulster. 253, 293
Ultraviolet protection. 53
Umbrella .289, 291
Unconstructed suit. 303
Under pressing 196, 197
Underlaps 98
Underlay 197
Underwear . . . . 92 ff, 240 ff, 258
Uni(color). 117
Uniform details. 296
Unravelling edge. 92, 94
Unstabilised yarn 67
Uraeus. 265
Usable width. 156

V

Variable feed 171
Vat dyes. 105
Vector (insect) protection 113
Vegetable dyes 105
Vegetable fibres . . . . 6 ff, 15, 41, 57
Vegetable tanning 142
Veil. 269, 273, 278
Velcro® 140
Velour, leather. 143
Velour, warp knitted 98
Velour, weft knitted 93
Velour, woven 74, 86, 110, 135
Velvet 87, 110, 133
Velvet ribbon. 139
Velveteen. .87, 135
Velveton. .135, 138
Venetian. 83, 123
Ventilating top 258
Ventilation, in clothing. . . . . 48 ff
Vertical continuity 153
Vertical hook .174
Vestolan®. 39
Vests .241, 243, 285
Vichy 136
Victorian Era . . . . 290 ff
Vicuna 7, 20
Vigoureux yarns 70
Vinyl chloride 7
Vinylal 7, 39
Vinylidene chloride. 7
Virgin wool 7, 17, 19
Viscose . . . . .7, 26, 28 ff, 41 ff
V-line 238, 298
Voile 80, 99, 136
Voile rayé ombré. 99
Vortex spinning. 65

W

Wadding 88, 89
Waffle. 89, 136
Waist measuring tape 160
Waistcoat lining 138
Waistcoats. 245, 250, 252, 289
Wale 91
Walking stick. 289
Warehouse 216
Warp backed fabrics 86
Warp knitted fabrics . . 90, 97 ff, 101, 137
Warp knitting . . . . 97 ff
Warp printing 109
Warp rib 80
Warp satins 83
Warp sheet . . . . 97 ff
Warp stitching. 88
Warp yarns. 76 ff
Warp-faced twill 81
Warping 77
Wash-away lace 100
Washing, aftercare . . . . . . 11, 14, 19, 24, 30 ff, 35, 37, 38, 46
Washing, finishing 103
Washing, pelt 146
Waste fibres. 58
Waste management. 56
Water 25
Water conservation 56
Water jet weaving. 78
Water repellent finish. 10, 50
Water resistance. 113
Waterproof gloves 259
Watteau pleats 284
Watteline. 137
Wave line. 298
Waved twill 82
Waxing leather 142
Wearable electronics 54
Wearer characteristics 239
Weatherproof clothing 50, 113
Weaving . . . . 76 ff
Weaving, preparation. 77
Web bonding. .75
Web formation 74
Web partition .61
Weft backed fabrics 86
Weft insertion devices 78
Weft knitting. . . . . 90 ff, 96, 101
Weft rib 80
Weft sateens 83
Weft stitching .88
Weft yarn . . . . 76 ff
Weft-faced twill. 81
Weighting 23
Welded seams. 193
Welding devices 193
Wellbeing, health 113
Welliné. 117
Wellness 303
Wellness finishing. 113
Welted tape. .139
Welts 89
Werther costume . . . . 286 ff
Western style hat 260
Wet cling 49, 52, 95
Wet processing . . . . 102 ff
Wet spinning, bast fibres 64
Wet spinning, man-made fibres . . 27, 32
Wet-laid webs. .74
Wetting 113
Weveknit 94, 136
Whipcord. .81, 136
White tie 256
Whole garment knitting. 96
Whole garment lay 155
Wicking .39, 49, 52
Wigs. .265, 283, 285
Wild leather. .143
Wild silk. 21 ff, 136
Wimple 275, 305
Winch reel 106
Wind chill. 49
Wind jacket 259
Windcheater vest 258
Winding. 77
Wire weaving .87
Wiredrawn filaments 40
Womenswear . . . . 246 ff, 254
Wood buttons 140
Wool fabrics. 19, 104
Wool felt . . . . 74 ff, 101
Wool finishing. 111, 112
Wool interlinings. 137
Wool spinning. . . . . 61 ff
Wool. . . . . .6, 7, 16 ff, 41 ff, 57
Woollen 74, 135
Woolmark® 19, 20, 45
Wool-type fibres 27
Work measurement . . . . 217 ff
Working conditions 221
Working environment 204, 222
Workstation design . . . . 221 ff
Workwear 245
World population 6
World production of textile fibres. 6
Worn-out appearance. 114
Worsted flannel. 111
Worsted spinning 62, 63
Woven fabrics . . . . 74, 76 ff, 101
Woven interlinings 137
Wrapped yarns 60, 69
Wrapping fibres 65

X

Xanthation 29
X-line 238, 298

Y

Yak 7, 20
Yarn count . . . . 72 ff
Yarn dyeing . . . . .102,105 ff
Yarn fineness. . . . . 72 ff
Yarn numbering. . . . . 72 ff
Yarn properties 66, 68, 70, 71
Yarn types .66, 71
Yarns . . . . 6, 60 ff
Yearling wool. .17
Y-line 238
Youth fashion . . . . 299 ff

Z

Z twist 60
Zephyr 136, 153
Zip fastener 140